Register Now for … s
to Your

MW00837270

SPRINGER PUBLISHING
CONNECT™

Your print purchase of *Addiction Counseling* **includes online access to the contents of your book**—increasing accessibility, portability, and searchability!

Access today at:
http://connect.springerpub.com/content/book/978-0-8261-3586-5
or scan the QR code at the right with your smartphone. Log in or register, then click "Redeem a voucher" and use the code below.

H8JSXHFA

Scan here for quick access.

Having trouble redeeming a voucher code?
Go to https://connect.springerpub.com/redeeming-voucher-code

If you are experiencing problems accessing the digital component of this product, please contact our customer service department at cs@springerpub.com

The online access with your print purchase is available at the publisher's discretion and may be removed at any time without notice.

Publisher's Note: New and used products purchased from third-party sellers are not guaranteed for quality, authenticity, or access to any included digital components.

SPRINGER PUBLISHING
View all our products at springerpub.com

ADDICTION COUNSELING

Alan Cavaiola, PhD, LPC, LCADC, is a full professor and a member of the Graduate Faculty at Monmouth University (West Long Branch, New Jersey) where he serves as director of the Addiction Studies program. He served as an associate editor of the journal *Substance Abuse* from 2013 to 2018. He is also a member of the Board of Directors of the International Coalition of Substance Abuse Educators (INCASE) from 2014 to the present. He has coauthored several books, including *Assessment and Treatment of DWI Offenders, Crisis Intervention: A Practical Guide*, and *Crisis Intervention Case Book*. In addition, he has authored several scholarly research publications and has presented his research at several national and international conferences. Prior to beginning his teaching career, he served as the clinical director of addiction treatment programs at Monmouth Medical Center, which included an inpatient adolescent treatment program as well as adult outpatient services.

Amanda L. Giordano, PhD, LPC, is an associate professor of counseling at the University of Georgia. She specializes in addiction counseling and has clinical, instructional, and scholarly experience related to both chemical and behavioral addictions. She is the sole author of a clinical reference book titled *A Clinical Guide to Treating Behavioral Addictions: Conceptualizations, Assessments, and Clinical Strategies*. She works to advance the counseling field with rigorous research and has published over 45 peer-reviewed articles and book chapters. She regularly teaches addiction counseling courses at both the undergraduate and graduate levels. In 2018, she was awarded the Addictions/Offender Educator Excellence Award from the International Association of Addictions & Offender Counselors. Additionally, she has experience as an editorial board member for several prominent counseling journals, including the *Journal of Addictions & Offender Counseling, Journal of Counseling & Development*, and *Counseling and Values*. She serves on the American Counseling Association (ACA) of Georgia Leadership Council and the board of the Association for Assessment and Research in Counseling (AARC) and is a member of several other ACA divisions.

Nedeljko Golubovic, PhD, is an assistant professor in the Department of Counseling and Marital and Family Therapy at the University of San Diego. He also serves as a program director for the Opioid Workforce Expansion Program funded by the Health Resource and Service Administration. The primary goal of his scholarly work is further exploration of addiction issues and trauma. More specifically, he is interested in assessing the intersection between addiction and trauma and examining the consequences of stigmatization and bias related to both areas. In the past, he was a part of the National Institute on Drug Abuse–sponsored teams for monitoring drug trends in the United States. Regarding his teaching experiences, he has been dedicated to training master's level professional counselors. He has experience in teaching a variety of core counseling classes, but his primary focus has been on preparing future counselors to work with addiction and trauma-related issues. In 2020, he was awarded the Addictions/Offender Educator Excellence Award from the International Association of Addictions & Offender Counselors. He also has experience as an editorial board member, and he currently serves on the editorial board of the *Journal of Counseling Leadership and Advocacy*. His service involvement includes committee cochair of the Emerging Leaders Program for the Association for Counselor Education and Supervision, Leadership Committee for the Association for Counselor Education and Supervision, and a grant reviewer for the Chi Sigma Iota International, as well as involvement in several ACA divisions.

ADDICTION COUNSELING

A Practical Approach

Alan Cavaiola, PhD, LPC, LCADC

Amanda L. Giordano, PhD, LPC

Nedeljko Golubovic, PhD

Copyright © 2022 Springer Publishing Company, LLC
All rights reserved.

No part of this publication may be reproduced, stored in a retrieval system, or transmitted in any form or by any means, electronic, mechanical, photocopying, recording, or otherwise, without the prior permission of Springer Publishing Company, LLC, or authorization through payment of the appropriate fees to the Copyright Clearance Center, Inc., 222 Rosewood Drive, Danvers, MA 01923, 978-750-8400, fax 978-646-8600, info@copyright.com or at www.copyright.com.

Springer Publishing Company, LLC
11 West 42nd Street, New York, NY 10036
www.springerpub.com
connect.springerpub.com/

Acquisitions Editor: Rhonda Dearborn
Compositor: Amnet Systems

ISBN: 978-0-8261-3585-8
ebook ISBN: 978-0-8261-3586-5
DOI: 10.1891/9780826135865

A robust set of instructor resources designed to supplement this text is located at **http://connect.springerpub.com/content/book/978-0-8261-3586-5.** Qualifying instructors may request access by emailing **textbook@springerpub.com.**

Instructor's Manual ISBN: 978-0-8261-3623-7
Instructor's PowerPoints ISBN: 978-0-8261-3624-4

Downloadable Forms ISBN: 978-0-8261-3586-5

The accompanying downloadable forms for this book are available through Springer Publishing Connect; use the code on the opening page of this book to access the ebook, select the Show Supplementary dropdown button, and select Student Materials to access the downloadable forms.

21 22 23 24 25 / 5 4 3 2 1

The author and the publisher of this Work have made every effort to use sources believed to be reliable to provide information that is accurate and compatible with the standards generally accepted at the time of publication. The author and publisher shall not be liable for any special, consequential, or exemplary damages resulting, in whole or in part, from the readers' use of, or reliance on, the information contained in this book. The publisher has no responsibility for the persistence or accuracy of URLs for external or third-party Internet websites referred to in this publication and does not guarantee that any content on such websites is, or will remain, accurate or appropriate.

Library of Congress Control Number: 2021033822

Contact sales@springerpub.com to receive discount rates on bulk purchases.

Publisher's Note: New and used products purchased from third-party sellers are not guaranteed for quality, authenticity, or access to any included digital components.

Printed in the United States of America.

I (AC) am very grateful to my friends and colleagues on the Board of the International Coalition of Addiction Studies Educators (INCASE) for their valuable recommendations and support. The Board and Membership of INCASE are professionals truly dedicated to competent, compassionate teaching and training of future generations of addictions treatment professionals. I am appreciative of the administration of Monmouth University and their support of the Addiction Studies program, and I am most grateful for all the assistance I've received from the Faculty Librarians at Monmouth University's Guggenheim Library. Without you, this book would not have been possible. I also very much appreciate the assistance of my former graduate students, Erin Murphy and Brian Matlaga, who helped with editing and research for this book. Thanks also to my family for their support throughout this process and to all of my clients who have shared their strength, hope, and experiences with me over the past 30 years I've been in practice. Finally, I'm very appreciative to the addiction professionals who allowed me to interview them for the Notes From the Field feature. Thank you all so much.

I (ALG) want to express my sincere gratitude to the professionals who are working with clients with addiction, advocating for this population, and ensuring that they receive quality services. I am especially grateful for those clinicians who shared their wisdom and perspectives during our interviews for the Notes From the Field sections. I am also deeply appreciative of the individuals who are pursuing and maintaining recovery from addiction, as they are some of the strongest individuals I know. I am grateful to my professional colleagues in the counseling program at UGA (Brandee, Deryl, George, Jolie, and Missy) who have supported me and encouraged my work in the field of addiction counseling. Finally, I want to thank Theresa Taylor and Jessica Abraham for all the joy they brought to my life—I am blessed beyond measure to call you two my sisters.

I (NG) want to express my deepest appreciation for the selfless work of mental health professionals who have dedicated their professional lives to improving care and service delivery for persons with addiction issues. I am especially thankful for those who mentored me over the last 10 years and helped me develop as a clinician, researcher, educator, and advocate. Also, I want to thank my colleagues who have served many roles in my professional and personal life and have been incredible resources and sources of support. Additionally, I am grateful to my students who consistently showed remarkable levels of compassion and dedication that continued to provide motivation for my work. Finally, I want to thank the addiction professionals who shared their experiences for the Notes From the Field sections for enriching this textbook.

CONTENTS

PREFACE

When we began writing this textbook, the United States was in the grips of an opioid epidemic in which overdose deaths have been ever increasing, perhaps amplified by the coronavirus 2019 (COVID-19) pandemic. Although the opioid epidemic took center stage in the media, there were also surges in cocaine and methamphetamine use and related deaths, as well as increases in cannabis vaping, especially among adolescents and young adults. Additionally, behavioral addictions such as sex and pornography addiction, internet gaming addiction, and gambling continued to impact individuals and communities across the globe. History provides us with several lessons; one of those lessons is that substance use trends wax and wane over decades. For example, many say the "Summer of Love" of the late 1960s, in which hallucinogens played a key role, ended when amphetamines surged in popularity, bringing with them a whole new set of problems and deaths. Cocaine epidemics existed in the 1920s, coinciding with alcohol prohibition, only to resurface again in the 1980s. Morphine addiction was prevalent following the Civil War, especially among wounded soldiers, and opioid addiction again surged in the past five years. Therefore, it is imperative that each new generation of mental health professionals is equipped to recognize and respond to addiction.

As authors, we share the conviction that whatever area of counseling you decide to specialize in or whatever counseling program you work in, you will be treating individuals who are either directly or indirectly impacted by substance use disorders (SUDs) and behavioral addictions. Therefore, we wrote this textbook with this in mind. Chapter 1 sets the stage by providing students with an overview of the current state of the addiction counseling profession and the ever-increasing need for addiction counselors and mental health counselors who possess specific knowledge and skills pertaining to treating SUDs, as well as information on counselor credentialing and ethical concerns specific to addiction counseling.

Subsequently, you'll find chapters (e.g., Chapter 2, Addiction Theory, and Chapter 4, Substance Use Disorders and Case Management) that provide foundational knowledge about what causes or sustains SUDs as well as information on how treating a benzodiazepine use disorder (i.e., sedative-hypnotic use disorder) differs from treating a cocaine use disorder (i.e., stimulant use disorder). In Chapter 3, Neuroscience and Addiction, we explore the role of neurotransmitter imbalances as both precursors to and consequences of SUDs. Neuroscience provides the addiction treatment profession with some fascinating cutting-edge research and new insights into how substances alter brain functioning, as well as some promising pharmacological treatments for ameliorating substance craving.

We felt ethically responsible for providing readers with as many evidence-based (i.e., backed by research) treatments as possible. As we move into the 21st century, what we know for certain is that no longer is addiction treatment a "one-size fits all" proposition, but rather treatment planning necessitates treatment approaches that are tailored to the individual. The same holds true when writing treatment plans (covered in Chapter 5, Assessment/Diagnosis and Treatment Planning). From years of clinical experience, we feel that assessment and treatment planning go hand in hand. A thorough biopsychosocial assessment (that also includes the use of standardized measures) helps to identify those issues the client wishes to work on and areas needing to be addressed, while the treatment plan provides the roadmap of how to help clients attain those goals as stated in the treatment plan. In Chapter 4, we also provide information on various levels of treatment as described in the *American Society of Addiction Medicine Criteria* (*ASAM-3*).

In Chapters 6 (Individual Counseling), 7 (Group Counseling), and 8 (Family Counseling), you'll learn the basics of various approaches to treating SUDs and how to treat families and loved ones. The goal of these foundational chapters is to provide students with the basics of how and when to utilize particular counseling techniques, whether it be in a group or individual session. In the family counseling chapter, we cover various models that conceptualize the impact of SUDs on families and how those models are used to inform family treatment. Students will also learn the advantages and disadvantages of Johnsonian interventions as well as other noncoercive approaches (e.g., CRAFT) that assist families to encourage their loved ones to accept treatment.

The entirety of Chapter 9 is devoted to motivational interviewing, one of the most widely used treatment approaches for counseling individuals who are ambivalent about change. As William Miller, one of the co-originators of motivational interviewing, points out, ambivalence is inherent to SUDs because substance use involves engaging in behavior that on one hand feels good while on the other hand impacts people's lives in profound and devastating ways. Motivational interviewing provides ways to help individuals who come into counseling feeling that they don't want help or that change is impossible. Motivational interviewing can be a powerful tool for restoring hope and helping to move people toward change in a collaborative way. As David Rosengren, the author of *Building Motivational Interviewing Skills: A Practitioner Workbook*, so aptly states, "motivational interviewing is more like ballroom dancing, not wrestling" (2009, p. 24).

Chapter 10 covers one of the most important areas in addiction counseling: relapse prevention. Once abstinence has been established, one of the most important and challenging tasks for clients is to develop strategies and coping skills that will help to ensure their recovery. By helping clients to develop coping responses to triggers or cues associated with relapse, counselors are better able to prepare them to discover ways to maintain their recovery.

One of the newest areas within the addiction counseling profession deals with behavioral addictions. Currently, the *Diagnostic and Statistical Manual of Mental Disorders*, Fifth Edition (*DSM-5*; American Psychiatric Association, 2013), includes gambling disorders as a section of the SUD chapter under "nonsubstance related disorders," and internet gaming disorder and nonsuicidal self-injury disorder are listed in Section III as conditions in need of further study. Many addiction treatment professionals hope that, in the future, other behavioral addictions (e.g., food addiction, sex addiction, and compulsive shopping) will be included in the *DSM*. Chapter 11 explores behavioral addictions and how to offer effective treatments to clients.

Over the past 20 years or so, there has been a proliferation and wider recognition of the preponderance of individuals who manifest both SUDs as well as mental health disorders. Chapter 12 explores those mental health disorders that are most likely to co-occur with SUDs and how to effectively treat them as part of clients' overall treatment regimen. In past years, it was assumed that mental health and SUDs needed to be treated separately and by separate treatment providers. Today, there's greater appreciation of the need to treat both disorders simultaneously, ideally by the same treatment professional.

Chapter 13 explores how SUDs impact on one's overall growth and development and how these developmental issues need to be addressed as part of the client's overall treatment plan. Chapter 14 explores the importance of taking into account the cultural identities such as race, ethnicity, gender, socioeconomic status, sexual orientation, religion and spirituality, and other social-environmental influences when conceptualizing and treating addiction. It's often said that SUDs do not occur in a vacuum; therefore it's important to consider various social and cultural influences.

Finally, Chapter 15 looks at the role that addiction professionals play both in advocating for their clients as well as in advocating for very-much-needed societal change that will help to lessen stigma and increase treatment opportunities for all Americans.

This textbook is accompanied by a set of downloadable forms including questionnaires, a treatment plan template and example, sample consent and confidentiality forms, and more. The downloadable forms are available through Springer Publishing Connect; use the code on the opening page of this book to access the ebook, select the Show Supplementary drop-down button, and select Student Materials to access the downloadable forms.

We hope you're able to gather a lot of new information as you read the textbook and that you enjoy reading it just as much as we enjoyed writing it.

Alan Cavaiola
Amanda L. Giordano
Nedeljko Golubovic

REFERENCES

American Psychiatric Association. (2013). *Diagnostic and statistical manual of mental disorders* (5th ed.). https://doi.org/10.1176/appi.books.9780890425596

Rosengren, D. (2009). *Building motivational interviewing skills: A practitioner workbook.* Guilford Press.

ACKNOWLEDGMENTS

First and foremost, we wish to express our deepest appreciation to Rhonda Dearborn, senior acquisitions editor at Springer Publishing, for making this textbook possible and for guiding us through the process of creating the outline for the textbook and advocating for us every step along the way. Similarly, we are appreciative of all the support and guidance of Mehak Massand, assistant editor at Springer Publishing, for all of her support and guidance. We also wish to thank Rachel Haines for her editorial assistance and Vinodhini Kumarasamy and the team at Amnet Systems for their assistance in reviewing and editing the manuscript.

We are also most grateful to our academic reviewers who took time to offer us valuable feedback and recommendations for making this textbook unique and a valuable contribution to the addiction education profession. We're especially grateful to Professor Regina Moro from Boise State University, Boise, Idaho; Professor Devon Bowser, Waynesburg University, Waynesburg, Pennsylvania; Professor Kirk Bowden, Rio Salado College, Ottawa University, Kansas; Professor Philip Clarke, Wake Forest University, Winston-Salem, North Carolina; Professor Alfredo Palacios, Auburn University, Auburn, Alabama; and Professor Asha Dickerson, Adler Graduate School, Richfield, Minnesota.

1

INTRODUCTION TO ADDICTION COUNSELING

LEARNING OBJECTIVES

This chapter provides an introduction to addiction counseling and highlights the need for all mental health professionals to be equipped to respond to addiction. By the end of this chapter, you will be able to

- explain the cost of addiction both in terms of human life and economic resources;
- defend the need for all mental health professionals to be prepared to recognize and respond to addiction;
- summarize the prevalence of addiction and explain the opioid epidemic;
- describe how empathy, addiction-related knowledge, and self-care are necessary for effective clinical work with addiction;
- apply professional ethical standards, state laws and regulations, and addiction-specific ethical codes to your work with clients with addiction;
- discriminate between various forms of credentialing related to addiction counseling.

TERMS TO KNOW

active addiction current use of drugs of abuse or engagement in addictive behaviors that is out of control, compulsive, continued despite negative consequences, and leads to cravings or mental preoccupation

addiction setting specialized facility or program to treat addiction such as a residential treatment facility, intensive outpatient program, partial hospitalization program, or detoxification unit

binge drinking consuming five or more drinks in one sitting

burnout psychological detachment, negative feelings toward others, and a sense of ineptitude as a result of chronic job-related stress

compassion fatigue secondary or vicarious psychological and emotional distress resulting from entering into the suffering of others

empathy genuine and accurate understanding of another person's experience

long-term recovery	sustained abstinence from drugs of abuse and addictive behaviors and the pursuit of holistic wellness
opioid epidemic	public health emergency related to alarming rates of overdose deaths and addiction due to opioids, specifically prescription opioids, heroin, and fentanyl
overdose death	intentional or accidental death caused by the ingestion of drugs of abuse
self-care	intentional practices to protect and nurture one's physical, emotional, psychological, and spiritual well-being

INTRODUCTION

This course is for everyone. Regardless of the setting in which you plan to work, as a mental health professional, you *will* encounter addiction. You will have clients who are in *active addiction*, clients who are in *long-term recovery* from addiction, clients who are in relationships with others in active addiction, parents of children in active addiction, or children of parents in active addiction. The prevalence of substance use and addictive behaviors in today's society guarantees that all mental health professionals will encounter addiction in their work. Indeed, substance use disorders and addictive behaviors occur among members of all racial and ethnic groups, across genders and sexual orientations, across socioeconomic statuses and ability statuses, among affiliates of all religious and spiritual traditions, across the life span, and throughout geographic regions. In sum, addiction does not discriminate, and it is costly. It has been estimated that the financial costs associated with substance misuse exceed $600 billion annually in the United States (Miller & Hendrie, 2008; National Institute on Drug Abuse [NIDA], 2018). This number includes costs for treatment, incarceration for drug offenses, heathcare, crime and law enforcement, prevention efforts, social services, and the loss of productivity due to addiction.

More so than economic cost, however, addiction results in the loss of life. From May 2019 to May 2020, the Centers for Disease Control and Prevention (CDC; 2020) reported over 81,000 *deaths due to drug overdoses* in the United States (that is more than the amount of people who would fill the Mercedes-Benz Superdome in New Orleans). Yet, death rates only reveal part of the problem as addiction takes a staggering toll on those living with the disease. Indeed, individuals with addiction experience problems related to their health, family relationships, romantic relationships, finances, employment, education, wellness, and quality of life—repercussions that are hard to quantify. In sum, the number of Americans who have been affected by addiction is striking. Consider that in 2019, 28.2 million adults (11.4% of the adult population in the United States) reported ever having a problem with alcohol or other drug use (Substance Abuse and Mental Health Services Administration [SAMHSA], 2020). That means that more than one in 10 American adults feel as though drugs of abuse have become a problem in their lives. Now consider the friends, family members, relationship partners, community members, and employers of those individuals who may be affected by the substance misuse. Very quickly, the number of people impacted by addiction in the United States becomes immense.

In light of the number of people affected by addiction, the need for prevention and intervention efforts is clearly apparent, and mental health professionals are uniquely poised to join in this effort. We contend that *all* counselors should feel a personal responsibility to be able to identify, conceptualize, and respond to substance use disorders and behavioral addictions (whether that means making an appropriate referral or treating the addiction themselves). If not, clinicians may spend months addressing clients' presenting concerns without seeing treatment gains because addiction issues are left unidentified. Thus, part of addressing the problem of addiction in this country is to provide effective training to *all* mental health professionals so they are equipped to respond to addiction in their work.

LEARNING ACTIVITY 1.1
PREVALENCE OF ADDICTION

Beyond statistics and data, the prevalence of addiction often is revealed in our own experiences. Take a moment to do a quick exercise. List out the members of the last three generations of your family tree (first generation: you and your siblings; second generation: your parents, as well as their siblings, their siblings' spouses, and their siblings' children; third generation: your grandparents, as well as their siblings, their siblings' spouses, and their siblings' children). Among these three generations of your family tree, are you aware of anyone who struggled with addiction (which can include the misuse of alcohol, tobacco, illicit drugs, gambling, sex, pornography, internet gaming, work, shopping, or exercise)? Are you aware of anyone who attended a 12-step program? Are you aware of anyone who would identify as being in recovery? What comes up for you as you do this activity?

Now, the claim that *all* mental health professionals should be trained in addiction counseling may elicit some opposition. For instance, students may ask, "But what if I am not planning to work in an *addiction setting*? Is this course really that important for me?" That is a valid question, yet given the prevalence of addiction, counselors in all settings (schools, community agencies, private practice, college counseling centers, hospitals, marriage and family agencies, religious organizations) will see chemical and/or behavioral addiction as part of their professional responsibilities. In fact, it is likely that students need not wait until they start their postgraduation employment to begin responding to addiction. Indeed, researchers found that large numbers of counseling students worked with substance use issues in their graduate-level practicum and internship experiences (Salyers et al., 2006).

Another reason why all mental health professionals should be trained to respond to addiction is the fact that individuals with substance use disorders or behavioral addictions interact with many different types of professionals (e.g., doctors, teachers, dentists, law enforcement, clergy, school counselors, marriage and family counselors) before going to specialized addictions treatment (if they receive treatment at all). For example, individuals with addiction may make appointments with their primary care physicians about health issues (caused by their addictive behaviors). Or they may see a counselor or psychiatrist about anxiety or depression (again, symptomology resulting from addiction). Or perhaps they schedule an appointment with their pastor or clergy member to discuss marital problems (which are emerging as a result of addictive behaviors). By increasing knowledge related to addiction across disciplines, the recognition of chemical and behavioral addiction can occur earlier, and individuals with addiction may be able to get the help they need much faster.

A final consideration for the importance of this course for all counselor-trainees is the fact that the use of substances is greater among individuals with mental health concerns than those without mental health concerns (SAMHSA, 2020). Indeed, mental illnesses and substance use disorders often co-occur, and in 2019, 9.5 million people in the United States had both a mental illness and a substance use disorder (SAMHSA, 2020). Individuals may seek psychiatric or therapeutic services for a mental illness (e.g., depression, anxiety, phobia) while also simultaneously dealing with addiction. Therefore, mental health professionals must be able to recognize and respond to addiction in light of these co-occurrence rates.

The aim of this textbook is to help prepare you to recognize, conceptualize, and respond effectively to addiction regardless of the setting in which you will work. Although there is new knowledge to be learned and new counseling techniques to consider, counseling students are not "starting from scratch" as they learn to address addiction. Instead, the information provided in this textbook is meant to build upon your previously learned counseling skills, your use of counseling theory, your multicultural competence, and your ability to engage in client conceptualization and treatment planning. All of your foundational clinical skills will be applied to your work with addiction. And, for those students who are interested in pursuing a career in an addiction setting, this textbook will give you the information needed to begin specializing in addiction counseling. So, let's start by exploring the prevalence of addiction to fully understand the breadth of the issue.

PREVALENCE OF ADDICTION

There is no question that addiction is a serious, prevalent issue in the United States. According to recent data from the National Survey on Drug Use and Health (NSDUH), 7.4% of Americans aged 12 years or older had a substance use disorder in the past year—that is 20.4 million people (SAMHSA, 2020)! Of those with substance use disorders, 71.1% had alcohol use disorders, while 40.7% had a disorder related to an illicit drug (SAMHSA, 2020). Additionally, 21.2 million people identified as being a person in recovery from alcohol or other drug addictions (SAMHSA, 2020). With regard to addictive behaviors, researchers found a median prevalence rate of internet gaming disorder to be 2.0% among nonclinical samples of children and adolescents and 5.5% with clinical samples included (Paulus et al., 2018). Additionally, Karila and colleagues' (2014) literature review revealed prevalence rates of sex addiction ranging from 3% to 16.8%. It is clear that mental health counselors working with clients across the life span will need to be equipped to recognize and respond to addiction.

But what about school counselors? How is a course on addiction counseling relevant to them? Counselors who work in schools have the unique opportunity to provide early interventions among students who are using substances or engaging in addictive behaviors. According to the 2019 Monitoring the Future Survey, 8.5% of eighth graders, 19.8% of 10th graders, and 23.7% of 12th graders used an illicit drug (including marijuana) in the previous 30 days (Miech et al., 2020). In addition, 2.6% of eighth graders, 8.8% of 10th graders, and 17.5% of 12th graders reported being drunk in the previous 30 days (Miech et al., 2020). The majority of substance use disorders and behavioral addictions begin in adolescence (e.g., researchers have found the average age of first pornography exposure to be 12 years old; Kraus & Rosenberg, 2014), thus, as school counselors become more aware of addiction, they will be prepared to intervene effectively. Rather than waiting for substance use disorders to fully develop and wreak havoc on the lives of clients and those they love, early intervention in the school system may change the course of a person's life. And those who do not think addiction is relevant among student populations may be surprised to learn that 43 recovery high schools (i.e., schools for students in recovery from a substance use disorder) currently exist in the United States (Association of Recovery Schools, 2021).

Okay, but what about child counselors and play therapists? Why is this course necessary? It is true that clinicians working with very young children likely will not see clients with addiction, however, it is probable that they will work with children who currently live in homes with active addiction. In fact, data reveal that 12.3% of children 17 years old or younger live with at least one parent who has a substance use disorder—that is 8.7 million children (Lipari & Van Horn, 2017). Additionally, recent data from the Fourth National Incidence Study of Child Abuse and Neglect reveal that alcohol abuse of the perpetrator was involved in 12.7% of child abuse cases and 12.1% of child neglect cases (Sedlak et al., 2010). Additionally, drug abuse of the perpetrator was involved in 9.5% of child abuse cases and 12.5% of child neglect cases (Sedlak et al., 2010). The ability to recognize when addiction is present in the home of a child and to conceptualize the potential implications of parental substance use on child development are necessary skills for child counselors.

Alright, but what about college counselors or student affairs professionals? What can this course offer them? For decades, American colleges and universities have been known for their permissive social norms related to alcohol and other drug use. Indeed, recent Monitoring the Future data reveal that 47% of 19- to 22-year-old college students used an illicit drug (including marijuana) in the past year, and almost 6% used marijuana on a near-daily basis (Schulenberg et al., 2020). Additionally, 33% of college students (aged 19–22) reported binge drinking (consuming five or more drinks in a row) in the previous two weeks (Schulenberg et al., 2020), and 1,519 college students (aged 18–24) died from unintentional alcohol-related deaths in 2014 (Hingson et al., 2017). Along with high rates of substance use among college students, behavioral addictions are prevalent as well. Indeed, Giordano and Cashwell (2018) found that 84.4% of college counselors reported working with at least one collegiate client in the past year with sex-addiction related concerns. Moreover, a metaanalysis of gambling trends among university students revealed an average estimated percentage of probable pathological gamblers to be 6.13% (Nowak, 2018). Thus, it is clear that clinicians and student affairs' professionals who work in collegiate settings must be prepared to respond to both chemical and behavioral addiction.

LEARNING ACTIVITY 1.2 PREPARING COUNSELORS IN ALL SETTINGS TO ADDRESS ADDICTION

Think about the setting in which you would like to work once you graduate (e.g., community agency, school, college counseling center, private practice, hospital, residential treatment facility) or the population in which you would like to specialize (e.g., military, individuals with eating disorders, individuals with serious mental illness, couples, families, children, LGBTQIA+ populations). Come up with three reasons as to why it is important for you to be knowledgeable and equipped to address addiction in this particular setting or with this particular population.

Therefore, community mental health, school, child/play, and college/university counselors all need to be prepared to respond to addiction. Beyond clinical work, however, mental health professionals must be knowledgeable about addiction to understand its impact on public narratives, legislation, public policy, and historical contexts. Although more examples will be provided in Chapter 14

(Multicultural Considerations in Addiction Treatment) and Chapter 15 (Advocating for Addicted Populations), the breadth of the impact of drugs of abuse on American society can be seen clearly in the recent opioid epidemic.

THE OPIOID EPIDEMIC

The *opioid epidemic* is now common nomenclature in today's society. As you will read in Chapter 4 (Substance Use Disorders and Case Management), opioids are a class of drugs with pain-relieving, euphoric effects. Opioids can be natural (e.g., opium), semi-synthetic (e.g., oxycodone, heroin), or fully synthetic (e.g., fentanyl). The opioid epidemic emerged as a result of the alarming number of drug overdose deaths involving this specific class of drugs. For example, in 2019, 70,630 people died from a drug overdose, and opioids were involved in over 70% of those deaths (CDC, 2021a). Since 1999, there have been approximately 500,000 overdose deaths involving opioids (CDC, 2021b). To put that number in perspective, in the last 20 years, the number of people who have died due to opioids is roughly the same as the population of Miami, Florida. In 2017, the Department of Health and Human Services issued a public health emergency in response to the opioid epidemic.

Experts contend that the opioid epidemic has had three distinct waves: (1) rise in prescription opioid deaths beginning in the late 1990s, (2) rise in heroin deaths beginning in 2010, and (3) rise in fentanyl deaths beginning in 2013 (it has yet to be seen if the worldwide COVID-19 pandemic will be associated with a fourth wave of the opioid epidemic; CDC, 2021b). The first wave was largely fueled by false information about the addictive nature of prescription opioids, like OxyContin, a prescription medication containing oxycodone created by Purdue Pharma (Edgell, 2020). In the mid-1990s, Purdue Pharma began marketing OxyContin as a medication for pain that had a low addiction potential, which was a false claim. In response to the aggressive marketing strategies of Purdue Pharma, physicians began prescribing opioids at rapid rates, leading to a surge in addiction and overdose deaths. Once the addiction potential of OxyContin was realized, 49 states filed lawsuits against Purdue Pharma, and the company has since proposed a settlement deal (Edgell, 2020). Since the mid-1990s, opioid addiction and overdose deaths have continued to climb. Some individuals with opioid use disorders began by misusing prescription opioids and progressed to stronger drugs like heroin. Consider the case of Michael.

CASE EXAMPLE: MICHAEL

Michael loved sports since he was little. Throughout grade school, Michael played basketball in the fall and baseball in the spring. He was talented and dedicated and played on the varsity teams of his high school. During his junior year, Michael was injured during a championship basketball game. He severely hurt his back and was in an enormous amount of pain. He underwent an invasive surgery followed by six months of physical therapy. During this time, Michael was prescribed opioids (e.g., oxycodone) to manage the pain. Michael took the medication as prescribed and quickly realized he felt immensely better when he was on the medication, not only physically but psychologically as well. He noted that, along with his physical pain, all of his stress, problems, and anxiety also dissipated when he took the

(*continued*)

medication. Soon, he began craving the pills before it was time for his next dose, and he would take more pills in a 24-hour period than was recommended. He loved how he felt when he took the medicine and said it "just made all the problems go away."

Over time, Michael began to become fearful about what would happen when his prescription ran out. Therefore, each time he went to see his doctor, he exaggerated his pain level to ensure he received another refill. Finally, after almost a year, his doctor said he should be able to manage pain with over-the-counter pain medicine (e.g., ibuprofen) and refused to refill his opioid prescription. At that point, Michael was taking the drug around the clock and felt withdrawal symptoms if he went too long without it. He learned from one of his coworkers at his part-time job that he could buy OxyContin off the street from a local dealer. Michael was nervous at first, but he felt that he needed the drug to survive, so he began buying it from his coworker's dealer. One day, the dealer said he didn't have any more OxyContin, but he told Michael that heroin would give him "an even better rush." Desperately, Michael agreed and used heroin for the first time. The dealer was right—Michael had never felt as good as he felt when he used heroin. He knew immediately that he was hooked. Since that day, Michael has not gone 24 hours without using heroin. At first, he smoked it, but then he started injecting heroin to feel the high faster and more intensely. Now, as an adult in a residential treatment facility for opioid use disorder, Michael says he never thought he'd be a "dope fiend" and is not sure "how his life turned out this way."

The relationship between prescription opioids and heroin use is complex. A researcher found that among individuals who used heroin in the past year in 2008–2010, 77.4% used prescription opioids prior to initiating heroin use (Jones, 2013). Additionally, in a longitudinal study of high school students, researchers found that nonmedical prescription opioid use was linked to higher probabilities of future heroin use (Kelley-Quon et al., 2019). Moreover, among clients with opioid use disorder involving heroin, 49% reported filling at least one prescription for an opioid in the year prior to initiating heroin use (Hartung et al., 2021).

It is important to note that not all opioid use constitutes drug misuse or addiction. Many people are prescribed opioids for pain management and do not misuse the medication. They take the drug as prescribed and discontinue its use when the prescription runs out. However, for a small portion of the population, opioid use becomes compulsive and continues

LEARNING ACTIVITY 1.3
THE PERVASIVENESS OF OPIOIDS

About two years ago, the second author (ALG) needed to get a root canal for an aching tooth. After the procedure, the endodontist told her that he was giving her a prescription for hydrocodone (a prescription opioid) in case she felt any pain after the procedure. As an educator and researcher who specializes in addiction, ALG found it alarming that he was dispensing a prescription for an opioid without asking any questions about her history of drug use, addiction, or recovery. When she brought this to the endodontist's attention, he said he has never thought about asking those questions before giving patients a prescription for an opioid. Although ALG was not in recovery herself, the ease with which opioids are prescribed could make it very difficult for individuals with a history of addiction. After a lengthy discussion, the endodontist conceded that it may be in everyone's best interest to ask more specific questions about drug/addiction history prior to giving prescriptions for opioids.

Consider your own experience with prescription opioids or the experiences of others in your life. What are concrete examples of how we as a society can work to curb the opioid epidemic?

despite negative consequences. These individuals meet criteria for opioid use disorder in the *Diagnostic and Statistical Manual of Mental Disorders*, Fifth Edition (*DSM-5*; American Psychiatric Association [APA], 2013), and are in need of professional treatment. Thus, in light of the magnitude of the opioid epidemic and the manner in which it has shaped American history, it is imperative that all mental health professionals are knowledgeable about opioid use and opportunities for advocacy.

CURRENT STATE OF TRAINING FOR ADDICTION COUNSELING

Given the prevalence of substance use and addictive behaviors, the important question is whether or not counseling students are being adequately trained to address addiction in their clinical work. The answer to that question has mixed results. For instance, the study of 111 accredited counselor-education programs revealed that 84.5% had a substance abuse course as part of their program (Salyers et al., 2006). Although the course was available, data did not indicate whether the course was required or an elective. Despite the prevalence of addictions courses, researchers surveyed 131 master's- and doctoral-level counseling students and found that the counseling trainees reported feeling least competent and least trained to address substance use issues among clients as compared to posttraumatic stress disorder (PTSD), poverty, or self-growth concerns (Tucker et al., in press). Additionally, among high school counselors, 50.3% reported they did not have a substance abuse course during their graduate program (Burrow-Sanchez & Lopez, 2009). These counselors reported feeling the most competent consulting with teachers about substance use issues among students and the least competent providing screenings or assessments for students' substance use (Burrow-Sanchez & Lopez, 2009).

Thus, although the majority of counseling programs appear to offer substance abuse or addiction counseling courses, the number of students who take these courses, as well as the efficacy of the courses themselves, is unclear. Recent literature does describe efforts of professional training programs to equip their students to work with addiction in ways other than taking a graduate-level course. For example, graduate students in an accredited psychology program received training for screening, brief intervention, and referral to treatment (SBIRT; Martin et al., 2020). The students completed either a 7-hour in-person SBIRT training or a 4-hour online booster SBIRT training. Over 90% of the in-person participants and 96.3% of the online participants said the training was relevant to their careers. Furthermore, 51.7% of the in-person participants and 75% of the online participants utilized what they learned with a client within 30 days of the training (Martin et al., 2020). Thus, it appears that, although there is room to improve, counselor-training programs are working toward preparing students to recognize and respond to addiction in their clinical work, either by offering specific courses or providing relevant training experiences.

Accreditation Standards

Reputable accreditation bodies of counselor-training programs also emphasize the need to prepare students to work with addiction. The 2016 standards of the Council for Accreditation of Counseling and Related Educational Programs (CACREP) identifies the need for students to understand "theories and etiology of addictions and addictive behaviors" (Section 2, F.3.d). Specifically, as counseling students gain knowledge related to human development, they should have an awareness of factors influencing the emergence and progression of both chemical and behavioral addictions. Although the word "addiction" is found in only one standard, knowledge pertaining to addictions fulfills myriad other training standards across the CACREP common core, such as utilizing essential counseling and conceptualization skills (Section 2, F.5.g), developing effective treatment plans (Section 2, F.5.h), understanding dynamics of the group counseling process (Section 2, F.6.b), using assessments appropriately (Section 2, F.7.e), considering differences in help-seeking behaviors among diverse clients (Section 2, F.2.f), and understanding the various roles of counselors as well as relationships between counselors and integrated behavioral healthcare professionals (Section 2, F.1.b.). Either by creating one or more mandatory courses or by infusing addictions-related content throughout CACREP core courses, counselor-training programs can effectively meet these standards. Take a look at Table 1.1 for examples of addictions-related content that could be infused across several foundational courses in a counselor-training program. Can you think of other examples?

TABLE 1.1 Examples of Addictions-Related Content Across the CACREP Common Core

CACREP COMMON CORE AREA	EXAMPLE OF ADDICTION-RELATED CONTENT
Professional Counseling Orientation and Ethical Practice	- History of addiction counseling - Counselor's roles in addiction treatment settings - Counselor's role working with other members of an addiction treatment team - Specialty accreditations for addiction counseling - Self-care strategies when working with addiction - Ethics regarding confidentiality with mandated clients in addictions treatment
Social and Cultural Diversity	- Advocating for clients with addiction - Systemic oppression related to drug laws and policies - Origins of drug laws and relationship to marginalized group members - Integrating spirituality into addiction counseling - Relationship among race-based traumatic stress, minority stress, acculturative stress, and substance use
Human Growth and Development	- How substance use or addictive behaviors can impact the developing brain - Etiology of chemical and behavioral addiction - Systemic factors that contribute to the use of substance or engagement in addictive behaviors - Neuroadaptations caused by drugs of abuse or addictive behaviors - Biopsychosocial model of addiction and role of genetics - Substance use as a means of coping with adverse childhood experiences, trauma, and crisis - Using an ecological model to conceptualize addiction
Career Development	- Career options and restrictions for clients with felony drug charges - Advantages and disadvantages of various career options for clients in long-term recovery - Career assessments and career decision-making programs for clients in addictions treatment or incarcerated for drug charges

(continued)

TABLE 1.1 Examples of Addictions-Related Content Across the CACREP Common Core (*continued*)

CACREP COMMON CORE AREA	EXAMPLE OF ADDICTION-RELATED CONTENT
Counseling and Helping Relationships	- Applying various theoretical orientations to the conceptualization and work with clients with addiction - Applying motivational interviewing skills to clinical work with addiction - Creating a strong therapeutic alliance with clients in various stages of change - Assessing for suicide among clients with chemical or behavioral addictions - Integrating trauma-informed care into addiction counseling - Developing empathy for clients with addiction - Developing a treatment plan for clients with addiction - Clinical work with couples or families in which active addiction is present
Group Counseling and Group Work	- Applying various theoretical orientations and group counseling approaches with an addiction counseling group - Recruiting and screening processes for an addiction counseling group - Necessary group counselor skills for facilitating an addiction counseling group - Various types of groups utilized with clients with addiction (e.g., psychoeducational, process, skill-building) - Ethical considerations for addiction counseling groups
Assessment and Testing	- Suicide assessment among clients with chemical and/or behavioral addictions - Utilizing standardized instruments for assessing chemical and behavioral addictions - Recognizing and reporting child abuse related to parental substance use - Interpreting and processing addiction assessment results with clients - Ethics related to disclosing assessment results when working with mandated clients in addictions treatment
Research and Program Evaluation	- Critiquing research related to substance use rates among diverse cultural groups - Reviewing the literature to identify both evidence-based counseling practices for addiction counseling and culturally adapted practices for diverse clients - Conducting needs assessments in various settings related to chemical or behavioral addictions - Evaluating the efficacy and outcomes of prevention and intervention strategies for addiction - Conducting quality research to better understand the etiology, progression, and treatment of addiction

CACREP, Council for Accreditation of Counseling and Related Educational Programs.

Along with counselor-training programs, similar education and training standards can be found in the fields of psychology and social work as well. The same addictions-related content can be infused across foundational courses in several mental health disciplines (e.g., rehabilitation counseling, psychology, psychiatry, social work, pastoral counseling). In sum, the understanding of addiction among mental health professionals in graduate training programs is necessary to fulfill multiple accreditation standards and prepare competent clinicians.

EFFECTIVE CLINICAL WORK WITH ADDICTIONS

When students consider working with clients with chemical or behavioral addictions, they may ask, "But what does it take to be effective?" The answer includes many of the same characteristics and skills that make counselors effective with other presenting concerns (e.g., ability to build a strong therapeutic alliance, active listening skills, assessment skills, treatment planning, ethical and professional behavior, treatment optimism and hope, multicultural competence, cognitive flexibility, unconditional positive regard, genuineness). In addition to the skills necessary for clinical effectiveness with all presenting concerns, there are a few aspects that are particularly important when working with addiction. Let's consider a few of these traits:

Empathy

The crux of clinical effectiveness is a counselor's ability to enter into the inner world of their clients, understand their lived experiences, and communicate that understanding back to the client. This skill is called *empathy.* Counselors need not have personal experience with everything that their clients have experienced to be effective (e.g., divorce, miscarriage, chronic pain, mental illness, early trauma), yet they need to be able to thoroughly understand the clients' experiences and meaning-making process. In the same way, counselors working with clients with addiction need not have experience with addiction and recovery themselves in order to be effective. In fact, Culbreth (2000) conducted a literature review and found that treatment outcomes among clients with addiction were similar regardless of whether the counselor was in recovery or not.

Instead, the essence of effective clinical work with addiction is the ability to empathize with clients and communicate that empathic understanding in session. Importantly, Carl Rogers (1980) noted, "The highest expression of empathy is accepting and nonjudgmental. This is true because it is impossible to be accurately perceptive of another's inner world if you have formed an evaluative opinion of that person" (pp. 153–154). Therefore, if counselors have "evaluative opinions" of individuals with addiction, it will be challenging (if not impossible) to genuinely empathize with their clients. This lack of empathy will be a hindrance to effective clinical work and may lead to early client termination, a weak therapeutic alliance, or incomplete or inaccurate client conceptualizations. Therefore, prior to working with clients with addiction, counselors must do their own work to address personal *biases*, potential *countertransference*, and *stigma* related to addiction.

LEARNING ACTIVITY 1.4
OBSTACLES TO EMPATHY

There are many potential obstacles to cultivating empathy for clients with addiction. For example, our own personal experiences with alcohol or other drugs and addictive behaviors, the experiences of those in our family or friend group, and the messages we internalize from society, the media, and the news. Answer the following questions as honestly as possible to identify potential obstacles to your ability to foster empathy for clients with addiction:

What are the first images that come to mind when you read the following words: "addict," "drug user," "alcoholic," "junkie." To what extent do these images reveal personal biases or the endorsement of negative stereotypes?

What has been your own experience with alcohol and other drug use or addictive behaviors (e.g., sex, gambling, pornography, internet gaming, social media, nonsuicidal self-injury)? How might your personal experiences affect how you perceive future clients with addiction? What countertransference issues will you want to monitor?

What has been your experience with others with addiction? This can include family members in active addiction or long-term recovery, friends, neighbors, coworkers, or romantic partners. How might these experiences affect how you perceive future clients with addiction? Where might there be potential for countertransference?

What are your personal beliefs about addiction (including chemical and behavioral)? To what extent do you perceive addiction to be a moral issue? To what extent do you perceive addiction to be a health issue? How might these beliefs impact your perception of future clients with addiction?

Addiction-Related Knowledge

Along with the ability to empathize (without evaluation), counselors should have specific knowledge related to addiction in order to create accurate conceptualizations and treatment plans. This knowledge can come from an addictions course in a graduate-training program, continuing education workshops and presentations, self-study, or supervision during internship or practicum. Prior to beginning their counseling careers, all counselors should have a basic understanding of drugs of abuse and behavioral addictions, the neuroscience of addiction, and effective treatment strategies for individual, group, and family counseling related to addiction. A study of counselors in training revealed that accurate information about addiction and treatment correlated with a decrease in stereotypical perspectives about addiction, which was essential for cultivating an optimistic view of addictions treatment (Chasek et al., 2012). Thus, the more knowledge a counselor acquires related to addiction, the less they will adhere to stereotypical beliefs (or overgeneralizations about people with addiction, which often are influenced by societal stigma) related to drug use and addictive behaviors. Take a moment to consider ways in which you can acquire addiction-related knowledge during your time in your graduate-training program (starting with reading this textbook!).

Self-Care

The importance of self-care is relevant to all kinds of clinical work, including work with addiction. Counselors continuously immerse themselves into the experience of others, which may be wrought with hardship, trauma, stress, and pain. Thus, the risk of *burnout* or *compassion fatigue* is prevalent among all mental health professionals. Specifically, burnout refers to "a syndrome of emotional exhaustion, depersonalization, and reduced personal accomplishment that can occur among individuals who do "people work" of some kind" (Maslach, 2003, p. 2). A similar yet distinct construct is *compassion fatigue*, which also has been called *secondary traumatic stress*. *Compassion fatigue* occurs when counselors are affected by the trauma of others (Figley, 2002), specifically "those who work with suffering suffer themselves because of the work" (Figley, 2002, p. 5). Without intentional, regular efforts to engage in self-care, counselors can experience burnout, compassion fatigue, or both. Therefore, when working with clients with addiction, it is important that counselors have a routine for how to protect and nurture their physical, psychological, emotional, and spiritual well-being. In fact, the American Counseling Association (ACA) *Code of Ethics* mandates that "counselors engage in self-care activities to maintain and promote their own emotional, physical, mental, and spiritual well-being to best meet their professional responsibilities" (2014, p. 8).

Clients with addiction often have histories of trauma and adverse childhood experiences, may engage in risky or illegal behaviors while in active addiction, and likely will experience relapse (or a return to use after a period of abstinence). All of these factors can increase the risk of burnout or compassion fatigue among counselors who work with clients with addiction. Therefore, self-care practices are essential for providing effective client care and ensuring the well-being of the counselor. Take a moment to consider effective ways in which you nurture and care for yourself. If this is a deficit area, what might be one step you could take toward strengthening your self-care practices?

NOTES FROM THE FIELD

Will Atkins, MA, LPC, was not planning on pursuing a career in the addictions field, but after interning at MARR Addiction Treatment Center, everything changed. After his internship at MARR, he was hired as a residential manager, which led to him becoming the director of residential services, and now he currently serves as the director of the men's recovery center program. When asked what he finds so rewarding about working in the addictions field, Will replied, "Getting to witness the moment when clients first experience hope again. Most people come in to treatment with little to no hope, and then something clicks and they get a glimmer of hope. Cultivating that hope and watching it grow is what I find most rewarding."

Will has experience providing individual, group, and family sessions in his role at the men's recovery center. He operates from an existential, 12-step foundation, applying spiritual principles (e.g., cultivating core values such as honesty, integrity, and courage) and 12-step work into his clinical practice. He believes that an essential component of addictions treatment is helping clients make connections, stating, "Addiction, at the root, is a disease of disconnection and isolation." Will purports that helping clients find purpose and meaning and developing connections with other people as well as spiritual connections are at the core of addiction counseling.

In his years of experience working with clients with addiction, Will has learned that most of his clients have had experiences of trauma, and thus counselors must be prepared to provide trauma-informed care. In order to do this well, counselors must engage in their own self-care practices to stay healthy. Will notes, "We are containers, of sorts, for what our clients are dealing with...we hold it for them until they can hold it for themselves. If you are full of your own issues or struggles, you can't show up to be a container for your clients."

With regard to challenges facing the profession, Will identified the movement toward short-term, insurance-driven care. He stated, "Because of the longevity of addiction, it is hard to comply with a short-term time frame. The longer clients can be in treatment, the better." Will also describes the importance of a systems orientation when working with addiction. Focusing only on the individual, rather than the systems in which that individual exists (e.g., family, community), is ineffective.

Will emphasized that all counselors should be knowledgeable about addiction. He stated, "Regardless of your specialty area, addiction is going to show up." He encourages counselors to be aware of the models of addiction that exist, understand 12-step programs, and be informed about addictions treatment referrals and resources in their local area. Will noted that counselors who work in the addictions field should be well-rounded in their knowledge and training pertaining to mental health concerns given that "addiction is a symptom of an underlying emotional issue." From adverse childhood experiences to co-occurring mental health concerns, counselors in the addictions field should be prepared to address a wide variety of presenting concerns and symptoms.

ETHICAL CONSIDERATIONS IN ADDICTION COUNSELING

Some students may be hesitant to work with clients with addiction because of perceived ethical ambiguity. For instance, if an adolescent client is using illicit drugs, when and who should you tell? If an adult client comes to a counseling session intoxicated, what do you do? If you are working with a mandated client whose urine screen comes back positive for drugs, must you disclose this information? If you believe a client is likely to relapse on a dangerous drug, what is your responsibility? If a client discloses that they are making and using illicit drugs in a home with young children, how should you respond? What if a pregnant client is consuming alcohol? These are important ethical questions to consider and, thankfully, there are many available tools to help counselors engage in the ethical decision-making process.

First, all mental health professions have a code of ethics. These codes outline desired behaviors among members of the profession and professional values. For example, the ACA *Code of Ethics* (2014) describes six principles of ethical practice: (1) autonomy (recognizing and respecting clients' control over their own lives), (2) nonmaleficence (do no harm), (3) beneficence (do good), (4) justice (operate with equality and fairness), (5) fidelity (follow through on commitments and work with integrity), and (6) veracity (be truthful). As counselors engage in ethical clinical work and advocacy, they ensure that their actions are reflective of these broad principles. The remaining ACA *Code of Ethics* (2014) provides specific guidance for topics spanning from the counseling relationship to distance counseling. The ethical codes of a mental health professional's specific field are foundational for clinical work with all presenting concerns, including addiction. Just like counseling with other clinical concerns, counselors who work with addiction engage in a thorough informed-consent process, obtain all required documentation and releases of information, protect clients' confidentiality unless specific situations arise (which are outlined in the informed consent, such as intent to harm oneself or child abuse), and maintain accurate and timely client records. Therefore, counselors who work with addiction are required to be knowledgeable of their profession's ethical codes and continually assess whether they are adhering to these standards in their clinical work.

Along with the ethical codes of specific mental health professions, many states have their own codes and regulations related to mental health practice. Counselors who work with addiction must be knowledgeable and trained in the laws, codes, and policies of the state in which they practice. For example, the Texas Administrative Code has a chapter related to substance use services as well as behavioral health programs with codes and policies relevant to counselors working with addiction. The Georgia Composite Board of Professional Counselors, Social Workers and Marriage and Family Therapists also has rules and regulations for licensed professionals in the state of Georgia, including a code of ethics (which is relevant to all clinical work, including work with addiction). In addition, each state has laws related to confidentiality, mandated reporting, and duty to warn, which are all relevant to clinical work with addiction. For example, parental substance use may cause a "failure to provide" in which children are neglected and without access to basic necessities (e.g., food, water, medical care, shelter, access to education), "failure to supervise" in which children are unmonitored, or "endangering a child" in which children witness crimes, felonies, or violence or are put in situations in which they could experience harm (e.g., being present in a home where methamphetamine is being made or in a car in which the driver is intoxicated). In each instance, counselors may need to make a report to the appropriate authorities in their state given their status as mandated reporters. Therefore, along with the ethical standards of their profession, clinicians who work with addiction also must be aware of the laws, policies, and regulations in the state in which they practice.

Finally, there are specific laws and ethical considerations unique to working with addiction that should be considered. For example, the Code of Federal Regulations 42 Part 2 protects the confidentiality of individuals who are seeking addictions treatment. This policy was passed in the 1970s as a means of removing treatment barriers by ensuring clients' records would be kept confidential as they sought treatment in federally funded addictions programs. Additionally, the Association for Addiction Professionals (NAADAC, 2021) provides a *Code of Ethics* specific to its members and those certified as Master Addiction Counselors (MAC). These ethical standards provide guidance related to the counseling relationship, confidentiality, professional responsibilities, diversity and multiculturalism, assessment and evaluations, distance counseling and e-therapy, supervision, ethical decision-making processes, and publications (NAADAC, 2021).

Similar to other ethical codes, NAADAC promotes nine principles that should be considered in light of all ethical decisions (and some of these principles are the same as those listed in the ACA *Code of Ethics*): (1) autonomy, (2) obedience (commitment to obeying laws and ethical standards), (3) conscientious refusal (commitment to refuse illegal or unethical directives), (4) beneficence, (5) gratitude (to help others as a way to honor those who have helped us), (6) competence (to be equipped and current with skills and knowledge to help clients), (7) justice, (8) stewardship (to use one's resources in a manner that serves others), and (9) honesty and candor (to be truthful in all dealings). Along with these principles, the ethical code describes best practices for specific situations such as confidentiality with mandated clients, required documentation, culturally appropriate communication, advocacy, and engaging in evidence-based practice (NAADAC, 2021). Even counselors who are not members of NAADAC can refer to the *Code of Ethics* for guidance related to ethical work with clients with addiction.

Finally, SAMHSA (2017) has provided counseling competencies for work with addiction. Specifically, the *Addiction Counseling Competencies* were drafted as a means of guiding ethical and effective practice by outlining 123 competencies across four transdisciplinary foundations (i.e., understanding addiction; treatment knowledge; application to practice; professional readiness) and eight practice dimensions (i.e., clinical evaluation; treatment planning; referral; service coordination; counseling; client, family, and community education; documentation; professional and ethical responsibilities). Examples of competencies include "use a range of supervisory options to process personal feelings and concerns about clients" (SAMHSA, 2017, p. 156) and "record progress of client in relation to treatment goals and objectives" (SAMHSA, 2017, p. 146). The *Addiction Counseling Competencies* were first drafted in 1993 and have been revised regularly through 2017. They provide thorough guidance for clinical work with addiction and serve as an important consultation tool.

Therefore, counselors working with clients with addiction have a range of resources at their disposal to guide their work and ensure ethical practice. The ethical standards of their profession, the laws and regulations of their state, and competencies and codes specific to addiction counseling are all available to consult. Additionally, as situations arise that cause counselors to question the appropriate ethical response when working with clients with addiction, they are encouraged to follow standard ethical decision-making guidelines such as (a) consult with seasoned professionals; (b) seek supervision; (c) consider all relevant principles, laws, ethical codes, and standards; (d) apply ethical principles and values; (e) generate multiple potential options; (f) brainstorm risks and benefits of all options; (g) apply a plan of action; and (h) reevaluate plans and options as necessary (Forester-Miller & Davis, 1996; NAADAC, 2021).

CREDENTIALING IN ADDICTION COUNSELING

A final topic for us to consider in this introductory chapter is credentialing options for counselors who wish to seek advanced training in addiction counseling. Although all mental health professionals should be equipped to respond to addiction, some clinicians may want to work primarily with clients with addiction or in specialized addiction treatment facilities. To demonstrate advanced training and competence, these counselors can choose to pursue specific credentials related to addiction counseling. In the past, counselors who wanted to work in the addictions field did not need graduate-level training (Mustaine et al., 2003). Many individuals became substance abuse counselors by accruing hours of clinical experience and receiving education through workshops and seminars. Today, however, addiction counseling is not seen as a separate profession, but rather part of the counseling field, and many credentials now require a graduate-level degree (Mustaine et al., 2003).

Each state in the United States has its own board of professionals who oversee addiction counseling credentialing, and many rely on the standards provided by the International Certification & Reciprocity Consortium (IC&RC). The IC&RC monitors six addiction counseling-related credentials (Alcohol & Drug Counselor [ADC], Advanced Alcohol & Drug Counselor [AADC], Clinical Supervisor [CS], Prevention Specialist [PS], Certified Criminal Justice Addictions Professional [CCJP], and Peer Recovery [PR]) that are endorsed by many state certification boards. For example, the state of Arizona has the Arizona Board for Certification of Addiction Counselors (ABCAC) and offers all six IC&RC credentials (PR, CS, PS, AADC, ADC, and CCJP). The state of New York has the New York State Office of Alcoholism and Substance Abuse Services (NYS OASAS) and offers two IC&RC credentials (PS and ACD). South Carolina has the Addiction Professionals of South Carolina (SCAADAC) and offers four IC&RC credentials (PR, CS, ACD, and AADC). Not all states, however, are members of the IC&RC, and some have their own state-specific credentialing processes for addiction counseling. For example, North Dakota is not an IC&RC member and offers its own Licensed Addiction Counselor (LAC) credential and Licensed Master Addiction Counselor (LMAC) credential (see Table 1.2 for a description of credentialing standards among four states that are not part of the IC&RC). Therefore, for those interested in pursuing addiction-counseling credentials, it is important to research the options available in your state.

TABLE 1.2 Credentialing Standards for States That Are Not Members of the IC&RC

STATE	CREDENTIAL	STANDARDS
Alaska	Counselor Technician	*Nondegree Track* • 84 training hours in NAADAC ethics, confidentiality, HIV/AIDS, addictive behaviors, documentation, crisis intervention, client-centered counseling, group counseling, working with diverse populations, community resources use, recovery education • 3 references *With Higher-Education Degree in Behavioral-Health-Related Field* • 20 training hours in NAADAC ethics, confidentiality, HIV/AIDS, and addictive behaviors • 3 references
	Chemical Dependency Counselor I	*Nondegree Track* • Experience: 4,000 hours (2 years) • Practicum hours: 100 hours • Training hours:148 hours • References: 3 references, 1 from supervisor *With Higher-Education Degree in Behavioral-Health-Related Field* • Experience: 2,000 hours (1 year) • Practicum hours: 100 hours • Training hours: 20 hours • References: 3 references, 1 from supervisor

(continued)

TABLE 1.2 Credentialing Standards for States That Are Not Members of the IC&RC (*continued*)

STATE	CREDENTIAL	STANDARDS
	Chemical Dependency Counselor II	*Nondegree Track* • Experience: 8,000 hours (4 years) • Practicum hours: 100 hours in addition to practicum requirements for Counselor-I (totaling 200 practicum hours) • Training hours: 176 hours • References: 3 references, 1 from supervisor • Exam: NAADAC level I or II or MAC *With Higher-Education Degree in Behavioral-Health-Related Field* • Experience: 6,000 hours (3 years) • Practicum hours: 100 hours in addition to practicum requirements for Counselor-I (totaling 200 practicum hours) • Training hours: 48 hours • References: 3 references, 1 from supervisor • Exam: NAADAC level I or II or MAC
	Chemical Dependency Clinical Supervisor	*Nondegree Track* • Experience: 12,000 hours (6 years) • Practicum hours: 100 hours in addition to practicum requirements for Counselor-II (totaling 300 practicum hours) • Training hours: 206 hours • References: 3 references, 1 from supervisor • Exam: NAADAC level II or MAC *With Higher-Education Degree in Behavioral-Health-Related Field* • Experience: 10,000 hours (5 years) • Practicum hours: 100 hours in addition to practicum requirements for Counselor-II (totaling 300 practicum hours) • Training hours: 78 hours • References: 3 references, 1 from supervisor • Exam: NAADAC level II or MAC
Montana	Certified Behavioral Health Peer Support Specialist	• Diagnosis by a mental health professional as having a behavioral disorder • Has received treatment for the diagnosis • Be in recovery, which is defined as "a process of change through which the individuals improve their health and wellness, live a self-directed life, and strive to reach their full potential" • Recovery does not include any period of incarceration, or hospitalization or any inpatient admission related to a behavioral health disorder that exceeds 72 hours within two years immediately preceding application • 40-hour training course with examination • Supervision with a supervisor in the related field that is in good standing with their license
	Licensed Addiction Counselor	Degree Requirements Vary: • Associate's degree in alcohol and drug studies, addiction, or substance abuse OR an associate's degree other than that with a minimum of six credit hours in human behavior, sociology, psychology; three credit hours in psychopathology; and nine credit hours in counseling • Bachelor's degree or higher in alcohol and drug studies, addiction, or substance abuse OR a bachelor's degree or higher other than that with a minimum of six credit hours in human behavior, sociology, psychology; three credit hours in psychopathology; and nine credit hours in counseling • Minimum of 330 contact hours of addiction courses (1 semester credit equals 15 hours) • 1,000 hours of supervised addiction counseling experience

(*continued*)

TABLE 1.2 Credentialing Standards for States That Are Not Members of the IC&RC (*continued*)

STATE	CREDENTIAL	STANDARDS
		Pass ONE of the following exams: • NCC Level 1 or Level 2 Exam • Northwest Certified II Exam • Southwest Certification II Exam • National Association of Alcoholism and Drug Abuse Counselors Certification Commission MAC • IC&RC ADC Exam or AADC Exam
North Dakota	Licensed Addiction Counselor	• Bachelor's degree or higher in addictions or closely related mental health field • 960 hours of clinical training with 40 hours of direct, face-to-face supervision in each of the following clinical training areas: screening and ASAM assessment, treatment planning, counseling, and client/family/community education and 30 hours of training in the area of documentation • Either NCAC-II or MAC Examination
	Licensed Master Addiction Counselor	• Master's degree or higher in addictions or closely related mental health field • 700 hours of clinical training with 30 hours of direct, face-to-face supervision in each of the following clinical training areas: screening and ASAM assessment, treatment planning, counseling, and client/family/community education and 20 hours of training in the area of documentation • MAC Examination • Verification of completion of 2,000 hours of postlicensure supervised addiction counseling experience

Wisconsin	Substance Abuse Counselor-In-Training	• 100 hours of specialized education in the following content areas:
		  ○ Substance abuse assessment (15 hours)
		  ○ Substance abuse counseling (15 hours)
		  ○ Substance abuse case management (10 hours)
		  ○ Substance abuse patient education (15 hours)
		  ○ Substance abuse professional responsibility (20 hours)
		  ○ Electives within the performance domains listed previously (25 hours)
		• Proof of employment or volunteer hours at an agency providing substance use disorder treatment
		• Take and pass the Wisconsin Statutes and Rules Exam

	Substance Abuse Counselor	• 360 hours of substance use disorder specialized education in the following content areas:
		  ○ Substance abuse assessment (60 hours)
		  ○ Substance abuse counseling (60 hours)
		  ○ Substance abuse case management (60 hours)
		  ○ Substance abuse patient education (60 hours)
		  ○ Substance abuse professional responsibility (60 hours)
		  ○ Boundaries and ethics (6 hours)
		  ○ Electives within the performance domains listed previously (54 hours)
		• Take and pass the NAADC NCAC-I examination (may be taken after completion of education, before completion of experience)

		• Take and pass the Wisconsin Rules and Statutes Exam (unless previously passed in obtaining a substance abuse counselor-in-training credential) • 3,000 hours of work experience • 1,000 hours in substance use disorder counseling with at least 500 hours in a one-on-one individual modality setting

(*continued*)

TABLE 1.2 Credentialing Standards for States That Are Not Members of the IC&RC *(continued)*

STATE	CREDENTIAL	STANDARDS
	Clinical Substance Abuse Counselor	• An associate's degree or higher in behavioral science field • Evidence of one of the following: ○ Holding a substance abuse counselor credential ○ OR, 360 hours of substance use disorder specialized education (same requirement of content and hours as SAC) • 5,000 hours of work experience • Take and pass the NAADC NCAC-I examination • Take and pass the Wisconsin Statutes and Rules Exam (unless previously passed in obtaining a substance abuse counselor-in-training credential)

AADC, Advanced Alcohol & Drug Counselor; ADC, Alcohol & Drug Counselor; ASAM, American Society of Addiction Medicine; IC&RC, International Certification and Reciprocity Consortium; MAC, Master Addiction Counselor; NAADAC, National Association for Alcoholism and Drug Abuse Counselors; NCAC-I, National Certified Addiction Counselor-Level I; NCAC-II, National Certified Addiction Counselor-Level II; NCC, National Association of Alcoholism and Drug Abuse Counselors Certification Commission; SAC, Substance Abuse Counselor.

In addition to state-level credentialing, the National Certification Commission for Addiction Professionals (NCC AP; affiliated with NAADAC) offers national credentials for addiction counselors. Through the NCC AP, counselors can earn the following certifications: National Certified Addiction Counselor-Level I (NCAC I), National Certified Addiction Counselor-Level II (NCAC II), or Master Addiction Counselor (MAC). The requirements for each certification differ with regard to education and contact hours. For example, the NCAC I credential requires a GED or high school education in addition to at least 270 contact hours of education related to addiction or relevant counseling subjects. The MAC credential, on the other hand, requires at least a master's-level degree in a counseling or a related field as well as 500 contact hours of education related to addiction or relevant counseling subjects. Although differences exist, all individuals seeking one of these three national credentials (NCAC I, NCAC II, or MAC) must be licensed in their state (e.g., as a substance abuse counselor, addiction counselor, professional counselor, social worker), have at least three years of clinical experience (under supervision) as an addiction counselor, and pass the appropriate exam (e.g., ADC exam through the IC&RC or Examination for Master Addictions Counselors [EMAC] through the National Board of Certified Counselors). The NCC AP also offers specialized credentials, including the Nicotine Dependence Specialist (NDS), National Certified Adolescent Addictions Counselor (NCAAC), and National Certified Peer Recovery Support Specialist (NCPRSS).

What does all this information about credentialing mean for you? All counselors should have a basic understanding about addiction so that they can appropriately recognize and respond to it in their clinical work. If, however, as you journey through the chapters of this textbook you feel as though you may want to specialize in addiction counseling and gain advanced training, there are many options for you to pursue at the state and national level. According to the U.S. Bureau of Labor Statistics' *Occupational Outlook Handbook* (n.d.), employment opportunities for substance abuse, behavioral disorder, and mental health counselors are growing at a rate much faster than average. Specifically, from 2019 to 2029, employment rates are projected to increase by 25% (Bureau of Labor Statistics, n.d.).

Therefore, it is an ideal time to receive education and training related to addiction counseling and pursue employment in the counseling field.

SUMMARY

The prevalence of substance use disorders and addictive behaviors in the United States is well known and alarming. All counselors should be prepared to recognize and respond to addiction in their unique settings. Although many graduate-level training programs offer a course related to addiction counseling, there is a need to strengthen training efforts and ensure counseling students are competent to address addiction. Additionally, addiction-related content is necessary to fulfil a variety of accreditation standards across mental health disciplines. Rather than learning brand-new skills, counseling students can prepare to work with addiction by building upon their general clinical and conceptualization skills. In addition, by increasing empathy, acquiring addiction-related knowledge, and engaging in regular self-care practices, counselors can reduce the risk of burnout and compassion fatigue in their work with addiction. Finally, counselors can ensure ethical practice by consulting their profession's code of ethics, state laws and regulations, and specific ethical codes and competencies related to addiction counseling. For students interested in advanced training related to addiction counseling, there are several state and national credentials that they can pursue.

RESOURCES

American Counseling Association. (2014). *ACA code of ethics*. http://www.counseling.org/knowledge-center/ethics

Association for Addiction Professionals. (2021). *Code of ethics*. https://www.naadac.org/assets/2416/naadac_code_of_ethics_112021.pdf

Centers for Disease Control and Prevention. (2021). *Understanding the epidemic*. https://www.cdc.gov/drugoverdose/epidemic/index.html

National Board for Certified Counselors. (n.d.). *Master addictions counselor*. https://www.nbcc.org/certification/mac

National Certification Commission for Addiction Professionals. (2021). *Certification*. https://www.naadac.org/certification

Substance Abuse and Mental Health Services Administration. (2017). *Addiction counseling competencies: The knowledge, skills, and attitudes of professional practice* (Technical Assistance Publication [TAP] Series 21. HHS Publication No. [SMA] 15-4171).

KEY REFERENCES

Only key references appear in the print edition. The full reference list appears in the digital product on Springer Publishing Connect: connect.springerpub.com/content/book/978-0-8261-3586-5/chapter/ch01

American Counseling Association. (2014). *ACA code of ethics*. http://www.counseling.org/knowledge-center/ethics

Association for Addiction Professionals. (2021). *Code of ethics*. https://www.naadac.org/assets/2416/naadac_code_of_ethics_112021.pdf

Council for Accreditation of Counseling and Related Educational Programs. (2016). *2016 CACREP standards*. https://www.cacrep.org/for-programs/2016-cacrep-standards/

Edgell, C. (2020). It's time to finish what they started: How Purdue Pharma and the Sackler family can help end the opioid epidemic. *Penn State Law Review, 125*, 255–287.

Hartung, D. M., Geddes, J., Johnston, K. A., Leichtling, G., Hallvik, S., Hildebran, C., & Korthuis, P. T. (2021). Patterns of prescription opioid use prior to self-reported heroin initiation. *Journal of Addiction Medicine, 15*(2), 130–133. https://doi.org/10.1097/ADM.0000000000000708

Lipari, R. N., & Van horn, S. L. (2017). *Children living with parents who have a substance use disorder.* The Center for Behavioral Health Statistics and Quality. https://www.samhsa.gov/data/sites/default/files/report_3223/ShortReport-3223.html

Martin, J. L., Cimini, M. D., Longo, L. M., Sawyer, J. S., & Ertl, M. M. (2020). Equipping mental health professionals to meet the needs of substance-using clients: Evaluation of an SBIRT training program. *Training and Education in Professional Psychology, 14*(1), 42–51. https://doi.org/10.1037/tep0000258

Miech, R. A., Johnston, L. D., O'Malley, P. M., Bachman, J. G., Schulenberg, J. E., & Patrick, M. E. (2020). *Monitoring the Future national survey results on drug use, 1975–2019: Volume 1, secondary school students.* Institute for Social Research, The University of Michigan.

Mustaine, B. L., West, P. L., & Wyrick, B. K. (2003). Substance abuse counselor certification requirements: Is it time for a change? *Journal of Addiction & Offender Counseling, 23*(2), 99–107. https://doi.org/10.1002/j.2161-1874.2003.tb00174.x

Salyers, K. M., Ritchie, M. H., Cochrane, W. S., & Roseman, C. P. (2006). Inclusion of substance abuse training in CACREP-accredited programs. *Journal of Addiction & Offender Counseling, 27*(1), 47–58. https://doi.org/10.1002/j.2161-1874.2006.tb00018.x

Substance Abuse and Mental Health Services Administration. (2020). *Key substance use and mental health indicators in the United States: Results from the 2019 National Survey on Drug Use and Health* (HHS Publication No. PEP20-07-01-001, NSDUH Series H-55). Center for Behavioral Health Statistics and Quality, Substance Abuse and Mental Health Services Administration.

2

AN OVERVIEW OF ETIOLOGICAL MODELS

LEARNING OBJECTIVES

In this chapter, we will be exploring various models that help to explain why some individuals develop substance use disorders (SUDs), while others do not. Some of the models described are etiological in nature (e.g., genetic model), as those models explore what causes SUDs, while other models are better at explaining what sustains addictive behaviors over time (e.g., behavioral models). Addiction models are important because they represent biopsychosocial risk factors that place individuals at higher risk for developing SUDs. By the conclusion of this chapter, you will be able to

- describe the origins and basic tenets of the disease model, moral model, and wellness model;
- explain how the moral model is at the root of criminal sanctions for substance use and accounts for high incarceration rates in the United States;
- describe how genetics and inheritability account for a significant percent of SUDs;
- describe how the psychoanalytic model has contributed to our understanding of causality of SUDs through the lens of trauma, attachment, and self-medication hypotheses;
- explain how behavioral models, such as classical conditioning, operant conditioning, social learning theory, and opponent-process theory, sustain or influence the development of SUDs;
- describe personality theory and personality traits that correlate with SUDs;
- explain sociocultural factors that influence the development of SUDs;
- synthesize the various biopsychosocial theories of addiction in order to describe how the diathesis-stress model provides a capitulation of the "nature–nurture" debate.

TERMS TO KNOW

attachment one's ability to form close relationships or attachments to others, e.g., parents or guardians, friends, partners. Sometimes referred to as *object relations*

concordance rate the probability or likelihood that twins or two family members will have the same trait or characteristic based on genetic inheritance

dizygotic twins also referred to as "fraternal twins"; occurs when the male sperm fertilizes two separate eggs of the mother. Dizygotic twins do not have the exact same DNA

genetic marker refers to a particular gene or DNA sequence that can be used to identify a particular genetic trait that can be traced back through one's pedigree

genetic predisposition an inheritable characteristic, e.g., the risk of acquiring a disease like alcoholism or Huntington's Disease

genotype the genetic makeup of an individual organism (as distinguished from their physical appearance). The genetic constitution of an individual

high-risk environment a social environment in which substance use is ever-present or condoned; environments in which poverty, racism, high crime, and lack of safety are common

Human Genome Project an international human genetic research project conducted between 1990 and 2003, which determined the base pair sequences in human DNA with the purpose of storing this information in computer databases

monozygotic twins also referred to as "identical twins"; occurs when the male sperm fertilizes one egg (or zygote) of the mother. Monozygotic twins have the exact same DNA

phenotype the observable physical and biochemical characteristics of an individual that are determined by both genetic makeup and environmental influences

protective factors individual characteristics and environmental circumstances that reduce or mitigate one's vulnerability to develop a SUD or other disorder

risk factors biological, psychological, and/or social characteristics that create vulnerability for that individual to develop a SUD or other disorder

self-esteem feelings of confidence about oneself as manifested personally or in interactions with others

sensation-seeking a personality trait in which individuals seek out risky, thrilling, and sometimes potentially dangerous activity. This trait is often found in males with SUDs

INTRODUCTION

According to the Monitoring the Future survey (2019), approximately 19% of eighth graders, 37% of 10th graders, and 52% of 12th graders report having experimented with alcohol during the past year, while 7% of eighth graders, 19% of 10th graders, and 21% of 12th graders report having used cannabis within the past 12 months, with cannabis vaping showing the most dramatic increases over the past year. Yet, we also know that not all of these adolescents will go on to develop substance use disorders (SUDs). For example, the most recent national epidemiological surveys of American adults (see the Substance Abuse and Mental Health Administration's [SAMHSA; 2016a] Key Substance Use and Mental Health Indicators in the United States survey) indicate that approximately 5.6% will develop alcohol use disorders, while approximately 0.8% will develop cannabis use disorders.

This raises an important question as to why some individuals will develop SUDs while others will not. The data described above suggest that exposure to alcohol or drugs alone does not accurately predict who will go on to develop SUDs and who will not. In order to answer this question, it's helpful to examine both risk and protective factors. Risk factors are hypothesized to be the sum of biological traits (e.g., genetic traits), along with personality characteristics and social/environmental factors that predispose one to develop SUDs, while protective factors similarly consist of biological, psychological, and environmental factors that help to prevent or mitigate the chances of someone developing a SUD. In this chapter, we will explore a number of models that help to explain why some individuals will go on to develop SUDs, while others will perhaps "grow out" of earlier experimental use of alcohol or substance use during their teen years.

LEARNING ACTIVITY 2.1

How many of you have had oral surgery to remove wisdom teeth? Were you prescribed any pain medication? Do you recall what type of pain medication you were prescribed? If so, what was your experience taking that medication? Take an informal survey of your family and friends to see what their experiences were with taking pain medication. Do these experiences match with what you know about SUDs?

LEARNING ACTIVITY 2.2

Watch the following Ted Talk by Johann Hari entitled "Everything You Know About Addiction Is Wrong": www.youtube.com/watch?v=PY9DcIMGxMs

This Ted Talk is based on Hari's 2015 book titled *Chasing the Scream* in which he describes the research done by Bruce Alexander and colleagues in Canada in which they created "Rat Park." Alexander's research debunked the earlier research that found that when rats were given a choice between plain water and water laced with heroin or cocaine, the rats would press a bar to receive doses of the drug-laced water until they eventually dropped dead. What was unique about Alexander's research, and what does it tell us about drug exposure?

It may seem at first glance that addiction counselors really don't need to be aware of etiological or causal models. For those of you familiar with Father Martin's classic educational film, *Chalk Talk*, which was shown in nearly every alcohol use disorder Minnesota-model treatment program in the United States, he comments, "If your tooth aches, do you want to know why it hurts or do you just want it pulled?" He goes on to explain that knowledge of causes does not alleviate pain or distress; only proper treatment does. Implied in this statement is the contention that Father Martin was not an advocate of treatment that focused on underlying causes, such as psychoanalytically oriented therapies. In this regard, he cautions that insight alone does not necessarily translate into behavior change. Yet, there is another perspective that addiction counselors need to consider. That is, in order to effectively treat individuals who are experiencing SUDs, accurate assessment and diagnosis is essential. From clinical experience, counselors are well aware that many SUD clients enter treatment unwillingly, and, as a result, counselors may not get a forthright picture of a client's current substance use status or how their substance use has impacted their ability to function. There are other clients who lack awareness into how mood-altering substances have been negatively impacting their lives. With clients who may not be forthcoming about their substance use (and problems resulting from substance use), the goal of the biopsychosocial assessment would be to evaluate both risk and protective factors. In other words, a client may not be forthcoming about their substance use; however, counselors can still gain an understanding of the client's risk for developing a SUD. Let's begin by exploring some of the most widely known models and how those models conceptualize SUD risk factors.

DISEASE MODEL VERSUS MORAL MODEL OF ADDICTION

The disease model and the moral model are considered to be overarching models that sometimes encompass some of the other models we will be examining. For example, the disease model claims that SUDs are like other medical and mental health disorders in that there is a biological (e.g., genetic or neurochemical) basis. Indeed, SUDs are often described as "biologically based brain diseases" or as "biologically based, chronic, relapsing diseases" (Leshner, 1997; Volkow, 2008; Volkow et al., 2004). Similar to how pancreatic cancer, Alzheimer's, or diabetes would be considered biologically based diseases or disorders, so too can SUDs be viewed from the lens of this biological perspective. It's important to take into account that when the disease model came into popularity (some say as early as the 1930s), it coincided with the introduction of Alcoholics Anonymous (AA). The founders of AA (Bill W. and Dr. Bob), however, were very wary of using the word "disease" to describe alcoholism because they were concerned that it would discount the important role of recovery, which is attained by diligently working the 12 Steps of AA that were designed to promote personal growth, honesty, and humility (Kurtz, 1979). The origins of the disease model of alcoholism can be traced back to around 1924 when Dr. William Silkworth, the medical director of Charles B. Towns Hospital in New York City, treated (i.e., detoxified) Bill W. several times. From his years of treating individuals with alcohol use disorders, Silkworth concluded, "Alcoholism is not just a vice or habit. This is a compulsion, this is pathological craving, this is a *disease*" (Silkworth, 1939, p. xxvii). Silkworth (1937) likened alcoholism to having an allergy to alcohol and had written extensively regarding his contention that alcoholism was a disease and, therefore, not the result of a flawed personality or moral failing.

Yet the disease model is not without controversy, as critics feel that the disease model is very much a double-edged sword. On one hand, it helps bring addictions out from under the stigma that brands those with SUDs as being "weak or morally flawed" and into the realm of other medical diseases or disorders. However, there are those who view the disease model as exonerating the person with SUDs from personal responsibility. For example, from a legal standpoint, would a driver who's under the influence of alcohol and/or drugs be exonerated from responsibility for killing a pedestrian crossing the street? Most states would consider this type of crime to fall under vehicular manslaughter, which would result in prison time. Does this differ from a person with severe mental illness who kills someone in a paranoid rage? Here, the courts would most likely deem this individual "not guilty by reason of insanity." Others feel that that the disease model puts too much emphasis on addiction as a brain disease at the expense of the behavioral, personal sociocultural aspects of addiction. For example, Satel and Lilienfeld (2013) conclude that much of the neuroscientific explanations of addictions were not as convincing as they were initially proposed and tended to discount important personal and sociocultural factors that influence SUDs.

Diametrically opposed to the disease model is the moral model, which claims that SUDs come about as a result of moral failing or willful, sinful behavior on the part of substance users (see Box 2.1). Similar to how people suffering from severe mental health disorders were once considered to be possessed by evil spirits or the devil (a perspective very much endorsed during colonial times in America; Bleuler, 1963), the moral model suggests that substance users are intentional sinners who deserve scorn and punishment. Benjamin Rush, a physician in Colonial Philadelphia and a signer of the Declaration of Independence, was a staunch advocate for more humane treatment of people with mental illness and alcohol use disorders and one of the first to question the moral model. Rush established one of the first treatment programs for alcoholics, which was called the "Home for Inebriates." However, the moral model dictated that people with mental illness and SUDs be punished, hence many "public inebriates" were thrown in jail or prisons (White, 1998).

This trend toward viewing alcohol use disorders as a moral failure continued through the early 19th century, which was around the time the Women's Christian Temperance Union (WCTU) was formed. Although not prohibitionists at first, the WCTU advocated for "blue laws" that would close taverns on Sundays so that men would go to church rather than to the local taverns, which were centers of political and community life at the time. Just prior to the Civil War, however, there were growing sentiments toward prohibition. The Prohibitionist movement came to national attention when the mayor of Portland, Maine, passed a city ban on alcohol. This ban resulted in decreased rates of crime, domestic violence, and public intoxication. In 1851, Maine passed legislation that banned the manufacture and sale of liquor within that state. Following the Civil War, a prohibitionist movement again gained popularity, and the Prohibitionist Party ran a candidate against Ulysses S. Grant for president of the United States. Yet it was not until 1920, however, that the Volstead Act (the 19th Amendment) was passed, which marked the beginning of Prohibition. Interestingly, this seemed to have come about because of the strength and popularity of both the temperance and the more

BOX 2.1

ALCOHOLISM: A DISEASE

As described earlier, the moral model claims that SUDs come about as the result of willful, sinful behavior. This approach is often endorsed by particular religious groups as illustrated in the following passage that appeared on a religious webpage. The following is an adaptation of what appeared on the webpage. It states:

Alcoholism...A Disease? If so:

It is the only disease contracted by an act of will
It is the only disease that is habit forming
It is the only disease that comes in a bottle
It is the only disease causing hundred of thousands of family disruptions
It is the only disease which is sold in stores by state license
It is the only disease that is taxed by the government
It is the only disease advocated by advertising media
It is the only disease that given as a Christmas present
It is the only disease that is marketed

What do you think about these statements? Do they make sense? Do they seem true?

extreme prohibitionist agenda, which was being backed by many organized religious groups. Also, it was not coincidental perhaps that Prohibition was passed into law at the end of World War I. Many historians believe that because there was so much anti-German hatred in the United States following the war, Prohibition legislation was enacted because it essentially put the entire German brewing industry out of business (e.g., German brewers such as Anhauser-Busch, Miller, Schlitz, Schaeffer, and Blatz; White, 1998).

Depending on which historian you read, Prohibition can either be viewed as being successful (in terms of curbing medical and social ills resulting from alcoholism) or a dismal failure (in terms of creating tremendous black-market demand for alcohol and crime associated with bootlegging). When Prohibition was repealed in 1933 with the passage of the 21st Amendment to the Constitution during the Franklin D. Roosevelt administration, it immediately put many Americans back to work who lost their jobs during the Great Depression (White, 1998).

Even though Prohibition was repealed decades ago, the moral model persisted throughout the 20th century and was used as a rationale for many of the draconian drug laws that were passed, which basically targeted many racial and immigrant groups. For example, the targeting of Chinese Americans and the opium dens of San Francisco resulted in laws banning opium. Mexican Americans were targeted for allegedly bringing cannabis to Southwestern states. African Americans living in port cities like New Orleans would be given cocaine to help increase their work productivity; however, they were also targeted by harsh laws banning cocaine. In each of these instances, racial discrimination and fear-mongering among politicians were often at the heart of these draconian laws. Also, keep in mind that, prior to the passage of the Harrison Act in 1914, it was legal to purchase many of these substances over the counter. In the 1930s, the federal government created the Lexington Narcotic Farm in Lexington, Kentucky. Lexington was essentially a prison for those convicted of drug-related offenses who were sent there for often indeterminant sentences. Although some therapeutic activities were offered at Lexington, the treatment was essentially involuntary. Famous jazz musicians such as Billie Holiday, Sonny Rollins, Chet Baker, and Elvin Jones all spent time at the Lexington Narcotic Farm. Lexington was a 20th-century example of the moral model in action (Campbell et al., 2008).

Unfortunately, the moral model continues to influence public policy and legal sanctions in 21st century America. The moral model is being played out every day in the United States as we witness ever-burgeoning number of individuals with SUDs who are being incarcerated in America's jails and prisons. Also, when we look at the disproportionate percentages of racial and ethnic minorities being incarcerated, it's very clear how racial bias was built into American drug laws and continues to discriminate against people of color. This is also reflected in the language being used to describe crack cocaine use within the African American community with phrases such as "the war on drugs," while the increasing rates of both prescription opioid use and heroin among middle-class, White Americans as "the opioid epidemic." In the first example, the "war on drugs" characterizes drug use as something to wage war on (suggesting a moral interpretation), while the increase in opioid use and overdose deaths is characterized as an "epidemic" (suggesting a disease epidemic). The question remains as to whether the United States will continue to build more prisons to manage the current drug crisis or whether a more humane, public health approach will be taken and more affordable treatment centers will be built.

DISEASE MODEL VERSUS WELLNESS MODEL

As indicated above, the disease model takes the approach that SUDs are comparable to other medical diseases and, therefore, should be viewed from the same perspective. Also, as with other diseases, there are symptoms (or criteria) for diagnosing the disease, a course or progression, and a prognosis or prediction of outcome. The wellness model takes a different

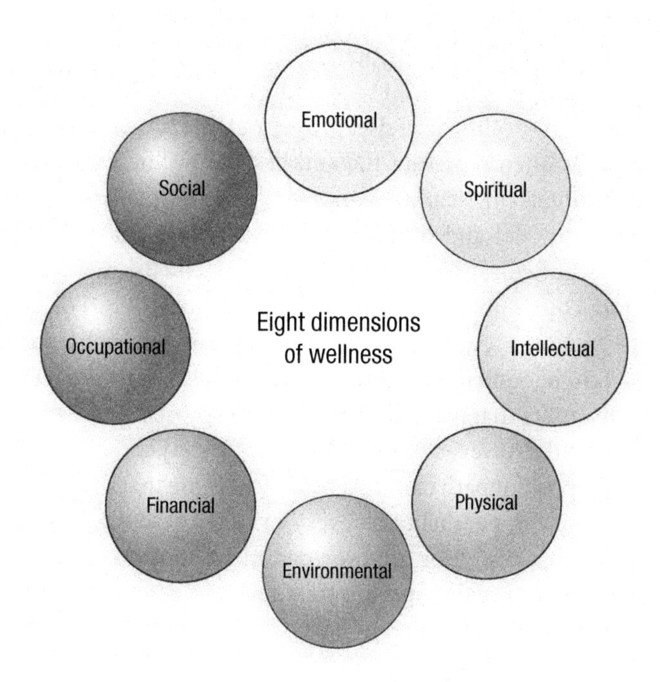

Emotional Wellness
The emotionally well person can identify, express, and manage the entire range of feelings and would consider seeking assistance to address areas of concern.

Occupational Wellness
The professionally well person engages in work to gain personal satisfaction and enrichment, consistent with values, goals, and lifestyle.

Social Wellness
The socially well person has a network of support based on interdependence, mutual trust, respect and has developed a sensitivity and awareness toward the feelings of others.

Spiritual Wellness
The spiritually well person seeks harmony and balance by openly exploring the depth of human purpose, meaning and connection through dialogue and self-reflection.

Physical Wellness
The physically well person gets an adequate amount of sleep, eats a balanced and nutritious diet, engages in exercise for 150 minutes per week, attends regular medical checkups, and practices safe and healthy sexual relations.

Financial Wellness
The financially well person is fully aware of financial state and budgets, saves and manages finances in order to achieve realistic goals.

Intellectual Wellness
The intellectually well person values lifelong learning and seeks to foster critical thinking, develop moral reasoning, expand worldviews, and engage in education for the pursuit of knowledge.

Environmental Wellness
The environmentally well person recognizes the responsibility to preserve, protect, and improve the environment and one's surroundings.

FIGURE 2.1 The eight dimensions of wellness.

Source: From Substance Abuse and Mental Health Administration. https://www.samhsa.gov/multi-site-search?search_api_fulltext=Wellness+Dimensions

approach by going beyond the "absence of illness" approach advocated by the disease model and by encouraging individuals to optimize their well-being. Wellness takes more of a *holistic or whole-person approach* by advocating that clients make changes in their diet, exercise regimens, stress reduction strategies, and improving sleep.

The concept of wellness was first promoted in the World Health Organization's 1948 (Zimmer, 2010) constitutional statement as follows: "Health is a state of total physical, mental and social well-being and not merely the absence of disease or infirmity." SAMHSA (2016b) recommends the wellness model be incorporated into all levels of SUD treatment by including the following eight areas: emotional, environmental, financial, intellectual, occupational, physical, social, and spiritual.

Wellness dimensions (see Figure 2.1) are addressed in addiction counseling by encouraging clients to engage in healthy exercise, proper nutrition, proper rest, and other self-care activities. Active SUDs often represent the antithesis of wellness in terms of negatively impacting lives of individuals physically, emotionally, and spiritually.

Unlike the disease model and moral models, which are diametrically opposed to one another in their conceptualization and approach to SUDs, the disease model and wellness model may be more compatible if we think of them sequentially. For example, in the early phases of SUD treatment, accurate assessment, diagnosis, and subsequent treatment planning are very much in alignment with the disease model. This is especially true when there are co-occurring disorders that need to be properly diagnosed in order for an effective treatment to be implemented. However, once abstinence/sobriety is established, then the wellness model provides an important path toward a healthy lifestyle that help to guarantee continued improvement when done in parallel to recovery-oriented activities (e.g., participating in 12-step meetings and counseling). Box 2.2 provides an illustration of how proper diagnosis is important in the terms of providing proper treatment.

BOX 2.2

BEAUTIFUL BOY

The author David Scheff has written two books about his son, Nic's, struggles with addiction to methamphetamines (i.e., crystal meth). His first book, *Beautiful Boy: A Father's Journey Through His Son's Addiction,* chronicles the father's attempts to come to grips with Nic's addiction and how it changed him over time. His second book, *Clean,* presents information on how Scheff tries to find appropriate treatment for his son who had cycled in and out of rehab centers about three times before attaining consistent recovery/sobriety. In an interview with Terry Gross (NPR's *Fresh Air* podcast; Gross, 2013), Nic was asked what made the difference during his third rehab treatment. Nic explained that during the course of his treatment, his counselor asked him if he ever had a psychological or psychiatric evaluation, to which Nic replied that he hadn't. The counselor had apparently picked up on a pattern to Nic's relapses which suggested that something else might be happening. Nic explained that when he was evaluated, he was diagnosed with bipolar disorder and was placed on a mood stabilizer. Nic emphatically stated that it wasn't that he didn't get anything out of his prior treatments, he did, however, there was a missing piece and that piece was bipolar disorder. At the time of the *Fresh Air* interview, Nic had himself become a successful author and screenplay writer and was married.

BIOLOGICAL MODELS

Genetic Theory

It is common knowledge that some diseases/disorders tend to run in families and the reason can often be based back to inherited traits or genetic vulnerability. For example, certain types of cancer, such as breast cancer, and essential hypertension or high blood pressure are considered to have genetic causes or etiologies. Similarly, it is widely accepted that SUDs and particular mental health disorders also tend to "run in families." For example, schizophrenia is about 50% heritable, while autism is about 70% heritable. Interestingly, there is a great deal of overlap in the genes involved in several distinct mental disorders such as schizophrenia, bipolar disorder, attention deficit hyperactivity disorder (ADHD), and depression (Winerman, 2019). Therefore, just as one inherits particular traits from their biological parents (e.g., eye and hair color, height, weight, or athletic, musical, or artistic talents), one can also inherit predispositions to develop SUDs and perhaps even process addictions like gambling disorders.

According to Donald Goodwin (1988), one of the leading researchers in the field of genetics and alcohol use disorders, the contention that alcoholism runs in families can be traced back to the Bible, Aristotle, and Plutarch. The well-known Greek philosopher Plutarch is quoted as writing, "Drunkards beget drunkards." However, one of the major challenges in determining whether SUDs have a genetic basis is to rule out the impact of environmental influences; that is, do sons or daughters learn to drink or use substances in ways similar to their parent because of modeling their parent's behavior? This is the true essence of the nature–nurture debate, or how much of a particular trait can be accounted for by genetic (nature) influences versus environmental (nurture) influences. Physical traits such as eye color or hair color indisputably have a genetic basis. In order to try to shed light on the nature–nurture conundrum, researchers began to study twins, particularly monozygotic or identical twins because they shared identical DNA, and ideally to study monozygotic twins who were reared apart (e.g., twins who were separated from their biological parents and raised by adoptive parents). Many of these early studies (e.g., Cadoret et al., 1985, 1987; Cloninger et al., 1981; Goodwin et al., 1973; Schuckit & Smith, 1997) were done in Scandinavian countries (e.g., Sweden, Norway) because those countries keep open adoption records; therefore, it was easier for researchers to follow-up on twins who were separated and raised by adoptive parents. The results of these early adoption studies found significantly higher rates of alcohol abuse and dependence among biological sons of alcoholic parents who were adopted at birth by nonalcoholic parents when compared to sons of nonalcoholic parents.

More recent studies examining both twins and adopted twins had definitively demonstrated that genetic influences had contributed to the development of alcohol use disorders in 50% to 60% for both men and women (McGue, 1999). For example, studies done at the Minnesota Center for Family Twin Research (MCTFR; often referred to as the "Minnesota Twins" research) had studied 1,400 pairs of monozygotic twins beginning at either age 11 or 17. At the time of the 12-year follow-up, this research has identified several genetic markers which were predictive of later alcoholism. These include personality factors such as impulsivity, sociability, rebelliousness and becoming easily bored; family background such as father's having a high tolerance to alcohol; and a low P300 brainwave pattern (a smaller P300 at age 17 was predictive of those who would develop alcohol and drug problems by age 20). Finally, precocious experimentation with alcohol (before age 15) was also predictive of later alcoholism (Legrand et al., 2005).

Although the research pertaining to genetics and SUDs is very convincing, there are several caveats to the genetic theory of addiction. One such caveat is that if SUDs are indeed inherited, *what exactly is inherited* that might predispose a person to becoming addicted? Are there differences in one's basic physiology that somehow gets inherited from parents or grandparents? Also, although there has been a great deal of research which examined the possibility of there being an "addictive personality" that predetermines whether one develops a SUD, the majority of research has focused on inherited physical characteristics (e.g., variations in how alcohol is metabolized or broken down in the body or depletions in particular neurotransmitters such as dopamine). Neurotransmitter models are discussed in Chapter 3.

PSYCHOLOGICAL MODELS

Psychoanalytic Theory

Classical psychoanalytic theory hypothesizes the key to determining psychopathology including depression, interpersonal problems, or SUDs lies in examining childhood conflicts and trauma. The goal of psychoanalytic therapy is to uncover these past traumas and conflicts in such a way that the client will develop insight into how their past is relevant to their present. Psychoanalysis has often been deemed an inappropriate treatment for SUDs, especially for those who are in early recovery because the very process of uncovering past trauma can be re-traumatizing. Yet, psychoanalytic theory provides counselors and clients with an understanding of how trauma impacts on people's lives, sometimes for years after the traumatizing incident (e.g., Heffernan et al., 2000) Examples of traumatic incidents can range from witnessing the death of fellow soldiers in combat to rape/sexual assault and being victimized by natural disasters such as devastating tornados or hurricanes.

Psychoanalytic theory also provides counselors with an understanding of defense mechanisms, such as denial, rationalization, and sublimation, which often fuel the addiction by distorting the painful reality of the impact that alcohol and/or drug use has on the individual. There's an old AA saying that addresses these distortions, "Alcoholism is a disease that tells you, you don't have a disease," and it's the defense mechanisms that account for these distortions. And yet, everyone employs defense mechanisms in their daily life, not just those with SUDs.

Another reason that psychoanalysis and psychoanalytic theory is not viewed as an effective treatment for SUDs is due, in part, to the fact that psychoanalytic theory is often viewed as outdated and psychoanalysis is very time-consuming and expensive. Also, most experienced addiction counselors realize that insight alone does not guarantee behavior change. Addiction counseling, especially in the early phases of treatment, tends to be very practical and more here-and-now focused (Washton & Zweben, 2006).

Yet, psychoanalytic theory has made, often indirectly, many contributions to the addictions treatment field. Let's begin by exploring Attachment Theory. Attachment Theory hypothesizes that one's ability to form healthy connections with others can often become the foundation how individuals form healthy (or dysfunctional) relationships later in life and can also help to describe how individuals form healthy relationships in sobriety, whether those connections be in 12-step programs or in counseling. Based on the early work of British psychoanalyst, John Bowlby, it was hypothesized that from the beginning of life, infants have a biological need to establish a bond with a caregiving adult (or parent) "by maintaining physical and emotional proximity to that loved one" (Fletcher et al., 2015, p. 109). According to Bowlby, attachment is a primary drive just as the need for food or sex. Early research by American psychologist Mary Ainsworth, who studied infant's reactions when separated from their primary caregiver (e.g., mother) and placed in the presence of a stranger; found that infants would respond to one of three attachment styles often reflective of their attachment to their mothers. Securely attached infants/children responded by continuing to explore their environment, undisturbed by the presence of a stranger. Insecurely attached infants/children responded to the stranger by crying, screaming, or showing other manifestations of fear or apprehension. Ambivalent infants/children showed no reactions whatsoever but would not explore their environment. These attachment styles are hypothesized to be pervasive and would therefore continue into adulthood. Attachment style is also associated with both the recognition and expression of emotion as well as emotional regulation (Ainsworth & Bowlby, 1991). Furthermore, it's thought that the inability to form secure adult attachments or relationships are predictive of those who develop SUDs. From an Attachment Theory perspective, those who have difficulty forming securely attached relationships to others are more prone to "attaching" to alcohol and other mood-altering substances. Recent research also finds that the ability to effectively regulate moods (especially negative mood states) is vital in resisting relapse triggers (Fowler et al., 2013). Also, being able to form a secure attachment with one's counselor is predictive of success in opioid maintenance treatment (Cavaiola et al., 2015). The very process of the counseling relationship (especially when there's a positive transference in the counseling relationship) that can be viewed as a healing experience which can sometimes repair the early damage caused by early loss, abandonment, or inconsistent parenting that may have caused insecure attachments.

Flores (2004) has written extensively on Attachment Theory as it applies to SUDs and addiction treatment. He concludes that attachment is a primary motivation and is not secondary to some other drive. He also states that affect regulation (i.e., the ability to regulate one's emotions) is determined by one's early attachment experiences. In other words, those who experienced secure attachments to parents or caretakers during infancy and childhood often are better able to regulate or modulate their emotions. Individuals who do not form these secure attachments are thought to be at higher risk for developing SUDs. Finally, Flores also concludes that the need for attachment is a lifelong process and not just something that occurs during infancy or childhood. Therefore, healthy adults seek attachments throughout the life span. Addiction counselors often observe that as individuals progress more deeply into their SUD, they tend to become more detached and isolated from others. One of the goals of recovery and sobriety is to form meaningful connections with others. For many, counseling and active participation in 12-step programs becomes a first step toward forming healthy, meaningful connections with others.

Khantzian (1984, 2014) is also a psychoanalytically oriented theorist who concludes that SUDs come about as a result of *ego deficits* which often result in feelings of low self-esteem and low self-worth. Many individuals who experience SUDs often report feeling as if "there's a hole inside" them which seems to disappear with the onset of drinking or drug use. Khantzian refers to this as the "self-medication" hypothesis (SMH) in which substance users are seeking to alleviate feelings of low self-esteem or low self-worth, depression, or anxiety. Khantzian appears to be one of the few psychoanalytic theorists who feels that one's stated drug of preference is not a mere coincidence (Khantzian, 1984). According to SMH, addiction is a "self-regulation disorder," that is, an attempt to manage painful emotions and an attempt to "self-repair." Painful emotions often pre-date SUD (e.g., childhood trauma, abandonment, loss), but keep in mind that addictions may often *cause* painful emotions (as would be the case when a person with a SUD is served with divorce papers because of alcohol or drug-related infidelities). Khantzian provides examples of the emotional self-regulation and self-medication function of specific substances. He proposes that those individuals who experience opioid use disorders seek to manage feelings of aggression or rage, while those with cocaine use disorders are thought to seek relief from depression, boredom, and symptoms of ADHD (not surprisingly, most medications for ADHD are stimulants) or bipolar disorder. Although common sense would suggest that people suffering from bipolar disorder would be likely to self-medicate the depressive cycle of bipolar with cocaine or other stimulant drugs, it's actually the opposite. People with bipolar disorder are more likely to use cocaine as a means to sustain the burst of energy that one experiences during a manic phase. Whereas, alcohol and cannabis are often attractive to those suffering from posttraumatic stress disorder (PTSD) who experience difficulty sleeping because it helps to "shut off" intrusive thoughts, nightmares, and other sleep difficulties related to the trauma. In addition, several research studies found that substance use was perceived as being helpful in reducing distressing symptoms among individuals with bipolar disorder (e.g., Bernardt & Murray, 1986; Dunner et al., 1979; Mayfield & Coleman, 1968; Weiss et al., 2004).

Behavioral Theories

In order to explore the relationship between behavioral theories and SUDs, it's best to accomplish this through the lens of five major behavioral theories: classical conditioning, operant conditioning, social learning theory, cognitive behavioral theory, and opponent process theory. Classical conditioning is most often associated with the work of Russian physiologist Ivan Pavlov. You may recall from your introductory psychology classes that Pavlov sought to explain how dogs can become conditioned to respond to a previously unconditioned stimulus. Utilizing dogs in his experiments, Pavlov presented them with meat and noted the amount of their salivation response. Since the dogs didn't have to be taught to respond to the presence of meat powder, he labeled the meat an *unconditioned stimulus* and the salivation as the *unconditioned response*. He then paired a bell sound with the meat powder and the dogs responded with the same unconditioned response; however, when presenting the dogs with only the bell sound, the dogs would salivate each time they heard the bell. The bell had become a *conditioned stimulus,* and this time it produced a *conditioned* (or *learned*) *response*, that is, salivation. Pavlov would even use different bell tones and the dogs would continue to salivate. This is known as *stimulus generalization*. In order to stop the dogs from salivating (to extinguish the conditioned response), Pavlov continued to ring the bell without pairing it with meat powder and eventually the dogs stopped salivating. This is known as *cue extinction*.

Classical conditioning is not as useful in explaining the etiology or cause of SUDs; however, it is helpful in describing how people with SUDs become conditioned to stimuli in their environment where they may be using substance. For example, just as Pavlov's dogs didn't have to be taught to salivate or respond to the meat powder, similarly, a person with or without an alcohol use disorder doesn't have to be taught to respond to a vodka martini. The physiological response to alcohol is a given (unconditioned response). However, think about all the things that may become paired with drinking alcohol, for example, the visual appearance of the martini glass, the aroma of the vodka, the sounds of ice cubes, or the music playing in the bar; all have the potential of becoming conditioned stimuli, and, therefore, all have the potential of becoming relapse triggers. The same conditioning occurs with substances other than alcohol, for example, the visual appearance of white powder on a mirror, the distinct aroma of cannabis or the aroma of crystal meth being "cooked," and the tactile sensation of injecting an opioid into a vein. These are all very powerful, conditioned stimuli. However, classical conditioning doesn't really explain why some individuals become easily conditioned while others may not like the sensations associated with substance use. For example, someone who has a tobacco use disorder and smokes two packs of cigarettes a day is conditioned to the aroma of cigarette smoke, while a nonsmoker may find the smell of cigarette smoke disgusting or aversive.

Operant conditioning is associated with Harvard psychologist B. F. Skinner. By utilizing what became known as a "Skinner box," rats would press a bar in order to receive food pellets. Here, the food pellet becomes a *positive reinforcement*. Skinner found that he could operantly condition a rat to press the bar numerous times before they would receive a food pellet. This was known as a *reinforcement schedule*, and Skinner discovered that rats would make several bar presses on an intermittent or fixed schedule. In researching the use of punishment (e.g., a bar press would be followed by a mild electrical shock), Skinner found that he could suppress responses (i.e., bar pressing). Also, *negative reinforcement* would also increase behavior; but in this model, the rat would make increased responses in order to avoid or escape the shock.

Operant conditioning doesn't explain why some people find certain substances reinforcing while others do not (think back to your informal survey of friends and family who were prescribed pain medication for major dental procedures like tooth extractions!). However, operant conditioning does help to explain why many individuals find particular substances positively reinforcing in the early stages of their use, while negative reinforcement helps to explain why later in one's progression they may be using NOT to get high (positive reinforcement), but rather to stop or avoid the pain associated with withdrawal (negative reinforcement). Remember, both positive and negative reinforcement increase behavior, while punishment tries to suppress behavior.

Social learning theory (Bandura, 1977) can be applied to our understanding of how SUDs are reinforced; only this time, the factors that influence substance use are among those in one's social environment. Social learning theory examines the influence of role models whom one perceives as being powerful or someone that one wishes to emulate. This theory explains how one's own substance use will be similar to those role models that individual is exposed to whether it be a parent, an older sibling, schoolmates, or influential role models such as celebrities. Social learning theory is most applicable to children who take on similar patterns of alcohol use as their parents as they grow older. In this instance, parents are powerful role models and can be very influential in determining drinking patterns of their adult children (Milgram, 1982). The reason why social learning theory falls under behavioral models is that emulating a powerful role model is perceived by the individual as positive reinforcement, and by mimicking that role model the individual is reinforced by those in their social circles.

Opponent process theory can best be conceptualized as a behavioral theory in that it focuses primarily on observable behavior and self-reported affective responses; however, when it was initially introduced in the 1970s by University of Pennsylvania psychologist Richard

Solomon, it was put forth as a theory that would describe "acquired motivations" (Solomon, 1980; Solomon & Corbit, 1974). Acquired motives include such things as love and social attachments, food and taste cravings, and thrill-seeking behaviors (e.g., bungee jumping, parachute jumping), as well as other motivated behaviors such as achievement and power. What Solomon found was that many of these acquired motives operated according to the same empirical principles as addictions. However, what also became evident from his research was that there were two unique and opposite processes that describe how addictive behaviors come about. The "a-process" is aroused by a stimulus that can be either pleasurable or aversive. An opponent loop or "b-process" occurs, which is directly opposite to the "a-process"; therefore, if the "a-process" after drinking alcohol is a pleasurable "buzz," then the "b-process" might include the discomfort of experiencing a hangover. It's important to take into account what happens with these two processes over time. Generally, the opponent process created by substance use becomes stronger over time and is only weakened by abstinence or disuse. Solomon (1980, p. 692) claims "in every case of acquired motivation *affective or hedonic* processes are involved," referring to either emotional (affective) or pleasurable (hedonic) experiences that are derived from the behavior or substance use. He then goes on to state, "In every case I have found, [I] describe or measure three affective or hedonic phenomena. These are a) affective or hedonic *contrast* (between a-process and b-process), b) affective or hedonic *habituation* (tolerance), and c) affective or hedonic *withdrawal* (abstinence) *syndromes*" (p. 692). Therefore, just as one experiences a high or euphoria upon first taking a substance, that is then contrasted with the aftereffect or withdrawal, and these emotional responses change over time as a result of habituation. Koob and Le Moal (2005) provide a neurological perspective that helps to explain this opponent process model:

> *"Our thesis is that addiction involves a long-term, persistent plasticity in the activity of the neural circuits mediating two different motivational systems: decreased function of brain reward systems driven by natural rewards, and recruitment of anti-reward systems that drive aversive states." (Koob & Le Moal, 2005, p. 1442)*

With opiate use disorders, over time the b-process or withdrawal becomes stronger such that continued opiate use is done primarily to alleviate withdrawal symptoms such as cramping, muscle aches, pain, nausea, and diarrhea. Finan et al. (2018) provide an explanation of how opioids, when prescribed as pain analgesics, produce dopamine deficits that regulate the motivational and emotional components of pain; however, there is an opponent or antireward process that also serves to perpetuate pain and, therefore, results in increased opioid use.

Solomon (1980) provides another example of an acquired motive that doesn't involve substance use: parachute jumping. In this example, the affective or hedonic contrast involves a negative reinforcer (fear), which is presented when jumping out of the plane but then is removed once the parachutist lands safely. Solomon describes the following example:

> *"During their first free-fall... military parachutists may experience terror... pupils dilated, eyes bulging... heart racing and breathing irregular. After they land safely, they may walk around stunned... for a few minutes and then... appear to be elated." (p. 693)*

Prior to jumping, the person is at baseline, but as the plane climbs, fear and terror (a-process) take over, and it's not until minutes after the parachutist lands that they begin to feel exhilaration or elation (b-process). Ask anyone who has parachuted and most will tell you that after their first jump, they would do it over again. Another acquired motive is that of getting a tattoo. What type of tattoo and where on the body the tattoo is placed often determines the level of pain. In this instance, as with parachute jumping, the a-process is something highly aversive (i.e., apprehension and pain from the tattoo needle) and the b-process is one of accomplishment, relief, or elation of seeing the finished product. It is often said that as a person is getting their first tattoo, they're often planning their second. Another behavioral example is that of nonsuicidal self-injury (NSSI). Prior to self-injury, most individuals will describe a tension or an obsession with cutting that builds in urgency and intensity over time. Once the person engages in self-injury, albeit painful, it is often experienced with a sense of relief (b-process; Klonsky et al., 2011).

As mentioned earlier, opponent process theory falls under behavioral theories in that it hypothesizes that both operant (e.g., positive and negative reinforcers) and classical (e.g., unconditioned stimuli) conditioning are at play. Opponent process theory doesn't look to replace or downplay the role of operant or classical conditioning but rather to incorporate how these conditioning models help to explain the role of both a-processes and b-processes in strengthening or reinforcing particular behaviors (Solomon, 1980). There appear to also be neurological changes that may also help to explain how and why opponent process explanations occur. For example, when one ingests a substance, it causes an activation of dopamine in the mesolimbic center of the brain that then projects onto the nucleus accumbens and amygdala, creating a feeling of positive reinforcement (a-process). The b-process then involves the downregulation or shutting down of the mesolimbic dopamine system (Koob et al., 1997; Weiss et al., 2001). The flood of dopamine in the mesolimbic system accounts for the subjective feeling of reward and hence is considered positively reinforcing. Keep in mind that this flood of dopamine can be activated by nearly all the drugs of abuse but also by particular food, pleasurable sexual encounters, gambling, and other process addictions.

Another way to conceptualize SUDs from a behavioral perspective comes from noted addiction neuroscientist George Koob (2009), who claims that SUDs involve both *impulsivity and compulsivity.* He defines *impulsivity* as the "tendency toward rapid, unintended reactions to internal and external stimuli without regard for the negative consequences of these reactions" (p. 1), while *compulsivity* is defined as "behavior that results in perseveration in responding in the face of adverse consequences or perseveration in the face of incorrect responses in choice situations and is associated with exaggerated response inhibition" (Koob, 2009, p. 1). Both impulsivity and compulsivity are characterized by emotional distress, whereby impulsivity coincides with a buildup of tension or arousal prior to committing the impulsive act and pleasure and relief once the act takes place, while compulsivity is also characterized by anxiety and stress before committing the act (i.e., drug use) and tension-relief once the act is committed. The aforementioned impulsivity–compulsivity is the behavioral recipe for addictive behaviors.

Personality Theory

As early as the 1960s, counselors working in SUD residential and outpatient programs began noticing similar personality traits among the men and women they were treating. Traits such as an inability to tolerate frustration, being very demanding of others, being quick to anger, immaturity, and tendencies to quickly develop addictions to other substances (e.g., caffeine, nicotine) and/or nonsubstance or process addictions (e.g., spending, eating, sex, gambling) were among the first personality characteristics noted. This resulted in many counselors hypothesizing that SUDs came about as the result of an *addictive personality*, that is, a set of personality traits that would predispose one to become addicted to alcohol and/or drugs (Nakken, 1988). Even during the early days of AA, there was a recognition that alcoholics tended to share particular personality traits that came to be known in Steps 4, 5, and 6 (of AA's 12 Steps) as "defects of character." Although AA made no claims as to whether these "character defects" were antecedents to alcoholism, the AA founders instead viewed these personality defects as being the result of years of heavy, problematic drinking.

Personality traits have also been studied as having etiological significance in the development of SUDs (e.g., Caspi et al., 1997; Galen et al., 1997; Sher et al., 1999, 2000). Although there were some similarities between the types of personality traits noted by those working in SUD treatment programs, there were also other traits that appeared to correlate consistently with SUDs. This second perspective originated as an attempt to describe key personality differences among individuals with SUDs, which turned out to be a very diverse or heterogeneous population. Many researchers concluded that there needed to be some way to describe some of these differences. While the *addictive personality* movement really helped to describe similarities among alcoholics and addicts noted by counselors, this second perspective attempted to describe differences among this rather diverse population. For example, Cloninger et al. (1981) hypothesized there were two distinct types of individuals who develop Alcohol Use Disorders. Type 1 includes individuals who are considered to be functioning alcoholics. These were men and women who tended to be more established in their jobs, careers, and families and who also tended to be more cautious, whereas Type 2 alcoholics were usually young men who were characterized as being impulsive risk-takers who often had histories of criminality and other acting out behaviors. Babor et al. (1992) also concluded that there were two types of alcoholics. Type A was associated with higher rates of anxiety and depression (i.e., internalizing pathology), while Type Bs tended to have higher rates of antisocial behavior and other substance use patterns (externalizing pathology). These typologies were developed because of the recognition that individuals with SUDs were a very diverse or heterogeneous population composed of individuals from all socioeconomic strata, races, ethnic groups, and educational levels (Hesselbrock & Hesselbrock, 2006; Jackson et al., 2014).

One of the difficulties with personality trait research was that most studies were done with individuals who already manifested SUDs, yet it was speculated that certain personality traits pre-dated the onset of SUDs and, therefore, could be considered as having a causal influence with several types of addiction (including process addictions such as gambling, sexual addictions, and internet gaming addictions). However, other researchers concluded that the so-called addictive personality traits were not the cause of addiction but rather were the result of the years of heavy and/or consistent alcohol or drug use and not the cause (similar to the view taken by the founders of AA). While most researchers conclude that there is no such thing as an "addictive personality" (Troncone, 2014), there are anecdotal accounts that conclude that there are personality traits that appear to be common among those with alcohol, substance, and some process addictions like gambling and sexual addictions. Also important to keep in mind is a phenomenon in the addiction treatment profession referred to as "cross-addiction" or "addiction transfer" (Hazelden, 2019) that occurs when an individual has two or more addictions. Whether addictive personality causes one to become addicted to more than one substance or whether certain personality traits develop as a result of years of alcohol or substance abuse is a classic "chicken and egg" dilemma. It is also worth noting that some of the personality traits associated with the "addictive personality" (e.g., sensation-seeking) are thought to be possibly inherited traits. Therefore, it's possible to have a crossover or interaction from the genetic model to the personality theory models, rather than these models being mutually exclusive.

What exactly are the personality traits that are thought to correlate with SUDs? There are several personality traits models that have attempted to answer this question. For example, the Big Five and Big Three Models both attempt to describe essential personality traits in the general population. The Big Five model evolved from attempts to describe essential personality traits using everyday language descriptions (Goldberg, 1993; John & Srivastava, 1999; McCrae et al., 2000). The five factors are (1) extraversion, (2) agreeableness, (3) conscientiousness, (4) neuroticism, and (5) openness. The Big Three dimensions (Clark & Watson, 1999; Clark et al., 1994; Markon et al., 2005) include (1) negative emotionality, (2) positive emotionality, and (3) disinhibition. In a large meta-analysis study, Kotov et al. (2010) found that individuals with SUDs had higher rates of disinhibition, low disagreeableness, and low conscientiousness. The authors of this study conclude that their research may have important implications for prevention efforts in terms of identifying particular personality types that may be at higher risk for developing SUDs.

Another personality theory model (similar to the Big Five and Big Three) that has been used to describe individuals with SUDs is referred to by the acronym UPPS-P, which stands for *urgency, premeditation, perseverance, sensation-seeking, and positive urgency. Urgency* is similar to impulsivity, whereby a person may experience an obsessive need to act on an impulse when in a negative mood state (such as feeling angry, irritable, or depressed), whereas *positive urgency* describes impulsive behavior that occurs during positive mood states (Smith et al., 2007). *Sensation-seeking* refers to the need to seek excitement and novel forms of stimulation. *Premeditation* refers to instances where individuals consider or weigh out the consequences of their decisions and/or actions, while *perseverance* describes one's ability to stick to a plan in order to achieve certain goals. In research utilizing the UPPS-P model with people with different types of SUDs (Moraleda-Barreno et al., 2018), stronger relationships were found between the severity of heroin and cocaine dependence and particular impulsive personality traits, while weaker relationships were found for alcohol and cannabis users.

Belcher et al. (2014) found that greater impulsivity and sensation-seeking were risk or vulnerability factors for SUDs, while positive emotionality and extraversion (PEM/E) constituted resilience or protective factors. The authors described PEM/E as "a state of positive affect, strong motivation, desire, wanting, as well as feelings of being excited, enthusiastic, active and optimistic" (p. 211).

Other personality research has examined particular SUD subpopulations. For example, Wieczorek and Nochajski (2005) and Jonah (1997) found that many driving under the influence (DUI) offenders scored high on sensation-seeking trait scales especially among repeat offenders. These authors hypothesized that because high sensation-seekers would become bored at one drinking location, they were more likely to drive to find another, more exciting drinking location, thereby increasing their likelihood of being pulled over by the police or getting into a motor-vehicle accident. Ball et al. (2000) also found in a group of DUI offenders they studied that there were more Type B alcoholics who also exhibited more psychiatric distress and lower abstinence self-efficacy (i.e., confidence in their ability to abstain) than the Type A alcoholics. Several other studies have also concluded that high novelty-seeking is highly correlated with impulsivity and high sensation-seeking, which are predictive of SUDs in general (Battaglia et al., 1996; Cloninger et al., 1995; Galen et al., 1997; Sher et al., 1995; Zuckerman & Cloninger, 1996). High sensation-seeking in cocaine-addicted adults was also found to positively correlate with having been diagnosed with ADHD in childhood (Ballon et al., 2015). Finally, particular personality traits were often found to correlate with drug of preference in several specific types of SUDs (McKernan et al., 2015).

SOCIOCULTURAL MODELS

The sociocultural models help to explain the profound influence of one's immediate environment (e.g., family and neighborhood) as well as ethnic and cultural influences that shape one's identity and behavior. As mentioned earlier, children are also influenced by their immediate family, which can be viewed though the lens of social learning theory or simply by the influence of one's social environment. When applied to behaviors like substance use, people tend to drink alcohol or use drugs similar to those in their immediate social circle, sometimes in order to become accepted by that social group or to fit in. As the old saying goes, "When in Rome, do what the Romans do."

CASE EXAMPLE: WILLIAM W.

Background Information: William was born on November 25, 1895 in East Dorset, Vermont to Emily Griffith and her husband, Gilman. The pregnancy and delivery were uneventful and both Emily and Gilman were looking forward to becoming parents. Emily had gone to college in Castleton and had become a schoolteacher, while Gilman worked as a supervisor at a local marble quarry. William was named for his paternal grandfather. Since Vermont was a dry state and therefore at the cutting edge of the growing temperance movement, William's grandfather had apparently taken several temperance pledges (agreements to abstain from alcohol) given his apparent struggles with drinking.

When William was 9 years old, his father had taken a job at a quarry in Rutland, Vermont. Rutland was one of Vermont's largest cities, and William went from attending a small one-room schoolhouse in East Dorset to attending a school in Rutland with hundreds of students. What made matters worse was that William's mother, Emily, had developed appendicitis that required surgery. Her recuperation was difficult, and her husband was not very helpful. It was rumored that he had an affair with the daughter of a local minister. The marriage began to unravel. Emily began to experience a number of "nervous breakdowns." In 1906, Emily and Gilman separated, and William went back to East Dorset to live with his maternal grandparents. Emily obtained a divorce and soon thereafter left to attend the Boston College of Osteopathy to study medicine and become a doctor. William's grandfather provided his grandson with a good life and became a father figure. Grandpa Griffith was a veteran of the Civil War and had done well in lumber and real estate businesses. William did not

(*continued*)

have much contact with his father after the divorce, and he saw his mother only during her scheduled breaks from her medical studies.

When it was time to enter high school, it was decided that William would attend the Burr and Burton Seminary in Manchester Village, Vermont. He boarded there during the week and then would take the train back to East Dorset on the weekends. William did well in his studies and was a pitcher on the school's baseball team. Burr and Burton students often went on to college at Harvard, Yale, or MIT, and it was his mother's dream that William would go to MIT to study engineering. During high school, William had fallen in love with Bertha Bamford, who was also a student at Burr and Burton and the daughter of the minister of the Episcopalian church in Manchester Village. On a fall weekend, Bertha's family took her to New York City to have a small tumor removed. When William returned to Burr and Burton on Monday, he expected to see Bertha; however, the headmaster informed everyone (including William) in an assembly that Bertha had died of "internal hemorrhaging." William was devastated. He sank into a depression and could hardly speak. William went from being a good student with good grades and athletic abilities to becoming dysfunctional. He failed his entrance exams for MIT. Instead, he enrolled in Norwich University, a small military college in Northfield, Vermont. William was still experiencing anxiety and depression, and being away at college probably contributed to his feelings of isolation and loneliness. When World War I broke out, Norwich students automatically became part of the U.S. Army Reserves, and William chose a coastal artillery unit and was sent to officers' training school. Coastal artillery was considered one of the safest units in the Army. William was stationed briefly in New Bedford, Massachusetts, which bordered the wealthy area of Newport, Rhode Island. It was here that William found he could lessen his social anxiety when he and other officers were invited to the mansions of Newport by having a few stiff drinks. Counter to his Christian and temperance upbringing in Vermont, William found that alcohol became an effective way to cope with depression and loneliness. When William was shipped over to France as a second lieutenant in the Coastal Artillery, he didn't see much combat, and, as a result, he felt guilty for selecting an artillery unit and, therefore, not doing more to serve his country.

Once William was honorably discharged from the military, he returned to the States and married his fiancé, Lois. They were living in New York City at the time, as William had taken a job as a stockbroker. It was during this time that William began to drink frequently and heavily. In many instances when William would drink, he would end up binge drinking for several days, and his wife, Lois, would end up bringing him to Towns Hospital in New York City where he was treated by a Dr. William Silkworth. There was one occasion where, after staying abstinent for a couple of weeks and promising not to pick up alcohol again, William had decided to take a day off to play golf. So, he gathered his golf clubs and jumped on a train to Westchester to play a round of golf. On the way, he struck up a conversation with a guy on the train, and when they arrived at their destination the fellow traveler suggested they stop in at a local bar to continue their conversation. William ordered a ginger ale, intent on making his tee time; however, because it was Armistice Day, the bartender bought everyone a round of drinks to celebrate. William could not turn down the drink, and he ended up drinking the entire day. Because he was so intoxicated, he passed out on a subway platform and later called Lois to pick him up. She once again brought her husband to Towns Hospital as she had done so many times before (Cheever, 2004).

Substance use can also be influenced by the country or region one grows up in. For example, if a person grows up in Russia, they may develop a preference for vodka, while someone growing up in France or Italy may develop a preference for Bordeaux wine or Chianti. In those particular countries, it is also considered a matter of nationalistic pride to drink alcohol that is produced in that country or region. However, it is also noted that the rates of alcohol use disorders are certainly higher in some countries than others. For example, United Kingdom countries are often referred to as "pub cultures," because much of the socialization that takes place occurs in neighborhood pubs. In Ireland (which also is considered a pub culture), it is considered a matter of nationalistic pride to drink Guinness beer or Jameson's or Irish whiskey.

While countries such as Italy and, to some extent, Israel are known to produce and consume wine, they tend to have lower rates of alcohol use disorders. Some attribute these lower rates to the fact that alcohol in those countries is consumed as part of family gatherings and also as part of religious rituals and celebrations. When looking at the impact of environment, it is also important to look at why some ethnic groups tend to have higher rates of addiction than others. Why do those of Irish ancestry have higher rates of alcohol use disorders than Israelis? Countries such as Australia, England, Ireland, Italy, and Israel have been investigated because of their variable rates of alcoholism as a means of discerning sociocultural differences that may influence those rates. For example, Australia, England, and Ireland have higher rates of alcoholism, which is hypothesized to be the result of being a pub culture. Pubs are central places of socialization and community life (Lyall, 2007), much like how taverns dominated American culture as places of communal gathering for information sharing and political discussion in the 18th and 19th centuries (remember, prior to 1776, America was a British colony). It appears that when alcohol is consumed among family and as part of holiday or religious rituals, this tends to have a buffering effect on excessive drinking. Another factor that supports the influence of culture is that many immigrant groups who relocate to countries with higher alcoholism tend to have low rates of substance abuse when they initially relocate; however, several years after relocation, their rates of substance abuse increase.

LEARNING ACTIVITY 2.3
RISK FACTORS CASE

Case Example: William W. is based on a rather well-known, deceased individual. As you read through the case history, see if you can pick out factors that would have placed this person at risk for a SUD. See if you can identify biological, psychological, and sociocultural risk factors. Once you've come up with the list of risk factors, discuss these in small groups in class or in your online discussion groups. See if you can identify who this well-known person is. If not, your instructor will provide you with information about this person's identity.

Many of the models or theories explored thus far tend to view SUDs as emanating from internal processes such as genetic factors or some types of physical or psychological anomaly, while the sociocultural models look primarily at the influence of the environment. It is widely accepted that SUDs do not occur in a vacuum; therefore, social and environmental influences must be taken into account as causal factors or factors that place individuals (and, in some instances, entire communities) at risk (Freeman & Dyer, 1993). Several social and environmental features have been identified as having greater influence. For example, it is not unusual to find that SUDs are more prevalent in areas that are profoundly impacted by poverty, racism, and a lack of occupational and educational opportunities. It should also be noted that both tobacco and alcoholic beverage corporations target low socioeconomic areas in the United States.

If one needs further convincing about the effects of environment on drinking and drug use, there are two examples to support these powerful influences. The first is the Vietnam War. The Vietnam War provided all the "main ingredients" for increasing addictive behaviors, for example, the constant threat of death, an everlasting supply of drugs (especially alcohol, marijuana, and heroin), and a lack of social support (tours lasted for 12 months, so there was a constant shifting of troops, which lessened the likelihood of cohesive social group support). Many U.S. soldiers who had not used drugs prior to being sent to Vietnam became addicted while "in country" (Frenkel et al., 1977; Robins, 1993; Robins & Slobodyan, 2003; Stanton, 1976). Some soldiers carried their addictions home with them; however, and very surprisingly, many gave up their addictions once they returned to the States.

The second example of environmental influence is drinking that is done while in college. According to research done with college-age populations (Wechsler et al., 2002a, 2002b), a sizeable portion of college students engage in binge drinking (defined as drinking five or more drinks per occasion); however, there is another body of research that suggests that many college students will "mature out" of this type of drinking behavior once they graduate and move on to establish careers and families (Kandel & Logan, 1984; Merline et al., 2004). College binge drinking can also be viewed as a good example of peer influence. The peer model views addictions as being either important as influencing initial alcohol and drug use or in influencing the continuation of substance use. As the old saying goes, "Birds of a feather, flock together"; so too will alcoholics feel more acceptance and comfort in drinking with other alcoholics, just as intravenous heroin uses will feel more acceptance and comfort with other similar heroin-addicted people. Individuals who abuse substances will often have greater social contact with those who also abuse similar substances (Blackson & Tarter, 1994). Although peer pressure from other drug-using adolescents to initiate drug use was thought to influence initial drug-taking behavior, research suggests that adolescents are more likely to initiate drug use in order to "fit in" or gain acceptance by a particular peer group that they perceive as being desirable. Peer role models who abuse alcohol or drugs are often perceived as being more powerful or admired; therefore, some teenagers will initiate drug use to become more like these envied peers. In some communities, drug dealers and drug gangs are seen as role models because they are perceived as successful and powerful (Westermeyer, 1999). An example of cultural influence discouraging alcohol and/or substance use is found in religious groups, for example, fundamentalist religious groups as well as Muslim and Buddhist worshipers whose beliefs prohibit substance use. The aforementioned religious groups socialize their children to believe that alcohol and drug use is considered sinful and therefore deviant.

Alcohol use disorders have been problematic within the African American community, however, this was not always the case. Historically, alcohol was used as part of ceremonial and religious rituals in Africa. Even during years of slavery and during the Reconstruction era, drunkenness was rare, although many states had enacted laws prohibiting the use of alcohol by freed slaves. With the passage of time, many of these laws were abolished, and African Americans gained their right to drink, although most did so at home or at neighborhood bars and mostly on the weekend. Because of these historical influences, it was thought that African Americans did not perceive alcoholism to be a danger. From a religious perspective, however, drunkenness was considered to be sinful. Given the struggles of African Americans to gain basic rights and given the lack of educational and job opportunities, these factors may have contributed to a perception that alcohol is a reward for living a hard life and that life's hardships entitle one to drink. Therefore, it is hypothesized that drinking in the African American community came to be perceived as a means of coping with life's hardships, rather than as a cause of problems. Rates of addiction in Hispanic and Latino barrios also provide evidence of how cultural influences in combination with poverty and the lack of economic and educational opportunity can impact on rates of addiction (Gillmore et al., 1990).

Similarly, Native American tribal nations being restricted to reservations has resulted in high rates of unemployment, school dropout, poverty, suicide, welfare dependence, and SUDs. Deaths due to alcoholism are five times higher for Native American adults and 17 times higher for Native American adolescents when compared with national averages. Rieckmann et al. (2012) compared a group of Native Americans living on reservations with a group living in urban areas and found that reservation-based Native Americans reported more severe medical and mental health problems, regular opioid use, and suicidal thoughts/attempts along with polysubstance use, while urban dwellers were more likely to report employment problems and polysubstance use. Some researchers posit that high rates of SUDs among Native Americans are the result of "soul wounds" and transgenerational trauma brought on by centuries of societal marginalization and oppression. It is noteworthy that in those tribal nations where casino gaming has become legal, this has resulted not only in economic and community growth but also in the amelioration of many health and social problems such as domestic violence, crime, and suicide rates, all of which are correlated with alcoholism. Overall, the positive social impact of legally sanctioned gaming has been demonstrated most dramatically with the Pequot and Mohegan tribal nations in Connecticut (Bubb, 2012) as well as some southwestern tribal nations.

Another compelling argument can be made regarding the profound influence of environment in the etiology of SUDs. While many addiction theorists conclude that biological models (such as genetic and neurotransmitter models) make the strongest case for SUD causality by pointing to the fact that some drugs of abuse are highly addictive when compared to others (e.g., crack cocaine, crystal methamphetamines, and opioids), the notion that certain mood-altering chemicals are inherently addicting and, therefore, irresistible to even casual users has been challenged. Johann Hari (2015), the author of *Chasing the Scream,* cites research that was well known in the 1970s in which rats could press a bar order to receive a drink of water containing morphine or cocaine or plain water. Invariably, the rats would bar press for the cocaine-laced/morphine-laced water until eventually they would literally drop dead from overdose (e.g., Pickens & Plunkett, 1970; Smith & Davis, 1973; Smith et al., 1975). Without doubt, morphine was considered to be a powerful, irresistible reinforcer even for rats! When Canadian researchers Alexander et al. (1978) replicated some of these earlier studies, they also included two bottles of water (one containing morphine-laced water and the other plain water); however, they also changed the rats' environment. These rat cages were filled with several "rat toys" like running wheels, balls, shiny objects, and female and male rats. The findings were startling. The rats who were in "rat park," or the enriched environment, did not prefer the morphine-laced water and, therefore, did not perish due to morphine overdose. Think of the implications for humans and the influence of one's environment!

Recently, two books were published that appear to provide support for the influence of environment. Princeton economists Anne Case and Angus Deaton (2020) were collecting data regarding chronic pain and its impact on overall health in America when they came across a rather startling discovery that White, working-age Americans who lacked college degrees were dying at ever-increasing rates from alcohol-related liver disease, suicide, and drug overdoses (particularly opioid-related overdoses that coincided with the opioid epidemic in the United States). In exploring the potential reasons for these sudden increases in death, Case and Deaton came upon several possible explanations. First, prescription opiates became very plentiful and very easy to obtain thanks in large part to pharmaceutical companies downplaying the addictive potential of these drugs and their aggressive marketing campaigns. With regard to opiate overdose deaths, Case and Deaton found that areas of the United States impacted by crushing poverty also happen to be areas reporting high rates of overdose deaths. These deaths seem to coincide with increased unemployment, underemployment, and a loss of job opportunities. There is a saying that has become popular in these areas: "When the factory moves out, heroin moves in." Some conservative authors (e.g., J.D. Vance's *Hillbilly Elegy* [2018]) tend to blame cultural factors or the fact that Americans are "taking the easy way out" by choosing alcohol/drugs, welfare, and disability income over hard work and commitment to supporting their family and communities. However, if this was a valid explanation, then wages would have risen in an effort to attract qualified workers back into the workforce. As Case and Deaton point out, wages have been stagnant for some time now. They also point out that while the economic surge (up until the impact of the coronavirus) had benefitted college graduates, it left behind the majority of the blue-collar, non–college-educated workforce, thus creating both economic and emotional despair (Gawande, 2020).

The second book to have come out in 2020 also echoes the research findings of Case and Deaton. Kristof and WuDann's (2020) *Tightrope: Americans Reaching for Hope* also chronicles the struggles of working-class Americans. By following the plight of the Knapp family of Yamhill, Oregon, the same town as Kristof grew up in, Kristof and WuDann make the case for how the booming economy following the Great Recession of 2008 had left many Americans struggling, as evidenced by several members of the Knapp family who died of overdoses and complications resulting from SUDs. Johann Hari (2015) explains these trends toward higher rates of addiction in society as being influenced by an American culture that prizes success, education, and good health but pushes aside and isolates those who are less fortunate. For example, those who live a meager existence with few comforts and few options for success tend to become marginalized in our society, which bears some similarity to the rats who were given only two bottles of water to choose from. However, Hari also mentions those at the other end of the economic spectrum, those with increased wealth, by pointing out that, as the total square footage of their "McMansions" has increased, they have also become more socially and emotionally isolated from others. Also important to consider is the availability of drugs and alcohol in particular neighborhoods and cities. Suffice it to say, environment plays a large role in the etiology of SUDs, especially if one is not fortunate enough to live in the human equivalent of "rat park."

THE DIATHESIS-STRESS MODEL

The nature–nurture debate has puzzled behavioral scientists for centuries. The debate takes opposing views on whether behavior and various mental health disorders (including SUDs) are the result of nature (e.g., biological influences such as genetics) or the result of nurture (such as family and environmental influences). Rather than this being an "either-or" question, many contend that behavior is essentially influenced by BOTH nature and nurture, not one or the other.

The nature versus nurture question was first raised by Sir Francis Galton in 1874 when he was investigating the influences of genetics on various human traits or characteristics. Finally, research initiated in the 1960s (Bleuler, 1963; Meehl, 1962) began to explore whether mental health disorders (more specifically schizophrenia and depression) might be the result of BOTH nature and nurture (e.g., Bebbington, 1987; Mednick et al., 1998; Robins & Block, 1988). In other words, isn't it possible for individuals to be influenced by both natural causes, like having a genetic predisposition for a SUD, and environmental factors, such as living in a poor section of town where drugs are readily available? Let's consider another scenario whereby a person has genetic influences (e.g., their father, paternal grandfather, and paternal great grandfathers all had alcohol use disorders), however, the son decides to join a monastery or a religious order where drinking alcohol is strictly forbidden. In this latter case, it is possible that, despite having genetic predispositions for alcoholism, this individual might not ever experience drinking problems if they live in an environment that doesn't condone drinking.

Mednick et al.'s (1998) research into the origins of schizophrenia came upon an interesting discovery. He and his colleagues were examining a group of sons born to mothers diagnosed with schizophrenia whom they followed for several years into their adolescence and young adulthood, which is when schizophrenia usually begins to emerge. The researchers used a factor analytic model in which they included a number of variables including the health of the schizophrenic mothers, childhood stressors of the sons, and educational performance. The one significant variable that was able to predict which sons developed schizophrenia was whether their mother had contracted the flu during the first trimester of pregnancy. In this example, the genetic influence of the mothers having been diagnosed with schizophrenia was not sufficient to account for their sons being diagnosed as schizophrenic; instead, the mothers having contracted the flu in the first trimester was the significant trigger. In this instance, the developing fetus's exposure to the flu (nurture or environment) was the crucial factor.

There is a saying that best summarizes the diathesis-stress model. It is as follows:

Biology loads the gun, psychology points the gun, but environment pulls the trigger.

The diathesis-stress model, therefore, very much follows the biopsychosocial assessment's exploration of risk factors that emanate from biological influences (such as genetics), psychological influences (such as particular personality traits), and environment influences (such as sociocultural factors). The diathesis-stress model takes into account not just nature or nurture but all three biopsychosocial influences. Without a doubt, SUDs are truly influenced by biological, psychological, and social influences, which is why the biopsychosocial model is so important for addiction counselors to understand and apply to assessment and treatment approaches.

NOTES FROM THE FIELD

David Dolan, LMHC, CSAC, LCADC, LPC, NCC, currently runs his own outpatient private practice (Bohdi Wellness and Psychotherapy) in Makawao, Hawaii, with his wife, Kim, where they specialize in treating people with SUDs with a focus on wellness. He started his career in the addictions field by developing and operating transitional housing for men coming out of residential treatment facilities for SUDs. When asked what he sees as one of the greatest challenges as an addictions counselor, David indicates it is striking a balance between being highly present with his clients and not getting overly invested in the specific outcomes of therapy. The thing he enjoys most about addictions counseling is when clients embrace recovery and "not only physical recovery from their addiction but transformation from a mental and spiritual standpoint." Also, when asked about the greatest challenges facing the addiction treatment profession, David indicates he is most concerned about the amount of unethical treatment that exists in the large-scale treatment industry*, where client brokering is a huge issue. He also expressed concerns about the shortage of treatment for individuals in long-term recovery.

*For more information on this topic, read the following: https://www.npr.org/2021/02/15/963700736/as-addiction-deaths-surge-profit-driven-rehab-industry-faces-severe-ethical-cris

SUMMARY

Etiological models of SUDs tend to fall under three main categories: biological, psychological, and social/sociocultural. The biological models take into account the etiological influences of genetics and neurotransmitter imbalances. Psychological influences take into account the role of particular personality traits such as sensation-seeking, low self-esteem, attachment difficulties, and the role of trauma in influencing SUDs. Finally, sociocultural models consider the role of environment, culture, race/ethnicity, poverty, family, peers, and other social influences. The diathesis-stress model represents a compromise of the age-old nature-versus-nurture debate by taking into account the influences of biological, psychological, and sociocultural influences.

RESOURCES

Alexander, B. K., Coambs, R. B., & Hadaway, P. F. (1978). The effects of housing and gender on morphine self-administration in rats. *Psychopharmacology, 58(2)*, 175–179. https://doi.org/10.1007/BF00426903

Flores, P. J. (2004). *Addiction as an attachment disorder*. Jason Aronson.

Hari, J. (2015). *Chasing the scream: The first and last days of the war on drugs*. Bloomsbury Press.

Kurtz, E. (1979). *Not God: A history of Alcoholics Anonymous*. Hazelden.

Nakken, C. (1988). *The addictive personality: Understanding compulsion in our lives*. Hazelden Foundation.

Robins, L. N., & Slobodyan, S. (2003). Post-Vietnam heroin use and injection by returning U.S. veterans: Clues to preventing injection today. *Addiction, 98*(8), 1053–1060. https://doi.org/10.1046/j.1360-0443.2003.00436.x

Satel, S., & Lilienfeld, S. O. (2013). *Brainwashed: The seductive appeal of mindless neuroscience*. Basic Books.

Solomon, R. L. (1980). The opponent process theory of acquired motivation: The costs of pleasure and the benefits of pain. *American Psychologist, 35*(8), 691–712. https://doi.org/10.1037//0003-066x.35.8.691

Volkow, N. D., Fowler, J. S., & Wang, G. J. (2004). The addicted human brain viewed in the light of imaging studies: Brain circuits and treatment strategies. *Neuropharmacology, 47*(Suppl. 1), 3–13. https://doi.org/10.1016/j.neuropharm.2004.07.019

White, W. L. (1998). *Slaying the dragon: The history of addiction treatment and recovery in America*. Chestnut Health Systems.

KEY REFERENCES

Only key references appear in the print edition. The full reference list appears in the digital product on Springer Publishing Connect: connect.springerpub.com/content/book/978-0-8261-3586-5/chapter/ch02

Alexander, B. K., Coambs, R. B., & Hadaway, P. F. (1978). The effects of housing and gender on morphine self-administration in rats. *Psychopharmacology, 58*(2), 175–179. https://doi.org/10.1007/BF00426903

Belcher, A. M., Volkow, N. D., Moeller, F. G., & Ferre, S. (2014). Personality traits and vulnerability or resilience to substance use disorders. *Trends in Cognitive Science, 18*(4), 211–217. https://doi.org/10.1016/.tics.2014.01.010

Cadoret, R. J., Troughton, E., & O'Gorman, T. W. (1987). Genetic and environmental factors in alcohol abuse and antisocial personality. *Journal of Studies on Alcohol, 48*(1), 1–8. https://doi.org/10.15288/jsa.1987.48.1

Flores, P. J. (2004). *Addiction as an attachment disorder*. Jason Aronson.

Hari, J. (2015). *Chasing the scream: The first and last days of the war on drugs*. Bloomsbury Press.

Kotov, R., Gamez, W., Schmidt, F., & Watson, D. (2010). Linking 'big' personality traits to anxiety, depressive and substance use disorders: A meta-analysis. *Psychological Bulletin, 136*(5), 768–821. https://doi.org/10.1037/a0020327

Robins, L. N. (1993). Vietnam veterans' rapid recovery from heroin addiction: A fluke or normal expectation? *Addiction, 88*(8), 1041–1054.

Robins, L. N., & Slobodyan, S. (2003). Post-Vietnam heroin use and injection by returning U.S. veterans: Clues to preventing injection today. *Addiction, 98*(8), 1053–1060. https://doi.org/10.1046/j.1360-0443.2003.00436.x

Satel, S., & Lilienfeld, S. O. (2013). *Brainwashed: The seductive appeal of mindless neuroscience*. Basic Books.

Solomon, R. L. (1980). The opponent process theory of acquired motivation: The costs of pleasure and the benefits of pain. *American Psychologist, 35*(1), 691–712. https://doi.org/10.1037//0003-066x.35.8.691

Volkow, N. D., Fowler, J. S., & Wang, G. J. (2004). The addicted human brain viewed in the light of imaging studies: Brain circuits and treatment strategies. *Neuropharmacology, 47*(Suppl. 1), 3–13. https://doi.org/10.1016/j.neuropharm.2004.07.019

Westermeyer, J. (1999). The role of cultural and social factors in the cause of addictive disorders. *The Psychiatric Clinics of North America, 22*(2), 253–273. https://doi.org/10.1016/s0193-953x(05)70075-7

White, W. L. (1998). *Slaying the dragon: The history of addiction treatment and recovery in America*. Chestnut Health Systems.

3

NEUROSCIENCE AND ADDICTION

LEARNING OBJECTIVES

This chapter focuses on the neuroscience and neurological influences on substance use disorder as well as some of the pharmacological and neurocognitive approaches that have resulted from this area of research. In addition, this chapter will explore the ways in which stress and trauma impact the brain. By the end of this chapter, you will be able to:

- describe various neurotransmitters and their roles in neurological functioning;
- describe how specific substances impact those neurotransmitters to create mood-altering effects;
- explain how neurotransmitter depletions cause post-acute withdrawal symptoms;
- describe how neuroscience research has influenced pharmacological treatment as well as trauma-informed care;
- describe what happens in the brain when individuals are exposed to substance cues and how those cue-activation responses contribute to relapse.

TERMS TO KNOW

agonist a chemical that binds to a receptor site and activates the receptor to produce a neurochemical action. It is a chemical entity that does not naturally occur in the body and acts on one or more receptors by mimicking the action of that receptor. Buprenorphine is a partial opioid agonist used in the treatment of opioid use disorders.

antagonist a chemical that binds to the receptor and prevents a substance from producing an effect

axon a thin nerve fiber that carries messages away from the nerve cell body

CNS central nervous system, which is composed of the brain and spinal cord

dendrite a thin nerve fiber that carries messages toward the cell body

endorphins includes any group of neuropeptides that bind to opioid receptor sites in the brain and throughout the body. Endorphins are thought to be the body's own analgesic or pain reliever. Endorphins are also involved in craving behavior and sexual functioning

epigenetics genetics is the study of genes, the functional units of DNA that direct the basic cellular activity, whereas epigenetics studies both functional and sometimes inherited changes in the regulation of gene activity. Environmental exposure can actually change or remodel the structure of DNA

hypodopaminergic suggests a condition of dopamine deficiency, usually following long intervals of alcohol or drug use

neurotransmitters substances manufactured in the neuron that aid in synaptic transmission of nerve impulses in the brain. Neurotransmitters are of two types: monoamines (e.g., serotonin, dopamine, norepinephrine, and GABA) and neuropeptides (e.g., endorphins, enkephalins, and dynorphins)

receptors a neurotransmitter receptor is at the end of a neural pathway or postsynapse and responds to particular neurotransmitters, e.g., serotonin and dopamine

synapse the junction or space between two neurons across which neural electrical impulses are transmitted

synaptic cleft the area through which nerve impulses cross from axon to dendrite

synaptic reuptake after a nerve impulse is transmitted from one synapse to another, the neurotransmitter that is released into the synaptic cleft or juncture is then reabsorbed back into the synaptic vesicles

synaptic transmission the process by which an electrochemical nerve impulse is transmitted or jumps from one end of the synapse to the next synapse

synaptic vesicles sac-like structures located at the end of a synapse that contain various neurotransmitters

INTRODUCTION

Within the past few decades, no other research area has resulted in such tremendous strides in our understanding of substance use disorders (SUDs) and their treatment than the field of neuroscience. These discoveries have occurred, in part, due to advancements in technology, such as brain imaging, and the measurement of neurotransmitters and neurotransmitter imbalances. These advancements have resulted in the development of a variety of pharmacological treatments which help to reduce severe acute withdrawal, post-acute withdrawal (PAW), and substance craving. While none of the aforementioned pharmacological treatments are "cure-alls" and, therefore, do not replace more traditional treatments such as counseling and participation in 12-step programs, they do hold promise in helping to strengthen sobriety and recovery. In this chapter, we explore some of the most recent findings in the area of neuroscience as they relate to SUDs, but most importantly we will provide examples where neuroscientific advances are practically applied to the treatment of individuals experiencing SUDs.

THE ROLE OF NEUROTRANSMITTERS AND THE "HIJACKED BRAIN"

At the simplest level, whenever one ingests alcohol or any mood-altering substance, the euphoric high or "buzz" one experiences is produced by neurochemical changes in the brain. The same holds true, however, for other things that produce pleasure or reward, such as eating chocolate cake, winning a bet, having sex, getting a job promotion, purchasing a new outfit, or getting an "A" on an exam. You may have noticed that some of the aforementioned pleasurable events or rewards fall within the framework of what we call "process addictions." For example, sex addiction, gambling, workaholism, shopping addiction, food addiction (such as overeating or addiction to sweets or high carb foods) share in common the fact that some individuals experience incredible pleasure in these activities, in part because they flood the brain with the neurotransmitter dopamine (see Box 3.1).

BOX 3.1

THE ROLE OF NEUROTRANSMITTERS

Each of the neurotransmitters in the brain has specific functions and produces certain emotional states. As mentioned previously, various drugs of abuse will tend to increase production of combinations of the neurotransmitters. For example:

Serotonin promotes feelings of well-being and sleep (serotonin is made from the amino acid tryptophan. Certain foods, such as turkey, contain high levels of tryptophan, which is why people feel sleepy after Thanksgiving dinner). Serotonin also reduces aggressive and compulsive behaviors such as excessive alcohol or drug intake and overeating. Serotonin also helps regulate the cardiovascular system.

Dopamine increases feelings of well-being and is associated with sexual arousal; however, dopamine may increase aggressive behavior and alertness. Excessive dopamine may actually cause psychotic behavior, while dopamine depletions are associated with anhedonia (i.e., the inability to experience pleasure).

Norepinephrine also increases feelings of well-being and reduces compulsive behaviors; however, an excessive amount of norepinephrine may increase anxiety, heart rate, and blood pressure and may cause tremors in those withdrawing from alcohol or drugs.

GABA reduces anxiety and compulsive behavior and may help to elevate one's threshold for pain. GABA is considered an "inhibitory" neurotransmitter in that it helps to reduce heart rate, blood pressure, and breathing rate.

Glutamate is also an excitatory neurotransmitter that helps us to form memories and helps with learning and cognitive processing. Glutamate also sends signals to other neurotransmitters and tends to be one of the most pervasive neurotransmitters throughout the brain. It is thought to also help in the development of neurons. Excessive glutamate has been found in people with strokes, autism, and intellectual disabilities.

Adenosine is an inhibitory neurotransmitter that produces drowsiness. Caffeine blocks this neurotransmitter; however, as the impact of caffeine wears off, drowsiness develops as adenosine is naturally produced during the course of the day and is involved in the onset of sleep.

In order to understand how a mood-altering substance produces a particular mood state, it is important that the aforementioned neurochemical changes (e.g., enhanced dopamine production) takes into account both the "what" and the "where." For example, when a person drinks a shot of tequila (or any beverage containing alcohol), dopamine gets released in the brain. Dopamine is the "what"; it is the neurotransmitter that helps to produce the anticipated pleasurable feeling or "buzz" (along with other neurotransmitters like GABA and serotonin). *Where* in the brain these neurotransmitters are released is also very important because mood-altering substances usually impact an area known as the nucleus accumbens, which is located about three inches behind the bottom of our eye sockets. The nucleus accumbens is part of the brain involved in emotions and reward. This area known colloquially as the "reward center" of the brain is also known as the *mesolimbic pathway* by neuroscientists (Grisel, 2019). In order to further delineate the so-called pleasure center of the brain responsible for allowing drugs to produce the sense of euphoria and drug-seeking behavior, Koob and Volkow (2010) put forth a four-circuit "map" of the areas of the brain involved: (1) reward located in the nucleus accumbens and ventral pallidum; (2) motivation/drive located in the orbitofrontal cortex and subcallosal cortex; (3) memory and learning located in the amygdala and hippocampus; and (4) control located in the prefrontal cortex and anterior cingulate gyrus (see Table 3.1). Therefore, while pleasure or reward (Circuit 1) appears to be "located" in the mesolimbic pathway, other aspects of substance use reactions are located in the other three neural circuits such as motivation/drive (2) to seek more of the substance, memory and learning (3) associated with how to use the substance based on past experiences, and the decision (4) to find and use the substance. Various substances of abuse produce specific mood and behavioral reactions depending on what combination of neurotransmitters are activated by that particular substance. Generally, central nervous system (CNS) depressants (e.g., alcohol, benzodiazepines, and opioids) will increase production of not only dopamine but also GABA (an inhibitory neurotransmitter), serotonin (a neurotransmitter associated with enhanced mood), and sometimes endorphins. CNS stimulants increase production

TABLE 3.1 Brain Structures and Role/Function

STRUCTURE	ROLE/FUNCTION
Nucleus accumbens	Reward/emotional responses
Mesolimbic pathway	Reward center
Brainstem	Breathing, sleep, sensory processing
Amygdala	Monitors and responds to threats and fear
Thalamus	Relay station located between brainstem amygdala and cortex
Hypothalamus	Controls hunger, thirst, body temperature hormone, and cortisol release
Hippocampus	Conscious and verbal memory
Prefrontal cortex	Decision-making, thinking, impulse control planning in future, predicts what others will do, responds flexibly to environment
Anterior cingulate cortex	Regulates emotions, motivation and goal-directed behavior, empathic response

of dopamine, norepinephrine, and acetylcholine, which produces feelings of stimulation, increased energy, and increased focus, along with heightened mood. We will explain this in greater detail later in this chapter.

Although it is widely accepted that dopamine is the main neurotransmitter responsible for producing the euphoria or "high" of most drugs of abuse, it does not explain how individuals become addicted or how the brain becomes "hijacked" by a particular substance, thereby producing dependence. Indeed, the flooding of the brain with dopamine will occur for anyone who drinks or engages in substance use, not just for individuals who have SUDs. To answer this question, Volkow et al. (2004) ran a series of experiments in which they provided participants with intravenous stimulant methylphenidate (MP). Approximately half of the subjects reported finding the MP injection "pleasant," while the other half found the injection "unpleasant." Those participants who found the injection "pleasant" had significantly lower levels of dopamine (DA and D2) receptors than the participants who described the injection as "unpleasant." These findings suggest that there may be an optimal range of dopamine receptors for someone to experience the MP injection as pleasant. In a very practical sense, this may account for why some individuals find particular drugs of abuse pleasurable while others do not. Addiction professionals agree that there is a genetic etiological (causal) component to SUDs; however, there has not been consensus among researchers as to what exactly gets inherited that predisposes one to develop a SUD. It is possible that neurotransmitter receptor depletions are the culprit.

The question of an inherited neurotransmitter deficiency was examined with regard to endorphin depletions. Endorphins are the neurotransmitters that are considered as the brain and body's natural analgesic or pain relievers. It has been hypothesized that SUDs may be caused by deficiencies in neurotransmitters such as dopamine and/or endorphins, which then determine whether certain individuals will find particular substances, such as alcohol or opioids, pleasurable, thereby placing these individuals at greater risk for SUDs. Blum and Payne (1991) point to a study done in Milan, Italy (Gennazzini et al., 1982) in which endorphin levels in the cerebral spinal fluid were measured in a group of individuals with long-term alcohol use disorders. Although the results of this study suggest there were indeed beta-endorphin depletions that were hypothesized to have caused the alcohol use disorders, there was no possible way to have measured the beta-endorphin levels of these individuals prior to the onset of their drinking. Therefore, at best, the researchers could only conclude that those who engaged in excessive, continuous drinking had depleted beta-endorphin levels.

As a result of the aforementioned research that attempted to answer the question regarding how genetic inheritance factors result in an increased likelihood of developing SUDs, Blum et al. (1996) put forth the *reward deficiency theory* (RDS), which claims that individuals who carry the A1 allele gene tend to inherit an insufficient number D2 receptors (a particular type of dopamine receptor), which then results in several psychological and emotional tendencies, for example, experiencing a lack of pleasure in activities that for most would be considered rewarding or pleasurable and high sensation or thrill-seeking behaviors. In other words, because of deficiencies in dopamine receptors, individuals who experience RDS do not derive much pleasure or gratification from normal, everyday activities and as a result are more likely to seek out high-sensation or extremely exciting activities. It is also hypothesized that RDS may be expressed in developing not only SUDs but also mood disorders, compulsive behaviors, and impulsivity. For example, it is found that 50% of those with gambling disorders and 48% of cigarette smokers also carry the A1 allele (Reward Deficiency Syndrome, 2020). This is what is known as a *hypodopaminergic effect,* in that the state of dopamine deficiency is the result of long intervals of alcohol or drug use.

How Specific Substances Impact the Brain

While alcohol, benzodiazepines, and opioid substances all tend to slow down the mind and produce a feeling of calm, what about substances like methamphetamines, crack, or cocaine, which produce incredible energy and elated mood? Alcohol, benzodiazepines, and opioids are all CNS depressants, while methamphetamines and cocaine are considered CNS stimulants. These depressant-versus-stimulation effects are produced by combinations of neurotransmitter and neuropeptide release at the synapses of particular nerve cells throughout our brains. For example, drinking a few shots of tequila will result in an increase in dopamine in the brain; however, GABA production is also increased along with glutamate. GABA is an inhibitory neurotransmitter, which means it will slow down (or depress) nervous system activity, thereby producing feelings of relaxation and reducing anxiety, worry, and sleepiness. Glutamate, however, is an excitatory neurotransmitter, which is responsible for helping the brain form memories (which helps explain why excessive drinking results in memory "blackouts"). Both GABA and glutamate are pervasive throughout the brain (Grisel, 2019), which may account for why those neurotransmitters have such a profound effect when people drink alcohol. Alcohol ingestion also impacts on endorphin release, which is why (prior to the discovery of other pain analgesics such as opioid "painkillers") alcohol was often used as an analgesic to reduce pain. Alcohol has such a pervasive effect on brain chemistry, no wonder Grisel (2019) likens its effect to a "sledgehammer." Also, it is important to consider that when a person drinks excessively and on a daily basis over the course of several years, they may develop neurological disorders such as Wernicke-Korsakoff syndrome, which is characterized by impaired cognitive (thought) processing, psychotic-like thinking, confusion, and profound memory deficits, which is the result of a combination of brain-cell damage and nutritional deficiency.

Let us examine the impact of other mood-altering substances. If alcohol impacts the brain "like a sledgehammer," then cocaine and amphetamines impact the brain more "like a laser" (Grisel, 2019). Cocaine, methamphetamines, and MDMA or ecstasy (ecstasy is often referred to as a "psychedelic amphetamine" because it contains chemical properties of psychedelics like LSD and amphetamines or stimulants) all impact the monoamine neurotransmitters, which include dopamine, serotonin, norepinephrine, epinephrine (or adrenalin), and melatonin (Grisel, 2019). All of the aforementioned neurotransmitters combine to produce a feeling of intense stimulation, incredible energy, and grandiosity (as if one could do or accomplish anything). For those who go on cocaine binges (which often last for several days or a few weeks) or use amphetamines daily over the course of several days, the stimulation thrill described earlier is replaced with psychotic-like, paranoid thoughts and something called stereotypy, a condition in which individuals repeat the same behaviors over and over again. In most instances, both conditions will usually resolve and diminish with abstinence.

According to Grisel (2019), cannabis use is likened to the brain being doused by "a can of red paint" (Grisel, 2019, p. 52), in the respect that the psychological-emotional impact of cannabis is pervasive and widespread, impacting a variety of neurotransmitters located throughout the brain. For example, glutamate neurotransmitter activation in the region of the hippocampus may account for why cannabis users have difficulty in forming short-term memories. Cannabis, like opioids, has its own special neural receptors in the brain called *endocannabinoids* (the prefix "endo" refers to these receptors being endogenous or internal, within the brain). Therefore, in addition to the release of neurotransmitters like dopamine and serotonin, which produce feelings of well-being, other neurotransmitters being released produce intense changes in sensory input (e.g., sound, taste, and vision) that are perceived as totally new and, therefore, incredibly interesting to someone who is stoned. This accounts for why, after smoking or ingesting cannabis, every sensation (whether visual, auditory, or gustatory) becomes amazing, as if being experienced for the very first time. However, the problem often encountered when individuals stop using cannabis is that *nothing* is very interesting, which clients may experience as an extreme version of PAW Syndrome (PAWS; see Box 3.2) including anhedonia (an emotion where pleasurable feelings are absent and feelings of boredom are prominent). Anhedonia is a common symptom of major depression and dysthymia.

Finally, opioids also have endogenous opioid receptors in the brain, which account for their analgesic or pain-relieving impact. Prescription opioids (such as hydrocodone [Oxycontin], hydromorphone [Vicodin], and oxycodone [Percoset]) are all considered to be analgesic substances because of their ability to change one's perception of pain. Interestingly, although these substances are known as "painkillers," they do not "kill pain" but rather alter one's perception of pain.

BOX 3.2

POST-ACUTE WITHDRAWAL

Each of the various mood-altering substances that result in substance use disorders (SUDs) produces "substance-specific" withdrawal symptoms. Generally, the withdrawal symptoms for central nervous system (CNS) depressant substances (e.g., alcohol, benzodiazepines, and opioids) tend to produce withdrawal symptoms that are opposite to the depressant impact of these substances, which in this case are agitation, restlessness, and overstimulation, whereas stimulant drugs of abuse (e.g., cocaine, methamphetamine, and amphetamines) tend to produce withdrawal symptoms of depression, lethargy, and malaise. All of the aforementioned withdrawal symptoms comprise what we know as "acute withdrawal," which generally lasts for a few days and at most several days. However, there is also a phenomena called ***post-acute withdrawal*** (PAW), which is thought to be the result of dopamine depletions in the brain. The thinking is that during the time a person is using mood-altering substances, they are essentially flooding their brain with dopamine. However, because of drug tolerance, the brain adapts and eventually stops producing dopamine on its own (referred to as "reward deficiency syndrome"). It is hypothesized that it takes several months (sometimes 6–12 months of total abstinence) before the brain begins to produce dopamine again. Not surprisingly, PAW is characterized by anhedonia (an inability to experience pleasure), lethargy, and lack of motivation to accomplish things. PAW is said to account for high rates of relapse in the first months of recovery.

Substance Withdrawal

Addiction counselors are all too familiar with both acute withdrawal and PAW because anecdotally many clients feel miserable when they first get clean and sober. Many also report sleep disturbance, which is hypothesized to be the result of months or years of drinking or drugging oneself to sleep. Unfortunately, this method of sleep induction often results in the blocking of rapid eye movement (REM) sleep. Generally, most adults go through about five or six REM stages through the course of an eight-hour night of sleep. REM is sometimes referred to as "paradoxical sleep" because the body and brain seem to be awake and aroused during REM sleep. People often have very vivid dreams during REM sleep, and both men and women experience sexual arousal during REM. It is hypothesized that REM helps us to "erase the tape" of the extraneous stimuli we have been bombarded with during the course of the day, while deep sleep helps us to rejuvenate from strenuous physical activity. Brain waves (electroencephalogram [EEG]) are able to measure REM and deep sleep. Now let us go back to our newly sober, recovering person. Because REM has been blocked or obliterated during active addiction, now in recovery, it comes back with a vengeance in something called *REM Rebound,* where the newly sober person is dreaming constantly and experiences a very restless sleep. It is estimated that it may take several months before REM and deep sleep become regulated again. Add this to the dopamine depletion, which is also part of PAW, and you have a person who feels pretty miserable...a perfect recipe for relapse. This is why as addiction counselors it is important to educate our clients about PAW while reassuring them that they will begin to feel better...eventually.

Coinciding with the aforementioned information on PAW derived mostly from the types of symptoms observed by addiction counselors among clients in the early stages of recovery, an area of research known as the *dopamine depletion hypothesis* began to validate these observations by providing neuroscientific explanations. When Dackis and Gold (1985) put forth the *dopamine depletion hypothesis,* they claimed that craving and substance-seeking and non–substance-seeking behaviors (as in the instance of process addiction) were the result of low dopamine levels in the brain. This model was used specifically to explain cocaine relapse that comes about as a result of cocaine craving. The hypodopaminergic state (or dopamine depletion following drug use) is said to be the result of both genetic predisposition as well as environmental elements or epigenetics (Blum et al., 2015). The RDS model has also been applied to explaining other drug craving (including alcohol) as well as food addiction (e.g., sugar binging). However, Blum et al. (2015) points out that while "it is universally agreed that dopamine is a major neurotransmitter in terms of reward dependence, there remains controversy regarding how to modulate its role clinically to treat and prevent relapse for both substance and non-substance related addictive behaviors" (p. 1862). Similarly, long-term opioid use disorders create endogenous endorphin depletions. These depletions contribute to relapse similar to RDS (Reed et al., 2017).

Additional research indicates that chronic use of opioids may actually result in alterations in neural circuitry in the brain. Epigenetics plays a key role in establishing a link between genetic expression and these changes in brain circuitry as a result of repeated opioid use. It is important to take into consideration that genes are not fixed and that they can be altered by experiences (e.g., continuous substance use). These experiences or life events (most importantly stressful life events) can trigger biochemical messages by attaching methyl groups to the outside of the genes (a process known as methylation) which, in turn, makes them more or less sensitive to messages from the body. These methylation patterns can be transmitted or passed on to offspring (i.e., sons and daughters), a process known as epigenetics (van der Kolk, 2014). These changes in neural circuitry or neuronal connectivity are hypothesized to explain why there is an increased likelihood of opioid use in response to exposure to cues associated with opioids. The aforementioned changes in neural circuitry appear to be most prevalent in the regions of the hippocampus, striatum, and midbrain (Brydnildsen et al., 2020). See Box 3.3.

Relevance of Psychopharmacological Research for Addiction Counselors

There have been several dopamine-enhancing (also referred to as dopaminergic) medications that have been researched as to their efficacy in reducing craving and subsequent relapse. Research has investigated several U.S. Food and Drug Administration (FDA)-approved medications, however, at best most have been only moderately effective in promoting "dopamine homeostasis" (Blum et al., 2015). For example, bromocriptine (Parlodel, Cycloset), a dopamine agonist that is FDA-approved for treating Parkinson's disease, had been shown to reduce cocaine craving (Maguire et al., 2014). Similarly, Weissenborn et al. (1996) found that bromocriptine, a dopamine antagonist, was helpful in reducing cocaine-induced operant responding. Other medications that have been investigated as potential craving-reducing,

BOX 3.3

COCAINE STUDY REVEALS HOW UNSEEN BRAIN CHANGES LEAD TO RELAPSE (BETUEL, 2020)

Follow-up research on individuals with severe cocaine use disorder reveals high rates of relapse, especially within the first year following inpatient treatment. For example, Simpson et al. (2002) found a 25% relapse rate to weekly cocaine use in a five-year posttreatment follow-up. Recent research by Paula Gajewski and Ian Maze (2019) suggests that cocaine alters or "rewires" the brain in such a way that results in gene expression, which results in high rates of relapse. The flooding of dopamine in the brain as a result of cocaine use does more than produce the euphoric cocaine high; it literally alters the brain in such a way as to create intense memories of the euphoric high in structures in the brain called histones (histones are a collection of proteins that act as spools for DNA). These molecular changes in genetic molecules are hypothesized to potentiate the likelihood of relapse in humans because dopamine will often attach to the histones. When mice were injected with a virus that prevented dopamine from attaching to the histones, the cocaine-addicted mice did not seek out cocaine. Therefore, the major focus of this research is to find out how these gene expression changes occur so that they can be reversed, thereby reducing cocaine-craving and the likelihood of cocaine relapse.

Sources: Betuel, E. (2020, April 9). Cocaine study reveals how unseen brain changes lead to relapse. *Inverse*. https://apple.news/AgDq_aBvKTwOozBslKqx56A; Gajewski, P. A., Eagle, A. L., Williams, E. S., Manning, C. E., McCornack, C., Maze, I., Heller, E. A., & Robison, A. J. (2019). Epigenetic regulation of hippocampal Fos*B* expression controls behavioral responses to cocaine. *Journal of Neuroscience, 39*(42), 8305–8314. https://doi.org/10.1523/JNEUROSCI.0800-19.2019; Simpson, D. D., Joe, G. W., & Broome, K. M. (2002). A national 5-year follow-up of treatment outcomes for cocaine dependence. *Archives of General Psychiatry, 59*(6), 539–544. https://doi.org/10.1001/archpsyc.59.6.538

dopaminergic drugs include baclofen (Gablofen, Lioresal), a skeletal muscle relaxant; gabapentin (Neurontin, Horizant), an anticonvulsant medication that also has been used to reduce nerve pain; lisuride (Dopergin), a dopamine agonist; and d-cycloserin, a partial glutamate/n-nitrosdimethylamine (NDMA) agonist. In addition, buspirone (Buspar) also has some efficacy in reducing cocaine craving. Similarly, verenicline (Chantix), a partial agonist at the nicotinic acetylcholine receptor, has demonstrated efficacy in reducing nicotine craving, thereby reducing the urge to relapse to active cigarette smoking (Crunelle et al., 2009). Another possible medication that has shown promise in reducing cocaine relapse is Brain-Derived Neurotropic Factor (BDNF), a common protein that occurs naturally in the brain (Bobadilla et al., 2018). In this study, BDNF targeted the nucleus accumbens, which is vital to reward-seeking behavior. This research found that when BDNF was injected in the brains of cocaine-addicted rats, it would interrupt cue-induced cocaine use, suggesting that cocaine relapse might be interrupted or prevented in humans. Interestingly, BDNF did not disrupt food-seeking behavior, which also activates reward circuitry, indicating that BDNF is specific in inhibiting drug-seeking behavior.

Naltrexone (ReVia, Vivitrol) and naloxone (Narcan) are opioid antagonists that act by occupying the mu, kappa, and delta receptor sites, thereby blocking the profound impact of opioids in the brain and body. Naloxone is often used in emergency situations to reverse opiate overdoses. It does so by occupying the opiate receptor site, which increases respiratory function, thereby preventing overdose death due to respiratory insufficiency. Naltrexone is used in oral or injectable (i.e., Vivitrol) form in the treatment of alcohol and opioid use disorders to help support abstinence by reducing cravings (National Center for Biotechnology Information [NCBI], 2020). Oral naltrexone is effective; however, medication compliance is an issue when clients might forget to take the oral, daily dose. Vivitrol is administered once a month in injectable form, which helps to reduce the disadvantage of oral medication compliance (Bisaga et al., 2018). Table 3.2 provides a list of medications that have been found to reduce substance craving.

There are three medications that have been utilized for reducing alcohol craving: acamprosate (Campral), naltrexone (ReVia), and topiramate (Topamax). Acamprosate is a GABA agonist and glutamate antagonist. Both GABA and glutamate are neurotransmitters that are activated during alcohol use, and acamprosate restores balance to these neurotransmitters, thereby reducing alcohol craving. Naltrexone hydrochloride is an opiate antagonist that acts as a competitive antagonist at the opioid receptor site. When used for reducing alcohol craving, Naltrexone hydrochloride modifies the hypothalamic-pituitary-adrenal (HPA) axis (Williams et al., 2004), which reduces alcohol craving. Finally, topiramate (Topamax) was originally developed as an antiseizure medication that also was found to treat migraines and cluster headaches. In its off-label uses, it has been used as an antipsychotic medication, which, unlike other antipsychotics, will promote weight loss. It is also used to treat binge eating disorder. More recently, topiramate has been used to reduce alcohol cravings. One of the advantages of topiramate is that, unlike the aforementioned anticraving medications, topiramate can be started while a client is still drinking and tapering their alcohol use. Similar to acamprosate, topiramate works by stabilizing the GABA and glutamate neurotransmitters.

There are some indications that ketamine (a rather potent N-methyl-D-aspartate [NMDA] glutamatergic receptor antagonist), in addition to treating severe depression, has

TABLE 3.2 Medications That Assist in Reducing Drug Craving

DRUG CAUSING CRAVING	MEDICATIONS THAT LESSEN CRAVING
Alcohol	Topirimate (Topamax)
	Acamprosate (Camprel)
	Naltrexone (ReVia)
Cannabis	Buspirone (Buspar)
Cocaine	Baclofen
Heroin/Prescription Opioids	Naltrexone
	Vivitrol (injectable Naltrexone)
Nicotine	Chantix
	Zyban (Wellbutrin)

also been effective in the treatment of SUDs. Jones et al. (2018) reviewed several studies in which ketamine (also known by its street drug colloquial term, "Special K") had beneficial impact on individuals with cocaine use disorder, alcohol use disorder, and opioid use disorder when administered at microdose levels, as opposed to the macrodose levels of the street drug. The studies reviewed noted reduced rates of substance use as well as better abstinence rates among participants. However, some of these studies were limited by small sample sizes.

There is another medication that was developed specifically for treating alcohol use disorders called disulfiram (Antabuse). Unlike the aforementioned anticraving medications, disulfiram works by blocking the oxidation of alcohol at the acetaldehyde stage. During alcohol metabolism following disulfiram intake, the concentration of acetaldehyde occurring in the blood may be 5 to 10 times higher than that found during metabolism of the same amount of alcohol alone, which results in a very unpleasant symptoms referred to as the disulfiram-alcohol reaction. This reaction is similar to being poisoned in that it produces vomiting, skin flush reaction, headaches, and fever. The disulfiram-alcohol reaction is proportional to the amount of alcohol ingested and the recency and amount of disulfiram taken. Disulfiram is considered to be an alcohol antagonist. Unlike the anticraving medications, which work primarily by modifying neurotransmitters, disulfiram blocks the liver's ability to break down or metabolize alcohol, which works according to principles of operant conditioning by pairing alcohol with an aversive competing response (Petrakis et al., 2005). With any aforementioned medications, we recommend that readers access www.drugs.com, which provides a list of side effects, contraindications, and adverse reactions.

Addiction counselors often have difficulty with the notion that taking a pill can aid in a client's recovery. Some may contend, "So you're going to treat a pill addiction (e.g., to prescription opioids or benzodiazepines) by giving someone a pill? That doesn't make sense!" Some counselors adhere to recommendation that to arrest the progression of a SUD the old saying, "Don't drink, don't use drugs, and go to meetings" is the simplest and most effective way to achieve sobriety/recovery. And while this recommendation does work for many, according to Timko and DeBenedetti (2007), approximately 64% of those who attend Alcoholics Anonymous drop out before their first year anniversary. The tendency in the addiction treatment profession has been to blame relapse on a lack of commitment, motivation, denial, or being stuck in the Precontemplation stage; all of which have merit; however, that still leaves counselors with the dilemma of how to motivate or assist clients toward change. Clients who are actively engaged in SUD will often perceive detox and a life of abstinence as inconceivable. Consider the following case example.

CASE EXAMPLE: TYLER

Tyler is a 20-year-old college junior who has been attending college on a lacrosse scholarship. During the regular season of his sophomore year, Tyler suffered a torn ligament in his knee, which required orthopedic surgery. Following the surgery, Tyler was prescribed Percoset, an opioid analgesic, to assist him with pain relief. He took the medication as prescribed; however, he developed an infection and needed another prescription. He continued to use Percoset for several months, and when he returned to college after the summer break he found he still needed the medication for pain relief. Tyler discovered that he could purchase Roxicette from a dealer on campus. "Roxies" or "blues" (also an opioid analgesic) were very popular on his college campus although they were expensive ($40 a pill). Tyler began to take cash advances on his credit card to buy Roxies, and eventually his parents confronted him with his spending, at which point Tyler admitted that he had become dependent on opioids and could not control his use. Tyler's parents insisted that he see an addiction counselor who recommended that Tyler see an American Society of Addiction Medicine (ASAM) physician who recommended a buprenorphine (Suboxone) detox on an outpatient basis. Tyler also attended an intensive outpatient (IOP) program for several weeks while also attending Narcotics Anonymous (NA) meetings regularly. Tyler was still struggling with craving, and when his drug dealer contacted him with an offer to sell him 20 Roxies for $50, it was an offer that Tyler could not refuse. His parents and counselor could tell something was wrong. Tyler initially denied he had relapsed, but when they insisted on a urine drug screen to provide objective verification of his claims of abstinence, Tyler angrily admitted he had relapsed. Tyler's ASAM physician suggested that following a suboxone detox he take naltrexone, an opioid agonist, which might help reduce his cravings. Tyler agreed to take the naltrexone as prescribed, and fortunately he experienced few side effects. After four months, Tyler was still abstinent. He was also attending NA three times per week and was working the steps with his NA sponsor. In addition, Tyler regularly met his counselor individually and also was attending an IOP program three times a week. Tyler reported that his cravings had lessened and he was feeling more committed to his recovery.

In this Case Example, once Tyler's addiction had come to light, he did begin to take steps toward recovery by seeing an addictions counselor for evaluation, detoxing, and then going into an intensive outpatient (IOP) program. Yet, Tyler continued to experience drug cravings, which contributed to his relapse. Being prescribed naltrexone helped in two ways: first, he subjectively reported a lessening of cravings, and second, if Tyler were to use opioids while taking naltrexone, he probably would not have felt the same euphoria because of the medication's opioid antagonist properties.

There is also a body of research that indicates that neurofeedback has efficacy as a treatment for SUDs. Much of this treatment research was based on the early work by Henri Begleiter at Downstate Medical Center in New York City (Begleiter & Kissin, 1983), who noted differences in brainwave activity among sons of fathers who were diagnosed with alcohol use disorders. Peniston and Kulkosky (1989, 1990, 1991) noted correlations between alcohol use disorders and poor synchrony as well as deficiencies in alpha brainwave activity (EEGs) measure different types of brainwave activities. Alpha brainwaves are slow, rhythmic waves that are associated with being in a relaxed state). Therefore, when individuals with alcohol use disorders drink, they increase their alpha brainwave activity, which coincides with pleasurable feelings. This raises the possibility that alpha brainwave deficiencies might be a predisposing factor in the etiology of SUDs. Alpha-theta brainwave neurofeedback training has proven effective in maintaining abstinence, significantly reducing self-reported depression and also accounting for significant reductions in several scales of the Millon Clinical Multiaxial Inventory (MCMI), suggesting improvement in overall mental health functioning (Saxby & Peniston, 1995).

It is well known that opioids prescribed initially for pain relief have contributed to the recent opioid epidemic. Now, there is recent evidence for the efficacy of genetic screening as a means of preventing postsurgical prescription opioid abuse. In this study (Larach, 2020), 20,885 participants underwent *CYP2D6* genotype testing (CYP refers to cytochrome P450, which is a group of enzymes responsible for most metabolism that occurs in the body). Of this sample, 8,157 had never been prescribed an opiate previously, however, they were prescribed a postsurgical opioid (e.g., hydrocodone, tramadol, or codeine). Of that group, 628 (7.7%) were deemed to be poor or intermediate opioid metabolizers (i.e., patients who would not respond well to opioid medication postsurgery) by genetic testing. Larach (2020) concludes that this group of poor-opioid-responder, postsurgery patients would not experience much relief from opioid medication and therefore would probably be more likely to seek more medication. This study has important implications for opioid analgesic prescribing.

LEARNING ACTIVITY 3.1
ALPHA BRAINWAVE DEFICIENCIES

The research quoted from Peniston and Kulkosky (1999) suggests that those who are predisposed to alcohol use disorders have deficient alpha brainwave activity that makes these individuals more vulnerable to the effects of alcohol, which serves to increase alpha and theta slow-wave activity, thereby producing a relaxed, pleasurable sensation. However, this could be a "chicken or the egg" phenomenon. In other words, do alpha deficiencies pre-date and predispose one to alcohol use disorders, or does years of drinking alcoholically result in changes in alpha-theta brainwaves? What is your opinion? How does the research in this area address this conundrum?

STRESS AND SUBSTANCE USE DISORDERS

Research indicates that there are significant correlations between trauma exposure and subsequent SUDs. This especially holds true for individuals with nicotine use disorders (Balk et al., 2009), cocaine use disorders (Pederson et al., 2008), and opioid use disorders (Mills et al., 2006; Sansone et al., 2009). In a study that compared these three groups, the opioid use disorders group reported an earlier age of onset of childhood trauma than the nicotine or cocaine use disorders group. In total, all three groups reported a 96.5% rate of having experienced at least one traumatic event in their lifetime (Lawson et al., 2013). There is also a body of research exploring the relationship between stress and the subsequent release of cortisol with craving, substance use, and relapse. Cortisol is a hormone that tends to get released into the bloodstream during times of stress. Stress responses induce changes in the HPA axis, which in turn can produce substance craving and negative mood states (Koob & Kreek, 2007). Stress also releases glucocorticoids (cortisol), which result in a decrease in dopamine production. For example, when individuals with SUDs are experiencing withdrawal, their cortisol levels increase (Koob, 2009) and dopamine levels decrease. The disruptions in cortisol response and dopamine depletions can extend for several months into abstinence, which may also account for PAW symptoms.

There are other examples that point to correlations between stress, trauma, and SUDs. Research examining adverse childhood experiences (ACEs), such as physical, emotional, or sexual abuse, points to increased levels of substance use and early drug initiation (Cavaiola & Schiff, 1988; Enoch, 2011; Widom et al., 1999). Felitti et al. (1998) and Felitti (2017) administered the ACE Scale to over 8,000 adults (ages 19 to 92) and found that individuals who had experienced one or more adverse life events in at least two of the seven categories had a greater likelihood of developing health risk factors later in life including both mental health and SUDs. In addition, ACEs were found to be reflected in the dysregulation of the HPA system. For example, high scores on the ACE Scale were found to correlate with increased cortisol levels. This research also discovered that administering intranasal oxytocin (the human-bonding hormone) would help to lessen the stress reaction in a group of cocaine-dependent participants (Flanagan et al., 2015). Brady and Back (2012) describe various mechanisms by which childhood adversities can be explained from a neurobiological perspective, including HPA disruptions resulting in an increase in cortisol levels. These disruptions in the noradrenergic receptor response (especially in the locus coeruleus area of the brain) help to explain how the positively reinforcing effects of alcohol/drugs (that result in dopamine increases in the mesocorticolimbic area) account for increased substance use during times of stress.

Veterans who suffered combat-related traumatic brain injuries (TBIs) that resulted in a loss of consciousness (LOC) were found to have increased SUDs and increased severity of both physical health and emotional (i.e., posttraumatic stress disorder [PTSD] symptoms; Gros et al., 2016). Similarly, increased alcohol use is often seen in individuals exposed to trauma. The *endorphin compensation hypothesis* (ECH) suggests that, following a traumatic event, endorphin activity increases as the brain and body attempt to lessen the pain of the trauma. ECH also indicates that alcohol use increases endorphin activity, which then becomes a way of coping with anxiety, irritability, and depression, which are common PTSD reactions. Alcohol use relieves these symptoms because alcohol compensates for the deficiencies in endorphin levels after a traumatic event (Volpicelle et al., 1999).

Relevance of Stress Research for Addiction Counselors

Given the significant rates of trauma within the SUD population, it is important that addiction counselors are mindful of this both when assessing as well as when treating addiction. In terms of assessment, it is important for counselors to explore early childhood history as well as any possible traumatic events the client may have experienced throughout their lifetime, including instances of disruption in parent–child relationships (such as abandonment or neglect). Traditionally, a more in-depth assessment would explore other childhood experiences such as early school/educational events, social/peer relationships, and family dynamics. There are some helpful assessment tools that can be utilized as part of the assessment process that helps counselors to gather background information. For example, the *Life Events Inventory*-Revised (Figure 3.1; Van Houten & Golembiewski, 1978); the *Adverse Childhood Experiences Scales* (ACES; Centers for Disease Control and Prevention, 2018); the *Life History Calendar* (Freedman et al., 1988); and the *Things I've Seen and Heard Interview* (Richters & Martinez, 1990) all provide a structured way of helping clients to disclose traumatic and stressful experiences they may have experienced during childhood and adolescent years. Clients may not readily disclose traumatic or adverse life events, especially in the early stages of treatment, however, the aforementioned assessment tools provide a means of informing clients that these issues will be important to disclose once trust in the counselor has been established. Volpicelle et al. (2019) recommend that in cases involving both PTSD and SUD both conditions be treated simultaneously because often both conditions are intertwined. Also, they recommend that addiction counselors consider referral for evaluation of whether an opioid receptor blocker might be helpful in encouraging abstinence given that both alcohol use and trauma increase endorphin activity. The recollection

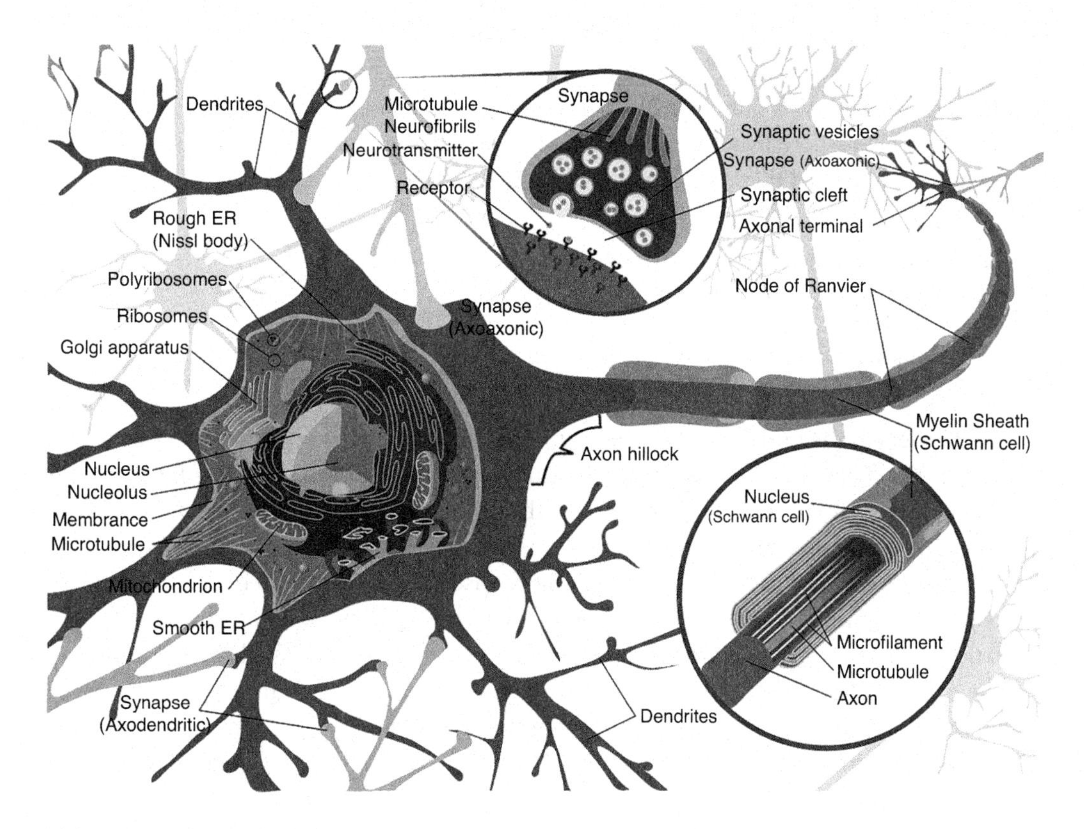

FIGURE 3.1 Synaptic Transmission.

Source: Courtesy of Pixabay, https://pixabay.com/vectors/red-science-diagram-cell-neuron-41524/

of traumatic memories in counseling sessions may result in a release of endorphins, which may plummet postsession, resulting in alcohol or drug craving. An opioid antagonist blocker, for example, altrexone, may help to decrease cravings brought on by these endorphin fluctuations. It is also important that counselors practice trauma-informed care, which is a therapeutic approach to managing trauma. The Substance Abuse and Mental Health Services Administration (SAMHSA; 2015) indicates that treatment programs are considered to be "trauma-informed" when they address the "4 Rs":

1. *Realizes* the widespread impact of trauma and understands the potential paths for recovery.
2. *Recognizes* the signs and symptoms of trauma in clients, families, staff, and others involved with the system.
3. *Responds* by fulling integrating knowledge about trauma into policies, procedures, and practices...AND
4. Seeks to actively resist *retraumatization* of the client.

It is important to explain what is meant by "actively resisting retraumatization of the client." Here, counselors need to take their lead from where the client is and not force the client to relive traumatic memories at times when they are not prepared or willing to do so. An example would be instances where combat veterans were essentially forced to reexperience traumatic combat experiences in order to do extinction training (this is a behavioral technique derived from classical conditioning models in which a client is asked to "relive" a traumatic memory either by having them describe the traumatic incident in great detail or watching videos that would simulate the traumatic memory). When a client is not prepared or willing to relive these traumatic memories, it can be devastating and retraumatizing. As counselors, it is important to work collaboratively with our clients to bring about change and not force them to relive traumatic experiences especially when feeling unprepared to do so. There are also six key principles to the trauma-informed therapeutic approach (SAMHSA, 2015):

1. Safety
2. Trustworthiness and transparency
3. Peer support
4. Collaboration and mutuality
5. Empowerment, voice, and choice
6. Cultural, historical, and gender issues.

Safety refers to the notion that trauma-informed counseling always provides a safe atmosphere for the client and their family. Counseling sessions become a safe place for the client and/or family to share their fears, concerns, difficulties, and any other areas they wish to explore. *Trustworthiness* and *transparency* are essential in any counseling relationship. Counselors must be conscientious in explaining the counseling process to clients and be faithful in keeping commitments. Trust is built upon consistency. There is an old saying, "People we trust are those who say what they do and they do what they say," such that actions and words are consistent. In terms of transparency, it is important to counselors to let clients know well in advance when they may be taking time off or may be unable to meet with their client. It is also important for counselors to be transparent about their own reactions and feelings and to provide clients with regular feedback. *Peer support* is also a key component of trauma-informed care because it provides traumatized individuals with opportunities to communicate with others who have experienced similar trauma. In addition, *collaboration and mutuality* refers to the need to work collaboratively when addressing trauma-related issues, while *empowerment, voice, and choice* addresses the need for trauma survivors to be able to tell their story and to begin to express to trusted others what they have gone through in an effort to gain better understanding and support. Finally, it is important for counselors and others working with trauma survivors to take *culture, history, and gender issues* into account when working with trauma survivors, as illustrated in the following case example.

CASE EXAMPLE: JULIA

Julia was awarded an Army Reserve Officer Training Corps (ROTC) scholarship that allowed her to attend a state university. She was the first person in her family to attend college, and her parents aunts, uncles, and grandparents were all very proud of her. This was especially important because Julia is from Mexico and her parents had immigrated to the United States when she was approximately 8 years old. At one point, there were concerns that her parents might be deported back to Mexico; however, Julia was protected under Deferred Action for Childhood Arrivals (DACA) laws and had been granted U.S. citizenship. Upon completion of her bachelor's degree, Julia was commissioned as a second lieutenant, and her infantry division was deployed to Afghanistan. Julia's platoon was out on patrol when her Humvee was hit by a rocket-propelled grenade. Julia was wounded and also suffered a traumatic brain injury (TBI), which resulted in her evacuation back to a military hospital in Germany and then back home to the United States. For several months, Julia found that she struggled with cognitive tasks as her organizational skills and short-term memory were both severely impacted by the TBI. As a result of the frustration that Julia experienced, she began drinking alcohol, which she felt would help to alleviate the anxiety and depression she experienced as a result of having suffered trauma in the explosion. With the encouragement of her doctor, Julia began working with an addictions counselor who was also Latina and also a veteran. Julia felt that her counselor understood how important it was for her to maintain her connection with the Army, even though her parents were angry that she had given so much for a country. Julia's counselor was careful in using a trauma-informed approach with her that allowed Julia to explore the trauma at a pace she was comfortable with.

There are many support groups for people who have experienced trauma. Peer support groups are often an essential component of trauma recovery just as 12-step and other addiction support groups (e.g., SMART recovery) are essential to SUD recovery. But here is the key thing: in referring someone to a counseling support group, it is best when the group is composed of individuals who have experienced similar traumatic incidents. For example, a group composed of combat veterans may be helpful; however, it may be countertherapeutic when mixing Vietnam veterans with Operation Iraqi Freedom veterans, just like it is not as helpful to mix Operation Desert Storm veterans with Operation Enduring Freedom (Afghanistan) veterans. Similarly, we would not mix sexual assault survivors with incest survivors. The SAMHSA website (2015) provides links to trauma-informed-care treatment models such as ATRIUM (Addiction & Trauma Recovery & Integration Model), Seeking Safety, and TAMAR (Trauma, Addiction and Mental Health Recovery), which are helpful models that provide counselors with ways to address both SUDs and trauma. See Box 3.4.

BOX 3.4

TRAUMA RESPONSE

In 2014, noted trauma specialist Dr. Bessel van der Kolk wrote a groundbreaking text entitled *The Body Keeps the Score: Brain, Mind and Body in the Healing of Trauma.* Based upon decades of clinical work and research with children and combat veterans suffering from posttraumatic stress disorder (PTSD) at Massachusetts General Hospital and Harvard University, van der Kolk has reached some important conclusions that are important for counselors working with traumatized clients. First, van der Kolk found that images and sensations of traumatic events tend to be "stored" in the right half of the brain (the right side of the brain is responsible for visual-spatial-tactile sensory processing, as well as emotional response). However, the left side of the brain is linguistic, sequential, and analytical, or as Dr. van der Kolk states, "the left half of the brain does all the talking, while the right half of the brain carries the music of experience" (p. 44). This is significant for counselors because many PTSD clients are unable to verbalize or explain their traumatic memories, which tend to be more sensory. This may also help to explain why techniques such as eye-movement desensitization response (EMDR) work so well with traumatized clients, as opposed to talk therapy types of approaches.

Source: van der Kolk, B. (2014). *The body keeps the score: Brain, mind and body in the healing of trauma.* Viking-Penguin Press.

Finally, Brady and Back (2012) delineate a number of *psychosocial interventions* as well as *pharmacological interventions* that are useful for treating trauma and co-occurring SUDs. Psychosocial interventions may include both cognitive behavioral therapy (CBT) and behavioral therapies. They point out three CBT-oriented approaches, that is, (1) exposure-based therapies, (2) cognition-focused therapies, and (3) anxiety/stress management therapy. Exposure-based therapies are designed to have clients confront anxiety-provoking traumatic memories in a gradual, safe way (e.g., recalling the location where the trauma took place). This is known as imaginal exposure (Foa et al., 2006). Cognition-focused therapy incorporates more traditional CBT approaches such as examining the meaning and client's interpretation of the trauma (e.g., challenging self-blame beliefs or other cognitive distortions). Finally, anxiety/stress management therapies would include stress-inoculation approaches such as those described by Meichenbaum and Novaco (1985). By teaching clients anxiety management (e.g., relaxation skills) and coping skills (e.g., thought-stopping techniques and assertiveness training), clients gain a better sense of self-mastery and ability to problem-solve in situations that might have been overwhelming in the past. Pharmacological interventions are also useful when combined with psychosocial interventions in reducing craving and relapse potential. In addition to some of the anticraving medications described earlier, research indicates that, when treating both SUDs and PTSD, sertraline (Zoloft), a serotonin-specific reuptake inhibitor, has been helpful in decreasing the severity of alcohol use as well as reducing reexperiencing PTSD symptoms, for example, nightmares, intrusive thoughts, and hyperarousal (Brady et al., 2005). In addition, a study utilizing 254 veterans with co-occurring alcohol use disorder, anxiety, and depression as well as PTSD found that prazosin (Minipress) was helpful in decreasing PTSD-related sleep disturbance and nightmares and also reduced alcohol intake (Petrakis et al., 2005). Prazosin is an antihypertensive medication.

CASE EXAMPLE: TINA

Tina is a 26-year-old single mother of a 4-year-old son, and she is currently seeking outpatient treatment after having tested positive for opioids by her probation office. Tina was placed on probation after having been arrested for trying to fill fraudulent prescriptions for OxyContin.

Tina's son was placed into the custody of her mother and stepfather until she successfully completed her substance abuse disorder (SUD) treatment. Tina indicated to the intake counselor that she has been using prescription opiates since her senior year in high school when she was introduced to OxyContin by her boyfriend. Tina was involved in this relationship for several years, and the boyfriend is the father of Tina's 4-year-old son. Tina describes the relationship as being both emotionally and physically abusive, and she reports that she still has nightmares about being beaten and threatened. She called the police on several occasions, and temporary restraining orders (TROs) have been issued; however, Tina would usually be intimidated into dropping the TRO or was worried that if she requested a permanent restraining order then her boyfriend would kill her, as he threatened to do on several occasions. Tina continued to use OxyContin in order to dull the nightmares and intrusive images of the abuse. It was clear that Tina was suffering from PTSD as well as an opioid use disorder. In addition, Tina's counselor had her take the Adverse Childhood Experiences Scales (ACES), which revealed that Tina had been sexually molested by a male cousin who was 6 years older than her, and she had been physically abused by her biological father. Tina's stated goal is that she wants to regain full custody of her son, and she states, "I am willing to do anything to make that happen." Tina agreed to an outpatient buprenorphine (Suboxone) detox and is now attending an intensive outpatient (IOP) program. In addition, she is actively participating in Narcotics Anonymous (NA) meetings and has a woman with several years of recovery as her NA sponsor. Tina's counselor recommends that Tina receive Vivitrol injections as a means of reducing her cravings for prescription opioids and also to block the high, should she relapse. Tina is very motivated to stay abstinent and to reduce her cravings, so she agrees to start on Vivitrol while attending the IOP program.

PREDICTING RELAPSE USING CUE ACTIVATION MODELS

There is also a large body of research within the field of neuroscience and SUDs that examines the brain's response to various substances in addicted versus nonaddicted groups. As you can imagine, SUD individuals had more profound neurological responses when presented with drug cues (e.g., visual and olfactory stimuli). For example, Cortese et al. (2015) found that most cue reactivity research would use unisensory visual cues to examine functional magnetic resonance imaging (fMRI) responses. However, their research employed both unisensory and multisensory smoking cues (e.g., visual cues plus the aroma of cigarette smoke), which resulted in significantly greater and more widespread response, especially in the frontal and temporal regions of the brain. See Box 3.5.

LEARNING ACTIVITY 3.2 TINA

Tina presents with several difficulties related to her opioid use disorder, first and foremost that she lost custody of her 4-year-old son. What are your thoughts about Tina's decision to take Vivitrol? See what you can find out about Vivitrol, and make a list of the advantages and disadvantages of this particular medication.

BOX 3.5

INDIVIDUAL DIFFERENCES IN NEUROTRANSMITTER RESPONSE

In the 1930s when laws governing cannabis (i.e., the Marijuana Stamp Act) were being enacted, Federal Bureau of Narcotics director Harry Anslinger sold Congress on the notion that marijuana use resulted in brutal violence. To make his case, Anslinger had a collection of cases (which became known as the "gore files"), all of which involved brutal murders, assaults, and rapes committed by individuals who were under the influence of marijuana. These national laws remained in effect until 2012 when Colorado and Washington became the first states to legalize marijuana. With the influx of tax money from cannabis sales, Colorado and Washington became the model for other states to legalize either medical or recreational cannabis or both. However, according to Alex Berenson, the author of *Tell Your Children: The Truth about Marijuana, Mental Illness and Violence*, not everyone agrees that cannabis will invariably mellow out users, make them more creative, or help them to fall asleep. There are instances where some individuals become paranoid or agitated as a result of using cannabis. However, citing evidence from crime statistics from states that have legalized cannabis and from a large epidemiological study done in Sweden in the 1980s (Andrésson, 1987, 1989), Berenson contends that not all individuals respond to cannabis in the same way and that correlations do exist between severe mental illness (i.e., schizophrenia), violence, and cannabis use. These studies suggest that, in certain individuals, the flood of dopamine resulting from continuous marijuana use may trigger psychotic reactions, which in turn incite some individuals to commit acts of violence. This is not to say that there are not other predisposing factors for these individuals to develop major mental illness and subsequent violent behavior. There are other examples of idiosyncratic reactions to drugs, for example, the use of MP (Ritalin), a stimulant used to treat attention deficit hyperactivity disorder (ADHD). For individuals diagnosed with ADHD, Ritalin creates a paradoxical reaction by stimulating the prefrontal lobes, thereby increasing beta brainwaves that allow for increased attention and concentration. For a non-ADHD individual, taking Ritalin would be like drinking 15 cups of coffee. Aldous Huxley once remarked, "It is human variability that accounts for why one man's meat being another man's poison."

Source: Adapted from Andrésson, S., Allebeck, P., Engström, A., & Rydberg, U. (1987). Cannabis and schizophrenia: A longitudinal study in Swedish conscripts. *Lancet, 330*(8574), 1483–1486. https://doi.org/10.1016/s0140-6736(87)92620-1; Andrésson, S., Allebeck, P., & Rydberg, U. (1989). Schizophrenia in users and nonusers of cannabis: A longitudinal study in Stockholm County. *Acta Psychiatrica Scandinavica, 79*(5), 505–510. https://doi.org/10.1111/j.1600-0447.1989.tb10296.x; Berenson, A. (2019). *Tell your children: The truth about marijuana, mental illness and violence.* The Free Press.

Research conducted at Stanford University (Collins, 2018) was able to predict relapse by using fMRI brain scans. Researchers MacNiven, Knutson, and colleagues were able to accurately predict those individuals who would relapse in 75% of the cases they studied. Their sample was composed of veterans who had completed a 28-day residential treatment program for stimulant use disorders (cocaine and methamphetamines). This research is based, in part, on the findings that, while self-reported drug craving is often not an effective predictor of relapse, brain activity as measured by fMRI scans does predict relapse. In this study, participants were shown several images of everyday objects like food and office supplies, but interspersed were images of drugs and drug paraphernalia. Those participants who experienced more intense brain activity in the mesolimbic (reward) center of the brain and especially in the area known as the nucleus accumbens were found to have relapsed within three months. In a somewhat similar study, only this time with opioids, Martucci et al. (2019) compared a group of patients who were prescribed opioids for fibromyalgia with another group of fibromyalgia patients who were not taking opioids and found distinct differences in their medial prefrontal cortex responses when presented with anticipated monetary rewards. The prefrontal cortex is responsible for judgment and decision-making.

Other research found increased limbic activation and blood flow using a PET scan in a group of detoxified male cocaine users when compared to a control group of noncocaine users. Cue activation was accomplished by presenting both groups with videos involving cocaine use. During the presentation of the cocaine video, the group of cocaine users experienced increased craving and increased cerebral blood flow in the limbic area (which corresponds to the pleasure or reward center of the brain; Childress et al., 1999). Similarly, cocaine craving and subsequent cocaine-seeking behavior was found to be influenced by changes to specific brain cells as a result of cocaine use. In this research, it was discovered that connections between brain cells were strengthened because of dendritic spines (i.e., the part of the brain cell that receives information from other neurons or brain cells). This strengthened or enhanced connectivity was hypothesized to increase cocaine craving in rats (Garcia-Keller et al., 2020).

Relevance of Cue Activation as a Cause for Relapse for Addiction Counselors

According to classical conditioning studies, drugs of abuse are without doubt very powerful unconditioned stimuli, which is proven in the aforementioned brain imaging research. Just as Pavlov's dogs did not need to be trained or conditioned to respond to the meat, so too individuals with SUDs respond to preferred substances very intensely. At the same time, there are other stimuli that may be present at the time of substance use that can also become conditioned stimuli or conditioned cues such as visual cues (such as the sight of a coke spoon or powder on a mirror) or the aroma of the substance (such as the smell of heroin being cooked) or sounds such as ice clinking in a glass. All of the aforementioned cues can trigger cravings, which in turn can trigger relapse to substance use.

When Pavlov wanted to extinguish (i.e., eliminate), the dog's conditioned response (i.e., salivation) to the sound of the bell (i.e., the conditioned stimulus) all he needed to do was to continue ringing the bell but refrain from pairing it with the sight and smell of the meat. Eventually, the dogs stopped salivating. Anyone who has a pet knows the power of a conditioned stimulus, for example, cats will come running at the sound of a can opener, and dogs will salivate when they hear a dog treat jar being opened or if they smell dog cookies. In order to extinguish cue reactivity in SUD individuals, it is necessary to present salient drug cues without having them paired with substance use. This is known as cue extinction training (CET) or Exposure Response Prevention (ERP). Since these cues can create substance craving, it is best to introduce CET in more controlled settings like residential programs where the client will be less likely to act on the craving and use. There are kits that can be purchased for the purposes of CET (e.g., www.killthecraving.com; Santoro et al., 2001), however, it is important for clients to be forthright about personal cues that they have found will induce craving. For example, for some clients, a particular time of year may bring on strong cravings to use (e.g., July 4 picnics or New Year's parties). For others, a particular song may have become associated with substance use (e.g., Price et al., 2010).

In providing relapse prevention planning with clients, it is important that addiction counselors assist clients in being able to respond proactively to both conditioned cues (such as those described earlier) as well as triggers. Marlatt and Donovan's (2005) research found four categories of relapse triggers, that is, (1) negative emotional states (which accounted for 35% of relapses), (2) social pressure (which accounted for 20% of relapses), (3) interpersonal conflict (which accounted for 16% of relapses), and (4) celebratory drinking/drug use (which accounted for 5% of relapses).

LEARNING ACTIVITY 3.3
COUNTERCONDITIONING TREATMENT

See what you can find out about the cue-exposure treatment and aversion therapy offered at the Schick-Shadel residential treatment program. What do you see as being advantages and limitations of these treatment approaches?

It is also important to be aware that there is one residential treatment program in Seattle, Washington that primarily uses aversive counterconditioning procedures as a mainstay treatment approach (see https://www.schickshadel.com/why-it-works/aversion-therapy/). This approach is based on classical conditioning cue exposure training; however, rather than refraining to pair the conditioned stimulus (e.g., aroma of alcohol) with the unconditioned stimulus (alcohol), aversion therapy pairs a negative stimuli with the unconditioned stimulus.

NOTES FROM THE FIELD

Sharon Moleski, MA, LPC, LCADC, BCN

Brain Health Center, Wall Township, New Jersey. Sharon currently is the codirector of the Brain Health Center, a private practice that specializes in using neurofeedback in treating individuals with substance use disorders (SUDs), as well as other mental health disorders (e.g., attention deficit hyperactivity disorder). Sharon has 15 years of addiction counseling experience. Within the past 8 years, she indicates having used neurofeedback (EEG-based biofeedback) with both adolescents and adults, and she reports it to be an efficacious treatment for several reasons. With regard to motivating a client, the saying applies, "A picture is worth a thousand words." When the client can "see his or her brain" and its dysregulation as depicted in a qEEG brainmap, that client is more likely to be invested in change. A client's initial EEG will often depict some combination of underarousal (brain disengaged—attention issues), overarousal (brain too fast—anxiety and worry), and inhibition (brain too slow—depression). Using this information neurofeedback allows clients to train their brain using classical and operant learning in conjunction with computer-assisted feedback. The holistic approach of neurofeedback training emphasizes clients' use of their own resources in the development of healthy brain wave patterns. Attention also is given to wellness strategies such as diet, physiology, exercise, and sleep. It is akin to "taking one's brain to the gym." The unique nature of neurofeedback is attractive to SUD clients who often have a propensity toward novelty and who may have a long history of treatment failure in traditional interventions.

The initial changes in the brain and the corresponding changes in feelings (e.g., anxiety and depression) are often rapid and noticeable, promoting commitment to therapy. They have been demonstrated to be long-lasting and without the side effects of medications.

SUMMARY

Research into how the brain responds to mood-altering substances by way of recent advances in neurological technology (i.e., CT scans, PET scans, fMRI) has produced some of the most cutting-edge research into our understanding of SUDs. Understanding the role of combinations of neurotransmitters that impact on specific areas of the brain (e.g., the mesolimbic pathways) provides a better conceptualization of how mood-altering substance produces profound changes in mood and behavior. This research has also resulted in a variety of treatments (e.g., anticraving medications; agonist and antagonist medications; neurofeedback; and cue-exposure counter-conditioning techniques) that result in improved treatment outcomes. Addiction counselors may need to work in collaboration with specially trained physicians (e.g., those board-certified by the American Society of Addiction Medicine) or with specially trained psychologists or programs that can properly administer neurofeedback training or cue-exposure training in order to help prevent relapse.

RESOURCES

Blum, K., & Payne, J. E. (1991). *Alcohol and the addictive brain: New hope for alcoholics from biogenetic research*. Free Press.

Grisel, J. (2019). *Never enough: The neuroscience and experience of addiction*. Doubleday.

Grisel, J. (2020). *Ted Talk: Never enough: The neuroscience and experience of addiction*. https://www.youtube.com/watch?v=rnt1eb9vQxA

Substance Abuse & Mental Health Services Administration (2015, August 14). *Trauma-informed care*. https://www.samhsa.gov/nctic/trauma-interventions

van der Kolk, B. (2014). *The body keeps the score: Brain, mind and body in the healing of trauma*. Viking-Penguin Press.

KEY REFERENCES

Only key references appear in the print edition. The full reference list appears in the digital product on Springer Publishing Connect: connect.springerpub.com/content/book/978-0-8261-3586-5/chapter/ch03

Blum, K., Febo, M., Thanos, P. K., Baron, D., Frantantino, J., & Gold, M. (2015). Clinically combating Reward Deficiency Syndrome (RDS) with dopamine agonist therapy as a paradigm shift: Dopamine for dinner? *Molecular Neurobiology, 52*(3), 1862–1869. https://doi.org/10.1007/s12035-015-9110-9

Blum, K., & Payne, J. E. (1991). *Alcohol and the addictive brain: New hope for alcoholics from biogenetic research*. Free Press.

Childress, A. R., Mozley, P. D., McElgin, W., Fitzgerald, J., Reivich, M., & O'Brien, C. P. (1999). Limbic activation during cue-induced cocaine craving. *The American Journal of Psychiatry, 156*(1), 11–18. https://doi.org/10.1176/ajp.156.1.11

Collins, N. (2018, December 28). Brain scans help predict drug relapse, Stanford researchers find. *Stanford News*. https://news.stanford.edu/2018/12/28/brain-scans-help-predict-drug-relapse/

Dackis, C. A., & Gold, M. S. (1985). New concepts in cocaine addiction: The dopamine depletion hypothesis. *Neuroscience & Biobehavior Review, 9*(3), 469–477. https://doi.org/10.1016/0149-7634(85)90022-3

Enoch, M. A. (2011). The role of early life stress as a predictor for alcohol and drug dependence. *Psychopharmacology, 214*(1), 17–31. https://doi.org/10.1007/s00213-010-1916-6

Felitti, V. J., Anda, R. F., Nordenberg, D., Williamson, D. F., Spitz, A. M., Edwards, V., Koss, M. P., & Marks, J. S. (1998). Relationship of childhood abuse and household dysfunction to many of the leading causes of death in adults: The Adverse Childhood Experiences (ACE) study. *American Journal of Preventative Medicine, 14*(4), 245–258. https://doi.org/10.1016/s0749-3797(98)00017-8

Grisel, J. (2019). *Never enough: The neuroscience and experience of addiction*. Doubleday.

Koob, G. F., & Kreek, M. J. (2007). Stress, dysregulation of drug reward pathways, and the transition to drug dependence. *American Journal of Psychiatry, 164*, 1149–1169. https://doi.org/10.1176/appi.ajp.2007.05030503

Koob, G. F., & Volkow, N. D. (2010). Neurocircuitry of addiction. *Neuropsychopharmacology, 35*(1), 217–238. https://doi.org/10.1038/npp.2009.110

Peniston, E. G., & Kulkosky, P. J. (1990). Alcoholic personality and alpha-theta training. *Medical Psychotherapy, 3*(1), 37–55.

van der Kolk, B. (2014). *The body keeps the score: Brain, mind and body in the healing of trauma*. Viking-Penguin Press.

4

SUBSTANCE USE DISORDERS AND CASE MANAGEMENT

LEARNING OBJECTIVES

In this chapter, we will be describing a variety of mood-altering substances along with intoxication and withdrawal symptoms and pathological impact that often occurs with prolonged use. In addition, we will also be explaining how to render a *Diagnostic and Statistical Manual of Mental Disorders*, Fifth Edition, substance use disorder diagnosis, how to create a treatment plan, and how to determine the most effective treatment level of care using the American Society of Addiction Medicine's Patient Placement Criteria. We will also discuss key case-management issues that counselors might anticipate depending on the substance being abused. At the conclusion of this chapter, you will be able to:

- describe the intoxication and withdrawal effects for each of the main substances of abuse;
- describe synergistic effects when similar substances are used concurrently;
- describe how various substances impact the brain and one's physical health;
- describe how detoxification for each of the main substances would transpire in the most efficacious and safest way possible;
- describe various methods of substance use (e.g., smoking, intramuscular injection, and oral);
- describe important case-management issues depending on the client's condition or status at the time they present for treatment.

TERMS TO KNOW

agonist — a compound or drug that activates a receptor site in the brain by being able to enhance or mimic the actions of that neurotransmitter

amotivational syndrome — condition attributed to continuous cannabis use in which client loses drive or ambition

anoxia — lack of oxygen to the brain (can occur as a result of an opioid overdose)

antagonist — a compound that is able to fit into a receptor (in the brain) that occupies it but does not activate it

anxiolytics — refers to medications that are prescribed to reduce anxiety

arrhythmia	irregular heartbeat
carcinogenic	cancer causing, e.g., many of the chemicals in cigarette smoke are carcinogenic
cross-tolerance	occurs when individuals who develop a tolerance to particular depressant or stimulant substances (e.g., alcohol or cocaine) also develop tolerance to similar depressant or stimulant substances
doping	taking steroids to increase athletic performance
formication	a tactile hallucination in which individuals feel a sensation of insects crawling under the surface of their skin
hypnotics	medications that are prescribed to promote sleep
insufflation	the use of drugs intranasally through inhalation
kindling	instances where continuous cocaine use potentiates an increased response to subsequent use of that substance
peripheral neuropathy	a neurological condition often resulting from continuous alcohol or other substance use that creates a discomforting "pins and needles" sensation in the extremities, such as hands, feet, and legs, during protracted abstinence
protracted abstinence syndrome	synonymous with post-acute withdrawal or protracted withdrawal symptoms
psychotogenics	substances that initiate psychotic behavior
pyramiding	slowly increasing the dose of a steroid, reaching a peak amount, and then slowly tapering
sensitization	a term pertaining to intermittent cocaine use in which the current use sensitizes a person to subsequent use
sniffing death syndrome	deaths resulting from inhalant use resulting from ventricular fibrillation
stacking	taking both oral and injectable steroids simultaneously
synergistic	the ability of one substance to enhance the impact of another substance by multiplying the impact
titrating or titration	a process by which the least amount of a chemical or drug is administered to achieve the desired effect, for instance, someone detoxifying from benzodiazepines is given titrated doses until abstinence is achieved
tolerance	occurs when the brain and body adapt to the current level of substance ingestion thereby creating a need to take in greater amounts of the substance in order to achieve the desired effect
tweaking	repeated use of methamphetamines in order to maintain the high
wax dabbing	use of a purer form of cannabis that contains extreme levels of tetrahydrocannabinol (THC) that is smoked and inhaled

INTRODUCTION

The purpose of this chapter is to provide an overview of different drugs of abuse, along with their unique intoxication and withdrawal symptoms and treatment protocols. Drugs of abuse differ from other substances in that they directly affect the reward system in the brain (specifically, the mesolimbic dopamine system). Therefore, ingesting a drug of abuse (e.g., methamphetamine) will be much more rewarding than ingesting a selective serotonin reuptake inhibitor (SSRI; e.g., Prozac) because of its effects in the brain. Also important to consider is that in some instances taking an opioid pain medication as prescribed may help individuals to cope and function, yet in other instances opioid pain medications often develop into a substance use disorder (SUD) that will continue to progress unabated unless treated.

Case management is one of the important skills that counselors need to develop in order to effectively match clients with the most effective level of care and treatment approaches. One of the overarching principles in both mental health and SUD treatment is that counselors try to match clients with the least-restrictive treatment environment (i.e., the level of treatment that will have the least impact on the client's life and their ability to meet their daily responsibilities). For example, if a client's substance use is not posing immediate dangers to their health, legal, emotional, or family/social life, an addiction counselor would not recommend a more intensive level of treatment such as a long-term residential or inpatient program. Instead, an outpatient program would provide the least-restrictive alternative. To help make a determination regarding the most effective level of care for particular clients, the American Society of Addiction Medicine (ASAM), offers a rubric that counselors can utilize. We will review the *ASAM-3* Patient Placement Criteria later in this chapter, and in doing so we will also describe various types or modalities of treatment. First, let us begin by examining some drugs of abuse.

ALCOHOL

Alcohol consumption is a worldwide phenomenon with the possible exception of countries that ban alcohol for religious reasons. Internationally, it is estimated that the per-capita consumption of alcohol is equal to 16 liters of 80-proof vodka annually, whereas in the United States the annual per-capita consumption is estimated to be equivalent to 23 liters of 80-proof vodka for every American 15 years of age and over (World Health Organization, 2014). Approximately $90 billion is spent on alcoholic beverages annually in the United States (Centers for Disease Control and Prevention [CDC], 2019). Without a doubt, drinking is very much a part of American culture but also accounts for a plethora of societal ills ranging from car accidents to domestic violence. While social drinking (i.e., rare or occasional alcohol consumption) is acceptable, problematic drinking (e.g., alcohol use disorders [AUDs]) can result in missed days from work, family problems, financial loss, emergency department (ED) visits, and a variety of other health problems (Hanson et al., 2018). AUD as defined in the *Diagnostic and Statistical Manual of Mental Disorders*, Fifth Edition (*DSM-5*; American Psychiatric Association, 2013), is described as a problematic pattern of alcohol use that results in significant impairment in life functioning. There are 11 diagnostic criteria described in the *DSM-5* for diagnosing AUDs that are described in Chapter 5, Assessment/Diagnosis and Treatment Planning (American Psychiatric Association, 2013).

Alcohol Metabolism and Pharmacology

Alcohol is primarily consumed in liquid form, so drinking is the primary route of administration. However, alcohol can also be ingested rectally (via alcohol enemas) or vaginally (a process known as "eyeballing" in which tampons are soaked with hard alcohol such as vodka and inserted; Doweiko, 2019). When alcohol is ingested orally, only about 10% to 20% is absorbed from the stomach into the bloodstream. The majority of alcohol (80%–90%) is absorbed into the bloodstream from the small intestine. Once in the bloodstream, alcohol travels through all the blood-rich organs of the body including the brain (where it produces mood-altering or intoxication effects) and the liver. The liver can be thought of as the "chemical processing plant" of the human body and is responsible for breaking down or metabolizing alcohol into inert chemical compounds that are then expelled from the body through one's breath, perspiration, or urine. Since the liver is able to metabolize approximately 1½ oz of alcohol (hard liquor such as gin, vodka, whiskey) per hour (1½ oz hard liquor is equivalent to 5 oz of wine and equivalent to 12 oz beer), if one were to have one hard-liquor drink (or the equivalent wine or beer) and wait an hour or so, they would probably not become intoxicated because they have allowed enough time for the liver to metabolize or break down the alcohol. For each of the drink equivalents mentioned earlier, the blood alcohol level (BAL) will increase to .03; however, if one were to wait for an hour or so after ingesting that one drink, glass of wine, or 12 oz beer, their BAL would drop back down to .00. Ingesting three drinks within an hour would likely increase the BAL to .09, and in most states that would be above the legal limit (.08) for being charged with a DUI. However, women tend to metabolize alcohol more slowly, therefore, the same three drinks may result in a much higher BAL. Body size also determines BAL; therefore, a male who weighs 190 pounds will have a lower BAL than a 110-pound woman. Eating fatty foods will slow down the absorption of alcohol into the blood stream (Doweiko, 2019); however, there is a common misconception that eating a full meal before drinking will prevent one from becoming intoxicated. Although eating a full meal may slow down alcohol absorption into the bloodstream, it will not ultimately prevent intoxication. Extreme BALs of .30 to .40 may result in a coma, whereas a BAL of .50 is associated with alcohol poisoning and possible death, as the increased BAL essentially shuts down the hypothalamus in the brain, which controls autonomic nervous system functions such as breathing, body temperature, and blood pressure.

Alcohol is essentially a central nervous system (CNS) depressant, which is why in the early stages of intoxication people slur their speech and may have trouble walking or performing simple tasks. Because of its depressant effects, alcohol is also considered a hypnotic in that it tends to make people feel drowsy and sleepy. However, some individuals report feeling stimulated by drinking. This is usually because alcohol tends to have a disinhibiting effect whereby individuals will often say or do things they ordinarily would not do or say. This disinhibition effect explains why acts of violence are sometimes committed as a result of intoxication.

Pathological Effects of Alcohol

Repetitive, heavy drinking often has profound impacts on various organ systems within the body. For example, the CNS is affected because of nerve-cell inflammation or destruction, which results in conditions such as Wernicke–Korsakoff's psychosis, alcoholic dementia, and a condition called *peripheral neuropathy* (which clients experience as a "pins and needles" sensation in their hands or feet). There is some research that suggests brain cells destroyed by alcohol can regenerate; however, repetitive drinking along with the lack of proper nutrition (resulting in vitamin B1 thiamine deficiencies) often contributes to neurological-cognitive decline, especially in older, chronic drinkers.

Drinking also takes a toll on the cardiovascular system. Although red wine has been promoted as helpful to cardiac functioning, this notion has recently been debunked, and total alcohol abstinence is promoted as the safest choice to ensure cardiac health. Conditions such as hypertension (high blood pressure), cardiomyopathy (heart muscle loss), and arrhythmias (irregular heartbeat) are all major problems that can develop as a result of chronic drinking.

Finally, the gastrointestinal (GI) system can be profoundly impacted by repetitive alcohol intake. Conditions such as steatosis (fatty liver), alcohol hepatitis (inflammation of the liver and hepatic system), cirrhosis (liver cell destruction that becomes replaced with scar tissue), gastritis (inflammation of the stomach lining), and pancreatitis (inflammation of the pancreas) can occur as a result of chronic alcohol use. Many of these aforementioned GI conditions are due to alcohol being an inflammatory or irritant substance (Woodward, 2013).

Alcohol Withdrawal and Detoxification

Individuals who drink increased amounts of alcohol on a daily basis often will develop physiological dependence. This is usually accompanied by one's developing a tolerance to how much they can consume in a given day. Tolerance is the result of the brain adapting to the amount of alcohol being ingested, therefore, more alcohol is required to achieve the desired effect. It is common for these individuals to drink quarts of hard liquor, wine, or beer daily, whereas for a social drinker these excessive amounts would most likely result in a coma or death. As alcohol is being metabolized over the course of several hours (e.g., during sleep), the body reacts to the slow depletion of alcohol in the bloodstream and withdrawal symptoms develop. Because alcohol is a CNS depressant, the withdrawal symptoms are those of agitation. (With stimulant drugs, the withdrawal effects are opposite, for instance, depressant effects.) Withdrawal is dependent on how much alcohol the person consumes on a daily basis and for how long (i.e., days, weeks, months, and years). Mild withdrawal symptoms include anxiety, vivid dreams, and headaches, while moderate withdrawal symptoms may include sweating, high blood pressure, irregular heartbeat, and alcohol hallucinosis (in which clients sometimes hear their name being called or other auditory sensations) and tremors (which can be observed by asking your client to hold their hand out, palm down, or by having them stick out their tongue). With more severe withdrawal, drinkers sometimes experience grand mal seizures (similar to epileptic seizures), which are especially dangerous if someone falls and hits their head. In addition, another severe symptom of withdrawal is delirium tremens (DTs), whereby individuals become incoherent, irrational, and extremely agitated. If DTs are not properly treated in a medical setting, death could occur as a result of cardiac arrest or heart attack due to extreme agitation and rapid heartbeat (Woodward, 2013).

When someone is physiologically dependent on alcohol, the first priority is to have them evaluated in an ED to be admitted for a medical detoxification. Withdrawal symptoms usually begin within 6 to 96 hours of one's last drink, so this time period is crucial in initiating detoxification treatment. Detox usually consists of medical personnel administering benzodiazepines (e.g., Librium) and anticonvulsant medication to help prevent seizures. Benzodiazepines are also CNS depressants, and therefore they work by reducing the agitation brought on by alcohol withdrawal. Once the dangers of alcohol withdrawal have passed (this often takes a few days), the dosage of the benzodiazepine is slowly reduced so that by the time the client is discharged from the detox unit, they are medication-free. Keep in mind, however, that detoxification is just the beginning of AUD recovery. Later in this chapter, we will discuss other necessary and effective treatments and case-management issues pertaining to AUD.

OPIOIDS

Prior to the onset of the coronavirus 2019 (COVID-19) pandemic, the United States found itself in the grips of another epidemic, the opioid epidemic. Although the death rates were substantially less than COVID-related deaths, each year there were increases in the overdose death rates. For example, in 2018, there were an estimated 60,000 overdose deaths; in 2019, there were about 72,000 overdose deaths; and by 2021, there were an estimated 81,000 overdose deaths. Although Narcan (naloxone) was able to reverse several of these overdoses and save lives, the death rates have continued to grow with each passing year, with the majority of these deaths coming from illicit heroin use. Yet, approximately 100 million Americans receive prescription pain medications annually (Barry et al., 2016), and an unfortunate yet common progression is for pain patients to go from legally prescribed pain medications like oxycodone hydrochloride (Oxycontin), fentanyl (Duragesic), roxicodone (Roxicette), hydromorphone (Vicodin), or oxymorphone (Dilaudid) to heroin. Within the past year, there have been several lawsuits settled against pharmaceutical corporations like Purdue Pharma, McKesson, and InSys for their marketing and distribution practices of opioid pain medication, which are alleged to have contributed to the opioid epidemic.

Heroin

From 2000 to 2010, there were an estimated 3.5 million Americans who used heroin, of which approximately 1 million are considered to be addicted (i.e., opioid use disorder [OUD]; Kreek et al., 2005). Admissions to treatment programs for heroin increased from 228,000 in 1995 to 254,000 in 2005, which constitutes approximately 15% of all SUD treatment admissions (Substance Abuse and Mental Health Services [SAMHSA], 2007). In order to understand the popularity of heroin, we need to go back to the plant it is derived from, that is, opium. Opium poppies grow wild in many countries, and while India supplies the world with much of the opium required for opium-based pain medications, most illicit opium poppies come from Afghanistan, Iraq, and Turkey (referred to as the Golden Crescent). America's War on Terror in the aftermath of the September 11th attacks also became intertwined with the War on Drugs, as many Afghan farmers found it more lucrative to grow opium poppies than to grow food crops such as wheat. Today, Afghanistan grows about two-thirds of the world's opium poppies. During the Vietnam war, much of the opium poppies used to produce heroin were being grown and imported from Cambodia, Laos, and Vietnam (sometimes referred to as the Golden Triangle). Opium poppies are also used to produce morphine (MS Contin), which was discovered by German chemist Friedrich Sertüner in 1804.

Codeine was created by another German chemist, Heinrich Dreser, who was working for the Bayer pharmaceutical company in Darmstadt, Germany. Although heroin was discovered by British chemist C. R. Alder Wright in 1874, it was the Bayer company that saw the marketing potential of heroin as a supposedly, nonaddictive alternative to morphine and codeine. With each new variant of opium (e.g., morphine and codeine heroin), these new drugs were marketed as being less- or nonaddictive compared to their precursors (a similar trend occurred with benzodiazepines).

From a psychopharmacological perspective, when ingested, heroin floods the brain with dopamine and norepinephrine, neurotransmitters that are associated with heightened euphoria. Norepinephrine has also been implicated in causing craving and subsequent drug-seeking behavior (Weinshenker & Schroeder, 2007). Depending on how much of the drug is ingested and route of administration (e.g., intravenous [IV] use vs. smoking), users may feel mild to intense euphoria (referred to as "a rush"), but in situations where overdose occurs, resulting in coma or death, the cause is due to respiratory depression (i.e., hypoxia). Here, the hypothalamus in the brain, which controls breathing, essentially shuts down (Gutstein & Akil, 2005). Fortunately, heroin overdoses can be reverse if detected and treated in time using naloxone (Narcan), which can be administered as a nasal spray or by injection. Naloxone works by occupying the opioid receptor sites in the brain, thereby allowing the remaining opioids to be metabolized without producing a prolonged coma. Another major difficulty with opioids, including heroin, is withdrawal. Generally, there is a period of acute withdrawal that can last anywhere from 5 to 14 days and includes symptoms such as anxiety, restlessness, runny nose, chills, stomach and muscle cramps, insomnia, diarrhea, increased blood pressure and heartbeat, and piloerection or "goose flesh" (which is where the term "going cold turkey" originated). A common misconception is that opioid withdrawal is the most severe and life-threatening among various substances; actually alcohol and benzodiazepine withdrawal result in more life-threatening medical complications. This is because of how taxing alcohol and benzodiazepine withdrawal are on the cardiovascular system. The intensity of opioid withdrawal is naturally determined by how much the client has been using and for how long. There is also a rather prolonged post-acute withdrawal (PAW) or protracted abstinence syndrome (Stine & Kosten, 2013) resulting from opioid dependence that can last for several months, characterized by anxiety, depression, and craving. Keep in mind that all of the aforementioned substances (opioids, alcohol, and benzodiazepines) are CNS depressants.

LEARNING ACTIVITY 4.1
RAPID OPIOID DETOX

See what you can find out about rapid and/or ultrarapid opioid detox. See if you can find information about programs or medical centers that offer this type of detox. Share what you have found out with your classmates.

Pathological Effects of Opioids

There are fewer medical problems that actually result from continuous opioid use, as evidenced by the millions of individuals who are prescribed opioids for chronic pain conditions. However, clients who use primarily heroin are at greater danger for overdose death, violence, and infectious diseases (e.g., HIV infection or abscesses) resulting from needle-sharing and alcohol-related problems for those with co-occurring AUD (Goldstein & Herrera, 1995; Hser et al., 1993). The one common physical problem that both licit and illicit opioid users often complain of is constipation and major dental problems (e.g., tooth decay and focal infections [abscesses]). Some research suggests that opioids caused rhabdomyolysis (a condition that results in the breakdown of skeletal muscles). However, once again, this condition may be caused by viral or bacterial infections most likely related to IV use with infected hypodermic needles. Another study found increased rates of neuropathy (a neurological condition experienced as a "pins and needles" feelings in extremities) in individuals using heroin, morphine, or pentazocine (Talwin), a synthetic opiate (Kleinschmidt et al., 2001).

SEDATIVES/HYPNOTICS

This group of legally prescribed medications is used primarily as anxiolytics or to reduce anxiety. Sedatives (aka tranquilizers) are prescribed primarily for daytime calming, while hypnotics are prescribed for nighttime promotion of sleep. Prior to the introduction of benzodiazepines (i.e., diazepam [Valium], patented by Hoffman LaRoche in 1959), barbiturates such as phenobarbital (Luminal), secobarbital (Seconal), and pentobarbital (Nembutal) were prescribed for treatment of insomnia, muscle spasms, and epileptic seizures and were used as tranquilizers. Although many epileptic patients took low doses of barbiturates often for years without problems or side effects, there were individuals who developed a tolerance to the sedative effects of barbiturates that resulted in taking increased doses and dependence. Marilyn Monroe was said to have overdosed on prescription barbiturates. Therefore, when benzodiazepines were introduced, they were marketed as being both safe and nonaddicting. From 1968 to 1982, Valium was one of the most-often prescribed medications in the United States (replaced once SSRI antidepressants were introduced). In 1978 alone, there were over 2 billion doses of Valium consumed in America (Calcaterra & Barrow, 2014).

Benzodiazepines (e.g., chlordiazepoxide [Librium], clonazepam [Klonopin], alprazolam [Xanax], and lorazepam [Ativan]) are used primarily to help lessen anxiety, to lessen alcohol withdrawal symptoms, and to reduce muscle spasms. When used on a short-term basis (i.e., a few weeks), benzodiazepines tend to have few side effects and are easily discontinued when no longer needed. Therefore, when used on a long-term basis, there is a risk of tolerance, dependence, and withdrawal developing, as well as difficulty in stopping or discontinuing the drug when no longer needed. The transition from short-term or occasional use to a sedative-hypnotic use disorder is often subtle and often occurs over time, as individuals progress to more frequent use in which they use up their prescriptions more quickly and then either turn to illicit use (i.e., purchasing from drug dealers) or by engaging in "doctor shopping" (i.e., searching for multiple doctors who will write additional prescriptions).

From a chemical and psychopharmacological perspective, benzodiazepines are somewhat similar to alcohol both in terms of being CNS depressants and how they work in the brain by increasing neurotransmitter output of dopamine and GABA. Although there is a low risk for overdose, when benzodiazepines are

LEARNING ACTIVITY 4.2
BENZODIAZEPINE WITHDRAWAL

There is a lot of information on the internet pertaining to benzodiazepine withdrawal, which includes first-person accounts as well as factual information. See what you can find out about benzodiazepines and watch some of the testimonies from people who have struggled with detoxifying from them. Share what you have found out with your classmates.

combined with other CNS depressant substances such as alcohol or opioids, there is a synergistic or multiplicative enhancement of both chemicals that may result in coma or overdose. Some of the newer benzodiazepines (e.g., alprazolam [Xanax]) are said to have a lower abuse and overdose potential than some of the older benzodiazepines such as diazepam (Valium), flurazepam (Dalmane), or chlordiazepoxide (Librium). Also, there are few medical or pathological problems caused by benzodiazepine use. One meta-analysis study noted an increased risk of cleft palate and other malformations in babies born to mothers using benzodiazepines at the time of conception when compared to the general population (Dolovich et al., 1998).

Hypnotics

One of the problems with most benzodiazepines is that they tend to block (or greatly reduce) REM sleep, which is necessary for maintaining cognitive functioning. Zolpidem (Ambien) is said to cause only minor reductions in REM sleep and also does not interfere with the normal progression of sleep stages (i.e., going from light to deep sleep). It is said that an average adult will go through approximately five or six REM stages during the course of a night's sleep. Zolpidem is taken in pill form and metabolizes throughout the course of the night and tends to metabolize more slowly in older adults and women (Doble et al., 2004; Mihic & Harris, 2011; Sadock et al., 2015). There are instances where clients may develop a tolerance to zolpidem when used at high-dosage levels for a number of years (Dundar et al., 2004), and mild withdrawal has also been noted, again depending on dose and frequency of use (Sadock et al., 2015). It is therefore recommended that clients maintain as low a dose as possible. There are also reports of next-day drowsiness, cognitive slowness, and sometimes dizziness.

When zolpidem was first introduced, it was assumed that it had a low abuse potential; however, over the past few years, there have been reports of increased tolerance (e.g., the average nightly dose is typically 5–10 mg); however, there are instances where individuals have used up to 800 mg nightly. It is thought that the increased abuse potential is greatest with individuals who have a history of other SUDs (Ciraulo & Knapp, 2009; Gitlow, 2007).

Eszopiclone (Lunesta) is not a benzodiazepine but is prescribed as a hypnotic that is intended for short-term treatment of insomnia (Doweiko, 2019). Similar to zolpidem, there is also an abuse potential, and those prescribing eszopiclone need to rule out whether there is a SUD history, especially a history of sedative or benzodiazepine misuse. Next-day effects also include drowsiness (similar to a hangover), anxiety, depression, nausea, and stomach pain. Some individuals have experienced amnesia after taking eszopiclone and yet will engage in rather complex behaviors (such as driving a car) without having any memory of having done so.

CANNABIS AND HALLUCINOGENS

Cannabis is classified as mild hallucinogen, however, it does not have the same psychological-cognitive impact as other hallucinogens such as LSD or MDMA, which we will be discussing later in this section. Although cannabis has been around for centuries, it only recently has become legalized for recreational and/or medical use in several American states. In the 1920s and 1930s, marijuana had been demonized as the "devil's weed," which gave rise to antimarijuana films such as *Reefer Madness* and draconian cannabis-possession laws that often targeted Mexicans living in the southwestern United States and African Americans living in the southeast. Harry J. Anslinger initially led the federal department responsible for enforcing alcohol Prohibition; however, when he saw that he would soon be out of a job with the upcoming repeal of Prohibition, he took on a new cause, the prosecution of marijuana users as the new director of the Federal Bureau of Narcotics. Although many of the marijuana myths perpetuated by Anslinger have since been debunked, many controversies still remain. The first controversy is whether marijuana is a "gateway drug," that is, a drug that results in a need to use more potent substances such as heroin. The second controversy pertains to whether marijuana is addictive and therefore produces substance-specific withdrawal symptoms. The third controversy is whether marijuana results in adverse medical and psychological consequences such as lung disease and something called "amotivational syndrome" (AMS). In Chapter 3, we described the pharmacology of cannabis; therefore, we will begin by examining some of the aforementioned controversies.

Cannabis Controversies

The supposition behind the "gateway hypothesis" controversy is based on the notion that there is a tendency to start with legal substances, such as alcohol and nicotine, followed by cannabis and then progressing to using more potent and more highly addictive illegal substances over time (e.g., cocaine or heroin). While some cannabis users will concurrently use other substances or will switch to using harder drugs (Wagner & Anthony, 2002), not all cannabis users will necessarily progress to more addictive drugs, and there are some studies that indicate that those individuals who do progress may have other co-occurring mental health disorders or SUD risk factors that might account for this progression (Hall & Lynskey, 2005). As Gossup (1987) pointed out, "There are only a few thousand opiate addicts in Great Britain, yet there are millions who have tried cannabis" (p. 9).

The second controversy revolves around whether cannabis is physically addicting. It is estimated that approximately 8%–20% of long-term, frequent cannabis users will become addicted (Budney et al., 2007; Volkow et al., 2014). While many cannabis users report using occasionally (much like the social drinker who consumes alcohol on specific occasions such as holidays), there are those who use daily over the course of weeks, months, or years. It is common for regular users to report developing tolerance. Also, the *DSM-5* includes criteria for cannabis withdrawal, which is characterized by such symptoms as irritability, anger, aggression, increased anxiety, depressed mood, restlessness, sleep (insomnia, disturbed dreams), and appetite disturbance. Interestingly, cannabis withdrawal usually does not require medical intervention or medication to help clients through the withdrawal process (American Psychiatric Association, 2013; Danovitch & Gorelick, 2012).

The third controversy pertains to whether cannabis causes adverse psychological, emotional, cognitive consequences and a condition known as "amotivational syndrome" (AMS) The hypothesis behind AMS is that regular cannabis use causes users to lose drive and ambition therefore making them unmotivated to accomplish or plan for anything. AMS is also associated with shortened attention spans and a tendency to become easily distracted (Gruber et al., 2003). In the aforementioned study, researchers found that individuals with the greatest level of cannabis use were found to have significantly lower incomes and educational achievement levels when compared to a control group. These findings are similar to research performed by Green et al. (2017), Brook et al. (2016), Juon et al. (2011), and Washburn and Capaldi (2015), all indicating that heavy cannabis use interferes with the ability to attain major developmental milestones of young adulthood such as completing an educational program beyond high school, establishing a consistent intimate relationship, and establishing oneself in a career. On the other hand, there are frequent cannabis users who are very achievement oriented, which leads many to question the veracity of AMS. Those who oppose AMS veracity contend that perhaps less ambitious, more distracted individuals are attracted to cannabis as their preferred substance.

Another psychological consequence of cannabis use is whether it contributes to mental health problems, including violent behavior. A series of Swedish studies (Allebeck & Andréasson, 1996; Andréasson et al., 1987, 1989) found that heavy cannabis use was correlated with the development of psychosis and schizophrenia. This research was rather compelling because it was based on a large national cohort of young men who were serving compulsory military service. Furthermore, "cannabis psychosis" was linked to violent behavior (somewhat similar to the type of violence seen in agitated paranoid schizophrenics). Meanwhile, in the United States, renowned psychiatrist Lester Grinspoon was advocating for decriminalization of cannabis in the United States based on the burgeoning number of arrests of young American men and women. In addition, the cannabis that was around in the 1960s and 1970s was rather low grade, often containing only 1%–2% tetrahydrocannabinol (THC), and certainly did not appear to cause the types of psychotic or violent reactions we see today. Recent estimates indicate that, on average, cannabis contains anywhere from 20%–25% THC content (Berenson, 2019). The Swedish research also raised the question whether the young men who experienced psychosis were predisposed to mental illness (Hamilton, 2017). Yet Allebeck and Andréasson (1996) concluded that, when 11 different risk factors (e.g., genetic risk) were controlled for, there was still over twice the risk for developing schizophrenia in those men who reported smoking cannabis more than 10 times. Berenson (2019) also indicated that states that have legalized marijuana for medical use have experienced increases in arrests for violent crimes and ED visits for mental health crises. In addition, for individuals who have been diagnosed with major mental health disorders (e.g., schizophrenia or bipolar disorder), there is an increased likelihood of rehospitalization for those who use cannabis regularly. So, although it appears that for the majority of users smoking cannabis will result in a relaxed, mellow type of euphoria, there will be a small percentage that will become paranoid, agitated, and perhaps more at risk for developing adverse reactions to cannabis.

The physical impact of cannabis appears to focus primarily on lung and pulmonary functioning. Some studies indicate that because marijuana smoke is inhaled more deeply and held in the lungs longer before exhaling, greater levels of tar may be retained in the lungs (Jones, 1980). Approximately 140 chemicals have been identified in marijuana smoke, and some of these are carcinogenic (Hollister, 1998; Jones, 1980). It is thought that this contributes to heavy cannabis smokers having higher rates of laryngitis, bronchitis, and asthma-like problems (Goldstein, 1995; Hollister, 1998). Currently, there has not been much research regarding medical complications related to vaporizing cannabis.

Methods of Cannabis Use

Most people associate cannabis use with smoking, whether it be in a rolled cigarette or "joint," or from a pipe or "bong" or vaping liquid THC. Depending on the quality/potency of the cannabis being smoked, all of these methods can produce an intense high that can last for hours. Since many states have legalized cannabis, the purity and potency have increased tremendously; however, so too has the cost, therefore illegal growers still operate successfully in many states that have legalized recreational marijuana. Hashish and hash oils are also considered to be potent forms of cannabis that are derived from the residue of the cannabis plant. Edibles have become very popular in states that have legalized cannabis. Several years ago, "pot brownies" were the most popular edibles; now THC can be found in gummy bears, toffee bars, chocolate bars, and other concoctions. Since THC absorption from edibles is much slower than from smoking or vaping cannabis, many individuals are fooled into thinking they did not consume enough of the edible to get them high and end up consuming more. This unfortunately has resulted in an increase in ED visits with complaints of panic-like anxiety. One of the newest and most potent forms of cannabis is referred to as "marijuana wax" or "wax dabbing." Cannabis wax is even more potent then smoking hash or hashish oil. The method of use is also rather unique in that cannabis wax is placed on a flat heating surface and then ignited with butane (Kimble, 2013). The resulting smoke is then inhaled through a metal tube (often referred to as a "nail"). Because the THC levels are so extreme, many cannabis users refer to wax dabbing as the ultimate high. However, because cannabis is fat soluble and therefore stays in the brain and body for extended periods of time, it also produces catatonic-like effects, which can often last for days, weeks, or months. Recently, "vaping" has become a popular way of smoking cannabis. Here, liquid THC is heated to produce a vapor, which is then inhaled. According to the 2019 Monitoring the Future survey, vaping THC has increased significantly among high-school-age adolescents and marked the largest single-year increases ever observed by the Monitoring the Future's 45-year history (Monitoring the Future, 2019).

Synthetic Cannabis

Currently, there are also a number of synthetic cannabinoid substances with street names such as "K-2," "bath salts," "spice," and "spike." Synthetic cannabinoids generally fall within the synthetic cathinone family of drugs and include substances such as "K-2" and "bath salts." These synthetic cathinones are often marketed as safer alternatives to cannabis, yet nothing could be further from the truth. Although most "fake weed" (as it is often referred to) is usually smoked, it can also be sold in liquid form and vaporized in e-cigarettes. Even the term *synthetic cannabis* is a misnomer, because these are natural plant materials (e.g., parsley or oregano) that are then sprayed with a variety of chemicals (there are over 700 chemicals found in some samples of synthetic cannabinoids, thereby making it difficult to predict its effects). According to the Monitoring the Future national surveys (Johnston et al., 2015), synthetic cannabinoids are most popular among high-school-age adolescents. Prior to becoming illegal, most of these drugs could be purchased in tobacco shops, gas stations, convenience stores, or online, usually in packaging that states "not for human consumption." Most synthetic cannabinoids are classified as Schedule I drugs because they are considered highly addictive and have no medical benefit whatsoever. The pathological effects of the synthetic cannabinoids are much greater than cannabis and include tremors, hypertension, nausea, vomiting, chest tightness, headaches, and blurred vision as well as psychological effects such as altered perception, panic, restlessness, euphoria, delusional thinking, and confusion (Castellanos, 2016).

If taken continuously, there can be withdrawal symptoms, which include headaches, anxiety, depression, and irritability. In 2015, a particularly troubling synthetic cannabinoid made its appearance in and around Syracuse, New York. Referred to by its street name "spike," users would become violent, aggressive, and hard to control. Syracuse EDs were flooded with spike overdoses (Featherstone, 2015).

Other Hallucinogens

Hallucinogens can also be divided according to those that are natural (such as peyote [derived from cactus] and psilocybin [mushroom]) and those that are synthesized in laboratories (e.g., DOM, MDMA, STP, and PCP). Interestingly, LSD is both natural and synthetic. Derived from the rye ergot fungus, LSD was first synthesized by chemist Albert Hoffman in 1936, who at the time was working for Sandoz pharmaceutical company when he happened to spill LSD liquid on his hand and began experiencing intense visual hallucinations. Hoffman kept his newfound chemical hallucinogen on the shelf of his lab until the CIA expressed interest in using LSD as part of its post–World War II interrogation methods (see Kinzer, 2020). It was not until the 1960s that Harvard psychologist Dr. Timothy Leary began experimenting with LSD as a mind-expanding drug that could have therapeutic benefits. Although LSD fell out of favor and Leary became discredited in the academic community, best-selling author Michael Pollan (2019) has recently become an advocate for hallucinogen "microdosing" as having therapeutic potential in treating posttraumatic stress disorder (PTSD), particularly in soldiers impacted by combat-related PTSD. Ketamine (similar to PCP) was originally developed as an anesthetic used for medical and veterinary surgery but was eventually diverted as an illegal substance. Because ketamine produced amnesia or memory loss, it had also become known as a date-rape drug. There have been recent clinical anecdotal reports that ketamine infusions may have beneficial use in preventing suicide in clients with chronic, severe depression (Velaquez-Manoff, 2018).

Unlike other substances discussed in this chapter, hallucinogens are generally not drugs that produce physical dependence or addiction. And although there is an aftereffect (i.e., "crashing") from taking hallucinogens, it is not similar to withdrawal whereby individuals experience cravings to resume use in order to prevent or diminish the aftereffect symptoms. Also, nearly all of the hallucinogens presented here are ingested orally, which suggests slow absorption into the bloodstream and up to the brain. Slow absorption generally precludes there being a euphoric rush. Instead, the visual hallucinations and delusion that hallucinogen users experience tend to occur slowly after ingestion. Another common phenomenon of an LSD trip is *synthesia,* which is a cross-over of sensory stimuli. Here, one may claim to "see music" or to "taste colors." A typical LSD trip may last anywhere from 6–10 hours, while an MDMA (ecstasy) trip would last 10–20 hours or more because MDMA is often laced with a stimulant. Hence, ecstasy is often referred to as a "psychedelic amphetamine."

Pathological Effects of Hallucinogens

From a psychological perspective, LSD has been known to precipitate psychotic reactions; however, it remains to be determined if these reactions are more common in individuals predisposed to major mental illness. Also, more frequent LSD users may experience *flashbacks* that may occur several days or weeks after an LSD trip. Flashbacks are characterized by visual hallucinations and delusions similar to having recently ingested LSD. The mechanisms by which flashbacks occur are not well understood (Doweiko, 2019); however, it is hypothesized that LSD molecules may get stored in the brain (similar to how THC is stored in fat cells throughout the body and brain) and may get released after physical exertion. Generally, flashbacks are of brief duration (10–20 minutes) and tend to dissipate on their own without medical intervention. These are referenced in the *DSM-5* (American Psychiatric Association, 2013) as "hallucinogen perceptual persisting disorder." While most individuals find LSD tripping to be pleasant, some experience "bad trips" that are usually characterized by extreme anxiety, panic, and/or paranoid delusions. These symptoms can be treated with antipsychotic medications such as haloperidiol (Haldol), which helps to alleviate these distressing symptoms. Because LSD produces both hallucinations and delusions and also because these experiences could be ameliorated or lessened with antipsychotic medications, LSD was studied in the 1970s as a biochemical model for schizophrenia that later became known as the "dopamine hypothesis of schizophrenia."

Ecstasy (MDMA) has a similar history as LSD with regard to having been developed in the lab and then making its way into American culture as a street drug. When MDMA was first discovered (Shulgin, 1986), it was found to produce not only euphoria but compassion, a universal feeling of love of fellow humans as well as pain relief or analgesia. This universal feeling of love and compassion is attributed to the fact that MDMA results in the release of oxytocin, a hormone that is released during bonding (e.g., an infant's bonding to their mother during breastfeeding). For those reasons, it was thought that MDMA might be useful as an adjunct to counseling and psychotherapy, and there were a few studies that found it to be therapeutically effective. Unfortunately, MDMA was classified as a Schedule 1 substance (so is marijuana), which means it has a high addictive potential and little if any therapeutic value. Prolonged MDMA use can also result in cardiac complications such as arrhythmias, increased heart rate/blood pressure, and inflammation of the heart (Badon et al., 2002; Shenouda et al., 2008). In addition, MDMA causes hyperthermia, or overheating of the body, which is the result of the drug's impact on the hypothalamus, which regulates one's body temperature along with other autonomic nervous system responses (e.g., breathing and heartbeat). The other problem with ecstasy is that long-term use was found to result in neurocognitive deficits (e.g., poor strategic self-regulation, increased reflective impulsivity, and overall lowered cognitive functioning; Halpern et al., 2010). What was particularly noteworthy in this study was how it was able to rule out possible confounding variables such as concurrent other substance use. Prolonged MDMA use is also said to cause memory problems (McDowell, 2004) that may last for months after one's last use of MDMA.

COCAINE AND STIMULANTS

Cocaine has a rather interesting history dating back centuries, when indigenous people living in the Andes Mountains of South America were said to have chewed on coca leaves to help boost their energy levels and to cope with high altitudes. In 1860, German chemist Albert Neimann came up with a process for isolating cocaine from coca leaves. Subsequently, cocaine became popular throughout the United States and Europe as an elixir that was combined with wine (called Marianni wine) and used for medicinal purposes (e.g., a topical anesthetic for eye, ear, nose, and throat surgery, for which it is still used today; Gorelick, 2013). When Coca Cola was introduced in Atlanta, Georgia in 1886, it contained cocaine. In 1884, Sigmund Freud published his findings on the psychological benefits of cocaine, especially as a treatment for depression. It was not until Freud became dependent on cocaine and a colleague of his died as a result of cocaine use that he began to rethink his perspective on cocaine as a wonder drug.

There have been several cocaine epidemics in the United States. The first coincides with the isolation of the psychoactive component of coca began in Germany and then spread to most of Europe and the United States. The second cocaine epidemic occurred during Prohibition (from 1920 to 1933) during which time cocaine was very much in vogue in speakeasys and night clubs. The third epidemic coincided with the economic expansion of the 1980s when cocaine was ever present in most cities, especially throughout the Wall Street financial district in New York City. Although much of powder cocaine was imported primarily from Columbia, South America, and, to a lesser extent, Mexico, a less expensive but more widespread version of cocaine referred to as "crack" or "crack cocaine" found its way into many poor urban neighborhoods. As heroin (especially black-tar heroin imported from Mexico) became cheaper and more plentiful (Quinones, 2016), interest in cocaine began to dwindle.

Cocaine is a CNS stimulant. Although it is estimated that 85% of cocaine users tend to use intermittently and therefore do not develop dependence, it is noted that tolerance does increase with prolonged use. Earlier editions of the *DSM* did not include cocaine dependence as a diagnostic category because the belief was that cocaine use tended to be intermittent and not continuous. It was not until the establishment of the 1-800-COCAINE hotline by Dr. Mark Gold in the mid-1980s that callers were mostly describing continuous daily use of cocaine and often spending thousands on the substance per week (Washton et al., 1984).

Methods of Cocaine Use

The most common method of cocaine use is intranasal, or "snorting" powder cocaine. This route of administration (also known as insufflation) guarantees that it will be rapidly absorbed into the bloodstream via the nasal mucosa. It will then reach the brain in about 30–90 seconds, and the peak intensity or "rush" will last about 15–20 minutes. Users will arrange the cocaine powder in lines about 2 inches in length. One gram of cocaine will yield about 30 lines (Doweiko, 2019). Because cocaine is sold illegally, the purity often varies, and most often it is only about 50%–60% pure (U.S. Drug Enforcement Administration, 2008). It is also possible to mix cocaine hydrocholoride powder with water and inject it intravenously, where it will reach the brain within 30 seconds. The danger with this method of use is that it is impossible for the user to know exactly how much cocaine they have ingested (again given purity variations), which can result in extreme agitation or cardiovascular complications. Cocaine can also be smoked, a method that is referred to as "freebasing." Since cocaine hydrochloride powder is not flammable, it must be mixed with ether (a highly flammable compound). Freebasing means that about 70%–90% of the cocaine will reach the brain within seconds, producing an intense rush. However, because freebasing is highly flammable and potentially explosive, there were several injuries associated with this method. It was at this point that cocaine dealers introduced "crack," a ready-to-smoke form of cocaine.

(Crack got its name because of the cracking sound it makes when ignited.) Smoking crack is considered safer than IV cocaine administration.

Cocaine can also be used sublingually by placing it under the tongue where it is absorbed through the blood-rich tissues of the mouth; however, this method of use has not been studied extensively. Also, cocaine can also be absorbed by ingesting it orally. Such would be the case with "body packers" (i.e., those who smuggle packets of cocaine by eating them). If these packets were to rupture, however, it would usually cause immediate death due to overdose (Esterson et al., 2017).

Another important aspect of cocaine use is that it results in both a sensitization and kindling effect. Sensitization occurs with intermittent use and is characterized by an "enhanced response to later (cocaine) exposure" (Gorelick, 2013, p. 197). Kindling is described as a process whereby "intermittent electrical activity of neurons results in a progressive increase in cellular response to subsequent stimulation" (Gorelick, 2013, p. 197). Therefore, both intermittent and continuous use of cocaine appear to hardwire the brain to respond more robustly to subsequent use. This phenomenon is thought to account for cocaine-induced seizures (Witkin et al., 2008).

Cocaine Metabolism and Pathological Effects

Cocaine is water soluble, which accounts for its rapid absorption into the bloodstream; however, the route of administration has a major impact on how quickly cocaine is absorbed into the bloodstream and travels to the brain. Cocaine is metabolized or broken down primarily by the liver at which point it is eliminated from the body via urination. Because cocaine is metabolized so quickly, this often results in subjective feelings of extreme craving (Preston et al., 2009).

The majority of physical problems related to cocaine come about as a result of the route of administration. For example, inhaled cocaine may result in a perforated septum (the tissue that divides nasal passages) or can contribute to a condition known as "crack lung," an asthma-like condition often accompanied by chronic bronchiolitis. It is suspected that this condition is the result of the many contaminants in cocaine when it is "cut" or adulterated with a variety of white powdery chemicals (e.g., talcum powder; Mendelson & Mello, 2008). Other pathological effects impact the cardiovascular system. These include potential heart attacks (Gorelick, 2013), atherosclerosis (i.e., the buildup of plaque in the coronary arteries), severe and sudden hypertension (upon ingesting cocaine), cardiac ischemia, cardiomyopathy (i.e., heart muscle atrophy), and sudden cardiac death (Bachi et al., 2017; Greenberg & Bernard, 2005; Stahl, 2008; Tomb, 2008).

Continuous cocaine use also causes many psychological and pathological effects. Cocaine users describe a euphoric rush after ingesting cocaine, which is said to be similar to sexual orgasm. Many users experience feelings of power and a surge of energy. For this reason, cocaine is often described as a "fountain of youth" drug (Cavaiola & Arillo, 1999). However, with prolonged use, users often report depression (associated with "crashing" or cocaine withdrawal), paranoid ideation, agitation, restlessness, and anxiety. Although cocaine withdrawal is not life-threatening, it is often associated with depressive symptoms (i.e., the opposite of the intoxication effects of cocaine), which include anhedonia, fatigue, difficulty concentrating, and disturbed sleep (Morgan et al., 2010). Those who develop cocaine use disorders are usually those who smoke crack cocaine or partake in freebasing or IV use. Research indicates that the lowest rates of cocaine dependence are found in individuals who use intranasally (Doweiko, 2019).

Amphetamines and Other Stimulants

According to preliminary data from the CDC (2020), in 2019 in the United States more than 16,000 of over 70,000 deaths due to drug overdoses were methamphetamine related. Amphetamine-type stimulants (ATSs) are used for treating conditions such as narcolepsy, ADHD, and depression, and sometimes to counter the sedation effects of other medications (Ling et al., 2013). Yet it is estimated that 52 million Americans between the ages of 15 and 64 have used ATS substances for nonmedical reasons in the past year. From 1994 to 2006, admissions to drug treatment programs increased from 2.7% to 8% (SAMHSA, 2006). ATS medications are classified as Schedule II drugs, meaning that they have treatment applications and abuse potential.

ATS medications include drugs such as methylphenidate (Ritalin, Concerta), Dextroamphetamine (Dexedrine), and modafinil (Provigil), which is not a true ATS; however, it is a stimulant that promotes wakefulness (Ling et al., 2013). Ephedrine is non-ATS stimulant drug that was once sold over the counter as an appetite suppressant. It is difficult to ascertain the true scope of ephedrine misuse (Karch, 2009). Also, ephedrine became popular as a precursor chemical in the production of methamphetamines. In 2004, ephedrine-containing cold remedies were placed behind the counter of pharmacies to help restrict their use. However, savvy methamphetamine dealers would pay several individuals to purchase ephedrine products. These purchasers became known as "smurfs." Methamphetamine or "crystal meth" is an illicitly produced stimulant and accounts for the majority of overdoses deaths. Crystal-meth labs have proliferated throughout the Midwestern states, especially in unpopulated, rural areas where many labs go undetected.

LEARNING ACTIVITY 4.3
AMPHETAMINE USE DISORDER

Look over the case of Richard Fee referenced in Appendix 4.1 (Case Example: Amphetamine Use Disorder). After familiarizing yourself with the case, think about the following case management questions: Could Richard's life have been saved? Following his hospitalization in 2011, what would have been the best course of action? As often occurs in most psychiatric hospitalizations, the goal is to help stabilize the patient (which in this case meant reducing his delusional symptoms); however, what else needed to take place beyond stabilization that might have helped Richard to resolve his amphetamine use disorder?

Amphetamine-Type Stimulants: Metabolism and Pathological Effects

Similar to cocaine, amphetamines are water soluble and are metabolized or broken down by the liver. Because ATS medications and methamphetamines are CNS stimulants, they tend to increase body temperature, blood pressure, heart rate, and breathing. These effects can last for up to 12 hours. Methamphetamine users often describe a "rush" after smoking or injecting crystal meth and feel a heightened sense of energy, libido, and alertness. However, continuous abuse of ATS drugs (or binge use) can result in paranoia, hallucinations, delusions, mood disturbance, and a condition known as "formication" (a tactile hallucination of bugs crawling under the skin; Ling et al., 2013). Continuous and binge ATS users may also experience compulsivity and the need to repeat the same behaviors over and over again. Finally, misuse of amphetamines has been demonstrated to cause brain damage although it has not been determined which amphetamines are more likely to cause damage. Apparently, at high doses amphetamines tend to be toxic to the neurotransmitter serotonin's neural networks (Yudko et al., 2009). Also, animal research indicates that the neurotransmitters dopamine and norepinephrine (also implicated in ATS drug stimulation) may require up to 6 months of abstinence to return to normal again (which may account for PAW symptoms if this research proves applicable to humans; King & Ellinwood, 2005). There are various hypotheses as to how ATS substances cause neurotoxicity (Jaffe et al., 2005; King & Ellinwood, 2005).

Most of the physical effects of ATS drugs impact the cardiovascular system in terms of arrhythmias and coronary artery damage (Karch, 2002) and pulmonary complications such as pneumonia. Liver damage is found in 40% of methamphetamine users. Methamphetamine-dependent users often develop severe dental problems including fractured or missing teeth, tooth decay, and gum/periodontal disease. This results in a condition known as "meth mouth" (Shaner et al., 2006).

TOBACCO

Tobacco use poses a problem as a substance of preference for several reasons. First, although chemically it is CNS stimulant, most smokers indicate that they smoke in order to relax (e.g., having a cigarette with a cup of coffee while reading the morning newspaper or after a meal). Second, although it is legal to grow and purchase tobacco in the United States, tobacco use disorders (including cigarette smoking, pipe, cigar, and chewing tobacco) account for approximately 480,000 deaths in America annually, more than all other substances combined (Hanson et al., 2018). Finally, there are very few recreational or social smokers (i.e., individuals who smoke occasionally). Therefore, when it comes to smoking, most are either tobacco dependent, daily smokers, or nonsmokers. There are very few individuals who fall in the middle.

Many centuries ago, some countries tried to ban or prohibit tobacco from being imported to their shores (England and Russia are examples of countries that attempted to ban tobacco); however, these prohibitions were ineffective and later lifted. Tobacco was an important crop especially in the southeastern United States. In North Carolina in the late 1800s, James Buchanan Duke had recruited Eastern European Jewish immigrants to roll cigarettes in his factories. Eventually, he invented a cigarette-rolling machine that could produce thousands of cigarettes per hour. The fortune that the Duke family had amassed was used to build a women's hospital and also funded Duke University.

Cigarettes are one of the most heavily marketed products in the United States and are currently marketed to poor African American, Latinx American, and Asian American communities. Within the past few decades, cigarette ads have been banned from television, however, ads still appear regularly in many magazines. In the 1950s and 1960s (when cigarettes cost 25 cents a pack), television ads often featured TV celebrities who extoled the benefits of smoking while downplaying any potential risks. One ad featuring TV personality Arthur Godfrey claimed that "4 out of 5 doctors preferred Chesterfield cigarettes and recommended them to their patients." Later in life Godfrey quit smoking and broke off his relationship as a Chesterfield spokesperson; however, in a cruel twist of fate, Arthur Godfrey was diagnosed with lung cancer (which he managed to survive) but ended up dying of emphysema in 1983 (thought to be caused by years of smoking). Also, cigarette smoking is pervasive among people diagnosed with mental health disorders, especially among individuals diagnosed with schizophrenia where it is estimated that approximately 90% smoke (Pankiewicz, 2008).

Worldwide cigarette smoking yields approximately $400 billion annually, and it is estimated that approximately 800 men and 200 million women smoke daily (Levinson et al., 2004). China is one of the largest cigarette consumers in the world. When smoking seemed to be waning in the United States (just under 18% of Americans currently smoke according to Striley and Nutley [2020]), electronic cigarettes (or vaping) were introduced in 2003. Electronic cigarettes (such as Juul) claimed to be safer because liquid nicotine was heated into a vapor, as opposed to traditional cigarettes in which tobacco was burned. Vaping was also marketed as a way to cut down on cigarette smoking because nicotine levels could be titrated (or reduced) over time; however, most vape users found they were continuing to smoke at about the same rate. Many adolescents were attracted to vaping because they could easily conceal their use from teachers and parents. Also, many vape manufacturers attracted teens by offering candy-flavored nicotine vape cartridges that many states have since banned.

Tobacco Metabolism and Pathological Effects

Nicotine is the main psychoactive ingredient in cigarettes, cigars, and chewing tobacco. With each puff of a cigarette, a small dose of nicotine is absorbed through the lungs where it is absorbed into the bloodstream and carried to the brain within seconds (Blank et al., 2008). In the brain, nicotine breaks down an enzyme (monoamine oxidase β), which then allows the neurotransmitter, dopamine (a neurotransmitter associated with pleasure and reward), to have a more profound impact. Nicotine also increases levels of epinephrine (a stimulant neurotransmitter), which accounts for why smokers feel a sense of alertness and reduced fatigue. Nicotine concentrations peak within the first few minutes after smoking a cigarette but then begin to be metabolized by the liver, at which point nicotine levels drop, which results in the craving to have another cigarette. Smokers appear to build up a tolerance to nicotine throughout the day (Hughes, 2006).

In addition to nicotine, tobacco smoke contains many other chemicals (approximately 4,700 chemicals [Fiore, 2006]). Many of these chemicals are present as the result of fillers and additives (e.g., perfumes and spices) that are added to make the aroma of tobacco smoke more appealing. It is estimated that up to 40% of cigarettes are composed of fillers (Hanson et al., 2018), which includes the poison arsenic. Additionally, cigarette smoke contains radioactive gases such as radium and polonium. It is estimated that daily smokers' radiation exposure is roughly equivalent to having 250 chest x-rays within a year's time. Unfortunately, filtered cigarettes do not provide protection against some of these carcinogenic (i.e., cancer-causing) chemicals. And yet, nicotine itself is NOT carcinogenic; if it was, the U.S. Food and Drug Administration (FDA) would never have approved nicotine-replacement products like Nicoderm or Nicorette gum (U.S. Department of Health and Human Services, 2016). It is the burning of tobacco that produces most of the carcinogens, whereas with cigar and chewing tobacco it is the mixing of tobacco with saliva that creates a chemical alkaloid reaction that increases the likelihood of developing cancers of the throat, jaw, and mouth. (Freud was said to have smoked on average 10 cigars a day and eventually died of jaw cancer.)

The physical pathological effects of smoking (and secondhand smoke exposure) are well known and well documented. In addition to the obvious pulmonary complications such as coronary obstructive pulmonary diseases (COPD) and emphysema, there are numerous cancers linked to smoking and tobacco, such as lung, throat, mouth, and jaw cancers, as well as pancreatic, esophageal, and gastric/stomach cancers. Smoking also contributes to gum disease and tooth loss. In addition, those who smoke are at increased risk for developing Type 2 diabetes (Willi et al., 2007; Yeh et al., 2010). Smoking also contributes to several types of cardiovascular diseases, most of which are caused by reduced oxygenated blood flow to the heart muscle, which appears to be caused by constriction of coronary arteries while smoking (Doweiko, 2019). Smoking also increases one's risk for developing hypertension, which greatly increases the risk of stroke. Approximately 26,000 fatal strokes are linked to smoking annually (Carpenter, 2001).

LEARNING ACTIVITY 4.4
SMOKING CESSATION

Do you know anyone who stopped smoking cigarettes or cigars or stopped chewing tobacco successfully? If so, find out why they stopped and what helped them to quit. According to Rustin (1996), most smokers that he surveyed stopped for personal reasons ("cigarettes became too expensive" or "my family wanted me to quit"), not because they were afraid of developing medical problems.

See if that matches up with the people you know who quit smoking. Also, see what you can find out regarding the possible side effects of or adverse reactions to Chantix and Zyban. Given those side effects, would you still recommend either one to your clients or friends?

With regard to the psychological impact of smoking, as mentioned earlier, many smokers indicate that smoking relaxes them or reduces stress; however, research by Parrott (1994, 1999) suggests that since nicotine is a stimulant it actually increases anxiety and stress levels. It is not uncommon (once detoxified from nicotine) for ex-smokers to report that they feel more relaxed. Also smoking tends to increase feelings of fatigue and appears to disturb sleep patterns (Hicks et al., 2003).

INHALANTS AND STEROIDS

Both inhalants and steroids are somewhat unique from the other substances presented thus far in this chapter. Inhalants are unique because they have one route of administration, that is, inhalation, and steroids are unique because generally they are not abused for mood-altering purposes but rather for athletic performance enhancement or appearance enhancement. Both substances, therefore, tend to have a distinctive group of users. For example, inhalants tend to be popular among younger adolescents (average age of inhalant users is 13 years) as well as Native American youth (Anderson & Loomis, 2003; Beauvais et al., 2002), whereas steroid abusers tend to be comprised of athletes and body-builders as well as police and correctional officers.

Although inhalant use was said to be around for decades, it was not until the 1950s and 1960s that glue-sniffing became popular when a Detroit newspaper ran an article that was intended to warn parents of the dangers of model-airplane glue-sniffing. Unfortunately, the article was said to have piqued curiosity about glue-sniffing and subsequently resulted in an increase in use. Epidemiological surveys indicate that only about 4% of adolescents who use inhalants are dependent or continuous users (Brust, 2004). Generally, as younger adolescents mature, they tend to have access to a wider variety of mood-altering substances and therefore move on from inhalant use to other substance use (perhaps with the exception of "dry" periods when these other drugs are unavailable).

Methods of Inhalant Use

There are several ways in which inhalants are used. *Sniffing or snorting* refers to direct inhalation from a container, as is the case with helium (inhaled from balloons) or nitrous oxide (inhaled directly from whipped-cream cans). *Bagging* refers to instances where the inhalant is poured into a plastic bag (e.g., lighter fluid or gasoline) and then inhaled by placing the bag over one's mouth. *Huffing* refers to instances where the inhalant is poured onto a rag and the rag is then placed over one's mouth (Anderson & Loomis, 2003; Nelson, 2000). Inhalants are absorbed rapidly into the bloodstream through the lungs and take effect within 5–15 minutes. Inhalants are lipid soluble (similar to cannabis) and therefore tend to be stored or deposited in fat cells throughout the brain and body where they are stored for lengthier periods (days, weeks, or months depending on the amount and frequency of use).

Types of Inhalants

Look under your kitchen sink or wander around your garage and chances are you will come across a variety of mood-altering inhalants. Aliphatic hydrocarbons includes volatile substances such as propane, butane, gasoline, cigarette-lighter fluid, model glues, and rubber cement. Alkyl halides include trichloroethane and trichlorofluromethanes such as dry-cleaning chemicals, degreasing agents, and spot removers. Aromatic hydrocarbons include benzenes, toluene, xylenes such as refrigerants (e.g., freon), aerosol propellants (e.g., hairsprays and spray deodorants), resins, lacquers, paint strippers, and varnishes. Nitrites such as butyl and amyl nitrate ("poppers") include inhalants such as adhesives, spray paints, glues, wood glues, and paint thinners. Many inhalant users are aware that gold and silver spray paints (often inhaled via bagging) are more powerful because of their higher concentrations of toluene propellants. Finally, ester ketones include acetones and butanones such as air fresheners, nail-polish removers, paints, and solvents.

Inhalant Metabolism and Pathological Effects

The long-term effects of inhalant use tend to be serious and potentially long lasting. Unlike alcohol, the human body is not equipped to efficiently metabolize inhalants (Pandina et al., 2013). Once metabolized or broken down by the body, inhalants are excreted or eliminated through the lungs, kidneys, or liver.

The intoxication effects of inhalants are very similar to the intoxication effects of alcohol in terms of the euphoria, the slowing of motor activity, lack of coordination, disinhibition, and ringing in the ears. Pathological physical effects include neurological problems, for example, cerebral atrophy (loss of gray matter of the brain) and enlargement of cerebral ventricles (spaces in the brain) and interference with brain development (Brouette & Anton, 2001; Cairney et al., 2002; Lubman et al., 2008; Meggs, 2003). Approximately 50% of deaths resulting from inhalant use are the result of ventricular fibrillation or what is commonly referred to as *sniffing death syndrome.*

The pathological psychological impact of inhalants includes impaired cognitive functioning (e.g., attention deficits, slowed information processing, decreased IQ, and memory loss). Other impairments include apathy and depressive affect, which in some clients can also be long term (e.g., Brouette & Anton, 2001; Yücel et al., 2008).

Steroids

While there are many medical uses of steroids (e.g., to reduce inflammation and to promote muscle growth), they are also known as appearance- and performance-enhancing drugs (APEDs). Steroids are chemically synthetic hormones that fall within two main categories, anabolic (refers to muscle tissue growth) and androgenic (refers to hormonal or masculinization effects). Steroids come in both oral and injectable forms. Individuals using steroids for APED purposes usually use them in cycles, often referred to as "stacking" (i.e., taking oral and injectable steroids simultaneously) and "pyramiding" (i.e., starting off with low doses of steroid but increasing over time, followed by tapering). "Doping" refers to steroid use to increase athletic performance (e.g., Olympic athletes or professional baseball or football players). Unlike other substances, steroids are usually not taken for their mood-altering effects. Yet individuals using steroids as APEDs do risk developing psychological dependency (Kanayama et al., 2009) and often experience tremendous anxiety over stopping steroids.

Steroid Metabolism and Pathological Effects

Steroids are metabolized or broken down by the liver, hence most of the pathological physical effects are those resulting in elevated liver enzymes. Also, long-term steroid cycling can result in hormonal impacts on both men (e.g., lowered sperm count and breast enlargement) and women (e.g., increase in body hair, enlargement of the clitoris, and other masculinization effects).

The main psychological effect is increase in aggressive behavior, especially in males. Commonly known as "roid rage," men will often experience explosive outbursts of anger that can result in legal and interpersonal problems. It is hypothesized that "roid rages" and aggressive behaviors are more likely during periods of tapering. Also, for those using steroids for APED purposes, there are difficulties encountered when trying to come off of steroids. Often there are anxieties about muscle-mass loss and accompanying loss of self-esteem or a loss of sense of well-being (Pandina et al., 2013).

LEVEL OF CARE AND PATIENT PLACEMENT: THE *ASAM-3*

The *ASAM-3* patient placement criteria provides an objective means to determine the safest level of care for individuals experiencing SUDs (Mee-Lee, 2013). The *ASAM-3* was developed specifically to provide objective patient placement criteria (applicable to both adolescents and adults). The *ASAM-3* utilizes a 2-axis grid consisting of 6 client dimensions (by which counselors assess their clients) on the horizontal axis and 10 levels of care on the vertical axis ranging from Early Intervention to Medically Monitored Intensive Inpatient Treatment. The 6 client dimensions are

1. **Acute Intoxication and/or Withdrawal Potential** (assess whether the client is currently under the influence of alcohol or substances or if there is a possibility the client might experience substance-specific withdrawal symptoms);
2. **Biomedical Conditions and Complications** (assess whether the client reports having any current medical problems, e.g., diabetes, respiratory illnesses, or other medical conditions that would need to be addressed if they client enters a SUD treatment program);
3. **Emotional, Behavioral, or Cognitive Conditions and Complications** (assess how the client is coping emotionally; are they able to think logically/rationally, do they exercise sound judgments, do they have insight into ways in which their SUD is interfering with their functioning?; and determine if there might be a co-occurring mental health condition);
4. **Readiness to Change** (assess if the client express ability, need, reasons, or desire to change substance use. Assess client's stage of change: Precontemplation, Contemplation, Determination, Action, Maintenance);
5. **Relapse, Continued Use, or Continued Problem Potential** (if client is currently abstinent, assess whether they are prone to relapse. Assess whether client express intentions to continue substance use or if there are continuing legal, social, or occupational problems that place this client at risk for continued use or relapse);
6. **Recovery/Living Environment** (assess whether client has support from family or significant others. Also assess whether client lives in an area in which substances are available and ever present).

Based on the counselor's assessment of these six biopsychosocial dimensions, determinations can be made as to the best level of care or treatment. For example, if a client being screened is clearly under the influence of alcohol or other substances and is at risk for withdrawal, then Dimension 1, Acute Intoxication and/or Withdrawal Potential, indicates that a hospital or a residential/inpatient program that provides medical monitoring is the safest level of care. Similarly, if this same client has medical complications (such as high blood pressure or diabetes), they would need to be referred to a residential program that offers medically supervised detoxification (see Level 3.7).

The *ASAM-3* specifies 10 levels of care ranging from the least restrictive/least intensive to most restrictive or most monitored treatment. Let us take a moment to review each level of care.

Level 0.5: Early Intervention is targeted for individuals who are considered at risk for developing a SUD, but at the time of screening there is not enough information to diagnose a SUD or the client does not meet the *DSM-5* criteria to diagnose a SUD (American Psychiatric Association, 2013). This level of care would also be best suited for those who are ambivalent about change or may not be aware or able to admit that their substance use is creating problems in functioning (i.e., Precontemplation stage).

Level 1: Outpatient Treatment includes a variety of addiction counseling modalities, for example, individual, group, family, and couples counseling, which often take place on a once-a-week type of schedule. Level 1 treatment may be offered to individuals (including those with co-occurring disorders), who are at the beginning of their recovery and for those who are uncertain if they have a SUD. This would include clients who present as having reasons to change but also have reasons to continue their substance use (i.e., Contemplation stage). Level 1 treatment is also appropriate for clients who have successfully completed an inpatient program or intensive outpatient (IOP) treatment program and are ready to step down to a less intensive level of care.

OTP-Level 1 encompasses opioid treatment programs (OTPs) or medication-assisted treatments (MATs) such as methadone or buprenorphine (i.e., Suboxone) programs. OTPs take place on an outpatient basis where clients may receive medication on a daily basis and then, once stabilized, are seen less often while provided with "take-home" doses to self-administer at home. OTP-Level 1 treatment would not be appropriate for clients experiencing severe withdrawal (ASAM-Dimension 1) or concurrent medical problems (ASAM-Dimension 2).

Level 2: Intensive Outpatient (IOP)/Partial Hospitalization Services is also a level of care that is recommended when a client is living at home or perhaps in a sober living facility (SLF). This level of care consists of multiple treatment contacts throughout the course of a week. IOP or partial hospital (PH) programs usually offer daytime, evening, and weekend tracks that allow clients to work or attend school. Whereas IOP programs usually meet 3 or 4 days a week, PH programs meet 5 days a week for 8 hours or more per day. Some IOP and PH programs are able to meet the complex needs of individuals with SUDs as well as those with co-occurring mental health disorders. Although group counseling is the primary treatment modality offered, these groups are often supplemented with individual, couples, and family sessions as needed. Level 2 IOP/PH programs are most often appropriate for individuals who are able to maintain abstinence and are not experiencing withdrawal (ASAM-Dimension 1). In addition, IOP/PH clients are not experiencing any co-occurring medical problems (ASAM-Dimension 2) or a severe mental health conditions (ASAM-Dimension 3).

Level 3: Residential/Inpatient Services is a more intensive level of care designed to treat individuals for whom outpatient treatment would not be adequate. *ASAM-3* Level 3 is appropriate for clients who need a structured live-in or residential program where clients can be closely monitored and abstinence is guaranteed. There are four sublevels of care under *ASAM-3* Level 3 that include *Level 3.1*: Clinically Managed Low Intensity Residential Services, *Level 3.3*: Clinically Managed Population-Specific High Intensity Residential Services, *Level 3.5*: Clinically Managed High Intensity Residential Services, and *Level 3.7*: Medically Monitored Intensive Inpatient Services. To further delineate these four Level 3 programs, Level 3.1: Clinically Managed Low Intensity Residential would include halfway houses and supported living environments where addiction counselors are present and individual, group, and family counseling occurs; however, clients might also be working or going to school. Level 3.3: Clinically Managed Population-Specific High Intensity Residential would include residential program for individuals with co-occurring disorders or programs for individuals with SUDs plus traumatic brain injuries or other medical conditions and would include SUD programs offered within veteran's hospitals. Level 3.5: Clinically Managed High Intensity Residential Services are designed to serve individuals with SUDs so severe that they are unable to function in society because of continual dangerous substance use, antisocial behavior, or serious, chronic mental health disorders (e.g., schizophrenia, bipolar disorder, and major depression). Level 3.5 programs would therefore include long-term therapeutic community-types of programs and co-occurring disorder residential programs for individuals with severe mental illness. Level 3.7: Medically Monitored Intensive Inpatient Services would include SUD programs that are sometimes housed within hospitals or acute medical care facilities that serve individuals who are experiencing severe withdrawal, which requires medical monitoring (Dimension 1) or individuals who are experiencing significant medical problems (Dimension 2) such as hypertension, diabetes, asthma, or a chronic pain condition that would preclude them from being treated in a traditional SUD residential treatment setting. Medical monitoring includes facilities where nursing staff or physicians' assistants are present to monitor the client's physical condition and where a physician would be on call for emergencies.

Level 4: Medically Managed Intensive Inpatient Services would also take place in acute care general hospitals, acute psychiatric hospitals, or a psychiatric unit within a medical center or an addiction treatment specialty hospital that includes acute care medical and nursing staff being present 24 hours a day, 7 days a week. This type of program is designed for individuals with severe risk of withdrawal (*ASAM-3*, Dimension 1) and for individuals with medical conditions that require 24-hour medical monitoring (*ASAM-3*, Dimension 2; Mee-Lee, 2013). As mentioned earlier, one of the overriding principles in determining an appropriate level of care is to start with the least restrictive treatment environment and, if necessary, to recommend more restrictive/intensive treatment. Therefore, counselors may begin with recommending an outpatient (Level 1) or IOP program (Level 2), and if the client is not making progress then a residential program (Level 3.1) might be more appropriate. Another important consideration is that as clients are moving from more-intensive treatments (e.g., Level 3.1: residential treatment) to less-intensive treatments (e.g., Level 1: outpatient), appropriate aftercare treatment is provided seamlessly.

It should be noted that these levels of care represent the ideal when it comes to placing patients in appropriate treatment programs. More often, treatment decisions are made on the basis of availability or whether the patient's insurance coverage (or lack thereof) will cover the cost of treatment. In rural areas, levels of care/treatment programs may be more limited, thereby making referrals to appropriate levels of care more difficult.

TREATMENT MODALITIES

While the *ASAM-3* provides some information regarding various levels of treatment that are common used for treating SUDs, there are some levels of care that are not included in the *ASAM-3* (Mee-Lee, 2013), such as halfway houses and SLFs. The *ASAM-3* does provide rather detailed descriptions of both medically monitored and nonmedical detoxification programs as well as traditional outpatient, IOP, and partial-hospitalization and residential-treatment programs (with detoxification and residential programs being the most intensive and most restrictive). Traditional outpatient counseling usually consists of once-a-week counseling sessions that last approximately 50 minutes per session. Outpatient counseling may consist of individual, group, couples, and/or family counseling. Whereas IOP programs usually rely on group counseling as the main treatment approach, IOP programs also offer individual and couples/family counseling. IOP programs usually require that clients are seen at least 3 or 4 times a week usually for 3-hour sessions; PH programs usually meet daily Monday through Friday from 9 to 5 pm. Some PH programs offer weekend and evening sessions. PH programs also rely on group counseling as their main treatment approach; however, those programs also offer individual, couples, and family sessions.

Halfway-house programs usually are recommended for those individuals who have completed residential SUD treatment but are not yet ready to return home or when the client's home environment is not conducive to or supportive of their sobriety. Similar to residential programs, the client fully resides at the halfway house; however, instead of being in counseling groups all day, clients are expected to work or go to school during the day and return to the halfway house in the evening where they participate in relapse-prevention-oriented counseling groups or will attend 12-step meetings. Counselors are on site and available all day, everyday to make certain that clients are following the rules of the program and are actively working on their recovery.

SLFs and Oxford houses are homes where recovering individuals live and share living expenses; however, there generally is no formal treatment that takes place at the home. Usually, SLFs and Oxford houses are gender-specific, and there may be anywhere from 4–7 men or women living in the home at one time. A house manager (usually someone with established recovery) oversees that home and makes certain that residents are living by the rules of the house. For example, residents are required to maintain abstinence (as a condition of their being allowed to live there) and participate in daily chores. Any formal treatment (such as attending outpatient counseling or IOP/PH) would take place outside of the SLF or Oxford house. Most often, SLFs and Oxford houses are situated in residential neighborhoods, and more often than not next door neighbors might not even be aware that a SLF or Oxford house is in their neighborhood.

CASE-MANAGEMENT CONSIDERATIONS

Case management refers to a collaboration of process and planning on behalf of a client that is designed to promote client wellness. Case-management functions involve assessment, planning, facilitation, care coordination, evaluation of plan, and client option advocacy (Greenwood, 2021). In some larger SUD treatment programs, case managers serve a specified role that differs from that of addiction counselors. While counselors are responsible for collaboratively coming up with a treatment plan and implementing that plan, a case manager would be responsible for making sure the client is receiving necessary services. The following case examples illustrate case-management functions.

CASE EXAMPLE: SHOWANDA

Showanda is 27 years old and is currently attending a medication-assisted treatment (MAT) program where she receives daily methadone maintenance doses in order to help with her opioid use disorder (OUD). She started the MAT program 8 months ago, and so far she feels it has helped her to stabilize and to "get her life back." Showanda had a 5-year history of opioid use, and she indicates that she was "sick and tired" of living on the streets. When Showanda arrived at

(*continued*)

the MAT clinic this morning, the dispensing nurse noticed that she seemed unsteady on her feet, had bruises on her face, and that her speech was somewhat incoherent. When the nurse asked what happened, Showanda indicated she had gotten into a fight with her roommate, who punched Showanda in the head. The nurse felt it was medically necessary to have Showanda checked out in the emergency department (ED) of the local medical center and that she be medically cleared before receiving her methadone. A friend of Showanda's who drove her to the MAT clinic offered to drive her to the ED. Two hours later, Showanda returned from the ED with a medical clearance indicating that her shoulder injury had been evaluated and treated.

Case-Management Issue: In this case, it was assumed that Showanda would have been able to tell the ED physician and nurses that she had been suffered a head injury in the fight. However, instead, Showanda complained that her shoulder had been injured, and that is what the ED assessed and treated her for. From a case-management perspective, the dispensing nurse at the MAT clinic should have called the ED to let them know why Showanda was being referred and to express concerns over a possible head injury. It would have been helpful for Showanda to be transported by emergency medical technicians as opposed to her friend driving her (Collins & Kleber, 2004; Collins et al., 2005).

CASE EXAMPLE: GREG

Greg is 24 years old and has just completed a 45-day detox and inpatient program for an alcohol use disorder (AUD). He has been referred to a men's halfway house, and he plans to work in a fast-food restaurant and save money so that he can eventually transfer to a sober-living facility. He is also committed to attending Alcoholics Anonymous (AA) and Narcotics Anonymous (NA) meetings regularly to help support his recovery. Greg indicates that he had dropped out of high school in his junior year because he stopped going to class because he was "partying" just about every night with his friends. He had worked part-time in local restaurants and fast-food places mostly so that he would have money to drink and smoke pot.

Case-Management Issue: Greg has a limited employment history and limited employable skills. Once he is stabilized in his sobriety, it would be helpful to refer Greg for a vocational assessment at the State Employment Services and Vocational Rehabilitation Services. Given Greg's substance use disorder (SUD), he is eligible to receive employment and vocational training because SUDs fall under disabilities similar to mental health disabilities. Once referred to vocational services, Greg will be assessed as to his strengths and limitations and vocational interests. They will also make arrangements for him to complete his GED. Having a well-paying job in an area that Greg finds fulfilling would be helpful as Greg establishes himself as a recovering individual.

CASE EXAMPLE: CONNOR

Connor is 16 years old and has just been discharged from an inpatient substance abuse disorder (SUD) treatment program in Delray Beach, Florida, because his health insurance has run out. Connor's counselor had called his mother to make arrangements to pick him up, and Connor was told "don't drink or drug and go to [AA/NA] meetings." Connor has had a difficult relationship with his mother and older sister. They are doubtful that Connor is serious about turning his life around. In addition to Connor's history of cannabis and inhalant abuse, he also

(continued)

had experienced the trauma of his father's physical abuse. Connor's parents are divorced, and he does not have any contact with his father; however, he still holds onto the rage of having been abused for so many years and in part blames his mother for letting this go on for so long.

Case Management Issue: The lack of adequate aftercare planning is problematic, especially in residential treatment programs that are more focused on insurance reimbursement than on their clients. Once Connor's insurance ran out, he was essentially "kicked to the curb" rather than a thorough relapse prevention plan being discussed with Connor and his mother. Connor may have been referred to an adolescent halfway house rather than returning home right away. This would also have provided him more time to work through the trauma of his being physically abused by his father. Also, rather than returning to his old high school where he would get high everyday with his friends, he might benefit from being in a recovery high school.

In each of the case examples presented earlier, there were essential case-management considerations that were not adequately planned or implemented. In some instances, the lack of adequate and conscientious case-management planning can endanger clients. In Appendix 4.1, we will present other case-management considerations based on each of the substances we presented earlier in this chapter.

NOTES FROM THE FIELD

Tracy Wrocklage, MA, LPC, LCADC

Tracy has worked in a medication-assisted treatment (MAT) program for the past 16 years. She also had worked in an outpatient treatment program for 5 years and more recently has a part-time private practice. With regard to her work with opioid use disorder (OUD) clients, she feels that there just are not enough treatment resources for these clients. However, one of the most rewarding aspects of her work in MAT is being able to see clients make positive changes in their lives as a result of the stabilizing effects of being in a MAT program and participation in counseling. When asked what recommendations she has for counselors starting off, she states, "The work is rewarding but can be emotionally challenging, so it is imperative to have healthy ways to take care of yourself."

NOTES FROM THE FIELD

Susan Neshin, MD

Dr. Neshin is the medical director of Jersey Shore Addiction Services (JSAS) in Neptune, New Jersey, and has served in that role for the past 37 years! JSAS has served as a model program for primarily treating individuals with opioid use disorder (OUD). Based on her years of clinical experience, she finds, "without question, chronic opioid use results in structural and functional changes in the brain." She also finds there are often genetic predispositions to OUDs. She finds that patients with longer opioid use histories and who have a history of multiple relapses and higher scores on the Addiction Severity Index often do better with methadone than with buprenorphine (e.g., Suboxone or Subutex). She also finds that many of the same patients who benefit from methadone also have more psychiatric problems that require treatment. She finds that stigma and "self-stigma" of opioid users often prevents them from receiving necessary treatment that would address shame and trauma. She points out that the self-shame associated the OUD often interferes with patients being honest, because past honesty often resulted in punishment rather than necessary, appropriate treatment.

SUMMARY

In this chapter, we have reviewed basic information about various substances and how those substances impact individuals physically and psychologically. The second half of the chapter examines how to apply this basic information to working with clients with regard to determining appropriate levels of care and case-management challenges specific to drug type.

RESOURCES

Miller, N. S., Gold, M. S., & Mahler, J. C. (1990). A study of violent behaviors associated with cocaine use: Theoretical and pharmacological implications. *Annals of Clinical Psychiatry, 2*(1), 67–71. https://doi.org/10.3109/10400123909150009

National Institute of Alcohol and Alcohol Abuse (NIAAA): https://www.niaaa.nih.gov/ NIAAA is similarly devoted to advancing the science of alcohol and alcohol use disorders. The NIAAA website provides valuable information regarding alcohol use disorders, research, and the latest treatment alternatives, as well as a section on resources for health providers and counselors.

National Institute of Drug Abuse (NIDA): https://www.nih.gov/about-nih/what-we-do/nih-almanac/national-institute-drug-abuse-nida The mission of the National Institute of Drug Abuse is to advance the science on the causes and consequences of drug use and drug addiction. This website provides valuable information on the latest epidemiological trends, research, and treatment options available to those with SUDs and their families.

Substance Abuse and Mental Health Services Administration (SAMHSA): https://www.samhsa.gov/ SAHMSA provides an incredible amount of information for both professionals as well as concerned citizens. For counselors, there are a number of TIPs (Treatment Improvement Protocols) on topics ranging from group counseling, to women and addiction to trauma and addiction and co-occurring disorders. These TIP documents are free to download. They also provide lists of treatment centers throughout the United States. Their website also contains links to the many centers (e.g., Center of Mental Health, Center of Substance Abuse Treatment, and Center of Substance Abuse Prevention) that also are a great source of information on SUDs and mental health concerns.

KEY REFERENCES

Only key references appear in the print edition. The full reference list appears in the digital product on Springer Publishing Connect: connect.springerpub.com/content/book/978-0-8261-3586-5/chapter/ch04

Allebeck, P., & Andréasson, S. (1996). Drug induced psychosis. *The British Journal of Psychiatry, 169*(1), 114–115. https://doi.org/10.1192/bjp.168.2.135

Anderson, C. E., & Loomis, G. A. (2003). Recognition and prevention of inhalant abuse. *American Family Physician, 68*(9), 869–874, 876.

Andréasson, S., Allebeck, P., Engström, A., & Rydberg, U. (1987). Cannabis and schizophrenia: A longitudinal study of Swedish conscripts. *Lancet, 330*(8574), 1483–1486. https://doi.org/10.1016/s0140-6736(87)92620-1

Beauvais, F., Wayman, J. C., Jumper-Thurman, P., Plested, B., & Helm, H. (2002). Inhalant abuse among American Indian, Mexican American and non-Latino white adolescents. *American Journal of Drug and Alcohol Abuse, 28*(1), 171–187. https://doi.org/10.1081/ADA-120001287

Brust, J. C. M. (2004). *Neurological aspects of substance abuse* (2nd ed.). Elsevier Butterworth Heinemann.

Budney, A. J., Roffman, R., Stephens, R. S., & Walker, D. (2007). Marijuana dependence and its treatment. *Addiction Science and Clinical Practice, 4*(1), 4–16. https://doi.org/10.1151/ascp07414

Cairney, S., Maruff, P., Burns, C., & Currie, B. (2002). The neurobehavioural consequences of petrol (gasoline) sniffing. *Neuroscience and Biobehavioral Reviews, 26*(1), 81–89. https://doi.org/10.1016/s0149-7634(01)00040-9

Green, K. M., Doherty, E. E., & Ensminger, M. E. (2017). Long-term consequences of adolescent cannabis use: Examining intermediary processes. *The American Journal of Drug and Alcohol Abuse, 43*(5), 567–575. https://doi.org.10.1080/00952990.2016.1258706

Halpern, J. H., Sherwood, A. R., Hudson, J. I., Gruber, S., Kozin, D., & Pope, H. G. (2010). Residual neurocognitive features of long-term ecstasy users with minimal exposure to other drugs. *Addiction, 106*(4), 777–786. https://doi.org/10.1111/j.1360-0443.2010.03252

King, G. R., & Ellinwood, E. H. (2005). Amphetamine and other stimulants. In J. H. Lowinson, P. Ruiz, R. B. Millman, & J. G. Langrod (Eds.), *Substance abuse: A comprehensive textbook* (4th ed.). Lippincott, Williams & Wilkins.

Lubman, D. I., Yücel, M., & Lawrence, A. J. (2008). Inhalant abuse among adolescents: Neuro-biological considerations. *British Journal of Pharmacology, 154*(2), 316–326. https://doi.org/10.1038/bjp.2008.76

McDowell, D. M. (2004). MDMA, ketamine, GHB and the "club drug" scene. In M. Galanter & H. D. Kleber (Eds.), *Textbook of substance abuse treatment* (3rd ed.). American Psychiatric Press.

Meggs, W. J. (2003). Neuropsychologic impairment, MRI abnormalities, and solvent abuse. *Journal of Toxicology-Clinical Toxicology, 41*(2), 209. https://doi.org/10.1081/clt-120002883

Parrott, A. C. (1999). Does cigarette smoking cause stress? *American Psychologist, 54*, 817–820. https://doi.org/10.1037//0003-066x.54.10.817

Pollan, M. (2019). *How to change your mind: What the new science of psychedelics teaches us about consciousness, dying, addiction, depression and transcendence*. Penguin Books.

Volkow, N. D., Frieden, T. R., Hyde, P. S., & Cha, S. S. (2014). Medication-assisted therapies-tackling the opioid-overdose epidemic. *New England Journal of Medicine, 370*(22), 2063–2066. https://doi.org/10.1056/NEJMp1402780

Yücel, M., Takagi, M., Walterfang, M., & Lubman, D. I. (2008). Toluene misuse and long-term harms: A systematic review of the neuropsychological and neuroimaging literature. *Neuroscience and Biobehavioral Reviews, 32*(5), 910–926. https://doi.org/10.1016/j.neubiorev.2008.01.006

APPENDIX 4.1

CASE-MANAGEMENT ISSUES RELEVANT TO SUBSTANCE TYPE AND DIAGNOSIS

For each of the various substance types, we will now explore ways in which counselors would intervene in situations where clients are experiencing difficulties. Case management sometimes involves referral to specific levels of treatment (such as those described in the American Society of Addiction Medicine Patient Placement Criteria [*ASAM-3*] levels of care described in Chapter 4; Mee-Lee, 2013) or may include referral for specific types of services (e.g., referring a client with difficulty finding employment for vocational or career counseling). For each substance type, we will be listing the major *Diagnostic and Statistical Manual of Mental Disorders*, Fifth Edition (*DSM-5*; American Psychiatric Association, 2013) diagnoses for each substance, however, we will not be able to provide case examples for each diagnostic category.

ALCOHOL

Alcohol Intoxication: Alcohol intoxication refers to clients who have recently ingested alcohol and are currently under the influence. This would be evidenced by behaviors such as slurred speech, unsteady gait (difficulty walking), incoordination, difficulties with attention and concentration and memory, and, in extreme instances, stupor or coma. Here, the role of the counselor is to make certain the client is safe and that no harm will come to them or others. This may require having your client evaluated in an ED, especially if it is clear that they are not going to be able to make reasonable decisions on their own behalf.

CASE EXAMPLE: ALCOHOL INTOXICATION

Fran is doing her internship in a community mental health center and is waiting to see her last appointment of the evening: Tom, a 32-year-old stockbroker, who is being treated for depressive affect as a result of a recent marital separation. Tom indicated in his intake that one of the issues leading up to the marital separation was his wife's complaints about his drinking and his coming home late several evenings per week. Tom disagreed with his wife's perceptions of his drinking excessively; however, when Tom shows up for his appointment with Fran, he is unsteady on his feet and slurring his words. Fran asks Tom if he's okay and he replies, "Sure, I'm okay. I had a horrible day though. I got served divorce papers and the stock market dropped 800 pts, but other than that, I'm doing just peachy." Fran thinks she smells alcohol and asks Tom if he had anything to drink. Tom replies, "Yeah, I had a few drinks on the train." He goes on to state that he was able to drive from the train station to tonight's

(*continued*)

appointment. Fran is concerned because Tom is incoherent and is very emotional. He nods off several times during their session. Fran calls her clinical supervisor to ask what she should do.

CASE MANAGEMENT

It is important that Fran consulted with her clinical supervisor in order to come up with a safety plan. The last thing Fran wants is for Tom to get back in his car and attempt to drive home. Plus, his blood alcohol level (BAL) could be .04 or .40; there is no way of knowing what his self-report of having "a few drinks" means or even whether he is taking other drugs or medications that could cause a synergistic effect with alcohol. The safest approach would be to have Tom transported to the ED (by police or emergency medication technicians [EMTs]) where he can be assessed and observed until such time that he is deemed safe to be discharged. What if Tom refuses to go to the ED and attempts to drive home himself? In this instance, Fran would be warranted to call the police to prevent Tom from driving and possibly injuring himself or others.

Alcohol Withdrawal: Alcohol withdrawal refers to a client's condition as a result of cessation of alcohol use after a lengthy period of continuous, daily use. As indicated earlier, alcohol withdrawal is characterized by agitation, increased heart rate, blood pressure, hand tremor, and possible seizures. Because alcohol withdrawal can be life threatening, the case-management goal is to have the client evaluated for admission to an inpatient or residential program where the client can be safely detoxified.

CASE EXAMPLE: ALCOHOL WITHDRAWAL

Sandra has been working from home for the past eight months or since coronavirus 2019 (COVID-19) restrictions began. She is 25 years old and currently lives alone. Because Sandra was unable to go out to dinner and bars with her friends, they would get together for "cocktail hour" on Zoom. This went on for several months, and Sandra was soon drinking about a pint of hard liquor per evening, plus one or two bottles of wine. On weekends, she would drink more. Sandra is also diabetic, and she knows she should not be drinking this much alcohol; however, she rationalizes that, because of COVID restrictions, this is her only way "to have fun." One evening, after her usual cocktails and wine, Sandra's cell phone rings, and as she gets up to retrieve it from the kitchen counter she becomes dizzy, falls, and hits her head on her coffee table. Because she is bleeding profusely, she calls a friend, who drives her to the hospital ED. As part of the routine screening, a blood test is given that reveals a BAL of .28 and a dangerously high blood-sugar level. After a few hours in the ED, Sandra begins to become agitated, and her hands begin to shake. The ED doctor recommends that Sandra be admitted to the hospital for observation given her head injury and so that her blood sugar level can be stabilized and she can be safely detoxified from alcohol.

CASE MANAGEMENT

It is important that Sandra is admitted to an ASAM Level 4: Medically Managed Inpatient program for detox given the complicating factor of her diabetes (Dimension 2: Biomedical

(*continued*)

Conditions and Complications) and her extreme BAL (.28) and the presence of alcohol withdrawal symptoms such as hand tremor and agitation. Most likely, she will be given a benzodiazepine such as Librium to help reduce agitation and a medication to prevent seizures. When Sandra is discharged from the hospital, she should be referred to either a SUD rehab program or an intensive outpatient SUD program.

Alcohol Use Disorders (AUDs): AUDs encompass pervasive patterns of alcohol use that result in clinically significant impairment and distress that impact clients medically, socially, financially, psychologically, and sometimes legally. It is possible that someone could be diagnosed with alcohol intoxication (e.g., anyone who had too much to drink), yet this does not mean that they would necessarily have an AUD, which requires that problems consequential to drinking would occur within a 12-month period.

CASE EXAMPLE: ALCOHOL USE DISORDER

Tyrone is 47 years old and claims that he has been drinking since he was a teenager. He indicates that drinking did not become problematic until he was in college and began drinking more regularly once he was away from home living in a dorm. It was around this time that he began missing classes because of "partying" the night before and also began to experience blackouts where he could not remember things he did or conversations he had while drinking. His friends began to turn their backs on him because Tyrone would sometimes get angry and belligerent when he drank. He eventually was placed on academic probation and never returned to finish his degree. Instead, he joined the military where his drinking became worse to the point where he was court martialed for showing up to his duty station drunk. Yet despite these problems, Tyrone continued to drink. When his wife told him she was leaving if he did not seek help, Tyrone went to his commanding officer and asked to be placed on medical leave so that he could go to rehab. He feels that he will be unable to stop drinking in his current living situation.

CASE MANAGEMENT

Given the symptoms reported, Tyrone can be clearly diagnosed with an AUD. Also, given the length of time he has been drinking and the impact drinking has had on his life, an ASAM Level 3: Residential/Inpatient Services would be appropriate. Although a least-restrictive environment approach would suggest that Tyrone enter an outpatient or intensive outpatient program, Tyrone indicates that he would be unable to stop drinking in his current living situation, which apparently is not conducive to his recovery (Dimension 6 Recovery/Living Environment). Here, Tyrone indicates that all of his friends and coworkers drink with him daily. Once Tyrone completes residential treatment, it will be important that he participates in some type of aftercare counseling whether it be ASAM Level 1: Outpatient Counseling or Level 2: Intensive Outpatient. At that point, Tyrone and his outpatient counselor could discuss whether he might benefit from an anticraving medication (i.e., topiramate [Topamax], acamprosate [Camprel], or naltrexone [ReVia]).

OPIOIDS

Opioid Intoxication: Opioid intoxication is usually characterized by drowsiness or coma, slurred speech, nodding (as if ready to fall asleep), difficulty with memory and attention, constricted pupils, and dysphoric (or depressed mood). The danger with opioid intoxication is whether the client could be overdosing, in which case pupils sometimes dilate as a result of anoxia or loss of oxygen to the brain. Opioid intoxication is also considered a medical emergency whereby clients should be evaluated in an ED.

Opioid Withdrawal: Often occurs within 12–24 hours after one's last dose of heroin or prescription opiates. Although opioid withdrawal is usually not life threatening, it can be very distressing and characterized by intense muscle and stomach cramps, nausea and vomiting, diarrhea, runny nose, fever, and insomnia. Some liken it to having a really bad flu. The following is a case example.

CASE EXAMPLE: OPIOID WITHDRAWAL

Jimmy has been using heroin intravenously for the past year. He began "getting high" following a car accident after which he was prescribed Percoset for pain relief as a result of breaking three ribs and his ankle in the accident. He required three surgeries to piece his ankle back together, and following each surgery he needed more Percoset to help him sleep because he was in so much pain. Once his doctor would no longer prescribe pain medication, Jimmy found a friend who supplied him with illicit painkillers, but once those proved to be too expensive Jimmy turned to using heroin to alleviate his pain. He lives in fear of going into withdrawal, because he did try to cut down from using 6 bags a day to 3 bags but found the discomfort of withdrawal to be too great. Jimmy had nearly overdosed when he shot up a "bad batch" of heroin that had been laced with carfentanil (a powerful pain medication used mostly with large animals). As a result, Jimmy promised his parents and girlfriend that he would get help.

CASE MANAGEMENT

Given that Jimmy's history of opioid use is relatively brief, he may be a candidate for buprenorphine (e.g., Suboxone), which can be prescribed by a certified doctor on an outpatient basis (ASAM Level OTP-Level 1). Jimmy will first be given a stabilizing dose of Suboxone (usually 8 mg) that he will take for a few days, at which point the dose will be slowly reduced over the course of a week to 10 days until Jimmy is completely detoxed. Two advantages of Suboxone are that it is taken sublingually and it is also a partial agonist, which means if Jimmy were to use heroin again while taking Suboxone it would block the high of the heroin. It is also recommended that Jimmy begin outpatient counseling, preferably that he attend ASAM Level 2: Intensive Outpatient Counseling along with 12-step meetings (preferably NA meetings) on a daily basis. If Jimmy had been using heroin for a lengthier time period, he may have been more of a candidate for a dolophine (i.e., methadone) detox. Methadone detoxes usually take place over a lengthier time period (e.g., 21 days or sometimes longer); however, in order to receive methadone, Jimmy would have to attend a licensed clinic on a

(continued)

daily basis. A starting dose of methadone would usually be around 80–120 mg, which is then slowly reduced over time. Methadone is dispensed as a cherry-flavored liquid. Another opioid detoxification option (although more expensive) is what is referred to as a *rapid* or *ultrarapid opioid detoxification*. In this type of detox, Jimmy would be admitted to a hospital that specializes in this type of detox protocol where he would be given naloxone or naltrexone (an opiate antagonist) that facilitates the withdrawal response by flushing the opioids from his system. In order to prevent Jimmy from experiencing severe withdrawal symptoms, however, he would be given some type of sedation (such as clonidine). For ultrarapid detoxification, Jimmy would be placed under anesthesia while being administered naloxone or naltrexone in which instance the detoxification is completed within several hours (Collins et al., 2005). Upon discharge from the hospital, Jimmy would be encouraged to remain on naltrexone to reduce opioid craving and also encouraged to attend counseling and NA. Finally, another recent approach to reducing the distress of opioid withdrawal is transdermal stimulation. Marketed under the name S. T. Genesis, this electrical apparatus is placed behind the client's ear and periodically will dispense an electrical stimulation to the trigeminal and vagus nerves, which results in the release of endorphins (the human body's natural painkiller), thereby reducing distressing opioid withdrawal symptoms. S. T. Genesis has just been cleared for use by the U.S. Food and Drug Administration (FDA; S. T. Genesis, 2021). This type of opioid withdrawal treatment is somewhat similar to acupuncture, which has also been found to reduce the extreme distress of opioid withdrawal (Liu et al., 2009; Collins & Kleber, 2004).

Opioid Use Disorder (OUD): In the case example of Jimmy, he would certainly qualify for an OUD diagnosis, given the pervasive impact that his continuous heroin use has had on his life and his ability to function. If we were to conduct a more in-depth assessment of Jimmy, we would probably find examples where his heroin use has interfered with several aspects of his ability to function. The question is how to best help Jimmy remain opiate-free. There are several ways to accomplish this goal.

Case Management: Opioid Use Disorder

Imagine that after an attempt to detoxify Jimmy using one of the recommended procedures described earlier that Jimmy relapses to active heroin use. What are the alternatives? One alternative would be to offer Jimmy Opioid Maintenance or Substitution Therapy (ASAM OTP Level 1) or what is also known as medication-assisted treatment. Here, Jimmy could be placed on a maintenance dose of either Suboxone or methadone to help prevent craving and also to prevent him from experience a heroin "rush" if he were to inject opioids again (given the antagonist or agonist blocking effects of these medications). Individuals with OUDs that do not respond to the aforementioned measures may benefit from medication-assisted treatment. Another possibility is that Jimmy might benefit from ASAM Level 3.5: long-term residential program or therapeutic community (e.g., Phoenix House, Odyssey House, and Integrity House). Therapeutic community length of stay would usually last for about a year, followed by another 3–6 months of halfway-house treatment (ASAM Level 3.1: Low-intensity residential).

CANNABIS AND HALLUCINOGENS

Cannabis Intoxication: Given that many states have recently legalized cannabis for medical and/or recreational use, there has been an increase in ED visits among individuals who have smoked or ingested too much cannabis accidentally and are experiencing agitation and distressing symptoms. Such is the case with someone who has ingested edible cannabis and feels it is not producing a high level, so they decide to ingest more edibles.

Cannabis Withdrawal: As indicated earlier, cannabis withdrawal is non–life-threatening and is often characterized by agitation, anxiety, sometimes depressed mood, insomnia, irritability, or anger. Although an antianxiety medication might help to alleviate some of these symptoms and perhaps help the person to fall asleep, generally these withdrawal symptoms will pass within a day or two, and therefore medication is rarely prescribed. Instead, social support is more helpful to help get the person through these uncomfortable couple of days.

Cannabis Use Disorder: As with AUDs described earlier, cannabis use disorders are also characterized by a pervasive or enduring pattern of cannabis use that results in problems in several areas of life functioning, along with cannabis craving and tolerance. The following case example illustrates a client with a cannabis use disorder.

CASE EXAMPLE: CANNABIS USE DISORDER

Josh is a single, 30-year-old, high-school graduate who currently works as a bartender at a local brew-pub. He is seeking counseling because of "mood swings" and "stress." Josh reports there are times when he "feels great" yet other times when feels depressed and cannot get out of bed in the morning. He adds that he has felt this way for the past two years but finally decided to seek help. Josh mentioned that he has been smoking cannabis since he was in high school, and upon graduating he decided to move to Colorado where cannabis was legal. He also mentions that he enjoys outdoor activities like snowboarding and hiking, so Colorado seemed like a good fit. However, Josh feels like he is at a crossroads in his life. He thought he would have done more with his life in terms of having a career and a stable love relationship. He feels that his daily cannabis use has held him back by becoming the "center of life." Josh describes that he is either high or thinking about getting high. Instead of having a girlfriend, he has a group of friends that he gets high with, snowboards with, and plays video games with. He admits he has not really done much dating. He says his job is fun but unfulfilling. In high school, Josh had done really well in a drafting class and had dreams of becoming an architect, plus he has been complimented on his artistic and creative abilities, but he feels he never put his talents to good use.

CASE MANAGEMENT

Although Josh does not have a lot of social support, he does appear to be motivated to make changes in his life (ASAM Dimension 4 Readiness to Change), and he is willing to attend 12-step support groups in addition to attending counseling. In the spirit of the "least restrictive treatment environment" approach, it is recommended that Josh attend an ASAM Level 2: Intensive Outpatient program where he will attend counseling groups 3 days a week that will help reinforce his efforts to maintain abstinence from cannabis.

SEDATIVES/HYPNOTICS

Sedative, Hypnotic, Anxiolytic Intoxication: Sedatives, hypnotics, and anxiolytics result in an intoxication that is somewhat similar to alcohol, characterized by slurred speech, incoordination, unsteady gait (walking), and memory/concentration difficulties. People who are intoxicated from taking too many sedatives such as benzodiazepines should not be allowed to drive or operate machinery and should be carefully monitored in order to prevent harm to self or others.

Sedative, Hypnotic, Anxiolytic Withdrawal: Withdrawal from this group of medications is usually characterized by agitation; anxiety; restlessness; hand tremor; seizures; and, in some instances, visual, tactile, or auditory hallucinations. Again, these are the symptoms that are characteristic of alcohol withdrawal.

CASE EXAMPLE: ANXIOLYTIC WITHDRAWAL

George is 43-year-old married man and was recently admitted to the detoxification unit of a local medical center for alcohol withdrawal. His admitting physician detoxed George using Librium (to reduce anxiety and agitation) and Phenobarbital (to help prevent seizures). After a week on the detox unit, at which point George's medication was slowly titrated (reduced), he was being discharged and was walking to the elevator when he suddenly fell to the floor as a result of a grand mal seizure. When George regained consciousness, he admitted to his doctor that he also had been taking Xanax for the past five years. George was successfully detoxed from alcohol; however, he would have needed to be in the hospital much longer to be detoxified from Xanax.

CASE MANAGEMENT

Withdrawal from sedatives, hypnotics, and anxiolytics is often a complex and lengthy process. Although these detoxes are most safely accomplished while in a hospital setting (ASAM Level 4: Medically Managed Inpatient), if the client has a responsible family member who can dispense the detox medication and there are no biomedical complications (e.g., hypertension), then the detox can be done while the client remains at home. Dr. Heather Ashton from the University of Newcastle in Great Britain maintains a detailed website that describes the risks of benzodiazepine abuse and provides detoxification schedules that physicians can follow to help their patients detoxify safely (https://benzo.org.uk/profash.htm).

Sedative, Hypnotic, and Anxiolytic Use Disorder: This group of disorders is characterized by pervasive use of sedatives, hypnotics, or anxiolytics, which cause clinically significant impairment in several areas of life functioning. Symptoms include taking these prescribed medications in larger amounts or for longer periods of time than intended (e.g., someone who sets out to use a sleeping medication while going through a stressful time at work but ends up taking them for months or years) or spending inordinate amounts of time obtaining prescriptions for these medications (e.g., doctor shopping). Central to this diagnosis is that the person continues their use despite knowing that it is causing psychological, social, and interpersonal problems. Drug craving and tolerance are also central to the diagnosis. The following is a case illustration.

CASE EXAMPLE: SEDATIVE USE DISORDER

Marisela is 32 years old and has two children aged 3 and 5. She is currently separated from her husband because of his history of flying into explosive rages. Marisela also works full time at a local bodega. When she began to experience dizzy spells, her primary care doctor understood that she was experiencing a great deal of stress and had prescribed Klonopin (a benzodiazepine) to help reduce her stress levels. At first, Marisela felt the medication really helped to reduce her anxiety; however, she soon found that she needed to take double the dosage to help her relax. Marisela was also taking additional Klonopin after getting into arguments with her husband. There were several times when Marisela would attempt to cut down on how much she was using but was unsuccessful. Knowing that she was going to run out of Klonopin, she went to an walk-in emergency medical clinic to get another prescription; this time she was prescribed Xanax. When she went back to her primary care doctor to get her prescription renewed several weeks prior to her renewal date, her doctor suggested she see a counselor who would work with her on stress management skills.

CASE MANAGEMENT

Marisela has many of the classic symptoms of a sedative/anxiolytic use disorder. This is what would be referred to as an *iatrogenic addiction* (i.e., when the treatment results in addiction). Iatrogenic addictions are common when physicians prescribe this group of medications as well as pain analgesics. Not all patients develop addictions when taking sedatives, hypnotics, or anxiolytics; however, as mentioned earlier, the current thinking is that these medications should only be prescribed for short-term use. Marisela's counselor will first focus on working with her prescribing physician to slowly cut down on the amount of Klonopin that she is using according to a schedule such as that recommended by Dr. Ashton. While doing so, her counselor will begin to work with Marisela on reducing her stress by using breathing techniques, progressive muscle relaxation, and mindfulness techniques.

COCAINE AND STIMULANTS

Stimulant Intoxication: Clients who are currently using cocaine and other amphetamine-type stimulants (ATSs) often present with symptoms of agitation, restlessness, and sometimes confusion. Most of the symptoms tend to be physical in nature, for example, irregular heartbeat, high blood pressure, dizziness, nausea or vomiting, sweats or chills, dilated pupils, chest pains, and sometimes seizures. For this reason, many clients will need to be evaluated by a medical professional and may be prescribed a sedative or anxiolytic medication for a couple of days to help reduce their anxiety and agitation. There are instances where clients have been known to experience fatal heart attacks or strokes as a result of stimulant overdose, which is why medical evaluation is important. In milder forms of stimulant intoxication, observation and support are the most helpful.

Stimulant Withdrawal: Remember, the withdrawal effect of most substances is opposite to the intoxication effect, therefore the withdrawal from cocaine and stimulants is characterized by "crashing" or depressive-type symptoms (e.g., drowsiness, fatigue, insomnia or hypersomnia, and increased or decreased appetite). Stimulant withdrawal is usually not life threatening. Unfortunately, antidepressants are usually not helpful in lessening the impact of stimulant withdrawal. Given that many antidepressants take several weeks to begin to work, most clients will have totally detoxed by the time the antidepressants begin to take effect.

Stimulant Use Disorder: The following is an actual case that was reported in the *New York Times* in 2013 that presents the tragic story of Richard Fee, a young, multitalented college student who began using prescribed amphetamines to enhance his academic performance (Schwarz, 2013).

CASE EXAMPLE: AMPHETAMINE USE DISORDER

Richard Fee, a gifted student athlete and aspiring medical student, graduated from college with a pre-med degree and in 2009 had moved back home with his parents to study for the MCAT exams. While in college, Richard had occasionally taken Adderall to help him study for final exams or write term papers, so when he began studying for the MCATs he figured that Adderall would help boost his grades. Stimulants such as Adderall and Ritalin are traditionally used to treat ADHD; however, within the past decade or so, these ATSs have been used by college students to boost their academic performance. What steroids are to athletic performance, stimulants are to academic performance. Richard had gone to a local mental health clinic and was assessed as having ADHD, at which point he was prescribed Adderall. Unfortunately, he continued to increase his dosages and frequency of use, believing that the medication would help him achieve higher MCAT scores. His use increased to the point where, in 2011, Richard had to be hospitalized for delusional behavior. His parents pleaded with his doctor to stop prescribing Adderall, yet Richard was given another 90-day supply. Right around the time that prescription ran out, Richard hanged himself in the closet of his parents' home (Schwarz, 2013).

CASE MANAGEMENT

Approximately 14 million prescriptions of ATSs are prescribed each month in the United States. For children, adolescents, and adults who are diagnosed with ADHD, these medications are vital to their everyday functioning whether it be academically, occupationally, or socially. The case of Richard Fee presents a tragic instance where these ATS medications were abused and contributed to a SUD.

INHALANTS

Inhalant Intoxication: As indicated earlier, inhalant intoxication is similar to that of alcohol intoxication; therefore, the same precautions should be taken when managing clients who are under the influence of inhalants. However, inhalant withdrawal is not a diagnosis included in the *DSM-5*. Yet, given the propensity of inhalants to slowly metabolize, they can remain stored in the body and brain for up to several months, which often creates many cognitive difficulties such as memory and concentration difficulties.

Inhalant Use Disorder: An inhalant use disorder would be characterized by a pervasive pattern of inhalant use that results in a plethora of life-functioning problems. As the criteria for inhalant use disorders are the same as with other SUDs, the types of problems seen with individuals with inhalant use disorders would be similar, except keep in mind that the majority of inhalant users are young adolescents and young Native Americans, two groups that are extremely vulnerable to the impact of these powerful chemicals.

CASE EXAMPLE: INHALANT USE DISORDER

Bobby is 13 years old and lives with his grandparents on the Tribal lands of the Lakota nation on the Pine Ridge reservation in South Dakota. Bobby's parents had divorced when he was 3 years old, at which time his mother left the reservation to live in Missouri with her new boyfriend. Bobby's maternal grandparents assumed custody of Bobby, who would only hear from his mother on his birthday. Bobby has struggled in school and does not really see much of a future for himself; however, he was well liked by his teachers and got along well with his classmates. One of Bobby's best friends introduced him to huffing acetone and varnish as an inexpensive way to get high. At first, they would get high occasionally after school, but since there was not much to do during the winter months, they began getting high daily. Bobby began to fail all of his school subjects and would become belligerent and aggressive with his teachers and his grandparents. The school suggested that Bobby be evaluated by a counselor.

CASE MANAGEMENT

Because of Bobby's abrupt change in behavior and attitude, the counselor who evaluated him was able to discern that Bobby was using drugs, specifically inhalants. Having seen problems with inhalants in their community, the counselor recommended that Bobby enter a residential treatment program for adolescents that had experience in treating inhalant use disorders. Bobby was admitted to the program for 6 months. Upon returning home to live with his grandparents, Bobby continued in counseling both at school and at a local mental health and substance use disorder treatment clinic.

TOBACCO

Tobacco Withdrawal: Withdrawal symptoms usually begin within 24 hours of smoking and are characterized by symptoms such as irritability, anger, frustration, insomnia, depressed mood, concentration difficulties, restlessness, and anxiety. If untreated, many smokers will resume smoking or tobacco use to alleviate these distressing symptoms. Withdrawal can be alleviated by administering nicotine replacement products such as nicotine gum (e.g., Nicorette) and/or nicotine transdermal patches (Nicoderm). In addition, there are a variety of nicotine nasal sprays, inhalers, and lozenges (U.S. Department of Health and Human Services, 2016). With the use of transdermal patches, instructions are provided for how to titrate or lessen the amount or dose of nicotine being absorbed into the bloodstream over the course of a few weeks until abstinence is achieved.

Tobacco Use Disorder (TUD): The *DSM-5* criteria for TUD (American Psychiatric Association, 2013) is identical to the other substance use disorders presented in Chapter 4. This is sometimes confusing to a layperson because generally people do not associate tobacco use with having the same type of profound mood-altering effects that alcohol, stimulants, or cocaine would have. The main consideration in treating TUDs is, once detoxified, how to help your client maintain abstinence. As American author Mark Twain once said, "Stopping smoking is easy. I have done it thousands of times." There are several behavioral techniques that can be used to help smokers maintain abstinence (Rustin, 1996). Also, there are oral medications that help clients to alleviate cravings. Medications such as varenicline (Chantix) and buproprion (Zyban or Wellbutrin) can be helpful adjuncts to help alleviate cravings to smoke.

One of the astounding things about TUD is that although tobacco kills more Americans that just about all other drugs combined, there are fewer treatment options, and what treatment options exist are all entirely outpatient. If you were to have a client who smokes upwards of two packs of cigarettes a day and they were to request inpatient treatment as a way to break their smoking addiction, it would be nearly impossible to have them admitted to an inpatient program. Health insurance companies will generally not pay for smoking cessation treatment, yet this is an area where smoking cessation will prevent other medical conditions that may require more costly medical interventions down the road.

CASE EXAMPLE UTILIZING *ASAM-3* CRITERIA

CASE EXAMPLE: TIFFANY

Tiffany is a 23-year-old female who currently works part time as a hairdresser at a local salon. She was referred for a SUD screening following an incident in which she was arrested for prostitution. Tiffany denies that she soliciting an undercover police officer for sex but does admit that she has been using opioids and cocaine (which was verified by a urine drug screen that Tiffany had submitted as part of this evaluation). She indicates that she has been using prescription opioids (hydromorphone or Dilaudid), which she had obtained from her aunt, who had been prescribed the pain medication after being in a car accident. When her mother had discovered that Tiffany had been stealing her aunt's prescription, she threw Tiffany out of the house, and since that time Tiffany has been staying with an older man who supplies her with drugs in exchange for sex. Tiffany's job at the hair salon does not provide her with enough money to get her own apartment. She has applied at other hair salons but has not been able to find work. Tiffany indicates that she has been using hydromorphone daily and has been using it intravenously. Her last use was 4 hours ago, and she reports that she is experiencing some mild withdrawal symptoms; however, she knows she will experience severe withdrawal if she goes without using for another 3 hours.

ASAM-3 Criteria

Dimension 1 (Intoxication/Withdrawal Potential)

Dimension 2 (Medical Conditions/Complications)

Dimension 3 (Emotional/Behavioral/Cognitive)

Dimension 4 (Readiness to Change)

Dimension 5 (Relapse/Continued Use Potential)

Dimension 6 (Recovery/Living Environment)

What is your level-of-care recommendation for Tiffany given the information provided?

REFERENCES

American Psychiatric Association. (2013). *Diagnostic and statistical manual of mental disorders* (5th ed.). https://doi.org/10.1176/appi.books.9780890425596

Collins, E. D., & Kleber, H. D. (2004). Opioids: Detoxification. In M. Galanter & H. D. Kleber (Eds.), *Textbook of substance abuse treatment* (pp. 265–289). American Psychiatric Publishing.

Collins, E. D., Kleber, H. D., Whittington, R. A., & Heitler, N. E. (2005). Anesthesia-assisted vs. buprenorphine or clonidine-assisted heroin detoxification and naloxone induction: A randomized trial. *Journal of the American Medical Association, 294*(8), 903–913. https://doi.org/10.1001/jama.294.8.903

Liu, T. T., Shi, J., Epstein, D. H., Bao, Y. P., & Lu, L. (2009). A meta-analysis of acupuncture combined with opioid receptor agonists for treatment of opiate-withdrawal symptoms. *Cellular and Molecular Neurobiology, 29*(4), 449–454. https://doi.org/10.1007/s10571-008-9336-4

Mee-Lee, D. (Ed.). (2013). *The ASAM Criteria: Treatment criteria for addiction, substance-related and co-occurring conditions* (3rd ed.). American Society of Addiction Medicine.

Rustin, T. A. (1996). *Keep Quit: A motivational guide to a life without smoking. Quit and stay quit: National Smoking Cessation Program.* Hazelden Publications.

Schwarz, A. (2013, February 2). Drowned in a stream of prescriptions. *New York Times.* https://www.nytimes.com/2013/02/03/us/concerns-about-adhd-practices-and-amphetamine-addiction.html

S. T. Genesis. (2021). *S. T. Genesis opioid addiction device highlighted on "Minding Your Business."* https://njbia.org/s-t-genesis-opioid-addiction-device-highlighted-on-minding-your-business

U.S. Department of Health and Human Services. (2016). *Using nicotine replacement therapy.* National Institutes of Health, National Cancer Institute. https://smokefree.gov/tools-tips/how-to-quit/using-nicotine-replacement-therapy

5

ASSESSMENT/DIAGNOSIS AND TREATMENT PLANNING

LEARNING OBJECTIVES

In this chapter, we will explore how substance use disorder (SUD) clients are assessed or evaluated in order to determine the nature and extent of their SUD. Assessment often utilizes structured interviews that help to guide the collection of relevant information. Often assessment measures are also utilized as part of the assessment process. At the conclusion of this chapter, you will be able to:

- describe the differences between screening and assessment;
- explain the main components of a biopsychosocial assessment and know how to conduct a biopsychosocial assessment;
- describe reasons why assessment measures are important as part of screening and assessment;
- employ a number of assessment measures as part of screening and assessment;
- explain the purpose and importance of test sensitivity/selectivity as well as reliability and validity;
- explain the reasons for utilizing measure that utilize both direct and indirect questions;
- describe the *Diagnostic and Statistical Manual of Mental Disorders*, Fifth Edition, criteria for rending a SUD diagnosis;
- describe how to write an effective, collaborative treatment plan;
- describe the American Society of Addiction Medicine patient placement criteria (*ASAM-3*) and how it is utilized in making level-of-care treatment decisions.

TERMS TO KNOW

biopsychosocial assessment a detailed client history that takes into account biological (e.g., genetic), psychological (e.g., sensation-seeking), and social (e.g., poverty) risk factors

cross-reactivity a term pertaining to drug screening that describes instances where a non-mood-altering substance (e.g., aspirin) is mistakenly detected on a drug screen as a drug of abuse (e.g., cocaine)

direct questions the types of questions contained on many questionnaires, tests, and inventories used to screen or assess individuals with SUDs. Direct questions include those types of questions that ask specifically about substance use and related problems, e.g. "have you ever experienced memory loss as a result of drinking?"

false negative refers to a situation whereby someone tests negative for a particular condition when in fact that person does have that particular condition

false positive refers to a situation whereby someone tests as having a condition (i.e., tests positive) when they in reality do NOT have that particular condition

gas chromatography/ mass spectrometry or GC/MS testing is considered the "gold standard" as it pertains to drug screening because it employs more accurate means of drug-screen analysis

indirect questions the types of questions on tests, inventories, and questionnaires that do not ask specifically about substance use or related problems but rather correlates of SUDs such as impulsivity or high sensation-seeking

reliability a test or questionnaire is considered reliable based on its ability to consistently measure over time and with similar participants what it sets out to measure. A test is considered reliable if it is consistent within itself across time

screening an abbreviated information-gathering or intake designed to determine if a client meets the criteria for admission into a particular treatment program or treatment regimen. For example, a screening to determine if a client meets the criteria for entry into a methadone maintenance program

social desirability refers to a person taking a test or questionnaire who wants to present themself in a favorable light. Sometimes referred to as "faking good"

structured interview a type of clinical interview in which the questions are specific and predetermined so that all questions are posed in a particular manner each and every time the structured interview is administered. The Addiction Severity Index (ASI) is considered an example of a semistructured interview

test sensitivity usually pertains to those tests that have cutoff scores. Tests with high sensitivity are able to correctly classify those who do have a particular condition (true positives), thereby lessening the possibility of false negatives

test specificity also pertains to tests with cutoff scores. Tests that have high test specificity are able to correctly classify those who DO NOT have

	a particular condition (true negatives), thereby lessening the possibility of false positives
thin-layer chromatography	refers to a type of drug screen analysis that is considered less accurate but is also less expensive and is therefore used as an initial drug screen
validity	a test or questionnaire is considered valid if it measures what it sets out to measure or is true to its purpose, thereby making the interpretations, inferences, and conclusions of the test results appropriate and meaningful

INTRODUCTION

When a client presents for substance use disorder (SUD) treatment (whether it be in an ED, an outpatient program, or a residential or rehab program), the first priority is to find out why the client is there (or their presenting complaint) and then to assess their treatment needs. This can be a challenging task depending on the client, the circumstances, and their reasons for seeking treatment. In this chapter, we will explore how to conduct a thorough assessment and will also describe why accurate assessments are important for both rendering a diagnosis and formulating treatment plans. Screening and assessments are also important for determining an appropriate level of care (e.g., medically supervised detoxification, inpatient rehab, and intensive outpatient), which will also be described in this chapter.

SCREENING VERSUS ASSESSMENT

There are many instances when SUD clients will present in crisis. This would certainly be the case if a client is brought to an ED as a result of having overdosed or because of being extremely intoxicated or because they are going into withdrawal. Needless to say, this is not the time to ask about early childhood issues or if they experienced any trauma as a teenager. Those types of in-depth questions are reserved for when counselors are conducting a more detailed biopsychosocial assessment. When clients are in crisis, the role of addiction counselors is to provide a quick yet thorough *screening* in order to determine the presenting problem and the most effective treatment recommendations or level of care. For example, does the client you are screening need to be admitted to a medical unit for detoxification for stabilization? Or do they need to be admitted to a short-term or long-term residential/rehab program? Or would the client benefit from referral to an outpatient addiction program or a program that treats both SUD and mental health disorders? To answer these questions, screenings usually focus on the following:

- **The Presenting Complaint:** Why is the client there and what symptoms are they experiencing?
- **The History Behind the Presenting Complaint:** When did the person begin using? What has the client used recently and how much? Has the the client received treatment in the past for the same condition? Are there any medical complications that need to be taken into account?

- **What Level of Treatment Is Safest and Most Appropriate:** Given the client's current condition, what level of care would be the most helpful, for example, detoxification, inpatient, intensive outpatient, or more.

The purpose of screenings is usually twofold: first, screenings are meant to determine whether a client truly manifests a SUD and second to determine whether the client meets the admissions criteria to be treated in your program or if they would be best treated at a different program that provides a different level of care. Therefore, when conducting a screening, addiction counselors are interested in the facts surrounding why the client has sought help at this particular time or the presenting complaint and the events and history surrounding that presenting complaint. However, imagine instances where clients are not able or willing to disclose information. What then? (See Learning Activity 5.1.) One thing to consider is whether you might be able to gather information from a more reliable source such as a significant other (e.g., a family member, a boyfriend, girlfriend, spouse, partner, or friend). Confidentiality regulations mandate that counselors obtain written permission (or at very least verbal or implied consent) in order to speak with significant others; however, there are exceptions to confidentiality in emergency and life-threatening situations.

Keep in mind that a screening is by no means as detailed as a biopsychosocial assessment, therefore, it may not be as definitive. An analogy would be a drug-screening test that is purchased at a pharmacy, which may not be as accurate as a drug-screening test administered by a physician or at a hospital; however, the screening test can provide valuable information.

LEARNING ACTIVITY 5.1

Imagine that you are working as an addiction counselor at a medical center ED and you are asked to see a 25-year-old woman who is extremely intoxicated, and she is rambling incoherently. She says something about "not taking her medication," but you are unable to get a straight answer from her. The hospital lab does a toxicology screen, which reveals a blood alcohol level of .28 along with benzodiazepines in her bloodstream. What would you do? What level of treatment would you recommend?

Screening: Level of Care and the *ASAM-3*

As indicated earlier, the purpose of screening is to determine the best level of care for a particular individual, given their presenting complaint and other information you have gathered pertaining to their substance use. The American Society of Addiction Medicine Criteria (*ASAM-3*; which was described in Chapter 4, Substance Use Disorders and Case Management) provides a framework or rubric for determining a level of care from which a client will derive the maximum benefit. The *ASAM-3* dimensions also provide counselors with a framework by which they write a screening evaluation. Commenting on whether a client is experiencing difficulties for each of the six dimensions provides a rationale for making a particular treatment recommendation.

In order to aid in the screening process, the Level of Care Inventory—3rd edition (LOCI-3) was developed for the purpose of assisting counselors to determine an appropriate level of care based on the *ASAM-3* criteria (Hoffmann et al., 2014; Mee-Lee, 2013). The LOCI-3 is a structured questionnaire that consists of a demographic information section, a section covering substance use and problems related to substance use, a summary of the *ASAM-3* criteria levels of care, an assessment chart that examines the six *ASAM-3* dimensions, and, finally, the level of care recommended and received. Information on the LOCI-3 can be obtained from the Change Company at www.changecompanies.net/products/?id=LO-3 or from EVINCE assessments at www.evinceassessment.com.

Biopsychosocial Assessment

The purpose of a biopsychosocial assessment is to gather more in-depth information about the client at a time when they are able to discuss their history in greater detail. In outpatient and intensive outpatient programs, this information would usually be gathered within the second or third sessions, once it has been determined that the prospective client is not in crisis or immediate danger and they can provide coherent information regarding their history. Exhibit 5.1 provides a sample of a biopsychosocial assessment form. Notice that the form begins with topics other than substance use. The reason is that it is usually better to start with less-threatening or less-contentious topics before moving into topic areas that may be more difficult to talk about. Also, it is important that counselors approach the assessment in a friendly, casual, yet professional manner. The purpose of the biopsychosocial assessment is not to catch your client in a lie, and it is also not an interrogation. Instead, this type of in-depth information gathering is more of a collaborative effort designed to gain a whole-person perspective of the client. Therefore, it is important that counselors spend time establishing rapport and helping the client feel comfortable before diving into information-collecting. There are some SUD treatment programs that utilize intake counselors who do nothing but screening and biopsychosocial assessments; however, most counselors working in outpatient mental health or SUD treatment centers will be responsible for screening and assessments that become part of the treatment process. This is a time for counselors to utilize all the counseling skills they have learned in order to make certain that clients feel comfortable in sharing their personal history. For example, it is important that counselors are empathic toward clients who may struggle to share information with someone they are meeting for the first time. Similarly, if a client is experiencing an immediate crisis or experiencing emotional distress, postpone any in-depth information gathering for another session.

The biopsychosocial assessment is an excellent way to get to know a lot about your client in a brief period of time (usually a biopsychosocial assessment takes approximately 60–90 minutes). It is important to keep in mind that some clients will be less willing to divulge personal information or history. Clients who are mandated to counseling by the courts or by an employer are usually less likely to disclose information; however, the reason why biopsychosocial assessments take a *whole person* approach is for two reasons. First, it is important to get a sense of the client's overall functioning in order to determine whether substance use has impacted their life functioning in particular areas. Second, it is important that we gather information about possible risk factors. *Risk factors* are usually evidence-based correlates of SUDs. For example, in exploring biological risk factors, we are interested in whether our client may have family members related by blood (not by marriage) who have also had struggles with SUDs. Similarly, there are mental health disorders that correlate or co-occur with SUDs, such as bipolar disorders, other mood disorders, eating disorders, attention deficit hyperactivity disorder (ADHD), and certain personality disorders, for example, antisocial personality disorder and borderline personality disorder. Many of the aforementioned mental health disorders also have genetic etiologies, therefore, it is helpful

Exhibit 5.1

BIOPSYCHOSOCIAL ASSESSMENT

Counselor: As you begin your counseling, it is important that I gather some information about your history so that I can get a more complete picture of some of the events leading up to your being here. If there are any questions that you are uncomfortable with or do not know how to answer, please let me know and move on to the next question. Once we are finished with gathering information, I will provide you with feedback on my impressions, and we will discuss what we will be doing from here. Does that sound okay to you? Before we get started, do you have any questions?

After we complete this part of our session, I will have you fill out some pencil-and-paper questionnaires that I will explain to you and that you will then take on your own. Do you have any difficulty with reading or writing? If so, would you prefer that I read the questions to you?

I. Medical History

1) Do you have any medical conditions for which you are currently receiving treatment?
2) Have you been hospitalized in the past five years? If so, why were you admitted?
3) Do you currently take any prescribed medication? If so, why are those prescribed?
4) Do you have any concerns about your health?
5) Do you have any family members who had medical problems?
6) If you have any family members who are deceased, what was their cause of death?

II. Developmental History

1) From what you were told, were there any complications when you were born?
2) From what you were told, did you begin to crawl, walk, and speak at the usual time frames (e.g., children usually take their first steps when they are about 1 year old)?
3) Did you have any illnesses as a child?
4) Were there any stressful events that occurred while you were growing up?
5) Were you accident-prone as a child?
6) Were you ever abandoned by a parent when you were growing up?
7) Were you ever verbally or physically abused as a child?
8) Did you feel safe and secure during your childhood?
9) When you were a child, did you look forward to holidays?
10) What was your happiest memory from when you were growing up?
11) Did you have many friends when you were in grammar school, middle school, or high school?
12) Did you have interests or hobbies that you enjoyed when you were a child?
13) What did you dream of becoming when you were a child?
14) If you could go back and change anything about your childhood, what would it be?

III. Educational/Occupational History

1) When you think back on your grammar-school years, what did you like best about going to school?
2) Did you recall having any difficulty or problems with any school subjects, for example, spelling, arithmetic, history, and so forth?
3) How did you get along with your teachers? With fellow students?
4) Did you have any learning problems? If so, did you participate in any evaluations?
5) Did you ever get into trouble when you were in grammar, middle or high school?
6) What is the highest grade you completed in school?
7) Did you have any problems with paying attention in class?
8) What type of work do you? Are you currently going to school?
9) Are you satisfied with your current job, and are you satisfied with your career or profession? If not, what would you rather be doing?
10) Have you ever been unemployed and, if so, for how long?
11) Do you have any current educational/training plans or things you would like to accomplish?

IV. Family History

1) Tell me something about your family growing up (e.g., something about who lived at home with you). How did everyone get along? Etc.
2) If you were having a problem, who would you turn to?
3) Who were you closest with when you were growing up?
4) How did your family resolve disagreements?
5) Did your parents show favoritism toward you or your siblings?
6) Did your parents argue? Did they argue over money problems? Other problems?
7) Did anyone in your family have any mental health problems such as problems with depression or anxiety? If so, was anyone in your family ever hospitalized?
8) When you were a teenager, did your parents experience any difficulties in allowing you more freedom? Were you rebellious as an adolescent?
9) Did you look up to or admire anyone in your family?
10) If you could change anything about your family, what would it be?

V. Psychological–Emotional History

1) Do you currently have any difficulties with anxiety, panic attacks, depression, anger, or distressing thoughts?
2) Have you experienced any emotional difficulties in the past, for example, during childhood or teen years? During adult years?
3) Do you feel you cope well with problems or that you are good at solving personal problems?

(continued)

4) Are you generally in a good mood? Do you feel you have a good sense of humor?
5) Have you ever experienced any suicidal thoughts? If so, did you ever think about how you might commit suicide?
6) Do you experience sadness during winter months? During spring or summer?
7) Would you say that you are the type of person who does not let stress get to them?
8) Do you have a good memory?

VI. Substance Use History

1) Do you have any concerns about your current use of alcohol or drugs?
2) What substances are you currently using? Most recent use?
3) How old were you when you started using alcohol or drugs?
4) Do you have a favorite type of alcohol or drug? What is it that you like most about that substance?
5) Did you ever experience a problem with controlling the amount you drink or use drugs?
6) Would you consider yourself a social or recreational drinker or drug user?
7) Would your family and friends consider you a social or recreational drinker or drug user?
8) Has your alcohol or substance use ever resulted in your getting into trouble?
9) Have there been any periods where you abstained or stopped drinking or drug use? If so, why did you quit, for how long, and what was that like for you?
10) Have you ever made any attempts to cut down your drinking or drug use?
11) Has anyone ever annoyed you by criticizing your alcohol or drug use?
12) Have you ever felt guilty about things you did or said while drinking or using drugs?
13) Have you ever taken a drink or drug in the morning in order to alleviate uncomfortable feelings caused by drinking or drug use the night before?

VII. Prior Treatment

1) Have you ever received treatment before for any alcohol- or drug-related issues?
2) If so, what type of treatment did you receive? Inpatient? Outpatient? Intensive outpatient?
3) Did you seek treatment on your own or did someone mandate that you seek help?
4) If you did receive prior treatment, do you feel it was helpful? Why or why not?
5) Have you ever gone to Alcoholics Anonymous (AA), Narcotics Anonymous (NA), or any other self-help type group?
6) If you have attended AA or NA, do you feel it was helpful? Why or why not?
7) Have you ever received any counseling for emotional problems?
8) What type of counseling do you feel would be most helpful to you at present?

VIII. Mental Status: These are your observations of your client as you are completing the biopsychosocial assessment:

Mood: Circle all that apply—overall mood was appropriate, inappropriate
friendly happy guarded sad angry
suspicious inconsistent (happy/sad/angry)
cooperative uncooperative animated flat

Behavior: Circle all that apply—calm restless agitated slow fidgety

Cognition/Thoughts Circle all that apply—logical/rational thought processes,
tangential thoughts (jumped from topic-to-topic)
irrational thoughts (did not make sense)
thoughts and speech hard to follow
short-term memory intact (have client repeat
the following numbers 2–7–3–9)
long-term memory (ask client to name four
presidents since 1960)
Ask client what today's date is.
Ask client what town/city they currently live in.

Judgement/Insight Ask client what they would do if someone started
to yell at them for pushing ahead of them in line
at the postoffice or supermarket.

Ask client why they were referred to your program.

to explore whether there is a family history of these mental health disorders. Just to be clear, we are not saying that everyone who experiences these particular mental health disorders will necessarily develop a SUD, nor are we saying that everyone who experiences a SUD will also experience one of the aforementioned mental health disorders; however, there are correlations or propensities toward these mental health disorders within individuals with SUDs that are well-documented in the research literature. Therefore, counselors need to be aware of these correlations because of the likelihood that co-occurring disorders tend to increase the risk for developing a SUD. However, it is also important to consider that, after years of alcohol or other substance use, a co-occurring mental health disorder may not surface until several months of abstinence.

There are also psychological risk factors that addiction counselors need to explore. For example, high sensation-seeking or novelty-seeking, low frustration tolerance, and anger issues as well as low self-esteem are all considered to be correlates of SUDs according to the research literature. Most notable, however, is whether your client has a history of trauma (e.g., childhood and/or adolescent physical or sexual abuse), as these also are often correlated with SUDs (e.g., Widom et al., 1999). Felitti et al. (1998) and Felitti (2017) administered the Adverse Childhood Experiences Scale to over 8,000 adults (aged 19–92) and found that individuals who had experienced adverse life events in at least two of the seven categories had a greater likelihood of developing health risk factors later in life, including SUDs. Therefore, it is important that counselors assess trauma history (see the Trauma Recovery Scale [Appendix 5.1] and the Adverse Childhood Experience Questionnaire [Appendix 5.2]).

Finally, it is also important to explore social (and sociocultural) risk factors. For example, research indicates that individuals who live in high-stress neighborhoods are often at risk for SUDs (Smith, 2020). By "high-stress" neighborhoods, we are referring to areas that are greatly impacted by crime, poverty, systemic racism, discrimination, and a lack of educational/occupational and healthcare opportunities. Although belonging to a particular racial or ethnic group does not destine one to develop a SUD, it can place a person at higher risk. For example, rates of alcohol use disorders (AUDs) tend to be higher in certain countries than others. England, Ireland, and Russia tend to have higher rates of AUDs when compared to other countries. Although it is difficult to pinpoint one reason for these differences in AUDs, we do often find distinct differences in how these various countries perceive drinking and most importantly excessive drinking. Also, if someone lives in country where alcohol or substance use is condoned (e.g., Ireland, England, and other United Kingdom countries are often referred to as "pub cultures," referring to the observation that most socialization and leisure time is spent in neighborhood pubs where people from communities gather to bond and exchange information), then it would be important to discuss how your client responds to these sociocultural risk factors (see Learning Activity 5.2).

LEARNING ACTIVITY 5.2

Take a look at the biopsychosocial assessment form which is included in Exhibit 5.1. Look through the questions and see if you can pick out questions that explore some of the aforementioned risk factors we have just presented (i.e., biological, psychological, and social).

ASSESSMENT MEASURES

When conducting evaluations of clients who present for treatment at SUD treatment facilities, it is always considered a "best-practices" approach to incorporate some type of objective assessment measure. There are several advantages to taking this approach:

1. Evaluations and diagnostic summaries are more likely to be accurate when assessment measures are included as part of the evaluation (Campbell & Fiske, 1959).
2. Assessment measures help to acquire additional information that may not be asked or covered in a biopsychosocial assessment.
3. Assessment measures provide an objective means to assess clients.
4. Assessment measures allow clients to "go on record" regarding their perceptions of problems (or lack of problems) they have experienced as a result of alcohol or drug use.

Let us say you have been asked to provide a substance use evaluation by the courts. Usually, in a situation like this, the courts request such evaluations to obtain treatment recommendations (such as level of care, e.g., inpatient, intensive outpatient, and outpatient) from someone with expertise in SUDs. While a biopsychosocial assessment is useful in obtaining information about the client, assessment measures help to provide objective diagnostic information that can then be incorporated into the written evaluation. Think about how you would explain to a client that you are going to ask them to fill out a questionnaire or some other measure as part of the assessment process. The following is an example of how counselors might introduce this to clients:

Counselor: As part of getting to know you and some of the issues you might be experiencing, I find it helpful to use questionnaires that help to gather information that we might not have time to discuss in our session. After you fill out the questionnaire, I will go over it with you to provide you with feedback. On this particular questionnaire, there are no right or wrong answers; you are simply asked to give your own opinion. Also, if you have any difficulty understanding the questions, we can go over those together. How does that sound to you? Do you have any questions or objections?

Client: That sounds okay. Will anyone see my answers?

Counselor: No, everything in your file, including these questionnaires, is confidential and therefore cannot be released to anyone without your knowledge and written consent.

We will now review some of these assessment measures.

Structured Interviews

There are several structured interviews available that go beyond a typical biopsychosocial assessment format such as that provided in Exhibit 5.1. Structured interviews are advantageous with regard to standardization and many include scoring systems that are useful when rendering a diagnosis. The most well-known semi-structured interview is the **Addiction Severity Index (ASI),** which was developed by McLellan et al. (1980). The ASI consists of 200 questions that were chosen to address seven potential problem areas that may come about as a result of substance use. The seven areas include medical status, employment and support, drug use, alcohol use, legal status, family/social status, and psychiatric status. The ASI takes about an hour to administer and gathers information pertaining to recent (i.e., past 30 days) and lifetime problems in all seven of the problem areas. The ASI is intended for use with adults, however, there is also a **Teen Addiction Severity Index** (TASI); (Kaminer et al., 1991) that has a similar structured interview format to the ASI. In addition to being utilized with individuals seeking SUD treatment, the ASI has also been used with psychiatric populations, those without homes, pregnant women, employee assistance clients, and prison populations. One of the unique features of the ASI is that it requires counselors to provide a subjective severity rating and to rate their level of confidence in the information the client has provided. The ASI yields two other scores: a severity rating, which is a subjective rating of the client's need for treatment, derived by the interviewer, and a composite score based on the seven problem areas. For the older editions of the ASI, scoring is done by hand, whereas for the newer Fifth Edition (Carise et al., 1999, 2005) there is a computer-scoring option that requires users pay a fee. Appendix 5.4 provides a sample report that might be derived after having administered the ASI to a client. As you can see, the ASI provides counselors with a great deal of information about a client, provided that the client has been forthright and honest with the counselor who administers it. Also, an online version of the ASI Fifth Edition can be found on the following website: https://addiction-severity.pdffiller.com and in Appendix 5.3. The online version of the ASI will also automatically provide scoring. Appendix 5.4 provides an example of evaluation reports derived from the ASI.

Other examples of structured interviews include the **Comprehensive Drinker Profile (CDP;** Marlatt & Miller, 1984) and the shortened version The **Brief Drinker Profile (BDP;** Marlatt & Miller, 1984). Both the CDP and the BDP provide counselors with information pertaining to a client's alcohol use and problems resulting from use. Both start off asking about demographic information (name, date of birth, age, address, etc.) as well as a few questions pertaining to family status, employment/income information, and educational history. Next, there are several questions pertaining to drinking history and alcohol-related problems, which includes the Michigan Alcohol Screening Test (MAST; Selzer, 1971). Both the CDP and the BDP are particularly adept at gathering information pertaining to quantity/frequency of alcohol use, when and where drinking takes place, drinking preferences (e.g., beer, wine, and distilled spirits), antecedents to drinking, and alcohol-related problems. Yet, these profiles are limited in that they rely on the client's recollections and their willingness to accurately self-disclose.

Finally, the **Comprehensive Addiction and Psychological Evaluation-5 (CAAPE-5®**; Hoffmann, 2000/2013) has the advantage of providing both an assessment of substance use as well as mental health problems. The substance use section of the CAAPE-5 asks questions that correspond to the 11 criteria for SUDs in the *Diagnostic and Statistical Manual of Mental Disorders*, Fifth Edition (*DSM-5;* American Psychiatric Association, 2013). For example, Criterion 2, "There is a persistent desire or unsuccessful efforts to cut down or control substance use" is addressed in CAAPE-5 question 18: "Have you ever set rules to control your drinking or drug use?" The client then responds whether they have experienced this criterion (yes or no) for alcohol, marijuana, cocaine, amphetamines/stimulants, heroin/opioids, hallucinogen/PCP, inhalants, and other drugs, and if they answered yes, the client then indicates how many times in the past 12 months have they attempted to cut down or control their substance use by responding 0, 1, 2, and 3+ times. This format is used for all 11 criteria with the exception of Criterion 3, "A great deal of time is in activities necessary to obtain the substance, use the substance or recover from its effects." Respondents are then asked the following questions: "On a typical Friday or last day of work for the week, how many hours do you spend drinking or using drugs and getting over the effects of use" and "For a typical Saturday or Sunday or two days when you do not work, how many total hours do you spend drinking or using and recovering from use?" or "When you drink or use during a typical work day, such as Monday through Thursday, how many hours would you typically spend drinking or using and recovering from use?" All of the aforementioned items correspond to Criterion 3 under SUDs in the *DSM-5* (American Psychiatric Association, 2013).

The mental health questions of the CAAPE-5 explore symptoms relating to disorders such as major depressive episodes, manic episodes, anxiety and phobias, panic disorder, posttraumatic stress, obsessions/compulsions, conduct disorders, antisocial personality, paranoid personality, schizoid personality, borderline personality, dependent personality, obsessive-compulsive personality, and psychosis indication with each mental health disorder consisting of 4 to 6 questions. Responses from both the SUD Criteria and the Mental Health Conditions section of the CAAPE-5 are then summarized. There are not particular cutoff scores, but rather counselors are able to discern whether clients meet the *DSM-5* criteria for SUDs (American Psychiatric Association, 2013); the corresponding level of severity of the SUD based on the number of criteria met and the CAAPE-5 also determine to what extent clients are distressed by the mental health conditions listed earlier. The CAAPE-5 can be found on The Change Company's website at www.changecompanies.net/products/?id=LO-3.

Questionnaires, Tests, and Inventories

There are also a multitude of questionnaires, tests, and inventories that were developed to screen and assess SUDs. Also, there are specific questionnaires, tests, and so forth that assess specific important aspects of SUDs, such as the intensity of one's alcohol/drug craving, their confidence in refusing a drink or drug, situations in which individuals may be more likely to feel tempted to use, their relapse proneness, and their readiness to change substance use behaviors. One of the limitations of using assessment measures pertains to the client's willingness to accurately self-disclose. In situations where clients are mandated for evaluation by the courts, there is a greater likelihood that they might attempt to present themselves in a more favorable light in order to avoid detection of SUD-related behaviors. Therefore, tests/questionnaires that rely solely on ***direct*** questions are at a disadvantage in being able to accurately identify those individuals who may be experiencing a pattern of risky or harmful behaviors as a result of alcohol or drug use (Fals-Stewart, 1996; Zaldívar et al., 2009). For example, tests such as the Michigan Assessment Screening Test for Alcohol and Drugs (MAST/AD; Westermeyer et al., 2004) or the Drug Abuse Screening Inventory (DAST; Skinner, 1982) are composed primarily of questions that ask directly about alcohol and/or drug use. A direct question such as "Have you ever lost a job because of drinking?" can easily be evaded by simply responding "no" to that and similar direct questions. Yet, as alluded to earlier, the advantage of direct questions is that it does allow clients to "go on record" regarding their perceptions of their alcohol and drug use and consequences of their use. In order to address the dilemma of direct questions, there are a several tests that have been developed that utilize ***indirect*** questions and/or subtle measurement scales. These indirect question measures are essentially attempting to determine SUD potential by examining evidence-based personality factors that are proven correlates of SUDs. For example, the MacAndrews Alcoholism Scale Revised (MAC-R) is composed almost entirely of indirect questions that are included within the Minnesota Multiphasic Personality Inventory-2 (MMPI-2). The MMPI-2 (Butcher, 1990; Butcher et al., 1989) is a widely known screening measure consisting of 567 true–false questions designed to assess psychiatric disorders (e.g., anxiety, mood, and thought disorders) as well as personality disorders. When the MacAndrews Alcoholism Scale was initially developed, it contained 54 items, and MacAndrew (1967) determined that a cutoff score of 24 could correctly classify 82% of self-admitted alcoholics who were administered the MMPI. The MAC-R (Butcher et al., 1989) consisted of 46 items; however, a cutoff score of 24 was still utilized. The MAC and MAC-R scales were developed using a factor-analytic method, whereby the MMPI was administered to many self-admitted individuals with AUDs and a factor analysis was employed to determine those items (when answered in a particular true–false direction) that successfully differentiated alcoholics from nonalcoholics. Examples of the indirect items of the MAC-R include the following: "I like to read newspaper articles on crime" (True); "I like to cook" (False); "I feel sad or blue sometimes" (True). As you can see, the aforementioned items have little relevance to SUD-related behaviors. Therefore, a score of 24 or greater on the MAC-R is interpreted as "indicative of a potentiality of having an AUD" given that the test-taker responded in a manner similar to individuals with AUDs.

Several of the other measures we will be reviewing also use cutoff scores that are designed to determine if one falls into the category of having a SUD or a SUD potential. The process of determining cutoff scores is an important aspect when developing an effective substance-abuse screening measure because the goal is to determine a cutoff score that possesses both ***sensitivity*** as well as ***specificity***. Sensitivity refers to the ratio of persons correctly screened as being "positive" for having a SUD or, in other words, the assessment measure is sensitive enough to correctly classify those who have a SUD (Altman & Bland, 1994). Specificity refers to the portion of individuals who are correctly identified as not having a SUD. The purpose of a cutoff score that has high sensitivity is that the measure will correctly class those who truly have a SUD, thereby minimizing false negatives, whereas the measure with high specificity will able to correctly classify those who do not have a SUD, thereby minimizing false positives (Altman & Bland, 1994). Tests that have a high degree of accuracy are considered to be ***reliable***, and although it is beyond the purpose of this chapter, there are several statistical ways to provide test reliability (e.g., test-retest reliability, split-half reliability). Tests that are true to their stated purpose are considered to be ***valid***. For example, a test such as the AUDs Identification Test (AUDIT), described in the "Alcohol Use Disorders Identification Test" section (also see Appendix 5.5), has high-face validity because the items ask direct questions that correspond to symptoms of AUDs.

There are two other measures that utilize indirect or subtle measures. They are the Substance Abuse Subtle Screening Inventory (SASSI)-4 and the Research Institute on Addictions Self Inventory (RIASI). Both the SASSI and the RIASI consist of direct questions pertaining to SUD-related problems and indirect questions that examine traits that correlate with SUDs. These measures along with others will be described in more detail in the following section.

Alcohol Use Disorders Identification Test (see Appendix 5.5)

The AUDIT was developed by the World Health Organization as a screening tool to identify harmful drinking patterns. The purpose or goal of the AUDIT is to identify AUDs as a means of providing recommendations for prevention, intervention, and treatment (Babor et al., 2019). The AUDIT is a 10-item questionnaire that covers three domains: (1) *Hazardous alcohol use,* that is, alcohol consumption including quantity/frequency, items 1–3; (2) *dependence symptoms,* for example, loss of control, need for morning drink, items 4–6; and (3) *harmful alcohol use,* or alcohol-related problems, for example, guilt over drinking, blackouts, and alcohol-related injuries, items 7–10. The AUDIT can be administered as a self-report written questionnaire or as a structured oral interview. The AUDIT is designed for use with adults and can be used in a variety of settings, for example, primary care, EDs, mental health settings, criminal justice (including DUI offender programs), and military settings, and can be used in employee assistance programs. The AUDIT is easy to score and interpret. Those taking the AUDIT are asked to respond on a Likert-type scale from 1–4 (with the exception of questions 9 and 10, which are scored on abbreviated scale of 0, 2, or 4). Given that there are 10 items, the maximum score that one can obtain is 40, while 0 is the lowest possible score. Overall scores falling between 1 and 7 are considered to be indicative of low-risk consumption, while scores of 8 to 14 are considered to be indicative of harmful alcohol consumption and scores of 15 or greater are considered to be a strong indication of an AUD.

Simple Screening Inventory for Alcohol & Other Drugs (see Appendix 5.6)

The Simple Screening Inventory for Alcohol & Other Drugs (SSI-SA) was developed by the Center for Substance Abuse Treatment (CSAT, 1994), which is part of the Substance Abuse and Mental Health Services Administration (SAMHSA). Because the SSI-SA was developed by a government entity, it falls within the public domain and can be downloaded and used without charge or copyright permission. The SSI-SA is a 16-item questionnaire (although only 14 items are used for scoring). Each of the 14 items, when answered affirmatively or "Yes," is scored as 1. Scores of 4 or greater are considered to be reason to refer clients for a full assessment. The advantages of the SSI-SA are that the measure is easily administered and scored. However, the SSA-SA is limited by relying on direct questions pertaining to alcohol and drug use and subsequent problems related to substance use.

The Michigan Assessment Screening Test for Alcohol and Drugs

The MAST/AD (Westermeyer et al., 2004) was based on the original MAST developed by Selzer (1971), which was initially used for screening DUI offenders. The MAST/AD is used with a variety of adult populations, and one of its main advantages is that it can be quickly self-administered and scored. Scores that fall between 1 and 3 are considered to be nonindicative of a SUD; however, a score of 4 is considered to be a likely indicator of a SUD. Scores of 5 or greater are interpreted as there being a greater likelihood of a more severe SUD. The advantages of the MAST and MAST/AD are that they are easily administered and can be quickly scored. The limitation of the MAST and MAST/AD is that they both are direct-questions measures, which means they are more likely to be easily faked, thereby yielding more false negatives. The MAST/AD can be accessed through Westermeyer et al. (2004).

The Drug Abuse Screening Test-20

The Drug Abuse Screening Test-20 (DAST-20; Skinner, 1982) consists of 20 items that examine substance use and problems related to substance use. The DAST was based on the earlier edition of the MAST (described in the "Michigan Assessment Screening Test for Alcohol and Drugs" section), and therefore it contains similar items. Scores are derived by adding affirmatively endorsed items (Yes responses). Scores of 6 or greater are considered to be indicative of a SUD. The DAST-20 is easily administered and scored. It is limited by its construction, which relies solely on direct questions related to substance use. The DAST-20 can be accessed at the following website: https://web.archive.org/web/20160325172655/http://projectcork.org/clinical_tools/html/DAST.html

Cannabis Abuse Screening Test (see Appendix 5.7)

The Cannabis Abuse Screening Test (CAST) was developed to screen adolescents who use cannabis (Legleye, 2018; Legleye et al., 2007). Consisting of only six questions (responded to using a five-point Likert scale), it was initially developed in France but was later translated into English for use in the United States. When the CAST was being developed, it was administered to approximately 20,000 adolescents from over 25 urban centers in France. The CAST examines cannabis use and subsequent harm or dysfunction resulting from cannabis dependence. The CAST is easily administered and scored, whereby three positive responses is considered indicative of problematic cannabis use (Sznitzman et al., 2008).

CAGE and TWEAK

The CAGE consists of four items, while the TWEAK consists of five items that can be woven into a biopsychosocial assessment or administered in written form. Both CAGE and TWEAK are acronyms. For the CAGE, the (C) item is "have you ever tried to **cut down** on your drinking," and (A) is for "has anyone ever **annoyed** you by criticizing your drinking?" The (G) asks "have you ever felt **guilty** about your drinking?" while the (E) asks "have you ever drank in the morning to relieve anxiety (i.e., withdrawal) known as an '**eye opener**.'" The CAGE was developed as a brief screening tool that would be used by physicians in primary-care settings and in EDs (Ewing, 1984). It is intended to differentiate severe AUDs from less-severe problematic drinking. Scoring is simple, where negative responses receive a score of 0 while positive or yes responses receive a score of 1. Scores of two or more are considered indicative of more severe AUDs (Ewing, 1984).

The TWEAK was developed to assess risky drinking during pregnancy (Russell, 1994; Russell et al., 1994). It consists of five items that address aspects of risky or problematic drinking. The (T) asks about tolerance, that is, the amount/quantity and frequency of drinking, while the (W) asks about significant others being worried or concerned about your drinking. The (E) asks about "eye-openers" or morning drinking to alleviate withdrawal symptoms such as anxiety. The (A) asks about amnesia, that is, has the person ever experienced a blackout or memory loss as a result of excessive drinking. Finally, the (K) asks whether the person has ever considered k/cutting down their use of alcohol. The TWEAK is scored similarly to the CAGE, however, positive/yes responses on the (T) tolerance question and the (W) worried significant others are both scored as 2, while the remaining items with positive/yes responses receive a score of 1. Scores of 2 or greater are considered indicative of harmful drinking, which would suggest the need for further evaluation (Cherpital, 1999).

Substance Abuse Subtle Screening Inventory (SASSI-4 and SASSI-A2)

The SASSI was developed by Glenn Miller in 1988. Dr. Miller was working at a federally funded program in Arizona that was tasked with assessing DUI offenders, and he saw the need for a questionnaire that would go beyond the existing screening questionnaires that relied solely on direct questions related to problematic alcohol use (Miller, 1988). The fourth edition of the SASSI (SASSI-4) consists of both direct and indirect or subtle questions. There are two Face Valid (Alcohol and Other Drugs) scales that consist of direct questions related to alcohol and other drug use and the nine subtle scales. The nine subtle scales include symptoms, obvious attributes, subtle attributes, defensiveness correctional, family versus control subjects, random answering pattern, supplemental addiction measure, and a new prescription drug scale that identifies individuals likely to be abusing prescription medications. One advantage of the SASSI-4 is that once each of the aforementioned direct and subtle scales are scored, there are nine Decision Rules that examine singular scale elevations and combinations of scale elevations to determine SUD potential. Another advantage of the SASSI is that, in addition to the Decision Rules, each scale provides counselors with information about the client. For example, a client who scores high on the Defensiveness Scale suggests that they may be in denial of substance-related problems, or the client may be attempting to present themselves in a favorable light, or the client may lack insight or awareness into how their substance use is impacting their life.

The SASSI-4 was developed for use with individuals 18 years old and older, while the SASSI-A2 was developed specifically for use with adolescents. Reliability and validity have been established for both measures. There are also audio versions of both SASSI measures for use with individuals who have reading disorders or reading difficulties. In addition, there are also Spanish versions of both measures. Information pertaining to training to administer the SASSI and purchase of test kits can be obtained via the following website: www.sassi.com

Marijuana Craving Questionnaire (see Appendices 5.8.1 and 5.8.2)

As noted in the current *DSM-5* diagnostic criteria for SUDs, craving is considered an essential aspect of SUDs (American Psychiatric Association, 2013). The Marijuana Craving Questionnaire (MCQ; Heishman et al., 2001; Heishman et al., 2009) was developed with the purpose of examining craving in individuals who use cannabis regularly. This can have both diagnostic as well as clinical significance because many cannabis users rationalize that cannabis does not cause physiological dependence, therefore it is impossible to develop an addiction to cannabis. (This is a point of contention given that Cannabis Withdrawal is included in the *DSM-5* [American Psychiatric Association, 2013].) Yet, cannabis craving can be significant even in individuals who do not use regularly. The MCQ has two versions, a 47-item version and a shortened 12-item version (Heishman et al., 2008). The MCQ was based on a model of nicotine craving that examined five theoretical categories: (1) desire to use marijuana, (2) anticipation of positive outcomes from marijuana, (3) anticipation of relief from withdrawal symptoms or negative mood states, (4) intention and planning to use marijuana, and (5) lack of control over cannabis use. Based on these five categories, four factors or subscales were developed, which include (1) compulsivity (i.e., how easy or difficult it is to limit cannabis use), (2) emotionality (i.e., feeling more in control of emotions, anxiety, and tension based on cannabis use), (3) expectancy (i.e., cannabis use associated with being able to sleep better or feeling more content), and (4) purposefulness (i.e., plans to use cannabis in order to feel pleasant in the moment). Individuals taking the MCQ are asked to respond on a 7-point Likert scale ranging from Strongly Disagree (1) to Strongly Agree (7). Each of the four factors is then scored. Generally, high craving scores are associated with greater likelihood to relapse (Heishman et al., 2008).

Alcohol Abstinence Self-Efficacy Scale

As people in recovery are accruing abstinence time and are working on their sobriety by participating in counseling and attending 12-step meetings, they develop self-efficacy or confidence in their ability to stay sober. The concept of self-efficacy was originated by Bandura (1977); in this instance, the Alcohol Abstinence Self-Efficacy Scale (AASES) was developed to measure self-efficacy or self-confidence in one's ability to successfully manage temptations to drink and to assess one's confidence in their ability to abstain (DiClemente et al., 1994). The AASES consists of 40 items total to which test-takers respond to using a five-point Likert scale (0 = Not at all, 1 = Not very, 2 = Moderately, 3 = Very, and 4 = Extremely). The first 20 questions ask test-takers to indicate "how ***TEMPTED*** you might be to drink in each situation." Examples of items include: #8. When I am being offered a drink in a social situation or #14. When I feel like blowing up because of frustration or #20. When I am excited or celebrating with others. The next 20 items consist of exactly the same questions, only this time, test-takers are asked, "how ***CONFIDENT*** are you that you WOULD NOT drink in each situation?" The AASES is then scored by adding the scores for each item. The higher the score on the first 20 items, the more tempted to drink the person feels they would be given the situations presented, whereas high scores on the second 20 items suggest that the individual feels confident that they would be able to abstain. The AASES is divided into four subscales (each subscale is composed of 5 questions). The subscales are as follows: (1) Negative Affect, (2) Social Interaction and Positive States, (3) Physical and Other Concerns, and (4) Withdrawal and Urges. From examining the scores on each of these subscales, counselors are able to gain information as to the types of situations or emotions where the client might be most tempted to drink and how confident the client is that they could refuse a drink given those situations or emotional states. Therefore, it is possible that a client may be tempted quite a bit by thoughts, urges, difficult emotions, and physical pain; however, it is possible that they may also feel confident or possess self-efficacy in their ability to refrain from relapsing. The AASES was developed for use with adults, and reliability and validity have been established.

Problem Oriented Screening Instrument for Teenagers

The Problem Oriented Screening Instrument for Teenagers (POSIT) is a self-administered screening questionnaire that was designed to assess adolescents ages 12–19 for SUDs as well as problems in life-functioning related to substance use (Rahdert, 1991). The POSIT consists of 139 true/false questions that yield the following scales: substance use/abuse, physical health status, family relationships, mental health status, peer relationships, educational status, vocational status, social skills, leisure/recreational interests, and aggressive behavior/delinquency. The POSIT does not require extensive training to score and administer and takes about 20 to 30 minutes to complete. The POSIT can be used by the counselor to begin discussions with adolescents in areas where they may be having difficulties (e.g., Santisteban et al., 1999). Because the POSIT falls within the public domain, the questionnaire can be accessed at https://mn.gov/doc/assets/DHS-4141A-ENG_1_tcm1089-275475.pdf or by contacting the National Clearinghouse for Alcohol and Drug Information, Rockville, MD 20847-2345 (Phone: 1-900-729-6686) and requesting the Adolescent Assessment/Referral System Manual, DHHS Publication No. (ADM 91-1735).

Drug Use Screening Inventory

Probably one of the more comprehensive screening questionnaires is the Drug Use Screening Inventory (DUSI; Tarter & Hegedus, 1991; Tarter & Kirisci, 1997; Tarter et al., 1994). The original DUSI consisted of 149 items, whereas the revised DUSI-R consists of 159 items. The DUSI takes approximately 20–40 minutes to administer (depending on reading comprehension level and reading speed) and another 5–10 minutes to score. The scoring yields 26 subscales that measure the severity of various problems including substance abuse (which covers drug preferences and drug involvement); psychiatric disorders; behavior problems; school adjustment; health status; work adjustment; peer relations; social competency; family adjustment; leisure/recreational; and prediction of violence proneness, legal recidivism and prediction of "adverse outcomes," that is, DUI, reoffending, selling, or dealing drugs. There is also a Lie Scale, which helps to alert counselors of the invalidity of the results due to the client's deliberate attempt to deceive the examiner or to minimize problems. Each of the 26 subscales yields a ***problem density score,*** which is expressed as a percentage and is calculated by adding the number of endorsed items within a particular subscale and then dividing by the total number of questions for that subscale. For example, six endorsed items among 12 total questions yields a problem density score of 50%. Problem density scores range from 0%–100%. There is also an ***overall problem index score,*** which is a composite score of all endorsed items for the entire questionnaire (i.e., 159 items) divided by the total number of questions. For example, a total of 40 items (out of the total 159 items) would yield an overall problem index of 25%. Finally, there is a third measure, the ***relative problem***

density score, which examines the relative contribution of each of the subscales, relative to one another. These scores basically rank order the severity of each subscale, which assists counselors in setting treatment priorities.

A computerized version of the DUSI-R is available that allows the DUSI-R to be scored via computer and produces a detailed interpretation report. A company called e-Insight provides information on DUSI-R scoring and interpretation, which can be utilized in client screening, in providing feedback to clients, and for program evaluation purposes (by assessing the client's progress). Here are two websites that provide information about the DUSI-R and contact information for e-Insight:

www.einsight.net/wp-content/uploads/2020/04/einsight-dusi-solution-sheet.pdf

www.einsight.net/solutions/dusi/

The DUSI and the DUSI-R appear to have good predictive validity. Tarter et al. (1994) studied a group of males from the time they were between 12 and 14 years old, again at age 16, and then again at age 19. Those who scored 24% or higher on the overall problem density score had a 75% likelihood of developing a SUD by age 19. Similar results were found at age 16 when the group of males was retested, and again a significant prediction of SUD at age 19 was found for those with overall problem-density scores of 24% or higher. Additional information regarding the DUSI-R can be found at https://pubs.niaaa.nih.gov/publications/AssessingAlcohol/InstrumentPDFs/32_DUSI-R.pdf or by contacting the author at:

Ralph Tarter, PhD
Department of Pharmaceutical Sciences
University of Pittsburgh, School of Pharmacy
711 Salk Hall
Pittsburgh, PA 15261

Internet Gaming Disorder Test

Internet gaming disorder (IGD) is a diagnosis that is currently listed under "Conditions for Further Study" in the *DSM-5* (American Psychiatric Association, 2013; Petry et al., 2015). However, IGD will be included in the upcoming *International Classification of Diseases (ICD)-11* published by the World Health Organization. The Internet Gaming Disorder Test (IGD-20; Pontes et al., 2014) consists of 20 questions that are responded to on a five-point Likert scale including Strongly Disagree (1), Disagree (2), Neither Agree nor Disagree (3), Agree (4), and Strongly Agree (5). Two items are reverse scored (Item # 2 "I never play games in order to feel better" and Item #19 "I know my main daily activity [i.e., occupation, education, homemaker, etc.] has not been negatively impacted by my gaming"). Scores range from 5 to 100, and a cutoff score of 71 and greater is considered suggestive of an IGD. In addition, there are six subscales: *Salience* (defined as a preoccupation with internet games: Items 1,7, and 13); *Mood Modification* (defined as the use of internet games to relieve or escape negative mood such as sadness, anxiety, or guilt: Items 2R, 8, and 14); *Tolerance* (defined as the need to spend increased time gaming: Items 3, 9, and 15); *Withdrawal* (defined as experiencing withdrawal symptoms when gaming is taken away, e.g., irritability, anxiety, or sadness: Items 4, 10, and 16); *Conflict* (defined as loss of interest in previous hobbies or interests as a result of internet gaming, continued gaming despite knowledge of psychosocial problems, deception of family members and therapists regarding extent of internet gaming and jeopardized or lost significant relationships, jobs, or educational opportunities because of gaming: Items 11, 17, 19R, and 20); and *Relapse* (defined as unsuccessful attempts to control participation in internet games: Items 6, 12, and 18). Although we have focused on a measure for IGD, keep in mind there are several other screening questionnaires that can be utilized for other behavioral addictions such as the South Oaks Gambling Screen (SOGS) for gambling disorders (Lesieur & Blume, 1987) and the Sexual Addiction Screening Test-Revised for screening sexual addictions (Carnes et al., 2010).

Readiness to Change Questionnaire

The Readiness to Change Questionnaire (RTCQ) was also developed by Heather and Rollnick (1992) for the purpose of determining a client's Stage of Change. The subscales of the RTCQ focus on three of the five Stages of Change as derived from the Transtheoretical Model (Prochaska et al., 1992): *Precontemplation, Contemplation,* and *Action*. The RTCQ consists of 12 items which test-takers respond to on a five-point Likert scale ranging from Strongly Disagree, Disagree, Unsure, Agree, Strongly Agree. The RTCQ is therefore quick to administer and score. Given that there are three subscales (Precontemplation, Contemplation, and Action), each subscale consists of 4 items. An example of a Precontemplation item from the RTCQ is "I don't think I drink too much," whereas an example of a Contemplation item is "I enjoy my drinking, but sometimes I drink too much." Finally, an example of an Action item is "I have just recently changed my drinking habits." High scores on one of the three scales (Precontemplation, Contemplation, or Action) is interpreted to mean that the client most likely falls within that particular Stage of Change.

It should be noted that there are two more assessment tools that measure Stage of Change. They are the Stages of Change Readiness and Treatment Eagerness Scale (SOCRATES; Miller & Tonigan, 1996) and the University of Rhode Island Change Assessment (URICA) scale (DiClemente & Hughes, 1990; Dozois et al., 2004). The SOCRATES is used to assess a client's level of motivation and readiness for change. As with the RTCQ, being able to provide clients with feedback as to where they fall according to their Stage of Change may be a useful educational tool that may help to guide treatment moving forward. The URICA was designed as a continuous measure of a client's attitudes toward change. Unlike the RTCQ, the URICA assesses where the client falls along four dimensions of the Stages of Change continuum: Precontemplation, Contemplation, Action, and Maintenance.

We have reviewed several questionnaires, inventories, and screening tests in this section. However, for a comprehensive listing of tests, we highly recommend the University of Washington Library's website (http://lib.adai.washington.edu/instruments/). Here, you can plug in specific search terms that will allow you to discover assessment tools for both adolescents and adults and for a variety of substances.

Advantages and Disadvantages of Drug Screening

Many SUD treatment programs utilize drug screening as a means of objectively determining that clients are remaining substance-free. Although urine screens remain the most popular means of drug screening, there are also many programs that have switched to utilizing saliva swabs. Swabs are less invasive as well as easier and less time-consuming to obtain samples.

When collecting a urine screen, there are many programs or situations when clients may be observed by a staff member urinating into a specimen cup. As an alternative to direct observation, some programs will modify the bathroom where the urine sample is collected in order to avoid tampering (e.g., hot water is turned off, bluing additive is placed in the toilet water, etc.). There are other ways to test for substances such as hair samples, blood tests, saccadic eye-movement testing, breath (i.e., breathalyzers), and spinal fluid. Each of the aforementioned measures has advantages and disadvantages. The purpose of this chapter is not to get into a debate about the purpose, efficacy, and constitutionality of drug testing. We would rather you do that as part of your classroom discussion (see Learning Activity 5.3); however, we feel it is important for addiction counselors to be aware that drug screens have their place as part of treatment; however, drug screens have several advantages and disadvantages (see Box 5.1). First and foremost, the issue of reliability or accuracy is of utmost concern because of the possibility of a false positive result (i.e., a drug test that comes up as positive for drugs in the client's system that is not accurate). False positives are of major concern because a positive drug screen may cost individuals their jobs, their livelihoods, or, as in the case of drug court or probation, their freedom. Therefore, it is important that the drug tests are reliable. Yet, reliability can depend on many factors such as the type of laboratory analysis being utilized, the type of drug being ingested (i.e., not all laboratories test for all substances being used), how recently the substance was ingested, and the potency of the substance.

LEARNING ACTIVITY 5.3
DRUG SCREENING

Many corporations use urine drug screening as part of a routine pre-employment medical exam, and random urine drug screens are routinely collected for those in safety-sensitive jobs (e.g., airline pilots, bus drivers, heavy-equipment operators, and military personnel). Discuss in small groups whether you feel this is an invasion of privacy and/or a violation of one's civil rights. Also, should schools be allowed to test students who are suspected of being under the influence or as a condition of participation in extracurricular activities (i.e., sports, clubs, etc.)?

There are also several disadvantages to drug screening, such as the issue of reliability mentioned earlier. In examining the issue of test reliability, it is important to take into account that not all drug urine screens are alike. For example, urine drug screens that provide immediate

BOX 5.1

ADVANTAGES OF DRUG/ALCOHOL SCREENING

1. Drug screening can be used to validate abstinence.
2. Drug screening can be used to monitor treatment progress.
3. Drug screening can be used in ED settings to determine what substances were ingested and in what quantities.
4. Drug screening can be administered to those in safety-sensitive jobs to make certain they are not operating equipment under the influence.
5. Drug testing can be used to measure treatment compliance (e.g. methadone and buprenorphine programs).

results are usually tests that rely on thin-layer chromatography (TLC). Although TLC tests are usually inexpensive, they are unfortunately not as accurate as gas chromatography/mass spectrometry (GC/MS) tests, which are generally more expensive but are reported to have an approximate 98.9% accuracy rate, thereby nearly eliminating the risk of false-positive test results. GC/MS testing is considered the gold standard in drug urine screening, and therefore it is the only type of testing allowed for use by the FBI and many other government agencies.

The other disadvantage to drug screening is with regard to cross-reactivity. This occurs when clients may test positive for substances as a result of having ingested over-the-counter (OTC) medications. Cross-reactivity is especially problematic for the older and less reliable immunoassay and TLC screens. For example, clients who take OTC remedies like Nyquil, Vicks Nasal Spray, Sudafed, or any ephedrine-containing product found in most asthma medications may test positive for amphetamines. Similarly, clients who have taken OTC analgesics like Motrin, Nuprin, or Advil may test positive for THC or cannabinoids. Clients who have received local or dental anesthetics like lidocaine or Novocain may test positive for cocaine, and clients who may be taking OTC antitussive cold medicine such as Robitussin may test positive for morphine or opioids (Hoffman & Silvers, 1987). Also, you may be familiar with the well-known urban legend that if someone eats a poppy seed bagel, they could test positive for opioids or morphine (which are derivatives from the poppy flower). Most drug testing laboratories and their chief laboratory scientists indicate that for a client to test positive for opioids they would have to eat a pound or more of poppy seeds. Therefore, the likelihood of a false positive from eating a poppy seed bagel is quite low according to the testing labs.

Finally, one of the main disadvantages of drug screening is that it places counselors into the role of "disbelieving skeptics," which contributes to a cat-and-mouse game of trying to catch clients who may be lying about maintaining abstinence. In our experience, clients who are successfully abstinent usually have little or no problem with submitting a drug screen. Take, for instance, the following case example.

CASE EXAMPLE: FRED

Counselor Robert Smith has been treating Fred, a 24-year-old, single male who works in the construction trade. Most of Fred's work involves framing houses, therefore, he works outdoors much of the time. Fred had originally been referred for outpatient counseling by his probation officer (PO) after Fred had tested positive for cocaine on one of the random drug screens administered by probation. At first, Fred was angry about being referred for counseling; however, as he started to trust his counselor, Fred began to open up about what it was like growing up in a home where both his parents were alcoholics. Fred verbalized his goal of wanting a better life than what he experienced growing up. He is currently involved in a serious romantic relationship and plans to marry next year, and therefore does not want substance use to ruin the relationship. Fred indicates that he has been "clean and sober" for the past four months, and in each session he and his counselor review situations and emotional triggers where he may have felt tempted to drink or use cocaine. One day, Fred comes into his regular weekly outpatient session and Counselor Smith notices that Fred's

(*continued*)

eyes are red. Counselor Smith does not observe other signs of possible drug use (e.g., changes in speech or behavior), yet he is suspicious but does not confront Fred with his suspicions as he feels it might impact the therapeutic relationship. Also, Fred happens to comment that the last few days have been especially windy at work. Since part of Fred's counseling involves random drug screening, Counselor Smith does a drug screen, which comes back negative.

In Case Example: Fred, the urine drug screen that Counselor Smith obtains provides objective verification of Fred's claims of abstinence. What would have happened if Counselor Smith had taken the view that "all addicts lie" and confronted Fred with his subjective suspicions? How might that accusation have impacted on the therapeutic relationship? Here is another case example.

CASE EXAMPLE: JIMMY

Jimmy is a 31-year-old, married male who is currently two years in substance use disorder (SUD) recovery. He regularly attends Alcoholics Anonymous (AA) and Narcotics Anonymous (NA) meetings and also sees a counselor once a week to work on strengthening his recovery and to learn how to improve his communication skills in his marriage. Jimmy reports that he has been totally abstinent from all mood-altering substances during the past two years. Jimmy works as a project manager for a large defense corporation that has many federal government contracts. Because Jimmy works on projects that involved classified information, he (along with his coworkers) has to submit to random urine drug screens. The drug testing is done by an outside company, and, in order to save money, they utilize one of the less-expensive thin-layer chromatography (TLC) drug tests. One day, Jimmy is called into the corporation's human resources department where he is told that he tested positive for amphetamines. Jimmy is shocked and outraged and explains to the human resources (HR) representative that he has been in recovery for two years. Jimmy swears that he has not used any substances. The HR representative tells him "that's all well and good, but the corporation has a zero-tolerance policy" (i.e., any positive drug screen results in immediate termination). Jimmy asks if the HR rep would be willing to talk with his counselor. Jimmy speaks with his counselor and grants verbal and written permission for her to speak with the HR rep. The HR rep agrees, and when she speaks with Jimmy's licensed alcohol and drug counselor, the counselor recommends that Jimmy submit a hair sample for drug analysis. The counselor explains to the HR rep that a hair drug analysis will not show if Jimmy is using presently, but it can tell if he has used any substances in the past 60 to 90 days. Jimmy agrees to the hair analysis and to a gas chromatography/mass spectrometry (GC/MS) drug urine screen and tests negative on both.

In this Case Example, Jimmy is in real danger of losing his job after testing positive for amphetamines on a TLC screen. As indicated earlier, if Jimmy were to have used one of the cross-reactive OTC medications, this type of false-positive test result would not be far-fetched. Fortunately, Jimmy's counselor was aware of the advantages of hair-analysis drug testing, which can reveal drug use in the past 60 to 90 days. The disadvantage to hair-analysis testing is that it is generally more expensive than even GC/MS urine screens; however, it was well worth the price in saving Jimmy's job, his career, and probably his marriage.

Before concluding this section on drug screening, it is important to mention a couple of important points. First, for the longest time, the only way to test for alcohol use was by either an invasive blood test or a noninvasive breathalyzer test. Most EDs will administer blood tests when patients are brought in for treatment after a motor vehicle accident. State and local police departments will use breathalyzer tests in instances where drivers are suspected of DUI of alcohol. Breathalyzers will test for recent alcohol use, and most states have a .08 BAC cutoff for arresting someone for DUI. Some SUD treatment programs keep inexpensive hand-held breathalyzers on premises to test clients who may be suspected of being under the influence of alcohol. In an outpatient program, having an objective measure of alcohol consumption is helpful because of the liability a treatment program would incur if a client were to leave their session and drive under the influence and hurt themselves or others in an accident. The dilemma programs run into, however, is that breath tests do not reveal alcohol use beyond immediate or recent drinking. With recent advances in technology, however, the EtG urine test has been developed, which helps to ascertain if a person has been drinking within the past 72 hours. Most drug-testing laboratories offer this EtG analysis option for an additional fee.

The second issue that counselors need to be aware of is with regard to cannabis drug testing. Because cannabis is fat-soluble, it tends to get stored in the fat cells in the brain and throughout the body where it is metabolized more slowly. Therefore, for individuals who smoke cannabis on a daily basis over the course of several weeks, months, or years, THC will still show up in urine, blood, or hair drug screens for quite some time (i.e., several weeks) and even after a person has ceased all cannabis use. Both blood and urine tests will provide not just a qualitative positive/negative result but also a quantitative result that is reported as nanograms per milliliter (ng/mL). Also, important to keep in mind is that today's cannabis is of higher potency than cannabis that was sold in the 1960s or 1970s. Therefore, it is not unusual that a person may test with levels as great as 600 to 800 ng/mL (which would be a very likely quantitative reading for someone who is "dabbing" or "wax dabbing" or using high-potency cannabis). However, clients who smoke heavily or those with a moderate-to-severe cannabis use disorder who have stopped using cannabis a few weeks prior will still test positive for THC, probably for many weeks. What counselors would likely see (if the client continued to remain abstinent from cannabis) are declining quantitative amounts over the course of those weeks of abstinence. However, this does not address the issue of DUI of THC or coming to work under the influence of THC where a person might test positive even when they have not smoked cannabis in several days or weeks and is not currently under the influence at the time of testing. There are a couple of labs that have developed breathalyzer-type tests that test for current THC use (e.g., see Hound Laboratories). These THC breathalyzer tests are currently being field tested by several state and municipal police departments with promising results.

Mental Health Screening

Although the main role of addiction counselors is to screen and assess people for potential SUDs, there are instances where clients may present with a suspected or potential co-occurring mental health disorders, in which case it may be necessary for addiction counselors to provide a basic mental health screening so that appropriate referrals or recommendations can be made. This type of screening would more likely fall within the scope of practice for master's-level counselors as opposed to bachelor's or associate's-level counselors. Appendix 5.9 provides a nonstandardized emotional health screening questionnaire that is easy to administer and score. However, there are several mental health screening measures available for purchase that provide standardized, reliable, and valid ways of screening potential mental health difficulties. These include the Symptom Checklist-90 Items-Revised (SCL-90-R; Derogatis, 1994), which provides a 90-item checklist that clients respond to on a five-point response scale. When scored, this provides measures on the following scales: somatization, obsessive-compulsive, interpersonal sensitivity, depression, anxiety, hostility, phobic anxiety, paranoid ideation, and psychoticism as well as a composite, general severity index that provides an overall measure of psychological distress. The SCL-90-R can be hand- or computer-scored and takes about 12–15 minutes to administer.

Similar to the SCL-90-R is the Brief Symptom Inventory (BSI; Derogatis, 1993). The BSI is also a screening tool of self-reported psychological distress that yields nine subscales and a composite subscale that are identical to the SCL-90-R. The main difference is that the BSI consists of 53 items that clients respond to with the following alternatives: "Not at all," "A little bit," "Moderately," "Quite a bit," and "Extremely." There are also more specific mental health screening measures such as the Beck Depression Inventory (BDI) Second Edition (Beck et al., 1996) and the Beck Anxiety Inventory (BAI; Beck, 1990/1993). Both the BDI and the BAI can be either computer- or hand-scored and take only a few minutes to administer. All of the aforementioned mental health screening measures can be obtained through the following website: www.pearsonassessments.com/professional-assessments/products/products-by-acronym.html.

Earlier in this chapter, we mentioned a structured interview format measure called the **CAAPE-5** (Hoffmann, 2000/2013). The CAAPE-5 has the advantage of providing an assessment of substance use as well as mental health problems. As discussed earlier, the mental health questions of the CAAPE-5 explore symptoms relating to disorders such as major depressive episodes, manic episodes, anxiety and phobias, panic disorder, posttraumatic stress, obsessions/compulsions, conduct disorders, antisocial personality, paranoid personality, schizoid personality, borderline personality, dependent personality, obsessive-compulsive personality, and psychosis indication with each mental health disorder consisting of 4–6 questions that correspond to *DSM-5* criteria (American Psychiatric Association, 2013).

BRINGING IT ALL TOGETHER: CASE CONCEPTUALIZATION, TREATMENT PLANNING, AND PROVIDING CLIENT FEEDBACK

After gathering information from the biopsychosocial assessment, scoring and interpreting any assessment measures that were administered, and obtaining results of drug screens that may have been collected, there are three main tasks that addiction counselors will need to do with all this information: (1) render a diagnostic impression; (2) provide feedback to the client; and (3) develop a treatment plan that includes both level-of-care recommendations as well as what issues or problems are to be addressed in treatment.

This is also the time when counselors will bring all that information together in a cohesive, concise summary. The downloadable forms that accompany this textbook (available through Springer Publishing Connect; use the code on the opening page of this book to access the ebook, select the Show Supplementary dropdown button, and select Student Materials to access the downloadable forms) provide an example of such a case conceptualization summary. The information provided in the case conceptualization summary is gleaned from the biopsychosocial assessment, assessment measures that were administered, and phone contact with the client's father. (The client had signed a written release of information form allowing for this phone communication.)

At this point, the intake counselor or primary counselor should provide the client with some initial feedback based on the information gathered. Feedback statements should be brief (i.e., not lengthy lectures) and concise, and should avoid the use of professional jargon including diagnostic terminology. An example of client feedback is included at the conclusion of Exhibit 5.1. At the conclusion of the client-feedback statement, the counselor should ask the client their reactions to the feedback provided and whether they agree or disagree with the information provided to them.

Once a client is accepted into a treatment program, the counselor and the client will then work on establishing the goals of treatment and will devise a treatment plan. Ideally, treatment planning should be a collaborative effort between the counselor and the client. The downloadable forms that accompany this textbook (available through Springer Publishing Connect; use the code on the opening page of this book to access the ebook, select the Show Supplementary dropdown button, and select Student Materials to access the downloadable forms) include a treatment plan template and a sample treatment plan based on the format used by most Joint Commission of Accreditation of Hospitals and Other Organizations (JCAHO) and Council for the Accreditation of Rehabilitation Facilities (CARF) accredited programs. Also, the majority of State-licensed outpatient and inpatient facilities will also use this type of treatment-plan format (Perkinson, 2017). Here are a few recommendations for how to write a treatment plan.

Problem This should be a behavioral statement of the presenting problem and not a diagnosis. It is also useful to include the statement "as evidenced by" in order to help substantiate that this is indeed a problem.

Goal Think of the goal as how things will look when the problem no longer exists. For example, client will develop a lifestyle consistent with sobriety or recovery. Or client will develop coping skills that allow them to function well on a daily basis.

Objectives There are things the client will be doing as part of their treatment, and the objectives should be observable. So, rather than, "client will work on positive self-esteem," which is a vaguely stated objective, instead "client will make a list of five positive qualities or talents and will share with group." This is an example of an observable objective.

Intervention/ Methods These are composed of things the counselor will be doing in order to help their client achieve their goals or objectives. Therefore, if an objective includes "client will practice cognitive coping statements," then in this section the counselor will be teaching the client what these statements sound like and how/when to use them.

Rendering a *DSM-5* Diagnosis

The most widely used and accepted classification system for diagnosing SUDs is the *DSM-5* (American Psychiatric Association, 2013). There are three main categories of substance disorders, which include: SUDs, substance intoxication, and substance withdrawal. SUDs is an overarching way to describe many different subtypes of disorders. In order to make an accurate *DSM-5* diagnosis, the counselor would need to specify the substance the client indicates that they are experiencing difficulties with, such as alcohol, caffeine, cannabis, hallucinogens, inhalants, opioids, sedatives/hypnotics/anxiolytics, stimulants, tobacco, or other substances. Counselors will try to determine if that individual is currently under the influence of drugs or alcohol (intoxication) or is experiencing substance withdrawal, as those are also separate diagnostic categories from SUDs and pertain to the client's status when they present for treatment (in other words, is the client presently under the influence or are they currently experiencing substance withdrawal?). In these instances, counselors would then specify if their client is experiencing Alcohol Withdrawal or Alcohol Intoxication, Opioid Withdrawal or Opioid Intoxication, and so forth. Please note that while a client may present as being under the influence of a hallucinogen like LSD, (which would be diagnosed as hallucinogen intoxication), because hallucinogens do not produce physiological or psychological dependence per se, there is not a diagnostic category for hallucinogen withdrawal. Both substance intoxication and substance withdrawal describe the client's condition at the time they are being evaluated, whereas the diagnosis of a SUD is given when an individual's alcohol or drug use had impacted on their ability to function over time. In other words, there is a pattern of life problems as a result of alcohol and/or drug use. It is common for clients who abuse substances to use more than one substance at a time, which will need to be noted in your diagnosis. The *DSM-5* includes 11 criteria that comprise the diagnostic category for SUDs. These 11 criteria include symptoms such as: (1) using substances over a longer period or using more of a substance than was intended; (2) express persistent desires to cut down, curtail, or quit substance use; (3) significant time and effort is spent obtaining the substance, using the substance or recovering from its effects; and (4) craving or strong desire to use the substance (American Psychiatric Association, 2013). Criteria 1 through 4 refer to a pathological pattern of substance use in which one experiences a loss of control over the amount used, an inability to cut down or quit, substance use taking up a great part of one's daily routine which includes recovering from hangovers and drug craving, or obsessions to use. Criteria 5 through 7 reflect social impairment and include (5) recurrent use which interferes with fulfilling major role obligations (e.g., work, school, and parenting responsibilities); (6) persistent or recurrent social or interpersonal problems as a result of substance use; and (7) social, occupational or recreational activities are reduced or eliminated due to substance use. Criteria 8 and 9 reference risky use, for example, (8) using substances in physical hazardous situations (like driving a car or operating machinery) and (9) continued use despite knowledge of persistent or recurrent negative physical or psychological consequences. Finally, Criteria 10 and 11 refer to physiological consequences such as (10) tolerance that is defined as needing to consume more and more of the substance in order to obtain the desired effect or experiencing a reduction in effect from using the same amount of the substance over time and (11) withdrawal as evidenced by experiencing extreme distress (specific to that particular substance) as a result of abruptly attempting to quit or curtail the use of that particular substance. SUDs can be further categorized by level of severity. Therefore, if a client were to experience two or three of the aforementioned criteria or symptoms, they would be categorized as having a mild SUD, whereas if a client manifested four or five of the criteria they would be categorized as having a moderate SUD. Finally, if a client were to manifest six or more of the criteria, they would be categorized as having a severe SUD. Other diagnostic specifiers include *in early remission* (the diagnostic criteria for that particular SUD has not been met for at least 3 months but less than 12 months); *in sustained remission* (none of the criteria for the SUD has been met for 12 months or longer); and *in a controlled environment* (this specifier would be given if the client is in an environment where substance use is restricted/prevented, that is, in an inpatient program or correctional facility).

In order for health insurance companies to reimburse clients or providers for treatment services rendered, counselors must include a diagnostic code based on the diagnosis the client has met the criteria for. Table 5.1 provides the *ICD-10* diagnostic codes for most of the SUDs.

TABLE 5.1 *ICD-10* Substance Use Disorder Diagnostic Codes

SUBSTANCE USE DISORDER	*ICD-10* CODES*
Alcohol Use Disorder (Mild)	F10.10
Alcohol Use Disorder (Moderate or Severe)	F10.20
Alcohol Intoxication	F10.129 or F10.229
Alcohol Withdrawal	F10.239 (without perceptual disturbances)
Alcohol Withdrawal	F10.232 (with perceptual disturbances)
Caffeine Intoxication	F15.929
Caffeine Withdrawal	F15.93
Cannabis Use Disorder (Mild)	F12.10
Cannabis Use Disorder (Moderate or Severe)	F12.20
Cannabis Intoxication	F12.129 (without perceptual disturbances)
Cannabis Intoxication	F12.122 (with perceptual disturbances)
Cannabis Withdrawal	F12.288
Hallucinogen Use Disorder	
Phencyclidine Use Disorder (Mild)	F16.10
Phencyclidine Use Disorder (Mod or Severe)	F16.20
Phencyclidine Intoxication	F16.129 (with a mild comorbid disorder)
Phencyclidine Intoxication	F16. 229 (with a moderate/severe comorbid disorder)
Inhalant Use Disorder (Mild)	F18.10
Inhalant Use Disorder (Moderate-Severe)	F18.20
Inhalant Intoxication	F18.129 (w/ mild comorbid inhalant use dis)
Inhalant Intoxication	F18.229 (w/ moderate/severe inhalant use dis)

(continued)

TABLE 5.1 *ICD-10* Substance Use Disorder Diagnostic Codes (*continued*)

SUBSTANCE USE DISORDER	*ICD-10* CODES*
Opioid Use Disorder (Mild)	F11.10
Opioid Use Disorder (Moderate-Severe)	F11.20
Opioid Intoxication	F11.122 (w/ mild opioid use disorder COD)
Opioid Intoxication	F11.222 (w/ mod-severe opioid use dis COD)
Opioid Withdrawal	F11.23
Sedative/Hypnotic/Anxiolytic Disorder	F13.10 (Mild)
Sedative/Hypnotic/Anxiolytic Disorder	F13.20 (Moderate or Severe)
Sedative/Hypnotic/Anxiolytic Intoxication	F13.129 (w/ mild Sedative/Hyp/Anx Dis)
Sedative Hypnotic/Anxiolytic Intoxication	F13.229 (w/ mod-severe Sed/Hyp/Anx Dis)
Sedative/Hypnotic Anxiolytic Withdrawal	F13.239
Stimulant Use Disorder (Mild)	F15.10 (amphetamine)
Stimulant Use Disorder (Mild)	F14.10 (cocaine)
Stimulant Use Disorder (Mod-Severe)	F15.20 (amphetamine)
Stimulant Use Disorder (Mod-Severe)	F14.20 (cocaine)
Stimulant Intoxication	F15.129 (w/out perceptual disturbance)
Stimulant Intoxication	F15.229 (w/comorbid Stim Use Disorder)
Stimulant Withdrawal	F15.23 (amphetamine or other stimulant)
Stimulant Withdrawal	F14.23 (for cocaine withdrawal)
Tobacco Use Disorder (Mild)	Z72.0
Tobacco Use Disorder (Mod-Severe)	F17.200
Tobacco Withdrawal	F17.203
Non–Substance-Related Disorder	
Gambling Disorder	F63.0

*The ICD-11 represents the new revision of the ICD-10 and is due to be released for practitioner use in January 2022.
ICD-10, International Classification of Diseases, Tenth Revision.

Please note that for many of the intoxication disorders, the F-code will depend on whether there is a comorbid or co-occurring SUD and whether that SUD is mild or moderate/severe.

Many counselors contend that rendering a diagnosis (even a provisional diagnosis) too early in the client's treatment increases the likelihood of misdiagnosis or an inaccurate diagnosis. This is a valid point. It is obviously better to wait until the client is fully stabilized and abstinent for several months before gaining a clearer diagnostic picture of the client and their symptoms, especially when making a determination of a possible co-occurring mental health diagnosis. However, addiction counselors are often put in the position of having to render a diagnosis in order for the client to be able to utilize their health insurance to cover the costs of treatment, or a diagnosis is often required by the state licensing authority that licenses that particular treatment facility. In these instances, it is important for counselors to specify that the early diagnosis is provisional at best and not a principal diagnosis.

NOTES FROM THE FIELD

Andrea Kusch, MA, CADC, works as an intake counselor at Preferred Behavioral Health's Child Protective Services Addiction Initiative in Ocean County, New Jersey. There, she does Substance Abuse Evaluations for those parents who have been involved with the State Child Protective Services when they have had DUIs or have endangered the welfare of their child(ren) by engaging in, possession of, or distribution of illegal substances or having had a domestic violence complaint. Once evaluated, if the client meets the criteria for a substance use disorder, they are then referred to an appropriate level of care at an addiction treatment facility. Andrea indicates that she utilizes the CAAPE and LOCI-3 when doing evaluations and finds both measures very helpful.

Ms. Kusch has over 15 years of experience working in the addiction treatment profession and has worked in residential treatment, detox facilities, and a women's halfway house. When asked what she views as the greatest challenge of her current position, Andrea states it is mandating someone to attend a treatment program when they believe they do not have issues with substance use. However, one of the greatest parts of her job is when clients are able to see things through someone else's eyes and "when the lightbulb goes on" and they begin their journey in sobriety/recovery. Ms. Kusch indicates that she likes being the "interventionist," that is, intervening at points in people's live when they are at their lowest. intervening at points in people's lives when they are at their lowest.

SUMMARY

This chapter focuses on how to assess clients who present with possible SUDs and incorporates information on the use of a biopsychosocial assessment, alcohol and drug screening/assessment measures, structured interviews, and laboratory drug screening. Information on how to summarize or conceptualize assessment information and how to determine an *ASAM-3* level of care and treatment plan are also presented. Finally, we also provided information on how to render both provisional and principal *DSM-5* diagnoses.

RESOURCES

Altman, D. G., & Bland, J. M. (1994). Diagnostic tests 1: Sensitivity and specificity. *British Medical Journal, 308*(June), 1552. https://doi.org/10.1136/bmj.308.6943.1552

American Psychiatric Association. (2013). *The diagnostic and statistical manual of mental disorders* (5th ed.). American Psychiatric Association.

Campbell, D. T., & Fiske, D. W. (1959). Convergent and discriminant validation by the multi-trait-multimethod matrix. *Psychological Bulletin, 56*(2), 81–105.

Felitti, V. J., Anda, R. F., Nordenberg, D., Williamson, D. F., Spitz, A. M., Edwards, V., Koss, M. P., & Marks, J. S. (1998). Relationship of childhood abuse and household dysfunction to many of the leading causes of death in adults: The Adverse Childhood Experiences (ACE) Study. *American Journal of Preventative Medicine, 14*(4), 245–258.

McLellan, A. T., Luborsky, L., O'Brien, C. P., & Woody, G. E. (1980). An improved diagnostic instrument for substance abuse patients: The Addiction Severity Index. *Journal of Nervous and Mental Diseases, 168*(1), 26–33. https://doi.org/10.1097/00005053-198001000-00006

Mee-Lee, D. (Ed.). (2013). *The ASAM Criteria: Treatment criteria for addiction, substance-related and co-occurring conditions* (3rd ed.). American Society of Addiction Medicine.

Miller, G. A. (1988). *The substance abuse subtle screening inventory manual.* The SASSI Institute.

Santisteban, D. A., Tejeda, M., Dominicis, C., & Szapocznik, J. (1999). An efficient tool for screening for maladaptive family functioning in adolescent drug abusers: The Problem Oriented Screening Instrument for Teenagers. *American Journal of Drug and Alcohol Abuse, 25*(2), 197–206. https://doi.org/10.1081/ada-100101855

Tarter, R. E., & Hegedus, A. M. (1991). The drug use screening inventory. *Alcohol Research and Health, 15*(1), 65–73.

Widom, C. S., Weiler, B. L., & Cottler, L. B. (1999). Childhood victimization and drug abuse: A comparison of prospective and retrospective findings. *Journal of Consulting and Clinical Psychology, 67*(6), 867–880. https://doi.org/10.1037//0022-006x.67.6.867

Zaldívar, F., Molina, A. M., López Rios, F., & Garcia Montes, J. M. (2009). Evaluation of alcohol and other drug use and the influence of social desirability: Direct and camouflaged measures. *European Journal of Psychological Assessment, 25*(4), 22–34.

There is a series of treatment planners published by Wiley & Sons that are very useful in learning how to write treatment plans. In addition to an addiction treatment planner (referenced later), there are also treatment planners on a variety of topics, e.g., couples treatment planner, depression treatment planner, anxiety treatment planner, and so forth.

Perkinson, R. R., Jongsma, A. E., & Bruce, T. J. (2014). *The addiction treatment planner* (5th ed.). John Wiley & Sons.

These references are useful for formulating a diagnosis and for level-of-care/patient placement:

American Psychiatric Association. (2013). *The diagnostic and statistical manual of mental disorders* (5th ed.). Author.

Mee-Lee, D. (Ed.). (2013). *The ASAM Criteria: Treatment criteria for addiction, substance-related and co-occurring conditions* (3rd ed.). American Society of Addiction Medicine.

The following video provides an example of how to conduct a biopsychosocial assessment: https://www.youtube.com/watch?v=59pj_03iJhk

KEY REFERENCES

Only key references appear in the print edition. The full reference list appears in the digital product on Springer Publishing Connect: connect.springerpub.com/content/book/978-0-8261-3586-5/chapter/ch05

Altman, D. G., & Bland, J. M. (1994). Diagnostic tests 1: Sensitivity and specificity. *British Medical Journal, 308*(June), 1552. https://doi.org/10.1136/bmj.308.6943.1552

American Psychiatric Association. (2013). *The diagnostic and statistical manual of mental disorders* (5th ed.). Author.

Fals-Stewart, W. (1996). The ability of individuals with psychoactive substance use disorders to escape detection by the Personality Assessment Inventory. *Psychological Assessment, 8*(1), 60–68. https://doi.org/10.1037/1040-3590.8.1.60

Hoffman, A., & Silvers, J. (1987). *Steal this urine test: Fighting drug hysteria in America.* Penguin.

Mee-Lee, D. (Ed.). (2013). *The ASAM Criteria: Treatment criteria for addiction, substance-related and co-occurring conditions* (3rd ed.). American Society of Addiction Medicine.

Prochaska, J. O., DiClemente, C. C., & Norcross, J. C. (1992). In search of how people change: Application to addictive behaviors. *American Psychologist, 47*(9), 1102–1114. https://doi.org/10.1037//0003-066x.47.9.1102

Russell, M., Martier, S. S., Sokol, R. J., Mudar, P., Bottoms, S., Jacobson, S., & Jacobson, J. (1994). Screening for pregnancy risk-drinking. *Alcoholism: Clinical and Experimental Research, 18*, 1156–1161. https://doi.org/10.1111/j.1530-0277.1994.tb00097.x

Widom, C. S., Weiler, B. L., & Cottler, L. B. (1999). Childhood victimization and drug abuse: A comparison of prospective and retrospective findings. *Journal of Consulting and Clinical Psychology, 67*(6), 867–880. https://doi.org/10.1037//0022-006x.67.6.867

Zaldívar, F., Molina, A. M., López Rios, F., & Garcia Montes, J. M. (2009). Evaluation of alcohol and other drug use and the influence of social desirability: Direct and camouflaged measures. *European Journal of Psychological Assessment, 25*(4), 244–251. https://doi.org/10.1027/1015-5759.25.4.244

APPENDIX 5.1

TRAUMA RECOVERY SCALE (TRS)

PART I

Score: ______ Name ________________

Directions: Please read the following list and check all that apply.

	Type Of Traumatic Event	Number of Times	Dates/Age(s)		
Δ 1.	Childhood Sexual Abuse	____	____	____	____
Δ 2.	Rape	____	____	____	____
Δ 3.	Other Adult Sexual Assault/Abuse	____	____	____	____
Δ 4.	Natural Disaster	____	____	____	____
Δ 5.	Industrial Disaster	____	____	____	____
Δ 6.	Motor Vehicle Accident	____	____	____	____
Δ 7.	Combat Trauma	____	____	____	____
Δ 8.	Physical Injury/Medical	____	____	____	____
Δ 9.	Childhood Physical Abuse	____	____	____	____
Δ 10.	Adult Physical Abuse	____	____	____	____
Δ 11.	Victim Of Violent Crime	____	____	____	____
Δ 12.	Captivity	____	____	____	____
Δ 13.	Torture	____	____	____	____
Δ 14.	Domestic Violence	____	____	____	____
Δ 15.	Sexual Harassment	____	____	____	____
Δ 16.	Threat of physical violence	____	____	____	____
Δ 17.	Accidental physical injury	____	____	____	____
Δ 18.	Humiliation	____	____	____	____
Δ 19.	Property Loss	____	____	____	____
Δ 20.	Death Of Loved One	____	____	____	____
Δ 21.	Neglect	____	____	____	____
Δ 22.	Witnessed Event (see below)	____	____	____	____
Δ 23.	Other:______________	____	____	____	____
Δ 24.	Other:______________	____	____	____	____

If you witnessed trauma and it has caused significant distress or problems in your life please identify the event(s) and people involved.

Witnessed Event: ____________________

Witnessed Event: ____________________

Witnessed Event: ____________________

Witnessed Event: ____________________

Witnessed Event: ____________________

Witnessed Event: ____________________

Witnessed Event: ____________________

Witnessed Event: ____________________

Witnessed Event: ____________________

Comments: ____________________

Source: Gentry, J. E. (1996). *Solution-focused trauma recovery scale (TRS)* [Unpublished]. Florida State University.

TRAUMA RECOVERY SCALE

PART II

Place a mark on the line that best represents your experiences during the past week.

1. ☐ I make it through the day without distressing recollections of past events.

   .______.______.______.______.______.______.______.______.______.______.

   0%____100% of the time

2. ☐ I sleep free from nightmares.

   .______.______.______.______.______.______.______.______.______.______.

   0%____100% of the time

3. I am able to stay in control when I think of difficult memories.

   .______.______.______.______.______.______.______.______.______.______.

   0%____100% of the time

4. I do the things that I used to avoid (e.g., daily activities, social activities, thoughts of events and people connected with past events).

   .______.______.______.______.______.______.______.______.______.______.

   0%____100% of the time

5. I am safe.

   .______.______.______.______.______.______.______.______.______.______.

   0%____100% of the time

   I feel safe.

   .______.______.______.______.______.______.______.______.______.______.

   0%____100% of the time

6. I have supportive relationships in my life.

   .______.______.______.______.______.______.______.______.______.______.

   0%____100% of the time

7. I find that I can now safely feel a full range of emotions.

   .______.______.______.______.______.______.______.______.______.______.

   0%____100% of the time

8. I can allow things to happen in my surroundings without needing to control them.

   .______.______.______.______.______.______.______.______.______.______.

   0%____100% of the time

9. I am able to concentrate on thoughts of my choice.

._____._____._____._____._____._____._____._____._____._____.

0%____100% of the time

10. I have a sense of hope about the future.

._____._____._____._____._____._____._____._____._____._____.

0%____100% of the time

Mean Score

Scoring Instructions: record the score for where the hash mark falls on the line (0–100) in the box beside the item (average 5a with 5b to get score for 5). Sum scores and divide by 10.

Interpretation: 100–95 (full recovery/subclinical); 86–94 (significant recovery/mild symptoms); 75–85 (some recovery/moderate symptoms); 74 (minimal recovery/severe); below 35 (probable traumatic regression).

Source: Gentry, J. E. (1996). *Solution-focused trauma recovery scale (TRS)* [Unpublished]. Florida State University.

APPENDIX 5.2

ADVERSE CHILDHOOD EXPERIENCE (ACE) QUESTIONNAIRE

Name: ____________________________ Date: ________________

This Questionnaire will be asking you some questions about events that happened during your childhood; specifically the first 18 years of your life. The information you provide by answering these questions will allow us to better understand problems that may have occurred early in your life and allow us to explore how those problems may be impacting the challenges you are experiencing today. This can be very helpful in the success of your treatment.

While you were growing up, during your first 18 years of life:

1. Did a parent or other adult in the household often:

   Swear at you, insult you, put you down, or humiliate you?

   Or

   Act in a way that made you afraid that you might be physically hurt?

   ☐ Yes ☐ No If Yes, enter 1 _____

2. Did a parent or other adult in the household often:

   Push, grab, slap, or throw something at you?

   Or

   Ever hit you so hard that you had marks or were injured?

   ☐ Yes ☐ No If Yes, enter 1 _____

3. Did an adult or person at least 5 years older than you ever:

   Touch or fondle you or have you touch their body in a sexual way?

   Or

   Attempt or actually have oral, anal, or vaginal intercourse with you?

   ☐ Yes ☐ No If Yes, enter 1 _____

4. Did you often feel that:

   No one in your family loved you or thought you were important or special?

   Or

Adverse Childhood Experience (ACE) Questionnaire

Your family didn't look out for each other, feel close to each other, or support each other?

☐ Yes ☐ No If Yes, enter 1 _____

5. Did you often feel that:

You didn't have enough to eat, had to wear dirty clothes, and had no one to protect you?

Or

Your parents were too drunk or high to take care of you or take you to the doctor if you needed it?

☐ Yes ☐ No If Yes, enter 1 _____

6. Were your parents ever separated or divorced?

☐ Yes ☐ No If Yes, enter 1 _____

7. Were any of your parents or other adult caregivers:

Often pushed, grabbed, slapped, or had something thrown at them?

Or

Sometimes or often kicked, bitten, hit with a fist, or hit with something hard?

Or

Ever repeatedly hit over at least a few minutes or threatened with a gun or knife?

☐ Yes ☐ No If Yes, enter 1 _____

8. Did you live with anyone who was a problem drinker or alcoholic, or who used street drugs?

☐ Yes ☐ No If Yes, enter 1 _____

9. Was a household member depressed or mentally ill, or did a household member attempt suicide?

☐ Yes ☐ No If Yes, enter 1 _____

10. Did a household member go to prison?

☐ Yes ☐ No If Yes, enter 1 _____

ACE SCORE (Total "Yes" Answers): _______

Adverse Childhood Experience (ACE) Questionnaire

PROVIDER INSTRUCTIONS ***(Revised April 11, 2019)***

Beginning June 1, 2019, the ACE Questionnaire shall be given to all adults ages 18 and older* who are seeking behavioral health services from the ODMHSAS and the OHCA (SoonerCare/Medicaid); with minimal exception**. The ACE score shall be reported on all CDC/PA 23 (admissions) and CDC/PA 42 (6-month updates/extensions). The questionnaire only has to be given once per person, per provider- but the score must be reported/carried forward on all subsequent CDCs like some of the other CDC responses (ex: gender and race are typically reported/carried forward on each CDC and rarely change). Valid ACE Scores should be entered on the CDC in one of the following formats: 00 to 10 or 0 to 10 (00 to 10, double digits, is preferred). For currently admitted/open adult clients, the ACE Questionnaire shall be given at the next 6-month treatment update and reported on the CDC/PA 42 (6-month update/extension).

*Note: This questionnaire should only be given to adults ages 18 and older; it should not be given to children or youth under the age of 18.

**Exceptions: Due to the nature of some levels of care and program types, there are circumstances in which the ACE Questionnaire shall not be required. They are as follows:

- *Community Living (CL) Level of Care* (ex: Homeless, Housing, Residential Care)
- *Service Focus-* 11 (Homeless, Housing, Residential Care); 23 (Day School); 24 Medication Clinic Only; and 26 Mobile Crisis.

GIVING THE ACE QUESTIONNAIRE

The ACE Questionnaire is to be given at the time of clinical assessment (at initial clinical assessment for new clients, and for currently admitted/open clients- at clinical assessment update completed as a part of the service plan update process at 6-month treatment update). This is to ensure ready access to a therapist should one be needed to address any issue that might arise from revisiting childhood trauma.

It is a self-administered instrument and shall be completed by the individual seeking services without intervention from staff (ex: staff may not reframe the question or give explanation regarding the intent of the question). The only assistance that staff may provide is with regard to literacy or vision challenges, and in that instance the introduction statement and questions must be read aloud to the individual exactly as written on the questionnaire. To ensure a trauma informed process, it is important that the introduction statement on the questionnaire is either read by the client or read to the client.

Due to the sensitive nature of the questions, the individual completing the ACE Questionnaire should be given a confidential space in which to complete it. They may choose to have someone with them in the room for support (ex: Peer Support Specialist, family, friend).

Scoring

For each of the ten (10) questions on the questionnaire, the individual will give a Yes or No answer. When scoring, each "Yes" answer will be given one (1) point. These points will be tallied to determine the individuals ACE Score.

Source: Felitti, V. J., Anda, R. F., Nordenberg, D., Williamson, D. F., Spitz, A. M., Edwards, V., Koss, M. P., & Marks, J. S. (1998). Relationship of childhood abuse and household dysfunction to many of the leading causes of death in adults. The Adverse Childhood Experiences (ACE) Study. *American Journal of Preventative Medicine, 14*(4), 245–258. https://doi.org/10.1016/S0749-3797(98)00017-8

APPENDIX 5.3

ADDICTION SEVERITY INDEX, 5TH EDITION

Clinical/Training Version

A. Thomas McLellan, Ph.D.
Deni Carise, Ph.D

INTRODUCING THE ASI: Seven potential problem areas: Medical, Employment/Support Status, Alcohol, Drug, Legal, Family/Social, and Psychological. All clients receive the same standard interview. All information gathered is ***confidential.***

We will discuss two time periods:

1. The past 30 days
2. Lifetime data

Patient Rating Scale: Patient input is important. For each area,
I will ask you to use this scale to let me know how bothered you have been by any problems in each section. I will also ask you how important treatment is for you in the area being discussed.
The scale is: 0–Not at all
1–Slightly
2–Moderately
3–Considerably
4–Extremely

If you are uncomfortable giving an answer, then don't answer.

Please do not give inaccurate information!
Remember: This is an interview, not a test.

INTERVIEWER INSTRUCTIONS:

1. Leave no blanks.
2. Make plenty of comments and include the question number before each comment. If another person reads this ASI, that person should have a relatively complete picture of the client's perceptions of his or her problems.
3. X = Question not answered.
   N = Question not applicable.
4. Stop the interview if the client misrepresents two or more sections.
5. Tutorial and coding notes are preceded by •.

INTERVIEWER SCALE: 0–1 = No problem
2–3 = Slight problem
4–5 = Moderate problem
6–7 = Severe problem
8–9 = Extreme problem

HALF TIME RULE: If a question asks for the number of months, round up periods of 14 days or more to 1 month. Round up 6 months or more to 1 year.

CONFIDENCE RATINGS:

- Last two items in each section.
- Do not overinterpret.
- Denial does not warrant misrepresentation.
- Misrepresentation is overt contradiction in information.

PROBE AND MAKE PLENTY OF COMMENTS!

LIST OF COMMONLY USED DRUGS:

Alcohol:	Beer, wine, liquor
Methadone:	Dolophine, LAAM
Opiates:	Painkillers = Morphine; Dilaudid; Demerol; Percocet; Darvon; Talwin; Codeine; Tylenol 2, 3, 4
Barbiturates:	Nembutal, Seconal, Tuinol, Amytal, Pentobarbital, Secobarbital, Phenobarbital, Fiorinol
Sedatives/ Hypnotics/ Tranquilizers	Benzodiazepines, Valium, Librium, Ativan, Serax Tranxene, Dalmane, Halcion, Xanax, Miltown Chloral Hydrate (Noctex), Quaaludes
Cocaine:	Cocaine Crystal, Freebase Cocaine or "Crack," and "Rock Cocaine"
Amphetamines:	Monster, Crank, Benzedrine, Dexedrine, Ritalin, Preludin, Methamphetamine, Speed, Ice, Crystal
Cannabis	Marijuana, Hashish
Hallucinogens:	LSD (Acid), Mescaline, Mushrooms (Psilocybin), Peyote, Green, PCP (Phencyclidine), Angel Dust, Ecstasy
Inhalants:	Nitrous Oxide, Amyl Nitrate (Whippets, Poppers), Glue, Solvents, Gasoline, Toluene, etc.

Just note if these are used:
Antidepressants
Ulcer Medications—Zantac, Tagamet
Asthma Medications—Ventoline Inhaler, Theo-Dur
Other Medications—Antipsychotics, Lithium

ALCOHOL/DRUG USE INSTRUCTIONS:
This section looks at two time periods: the past 30 days and years of regular use, or lifetime use. Lifetime use refers to the time prior to the past 30 days.

- 30-day questions require only the *number* of days used.
- Lifetime use is asked to determine extended periods of *regular* use. It refers to the time prior to the past 30 days.
- Regular use = 3+ times per week, 2+ day binges, or problematic, irregular use in which normal activities are compromised.
- Alcohol to intoxication does not necessarily mean "drunk"; use the words "felt the effects," "got a buzz," "high," etc. instead of "intoxication." As a rule of thumb, 5+ drinks in one day, or 3+ drinks in a sitting defines intoxication.
- How to ask these questions:
  ✓ How many days in the past 30 days have you used...?
  ✓ How many years in your life have you *regularly* used...?

Addiction Severity Index, 5th Edition **(Clinical/Training Version)**
GENERAL INFORMATION

G1. ID No.:

G2. Soc. Sec. No.: ___ - ___ - ___

G4. Date of Admission: ___ / ___ / ___
(Month/Day/Year)

G5. Date of Interview: ___ / ___ / ___
(Month/Day/Year)

G6. Time Begun: (Hour:Minutes) ___ : ___

G7. Time Ended: (Hour:Minutes) ___ : ___

G8. Class: 1. Intake 2. Follow-up

G9. Contact Code: 1. In person 2. Telephone
(Intake ASI must be in person)

G10. Gender: 1. Male 2. Female

G11. Interviewer Code No./Initials:

G12. Special:
1. Patient terminated
2. Patient refused
3. Patient unable to respond
N. Not applicable

Name

Address 1

Address 2

City State Zip Code

G14. How long have you lived at this address? ___ / ___ (Years/Months)

G15. Is this residence owned by you or your family?
0–No 1–Yes

G16. Date of birth: ___ / ___ / ___
(Month/Day/Year)

G17. Of what race do you consider yourself?
1. White (not Hispanic) 4. Alaskan Native 7. Hispanic-Puerto Rican
2. Black (not Hispanic) 5. Asian/Pacific Islander 8. Hispanic-Cuban
3. American Indian 6. Hispanic-Mexican 9. Other Hispanic

G18. Do you have a religious preference?
1. Protestant 3. Jewish 5. Other
2. Catholic 4. Islamic 6. None

G19. Have you been in a controlled environment in the past 30 days?
1. No 4. Medical Treatment
2. Jail 5. Psychiatric Treatment
3. Alcohol/Drug Treatment 6. Other: ___________
- A place, theoretically, without access to drugs/alcohol.

G20. How many days?
- "NN" if Question G19 is No. Refers to total number of days detained in the past 30 days.

ADDITIONAL TEST RESULTS

G21. ______________

G22. ______________

G23. ______________

G24. ______________

G25. ______________

G26. ______________

G27. ______________

G28. ______________

	SEVERITY PROFILE									
PROBLEMS	0	1	2	3	4	5	6	7	8	9
MEDICAL										
EMP/SUPPORT										
ALCOHOL										
DRUGS										
LEGAL										
FAMILY/SOCIAL										
PSYCH.										

GENERAL INFORMATION COMMENTS
(Include the question number with your notes)

MEDICAL STATUS

M1. How many times in your life have you been hospitalized for medical problems?
- Include ODs and DTs. Exclude detox, alcohol/drug, psychiatric treatment, and childbirth (if no complications). Enter the number of overnight hospitalizations for medical problems.

M2. How long ago was your last hospitalization for a physical problem? (Years/Months)
- If no hospitalizations in Question M1, then this should be "NN."

M3. Do you have any chronic medical problems that continue to interfere with your life? 0–No 1–Yes
- ***If Yes, specify in comments.***
- A chronic medical condition is a serious physical condition that requires regular care (i.e., medication, dietary restriction), preventing full advantage of the person's abilities.

M15.<**OPTIONAL**> Number of months pregnant: (Months)
- "N" for males, "0" for not pregnant.

M4. Are you taking any prescribed medication on a regular basis for a physical problem? 0–No 1–Yes
- ***If Yes, specify in comments.***
- Medication prescribed by an M.D. for medical conditions; ***not psychiatric medicines***. Include medicines prescribed whether or not the patient is currently taking them. The intent is to verify chronic medical problems.

M5. Do you receive a pension for a physical disability? 0–No 1–Yes
- ***If Yes, specify in comments.***
- Include worker's compensation; exclude psychiatric disability.

M6. How many days have you experienced medical problems in the past 30 days?
- Include flu, colds, etc. Include serious ailments related to drugs/alcohol, which would continue even if the patient were abstinent (e.g., cirrhosis of liver, abscesses from needles).

For Questions M7 & M8, ask the patient to use the Patient's Rating Scale.

M7. How troubled or bothered have you been by these medical problems in the past 30 days? (Restrict response to problem days of Question M6.)

M8. How important to you now is treatment for these medical problems?
- If client is currently receiving medical treatment, refer to the need for additional medical treatment by the patient.

Interviewer Severity Rating

M9. How would you rate the patient's need for medical treatment?
- Refers to the patient's need for ***additional*** medical treatment.

Confidence Rating

Is the above information significantly distorted by:

M10. Patient's misrepresentation? 0–No 1–Yes

M11. Patient's inability to understand? 0–No 1–Yes

MEDICAL COMMENTS

(Include question number with your notes)

EMPLOYMENT/SUPPORT STATUS

E1. Education completed: ☐☐/☐☐ (Years/Months)
- GED = 12 years, note in comments.
- Include formal education only.

E2. Training or technical education completed: ☐☐ (Months)
- Formal/organized training only. For military training, include only training that can be used in civilian life (e.g., electronics, artillery).

E3. Do you have a profession, trade, or skill? 0–No 1–Yes ☐
- Employable, transferable skill acquired through training.
- If Yes, specify ____________________

E4. Do you have a valid driver's license? ☐
- Valid license; not suspended/revoked. 0–No 1–Yes

E5. Do you have an automobile available for use? ☐
- If answer to E4 is No, then E5 must be No. 0–No 1–Yes Does not require ownership, requires only availability on a regular basis.

E6. How long was your longest full-time job? ☐☐/☐☐ (Years/Months)
- Full time = 40+ hours weekly; does not necessarily mean most recent job.

E7. Usual (or last) occupation? ☐
(specify) ____________________
(Use Hollingshead Categories Reference Sheet)

E8. Does someone contribute to your support in any way? ☐
0–No 1–Yes
- Is patient receiving any regular support (i.e., cash, food, housing) from family/friend? Include spouse's contribution; exclude support by an institution.

E9. Does this constitute the majority of your support? ☐
0–No 1–Yes
- If E8 is No, then E9 is N.

E10. Usual employment pattern, past 3 years? ☐
1. Full time (40 hrs/week)
2. Part time (regular hours)
3. Part time (irregular hours)
4. Student
5. Service/Military
6. Retired/Disability
7. Unemployed
8. In controlled environment
- Answer should represent the majority of the last 3 years, not just the most recent selection. If there are equal times for more than one category, select that which best represents the current situation.

EMPLOYMENT/SUPPORT COMMENTS
(Include question number with your notes)

EMPLOYMENT/SUPPORT (cont.)

E11. How many days were you paid for working in the past 30 days? ☐☐
- Include "under the table" work, paid sick days, and vacation.

For Questions E12–17:

How much money did you receive from the following sources in the past 30 days?

E12. Employment ☐☐☐☐
- Net or "take home" pay; include any "under the table" money.

E13. Unemployment compensation ☐☐☐☐

E14. Welfare ☐☐☐☐
- Include food stamps, transportation money provided by an agency to go to and from treatment.

E15. Pensions, benefits, or Social Security ☐☐☐☐
- Include disability, pensions, retirement, veteran's benefits, SSI, and worker's compensation.

E16. Mate, family, or friends ☐☐☐☐
- Money for personal expenses (e.g., clothing); include unreliable sources of income. Record ***cash*** payments only; include windfalls (unexpected), money from loans, legal gambling, inheritance, tax returns, etc.

E17. Illegal ☐☐☐☐
- Cash obtained from drug dealing, stealing, fencing stolen goods, illegal gambling, prostitution, etc. Do not attempt to convert drugs exchanged to a dollar value.

E18. How many people depend on you for the majority of their food, shelter, etc.? ☐☐
- Must be regularly depending on patient; do include alimony/child support; do not include the patient or self-supporting spouse, etc.

E19. How many days have you experienced employment problems in the past 30 days? ☐☐
- Include inability to find work, if actively looking for work, or problems with present job in which that job is jeopardized.

For Questions E20 & E21, ask the patient to use the Patient's Rating Scale.

E20. How troubled or bothered have you been by these employment problems in the past 30 days? ☐
- If the patient has been incarcerated or detained during the past 30 days, he or she cannot have employment problems. In that case, an N response is indicated.

E21. How important to you now is counseling for these employment problems? ☐
- Stress help in finding or preparing for a job, not giving the patient a job.

Interviewer Severity Rating

E22. How would you rate the patient's need for employment counseling? ☐

Confidence Rating

Is the above information significantly distorted by:

E23. Patient's misrepresentation? 0–No 1–Yes ☐

E24. Patient's inability to understand? 0–No 1–Yes ☐

EMPLOYMENT/SUPPORT COMMENTS (cont.)

(Include question number with your notes)

____
____
____
____
____
____
____
____
____
____
____
____
____
____
____
____
____
____
____
____

ALCOHOL/DRUGS

Route of administration:

1. Oral
2. Nasal
3. Smoking
4. Non-IV injection
5. IV injection

- *Note the usual or most recent route. For more than one route, choose the most severe. The routes are listed from least severe to most severe.*

	Past 30 Days	Years of Regular Use	Route of Admin.
D1. Alcohol (any use at all)			
D2. Alcohol (to intoxication)			
D3. Heroin			
D4. Methadone			
D5. Other Opiates/Analgesics			
D6. Barbiturates			
D7. Sedatives/Hypnotics/Tranquilizers			
D8. Cocaine			
D9. Amphetamines			
D10. Cannabis			
D11. Hallucinogens			
D12. Inhalants			
D13. More than one substance per day (including alcohol)			

D14. According to the interviewer, which substance(s) is/are the major problem?

- Interviewer should determine the major drug of abuse. Code the number next to the drug in Questions D1–12, or "00" = no problem, "15" = alcohol and one or more drugs, "16" = more than one drug but no alcohol. Ask patient when not clear.

D15. How long was your last period of voluntary abstinence from this major substance? (Months)

- Last attempt of at least 1 month, not necessarily the longest. Periods of hospitalization/incarceration ***do not count***. Periods of Antabuse, methadone, or naltrexone use during abstinence ***do count***.
- "00" = never abstinent

D16. How many months ago did this abstinence end?

- If D15 = "00," then D16 = "NN."
- "00" = still abstinent.

How many times have you:

D17. Had alcohol DTs?

- ***Delirium Tremens*** (DTs): Occur 24-48 hours after last drink or significant decrease in alcohol intake; includes shaking, severe disorientation, fever, hallucinations. DTs usually require medical attention.

D18. Overdosed on drugs?

- ***Overdoses*** (OD): Requires intervention by someone to recover, not simply sleeping it off; include suicide attempts by OD.

ALCOHOL/DRUGS COMMENTS

(Include question number with your notes)

ALCOHOL/DRUGS (cont.)

How many times in your life have you been treated for:

D19. Alcohol abuse? ☐☐

D20. Drug abuse? ☐☐
- Include detoxification, halfway houses, in/outpatient counseling, and AA or NA (if 3+ meetings within 1-month period).

How many of these were detox only?

D21. Alcohol ☐☐

D22. Drugs ☐☐
- If D19 = "00," then Question D21 is "NN."
  If D20 = "00," then Question D22 is "NN."

How much money would you say you spent during the past 30 days on:

D23. Alcohol? ☐☐☐☐

D24. Drugs? ☐☐☐☐
- Count only actual money spent. What is the financial burden caused by drugs/alcohol?

D25. How many days have you been treated in an outpatient setting for alcohol or drugs in the past 30 days? ☐☐
- Include AA/NA

D99. <**OPTIONAL**> How many days have you been treated in an inpatient setting for alcohol or drugs in the past 30 days? ☐☐

How many days in the past 30 days have you experienced:

D26. Alcohol problems? ☐☐

D27. Drug problems? ☐☐
- Include: Craving, withdrawal symptoms, disturbing effects of use, or wanting to stop and being unable to.

For Questions D28-D31, ask the patient to use the Patient's Rating Scale. The patient is rating the need for additional substance abuse treatment.

How troubled or bothered have you been in the past 30 days by these:

D28. Alcohol problems? ☐

D29. Drug problems? ☐

How important to you now is treatment for:

D30. Alcohol problems? ☐

D31. Drug problems? ☐

Interviewer Severity Rating

How would you rate the patient's need for treatment for:

D32. Alcohol problems? ☐

D33. Drug problems? ☐

Confidence Rating

Is the above information significantly distorted by:

D34. Patient's misrepresentation? 0–No 1–Yes ☐

D35. Patient's inability to understand? 0–No 1–Yes ☐

ALCOHOL/DRUGS COMMENTS (cont.)

(Include question number with your notes)

LEGAL STATUS

L1. Was this admission prompted or suggested by the criminal justice system? 0–No 1–Yes ☐
- Judge, probation/parole officer, etc.

L2. Are you on parole or probation? 0–No 1–Yes ☐
- Note duration and level in comments.

How many times in your life have you been arrested and charged with the following:

L3. Shoplifting/Vandalism ☐☐ L10. Assault ☐☐

L4. Parole/Probation Violations ☐☐ L11. Arson ☐☐

L5. Drug Charges ☐☐ L12. Rape ☐☐

L6. Forgery ☐☐ L13. Homicide/ Manslaughter ☐☐

L7. Weapons Offense ☐☐ L14. Prostitution ☐☐

L8. Burglary/Larceny/ Breaking and Entering ☐☐ L15. Contempt of Court ☐☐

L9. Robbery ☐☐ L16. Other: ______ ☐☐
- Include total number of counts, not just convictions. Do not include juvenile (pre age 18) crimes, unless client was charged as an adult.
- Include formal charges only.

L17. How many of these charges resulted in convictions? ☐☐
- If L3–16 = 00, then question L17 = "NN."
- Do not include misdemeanor offenses from questions L18–20 below.
- Convictions include fines, probation, incarcerations, suspended sentences, guilty pleas, and plea bargaining.

How many times in your life have you been charged with the following:

L18. Disorderly conduct, vagrancy, public intoxication? ☐☐

L19. Driving while intoxicated? ☐☐

L20. Major driving violations? ☐☐
- Moving violations: speeding, reckless driving, no license, etc.

L21. How many months have you been incarcerated in your life? ☐☐
- If incarcerated 2 weeks or more, round this up to 1 month. List total number of months incarcerated.

L22. How long was your *last* incarceration? ☐☐ (Months)
- Enter "NN" if never incarcerated.

L23. What was it for? ☐☐
- Use codes L3–16, L18–20. If multiple charges, choose the most severe. Enter "NN" if never incarcerated.

L24. Are you presently awaiting charges, trial, or sentencing? 0–No 1–Yes ☐

L25. What for? ☐☐
- Use the number of the type of crime committed: L3–16 and L18–20.
- Refers to Question L24. If more than one charge, choose the most severe.

L26. How many days in the past 30 days were you detained or incarcerated? ☐☐
- Include being arrested and released on the same day.

LEGAL COMMENTS

(Include question number with your notes)

____

____

____

____

____

____

____

____

____

____

____

____

____

____

____

____

____

____

LEGAL STATUS (cont.)

L27. How many days in the past 30 days have you engaged in illegal activities for profit? ☐☐
- Exclude simple drug possession. Include drug dealing, prostitution, selling stolen goods, etc. May be cross-checked with Question E17 under Employment/Support Section.

For Questions L28-29, ask the patient to use the Patient's Rating Scale.

L28. How serious do you feel your present legal problems are? ☐
- Exclude civil problems

L29. How important to you now is counseling or referral for these legal problems? ☐
- Patient is rating a need for ***additional*** referral to legal counsel for defense against criminal charges.

Interviewer Severity Rating

L30. How would you rate the patient's need for legal services or counseling? ☐

Confidence Rating

Is the above information significantly distorted by:

L31. Patient's misrepresentation? 0–No 1–Yes ☐

L32. Patient's inability to understand? 0–No 1–Yes ☐

LEGAL COMMENTS (cont.)

(Include question number with your notes)

____

____

____

____

____

____

____

____

____

____

____

____

FAMILY HISTORY

Have any of your blood-related relatives had what you would call a significant drinking, drug use, or psychiatric problem? Specifically, was there a problem that did or should have led to treatment?

Mother's Side	Alcohol	Drug	Psych.	**Father's Side**	Alcohol	Drug	Psych.	**Siblings**	Alcohol	Drug	Psych.
H1. Grandmother	☐	☐	☐	H6. Grandmother	☐	☐	☐	H11. Brother	☐	☐	☐
H2. Grandfather	☐	☐	☐	H7. Grandfather	☐	☐	☐	H12. Sister	☐	☐	☐
H3. Mother	☐	☐	☐	H8. Father	☐	☐	☐				
H4. Aunt	☐	☐	☐	H9. Aunt	☐	☐	☐				
H5. Uncle	☐	☐	☐	H10. Uncle	☐	☐	☐				

0 = Clearly No for any relatives in that category X = Uncertain or don't know
1 = Clearly Yes for any relatives in that category N = Never had a relative in that category
- In cases in which there is more than one person for a category, report the most severe. Accept the patient's judgment on these questions.

FAMILY HISTORY COMMENTS

(Include question number with your notes)

____

____

____

____

____

FAMILY/SOCIAL RELATIONSHIPS

F1. Marital Status: ☐
1–Married 3–Widowed 5–Divorced
2–Remarried 4–Separated 6–Never Married
• Code common-law marriage as "1" and specify in comments.

F2. How long have you been in this marital status (Question F1)? ☐☐/☐☐ (Years/Months)
• If never married, then since age 18.

F3. Are you satisfied with this situation? ☐
0–No 1–Indifferent 2–Yes
• Satisfied = generally liking the situation.
• Refers to Questions F1 and F2.

F4. Usual living arrangements (past 3 years): ☐
1–With sexual partner and children
2–With sexual partner alone
3–With children alone
4–With parents
5–With family
6–With friends
7–Alone
8–Controlled environment
9–No stable arrangement
• Choose arrangements most representative of the past 3 years. If there is an even split in time between these arrangements, choose the most recent arrangement.

F5. How long have you lived in these arrangements? ☐☐/☐☐ (Years/Months)
• If with parents or family, since age 18.
• Code years and months living in arrangements from Question F4.

F6. Are you satisfied with these arrangements? ☐
0–No 1–Indifferent 2–Yes

Do you live with anyone who:

F7. Has a current alcohol problem? 0–No 1–Yes ☐

F8. Uses nonprescribed drugs, or abuses prescribed drugs? 0–No 1–Yes ☐

F9. With whom do you spend most of your free time? ☐
1–Family 2–Friends 3–Alone
• If a girlfriend/boyfriend is considered as family by patient, then the patient must refer to that person as "family" throughout this section, not as a friend.

F10. Are you satisfied with spending your free time this way? ☐
0–No 1–Indifferent 2–Yes
• A satisfied response must indicate that the person generally likes the situation. Refers to Question F9.

F11. How many close friends do you have? ☐
• Stress that you mean close. Exclude family members. These are "reciprocal" relationships or mutually supportive relationships.

Would you say you have had a close, long-lasting, personal relationship with any of the following people in your life:

F12. Mother ☐
F13. Father ☐
F14. Brothers/sisters ☐
F15. Sexual partner/spouse ☐
F16. Children ☐
F17. Friends ☐

0 = Clearly No for all in class
1 = Clearly Yes for any in class
X = Uncertain or "I don't know"
N = Never had a relative in category

FAMILY/SOCIAL COMMENTS
(Include question number with your notes)

____
____
____
____
____
____
____
____
____
____
____
____
____
____
____
____
____
____

FAMILY/SOCIAL (cont.)

Have you had significant periods in which you have experienced serious problems getting along with:
0–No 1–Yes

	Past 30 days	In Your Life
F18. Mother	☐	☐
F19. Father	☐	☐
F20. Brother/sister	☐	☐
F21. Sexual partner/spouse	☐	☐
F22. Children	☐	☐
F23. Other significant family (specify) ______	☐	☐
F24. Close friends	☐	☐
F25. Neighbors	☐	☐
F26. Coworkers	☐	☐

- "Serious problems" mean those that endangered the relationship.
- A "problem" requires contact of some sort, either by telephone or in person.

Has anyone ever abused you? 0–No 1–Yes

	Past 30 days	In Your Life
F27. Emotionally • Made you feel bad through harsh words.	☐	☐
F28. Physically • Caused you physical harm.	☐	☐
F29. Sexually • Forced sexual advances/acts.	☐	☐

How many days in the past 30 days have you had serious conflicts with:

F30. Your family? ☐

F31. Other people (excluding family)? ☐

For Questions F32–35, ask the patient to use the Patient's Rating Scale.

How troubled or bothered have you been in the past 30 days by:

F32. Family problems? ☐

F33. Social problems? ☐

How important to you now is treatment or counseling for:

F34. Family problems ☐
- Patient is rating his or her need for counseling for family problems, not whether the patient would be willing to attend.

F35. Social problems ☐
- Include patient's need to seek treatment for such social problems as loneliness, inability to socialize, and dissatisfaction with friends. Patient rating should refer to dissatisfaction, conflicts, or other serious problems.

Interviewer Severity Rating

F36. How would you rate the patient's need for family and/or social counseling? ☐

Confidence Rating

Is the above information significantly distorted by:

F37. Patient's misrepresentation? 0–No 1–Yes ☐

F38. Patient's inability to understand? 0–No 1–Yes ☐

FAMILY/SOCIAL COMMENTS (cont.)
(Include question number with your notes)

____

PSYCHIATRIC STATUS

How many times have you been treated for any psychological or emotional problems:

P1. In a hospital or inpatient setting? ☐☐

P2. Outpatient/private patient? ☐☐
- Do not include substance abuse, employment, or family counseling. Treatment episode = a series of more or less continuous visits or treatment days, not the number of visits or treatment days.
- Enter diagnosis in comments if known.

P3. Do you receive a pension for a psychiatric disability? ☐
0–No 1–Yes

Have you had a significant period of time (that was not a direct result of alcohol/drug use) in which you have: 0–No 1–Yes

	Past 30 days	In Your Life
P4. Experienced serious depression, sadness, hopelessness, loss of interest, difficulty with daily functioning?	☐	☐
P5. Experienced serious anxiety/tension—were uptight, unreasonably worried, unable to feel relaxed?	☐	☐
P6. Experienced hallucinations—saw things or heard voices that others didn't see/hear?	☐	☐
P7. Experienced trouble understanding, concentrating, or remembering?	☐	☐
P8. Experienced trouble controlling violent behavior, including episodes of rage or violence? • Patient can be under the influence of alcohol/drugs.	☐	☐
P9. Experienced serious thoughts of suicide? • Patient seriously considered a plan for taking his or her life. Patient can be under the influence of alcohol/drugs.	☐	☐
P10. Attempted suicide? • Include actual suicidal gestures or attempts. • Patient can be under the influence of alcohol/drugs.	☐	☐
P11. Been prescribed medication for any psychological or emotional problems? • Prescribed for the patient by a physician. Record "Yes" if a medication was prescribed even if the patient is not taking it.	☐	☐

P12. How many days in the past 30 days have you experienced these psychological or emotional problems? ☐☐
- This refers to problems noted in Questions P4–P10.

For Questions P13–P14, ask the patient to use the Patient's Rating Scale.

P13. How much have you been troubled or bothered by these psychological or emotional problems in the past 30 days? ☐
- Patient should be rating the problem days from Question P12.

P14. How important to you now is treatment for these psychological or emotional problems? ☐

PSYCHIATRIC STATUS COMMENTS
(Include question number with your comments)

____
____
____
____
____
____
____
____
____
____
____
____
____
____
____
____
____
____
____
____

PSYCHIATRIC STATUS (cont.)

The following items are to be completed by the interviewer:

At the time of the interview, the patient was: 0–No 1–Yes

P15. Obviously depressed/withdrawn ☐

P16. Obviously hostile ☐

P17. Obviously anxious/nervous ☐

P18. Having trouble with reality testing, thought disorders, paranoid thinking ☐

P19. Having trouble comprehending, concentrating, remembering ☐

P20. Having suicidal thoughts ☐

Interviewer Severity Rating

P21. How would you rate the patient's need for psychiatric/psychological treatment? ☐

Confidence Rating

Is the above information significantly distorted by:

P22. Patient's misrepresentation? 0–No 1–Yes ☐

P23. Patient's inability to understand? 0–No 1–Yes ☐

PSYCHIATRIC STATUS COMMENTS (cont.)

(Include question number with your notes)

Source: Carise, D., McLellan, A. T., Gifford, L. S., & Kleber, H. D. (1999). Developing a national addiction information system: An introduction to the Drug Evaluation Network System. *Journal of Substance Abuse Treatment, 17*(1–2), 67–77. https://doi.org/10.1016/s0740-5472(98)00047-6

APPENDIX 5.4

ADDICTION SEVERITY INDEX (ASI) SAMPLE REPORT

CLIENT:	Susan T.
DOB:	12/21/1980
Date of Interview:	10/14/20
Interviewer:	William Smith, M.A, CSAC II.

General Information Section

The following evaluation report is a summary based on an in-person interview with Susan T. conducted on October 14, 2020. This ASI summary is based on the client's self-report regarding lifetime and recent Medical, Employment, Alcohol, Drug, Legal, Family/Social, and Psychiatric involvement and/or problems. Included in each of these sections is the interviewer's severity rating and confidence ratings as well as an overall level-of-care recommendation based on these findings.

Susan is a 40-year-old divorced woman who is the mother of two children, a son aged 11 and a daughter aged 9. She states she grew up in an intact family with both biological parents and an older brother, Ted, who was killed at age 18 in an auto accident. Susan states that she graduated from a Catholic high school when she was 17 years old and was accepted into a 4-year college. However, Susan indicates that she "flunked out by her sophomore year" because of "partying." Upon leaving college, Susan returned home to live with her parents and began working at a local bank as a teller. She received several promotions and eventually became manager of the bank, a job that she held until 2017. Susan was married when she was 22 to a high school sweetheart. They were married for 13 years and divorced when Susan caught her husband in an extramarital affair. Susan remained in the marital home and receives child support from her husband whom she shares custody of their children with. It was around the time of the divorce what Susan began socializing more with friends of hers who were also divorced by going out to bars. Susan was arrested for driving under the influence last August, which prompted this evaluation as a condition of the court.

Alcohol & Drug Section

Lifetime and Recent Alcohol Use: In her lifetime, Susan indicates that she began drinking intermittently in high school and did not begin to drink regularly until her divorce in 2015. For the next 5 years, Susan reports that she drank regularly and had progressively increased her alcohol intake. Client reports that she has never experienced alcohol withdrawal symptoms other than slight hand tremor and diaphoresis (perspiring). She has not experienced alcohol-related seizures or delirium tremens.

Lifetime and Recent Drug Use: Susan reports that, around the time of her divorce, she began to have difficulty sleeping. Her primary care physician prescribed Xanax for daytime calming and Ambien to help her fall asleep. She reports having smoked cannabis while in college and began smoking regularly with her roommate. Client also reports having used cocaine a few times and nonprescription use of Ritalin for when she had to study for exams or write term papers. She reports no other substance use.

Page Two
Client: Susan T.

In the past 30 days, Susan indicates that she drank everyday during the past month and that she used Xanax daily in the past 30 days and Ambien approximately 10 times in the past four weeks. Client reports that she has smoked cannabis approximately eight times in the past 30 days; she has not used any hallucinogens.

Alcohol and Drug Treatment History

Susan states that she saw an outpatient addictions counselor for individual counseling at her parent's insistence when she flunked out of college. She recalls that the counselor had her go to a few Alcoholics Anonymous (AA) meetings. After several weekly sessions, Susan convinced her parents that she did not need counseling and therefore dropped out of treatment.

Client Perception of Severity of Alcohol and Drug Problems and Desire for Treatment

Based on the Severity Rating (7), Susan has experienced significant alcohol-related problems during the past 30 days, which clearly indicates the need for treatment. She also indicates being extremely distressed by these problems, especially in the aftermath of having received a DUI offense approximately 2 months ago. Susan recognizes the need for treatment for her drinking; however, she does not feel that her benzodiazepine use is problematic (although she readily admits to using Xanax on a daily basis).

Interviewer Impressions and Recommendations—Alcohol and Drugs: Based on this counselor's Confidence Rating, it does not appear that Susan had difficulty understanding the questions posed to her, and she did not appear to misrepresent herself. It is my impression, therefore, that Susan was neither defensive nor guarded in this interview. Also, the client did not misrepresent her alcohol or drug use history, as evidenced by her readily admitting to past use and problems resulting from that substance use. It is this interviewer's belief that both alcohol and drugs are Susan's most significant problem that she is currently experiencing as it has impacted on her overall functioning in several areas. It is vital that Susan receive treatment for her substance use given the problems that she has reported.

Additional Alcohol and Drug Comments: Client appears sincerely motivated to participate in treatment for her alcohol-use problems. The client states that she wants to be a better parent and to resume her career in the banking industry. Susan believes that her use of alcohol is responsible for the majority of problems she has experienced. However, she tends to view her benzodiazepine use as something that helps her to function rather than something that impairs her functioning.

Family/Social Section

Susan is currently divorced and feels justified in her seeking a divorce based on her ex-husband's marital infidelity. She has been divorced for about 5 years. She has lived with her son and daughter in the marital home since the separation/divorce.

Recovery Environment and Social Contacts: A few months following the client's marital separation, she began to socialize with female friends who were also divorced. Much of her socialization consisted of going out to bars in the evening, leaving her children with her parents or a babysitter. On one of these outings, Susan was pulled over by the police when she swerved and hit a parked car. No one was

Page Three
Client: Susan T.

injured; however, this was a wake-up call for Susan, who states she recognized her "bar-hopping" had gotten out of hand. Susan states that she continued to drink cocktails at home following the DUI but under no circumstances has she drank and gotten behind the wheel of her car.

Other than her divorced female friends, the client states that she has few friends that she can rely on. She is friendly with another bank manager from another branch of the bank that she would have lunch with, however, this coworker is married and also has children.

Relationship Problems Lifetime: Susan reported that her drinking had caused tension between her and her parents. She also admits that her drinking was a source of conflict between her and her ex-husband. With the exception of one friendship what was similarly adversely impacted by her drinking; she indicates that her current friends tend to drink similarly to how she was drinking. The client did indicate that her drinking caused some difficulties in her relationships with coworkers and bosses, especially on those days when she would come into work feeling hung over. Susan did not report any history of emotional, physical, or sexual abuse or other childhood trauma, other than the loss of her brother who was killed in an auto accident when she was 16 years old.

Relationship Problems Past 30 Days: In the past 30 days, Susan reports no significant relationship problems, although her parents are "concerned" because of her DUI, and her two children have expressed their concerns to her as well. Susan reports no recent emotional, physical, or sexual abuse trauma.

Client Perception of Severity of Family and Social Problems and Desire for Treatment: Susan seems to accept the concerns expressed by her parents and her children as valid and is neither resentful nor defensive in her response to these concerns. The relationship problems that Susan has disclosed further warrant her referral to treatment.

Interviewer Impressions and Recommendations—Family and Social: It is this counselor's impression that Susan understood all of the questions and that she did not deliberately misrepresent this information. Susan's drinking has resulted in considerable social and relationship problems that she admits are warranted. She expresses a desire to improve her relationships with her parents and children.

Psychiatric Section

Serious Emotional and Psychological Problems—Lifetime: Susan does not appear to manifest any significant past history of emotional or psychological problems. However, she does have a history of being prescribed anxiolytic medications for several years, and she states that these have been beneficial to her well-being. Yet, the benzodiazepine medications are addictive, and Susan reports using one of them on a daily basis for quite some time. These meds are being prescribed by her primary care physician. Susan reports no history of treatment for psychological or mental health problems. In addition, she is not receiving any compensation for a psychiatric disability.

Page Four
Client: Susan T.

Recent Serious Emotional and Psychological Problems: Susan reports having had serious difficulties with anxiety in the past 30 days related to the DUI and subsequent accident. Susan is fearful of the legal repercussions of the DUI and whether she will face jail time.

Client Perception of Severity of Emotional and Psychological Problems and Desire for Treatment: Susan's anxiety and consequential benzodiazepine use represent significant co-occurring disorders. Her current reports of anxiety have been exacerbated by the DUI and pending legal charges. Susan admits that she should have sought mental health treatment for her anxiety and seems to have some insight into the limitations of anxiolytic medications. Susan also admits that her drinking and anxiety contributed to her job loss.

Interviewer Impressions and Recommendations—Psychiatric: It is this counselor's impression that Susan understood all of the questions and that she did not deliberately misrepresent her emotional/mental health information. She does, however, appear to manifest moderate psychiatric symptoms that suggests that treatment is warranted, especially if Susan were to be detoxed from benzodiazepine medication, in which case an SSRI might be more beneficial along with counseling to help her address her anxiety.

Legal Section

History of Charges and Arrests: As indicated earlier, Susan's referral for this substance abuse evaluation came about as a result of her recent DUI arrest that took place approximately two and half months ago. Susan reports that, at the time of her arrest, she had hit a parked car. Her BAC was reported to have been around .20, which is over twice the legal limit for this state. Susan reported no other arrests, although she did admit to being charged with Reckless Driving when she was home during summer break from college. Susan recalls that she had been drinking when she was pulled over for swerving but was not charged with a DUI.

Current Legal Involvement: In the past 30 days, Susan reports no other arrests or legal involvement other than her DUI offense. Her benzodiazepine prescriptions are obtained legally via her PCP's prescription. Susan is awaiting her court hearing on the DUI charges. She has not been on probation or parole.

Client Perception of Severity of Legal Problems and Desire for Treatment: Susan is clearly distressed by her pending legal charges resulting from the DUI arrest/accident. She reports that she has sought the advice of legal counsel and that her attorney was supportive of her seeking this substance-abuse evaluation.

Interviewer Impressions and Recommendations—Legal: This counselor's impression is that Susan understood all of the questions and that she did not deliberately misrepresent this legal information. She was not defensive in sharing this legal information, and she does appear to be very concerned about the implications a legal conviction would have on her future career in the banking industry.

Page Five
Client: Susan T.

Medical Section

Medical History: Susan had no history of any hospitalizations for any medical problems and reports that she is in good health. Similarly, Susan is not currently receiving Social Security Disability benefits nor has she in the past year.

Client Perception of Severity of Medical Problems and Desire for Treatment: Susan does not report any current medical problems or concerns in the past 30 days. She reports that she is currently in good health, therefore, she does not feel she is in need of medical treatment or assistance at this time.

Interviewer Impressions and Recommendations—Medical: This counselor's impression is that Susan understood all of the questions and that she did not intentionally misrepresent any of her medical history. She appears to have no need for medical treatment at this time.

Additional Comments Regarding Medical: Susan did express some concerns about how her drinking might affect her health in the future.

Employment Section

Employment History: Susan had been working full time as a manager of a bank up until 2017. She had begun working for the bank shortly after she left college and had received several promotions. Susan was asked to step down from her position as bank manager after an altercation with one of her staff. Susan states that she was "under a great deal of stress" at the time, attributing much of this stress to her divorce and lack of parenting support from her ex-husband.

Current Financial Resources: When Susan left the bank, she was offered a generous severance package, which has helped to support her two children and herself along with unemployment benefits and child support.

Education, Training and Resources: Susan is a high school graduate who has approximately 24 undergraduate college credits in business/finance and general education. She received a lot of trainings in banking and management as she was advancing in her positions at the bank where she worked for several years.

Client Perception of Severity of Employment Problems and Desire for Treatment: Susan indicates that she will need to work once her severance package is entirely spent and she is no longer eligible for unemployment benefits. The recent COVID crisis worked to Susan's advantage in that her unemployment benefits were extended. She is concerned, however, that a DUI conviction would adversely impact her ability to obtain a job in the banking industry. Susan also has some insight into how her drinking and coming to work hungover had exacerbated her ability to cope with day-to-day job stress.

Page Six
Client: Susan T.

Interviewer Impressions and Recommendations—Employment: It is this counselor's impression that Susan understood all of the questions and that she did not purposely misrepresent this information, nor was she defensive in responding to questions posed to her. Given her current unemployed status, vocational/employment counseling is highly recommended once the client is stabilized in her SUD recovery.

Additional Employment Comments: Client had a stable history of employment with the bank where she had risen to the position of bank manager. Her employment ended in 2017, and she has been living on her severance and unemployment and child support. Susan is receptive to vocational counseling and to receiving additional training.

Interviewer Comment

The previous information is based on Susan T's responses to questions from the Addiction Severity Index interview and was completed on 10/14/20. This information will be used to guide treatment recommendations pertaining to level of care for Susan and will also be used to develop a specific treatment care plan.

Submitted by:

____

James Carver, MA, LCADC

APPENDIX 5.5

ALCOHOL USE DISORDERS IDENTIFICATION TEST

The **AUDIT** is designed to help in the self-assessment of alcohol consumption and to identify any implications for the person's health and well-being, now and in the future.

It consists of 10 questions on alcohol use. The responses to these questions can be scored, and the total score prompts feedback to the person and in some cases offers specific advice.

Please select your gender.

❍ Male
❍ Female

1. How often do you have a drink containing alcohol?

❍ Never
❍ Monthly or less
❍ 2–4 times a month
❍ 2–3 times a week
❍ 4 or more times a week

2. How many standard drinks containing alcohol do you have on a typical day when drinking?

❍ 1 or 2
❍ 3 or 4
❍ 5 or 6
❍ 7 to 9
❍ 10 or more

3. How often do you have six or more drinks on one occasion?

❍ Never
❍ Less than monthly
❍ Monthly
❍ Weekly
❍ Daily or almost daily

4. During the past year, how often have you found that you were not able to stop drinking once you had started?

❍ Never
❍ Less than monthly
❍ Monthly
❍ Weekly
❍ Daily or almost daily

5. During the past year, how often have you failed to do what was normally expected of you because of drinking?
   - ❍ Never
   - ❍ Less than monthly
   - ❍ Monthly
   - ❍ Weekly
   - ❍ Daily or almost daily

6. During the past year, how often have you needed a drink in the morning to get yourself going after a heavy drinking session?
   - ❍ Never
   - ❍ Less than monthly
   - ❍ Monthly
   - ❍ Weekly
   - ❍ Daily or almost daily

7. During the past year, how often have you had a feeling of guilt or remorse after drinking?
   - ❍ Never
   - ❍ Less than monthly
   - ❍ Monthly
   - ❍ Weekly
   - ❍ Daily or almost daily

8. During the past year, how often have you been unable to remember what happened the night before because you had been drinking?
   - ❍ Never
   - ❍ Less than monthly
   - ❍ Monthly
   - ❍ Weekly
   - ❍ Daily or almost daily

9. Have you or someone else been injured as a result of your drinking?
   - ❍ No
   - ❍ Yes, but not in the past year
   - ❍ Yes, during the past year

10. Has a relative or friend, doctor, or other health worker been concerned about your drinking or suggested you cut down?
    - ❍ No
    - ❍ Yes, but not in the past year
    - ❍ Yes, during the past year

Source: As a World Health Organization-approved instrument, the AUDIT is in the public domain. Saunders, J. B., Aasland, O. G., Babor, T. F., de la Fuente, J. R., & Grant, M. (1993). Development of the Alcohol Use Disorders Identification Test (AUDIT): WHO Collaborative Project on Early Detection of Persons with Harmful Alcohol Consumption II. *Addiction, 88*(6), 791–804. https://doi.org/10.1111/j.1360-0443.1993.tb02093.x

APPENDIX 5.6

SIMPLE SCREENING INVENTORY

SIMPLE SCREENING INSTRUMENT FOR SUBSTANCE ABUSE (SSI-SA)
SCREENING INSTRUMENT

NAME:_______________ **SCREENING DATE:**_______________

I'm going to ask you a few questions about your use of alcohol and other drugs during the past 6 months. During the **past 6 months**...

1. Have you used alcohol or other drugs? (such as wine, beer, hard liquor, pot, coke, heroin or other opiates, uppers, downers, hallucinogens, or inhalants). YES ____ NO ____
2. Have you felt that you use too much alcohol or other drugs? YES ____ NO ____
3. Have you tried to cut down or quit drinking or using drugs? YES ____ NO ____
4. Have you gone to anyone for help because of your drinking or drug use? YES___ NO ____
5. Have you had any health problems? For example, have you:

___ had blackouts or other periods of memory loss?

___ injured your head after drinking or using drugs?

___ had convulsions, delirium tremens (DTs)?

___ had hepatitis or other liver problems?

___ felt sick, shaky, or depressed when you stopped?

___ felt "coke bugs" or a crawling feeling under the skin after you stopped using drugs?

___ been injured after drinking or using?

___ used needles to shoot drugs?

Give a "YES" answer if at least one of the eight presented items is marked
YES _____ NO _____

6. Has drinking or other drug use caused problems between you and family or friends?
   YES _____ NO _____
7. Has your drinking or other drug use caused problems at school or work?
   YES _____ NO _____
8. Have you been arrested or had other legal problems? (such as bouncing bad checks, driving while intoxicated, theft, or drug possession)? YES _____ NO _____
9. Have you lost your temper or gotten into arguments or fights while drinking or using other drugs? YES _____ NO _____
10. Are you needing to drink or use drugs more and more to get the effect you want?
    YES _____ NO _____
11. Do you spend a lot of time thinking about or trying to get alcohol or other drugs?
    YES _____ NO _____
12. When drinking or using drugs, are you more likely to do something you wouldn't normally do such as break rules, break the law, sell things that are important to you, or have unprotected sex with someone? YES _____ NO _____
13. Do you feel bad or guilty about your drinking or drug use? YES _____ NO _____

The next questions are about your lifetime experiences.

14. Have you ever had a drinking or other drug problem? YES _____ NO _____
15. Have any of your family members ever had a drinking or drug problem? YES _____ NO _____
16. Do you feel that you have a drinking or drug problem now? YES _____ NO _____

SCORING

SCORE: (Questions 1 and 15 are not scored)
Number of "Yes" Answers _____
. Screened positive = a score of 4 or greater.

Source: Center for Substance Abuse Treatment. (1994). *Simple Screening Inventory.* Government Printing Office.

APPENDIX 5.7

CANNABIS ABUSE SCREENING TEST

In the last 12 months, have you smoked cannabis?

Yes ☐ No ☐

In the last 12 months... Mark one box for each line	Never	Rarely	From time to time	Fairly often	Very often
Have you smoked cannabis before midday?	❒ 0	❒ 1	❒ 2	❒ 3	❒ 4
Have you smoked cannabis when you were alone?	❒ 0	❒ 1	❒ 2	❒ 3	❒ 4
Have you had memory problems when you smoked cannabis?	❒ 0	❒ 1	❒ 2	❒ 3	❒ 4
Have friends or members of your family told you that you ought to reduce your cannabis use?	❒ 0	❒ 1	❒ 2	❒ 3	❒ 4
Have you tried to reduce or stop your cannabis use without succeeding?	❒ 0	❒ 1	❒ 2	❒ 3	❒ 4
Have you had problems because of your use of cannabis (argument, fight, accident, bad result at school, etc.)?	❒ 0	❒ 1	❒ 2	❒ 3	❒ 4
Which ones?					

To calculate a score, the responses are coded on a scale of 0 to 4. The total score obtained (which can range from 0 to 24) indicates whether or not the questioned users are at risk. A score of less than 3 indicates no addiction risk. A score of 3 or less than 7 indicates low addiction risk, and a score of 7 or above indicates high addiction risk.

SCORE	

Source: Legleye, S., Karila, L., Beck, F., & Reynaud, M. (2007). Validation of the CAST, a general population Cannabis Abuse Screening Test. *Journal of Substance Use, 12*(4), 233–242. https://doi.org/10.1080/14659890701476532

APPENDIX 5.8.1

MARIJUANA CRAVING QUESTIONNAIRE: PART I

INSTRUCTIONS: Indicate how strongly you agree or disagree with each of the following statements by placing a check mark in one of the spaces between STRONGLY DISAGREE and STRONGLY AGREE. The closer you place your check mark to one end or the other indicates the strength of your agreement or disagreement. If you do not agree or disagree with a statement, place your check mark in the middle space. Please complete every item. We are interested in how you are thinking or feeling right now as you are filling out the questionnaire.

1. Smoking marijuana would be pleasant right now.

   STRONGLY DISAGREE ______________________________ STRONGLY AGREE

2. I could not easily limit how much marijuana I smoked right now,

   STRONGLY DISAGREE ______________________________ STRONGLY AGREE

3. Right now, I am making plans to use marijuana.

   STRONGLY DISAGREE ______________________________ STRONGLY AGREE

4. I would feel more in control of things right now if I could smoke marijuana.

   STRONGLY DISAGREE ______________________________ STRONGLY AGREE

5. Smoking marijuana would help me sleep better at night.

   STRONGLY DISAGREE ______________________________ STRONGLY AGREE

6. If I smoked marijuana right now, I would feel less tense.

   STRONGLY DISAGREE ______________________________ STRONGLY AGREE

7. I would not be able to control how much marijuana I smoked if I had some here.

   STRONGLY DISAGREE ______________________________ STRONGLY AGREE

8. It would be great to smoke marijuana right now.

   STRONGLY DISAGREE ______________________________ STRONGLY AGREE

9. I would feel less anxious if I smoked marijuana right now.

   STRONGLY DISAGREE ______________________________ STRONGLY AGREE

10. I need to smoke marijuana now.

    STRONGLY DISAGREE ______________________________ STRONGLY AGREE

11. If I were smoking marijuana right now, I would feel less nervous.

    STRONGLY DISAGREE ______________________________ STRONGLY AGREE

12. Smoking marijuana would make me content.

    STRONGLY DISAGREE ______________________________ STRONGLY AGREE

Scoring of the 12-Item Marijuana Craving Questionnaire (MCQ)

Factor analysis of the 47-item MCQ yielded four factors, which we have termed compulsivity, emotionality, expectancy, and purposefulness (Heishman et al. Addiction 96:1023-1034, 2001). The 12-item MCQ was constructed by selecting the three items from each factor that exhibited optimal within-factor reliability (Cronbach's alpha coefficient) and inter-item correlation.

All items are scored on a 1–7 scale (Strongly Disagree = 1 and Strongly Agree = 7). The scores of the three items in *each* factor should be summed for a total factor scale score (range 3–21).

FACTOR 1 (Compulsivity, alpha = 0.75, inter-item correlation = 0.50)
2. I could not easily limit how much marijuana I smoked right now.
7. I would not be able to control how much marijuana I smoked if I had some here.
10. I need to smoke marijuana now.

FACTOR 2 (Emotionality, alpha = 0.77, inter-item correlation = 0.52)
4. I would feel more in control of things right now if I could smoke marijuana.
6. If I smoked marijuana right now, I would feel less tense.
9. I would feel less anxious if I smoked marijuana right now.

FACTOR 3 (Expectancy, alpha = 0.55, inter-item correlation = 0.29)
5. Smoking marijuana would help me sleep better at night.
11. If I were smoking marijuana right now, I would feel less nervous.
12. Smoking marijuana would make me content.

FACTOR 4 (Purposefulness, alpha = 0.68, inter-item correlation = 0.42)
1. Smoking marijuana would be pleasant right now.
3. Right now, I am making plans to use marijuana.
8. It would be great to smoke marijuana right now.

Source: Heishman, S. J., Singleton, E. G., & Liguori, A. (2001). Marijuana Craving Questionnaire: Development and initial validation of a self-report instrument. *Addiction, 96*(7), 1023–1034. https://doi.org/10.1046/j.1360-0443.2001.967102312.x

APPENDIX 5.8.2

MARIJUANA CRAVING QUESTIONNAIRE: PART II

***INSTRUCTIONS:* Indicate how strongly you agree or disagree with each of the following statements by placing a check mark along each line between STRONGLY DISAGREE and STRONGLY AGREE. The closer you place your check mark to one end or the other indicates the strength of your agreement or disagreement. Please complete every item. We are interested in how strongly you are thinking or feeling right now as you are filling out the questionnaire.**

1. If there was marijuana right here in front of me, it would be hard not to smoke it.
   STRONGLY DISAGREE ___ : ___ : ___ : ___ : ___ : ___ : ___ STRONGLY AGREE
2. Smoking marijuana would not be pleasant right now.
   STRONGLY DISAGREE ___ : ___ : ___ : ___ : ___ : ___ : ___ STRONGLY AGREE
3. I would feel better if I could smoke marijuana.
   STRONGLY DISAGREE ___ : ___ : ___ : ___ : ___ : ___ : ___ STRONGLY AGREE
4. If I had the chance to smoke marijuana, I think I would use it.
   STRONGLY DISAGREE ___ : ___ : ___ : ___ : ___ : ___ : ___ STRONGLY AGREE
5. Smoking marijuana would be wonderful.
   STRONGLY DISAGREE ___ : ___ : ___ : ___ : ___ : ___ : ___ STRONGLY AGREE
6. Even if it were possible, I probably would not smoke marijuana right now.
   STRONGLY DISAGREE ___ : ___ : ___ : ___ : ___ : ___ : ___ STRONGLY AGREE
7. Right now, I miss smoking marijuana.
   STRONGLY DISAGREE ___ : ___ : ___ : ___ : ___ : ___ : ___ STRONGLY AGREE
8. I am going to smoke marijuana as soon as I possibly can.
   STRONGLY DISAGREE ___ : ___ : ___ : ___ : ___ : ___ : ___ STRONGLY AGREE
9. I would feel more anxious if I smoked marijuana right now.
   STRONGLY DISAGREE ___ : ___ : ___ : ___ : ___ : ___ : ___ STRONGLY AGREE
10. Smoking marijuana would make things seem just perfect.
    STRONGLY DISAGREE ___ : ___ : ___ : ___ : ___ : ___ : ___ STRONGLY AGREE
11. I have an urge to use marijuana now.
    STRONGLY DISAGREE ___ : ___ : ___ : ___ : ___ : ___ : ___ STRONGLY AGREE

12. Right now, I am not making any plans to use marijuana.

STRONGLY DISAGREE ___ : ___ : ___ : ___ : ___ : ___ : ___ STRONGLY AGREE

13. I would feel less in control of things right now if I could smoke marijuana.

STRONGLY DISAGREE ___ : ___ : ___ : ___ : ___ : ___ : ___ STRONGLY AGREE

14. Smoking marijuana would help me sleep better at night.

STRONGLY DISAGREE ___ : ___ : ___ : ___ : ___ : ___ : ___ STRONGLY AGREE

15. I could not stop myself from smoking marijuana if I had some here.

STRONGLY DISAGREE ___ : ___ : ___ : ___ : ___ : ___ : ___ STRONGLY AGREE

16. If I smoked a little marijuana right now, I would not be able to stop using it.

STRONGLY DISAGREE ___ : ___ : ___ : ___ : ___ : ___ : ___ STRONGLY AGREE

17. I want to smoke marijuana so bad that I can almost taste it.

STRONGLY DISAGREE ___ : ___ : ___ : ___ : ___ : ___ : ___ STRONGLY AGREE

18. Nothing would be better than smoking marijuana right now.

STRONGLY DISAGREE ___ : ___ : ___ : ___ : ___ : ___ : ___ STRONGLY AGREE

19. I would do almost anything for a “joint”.

STRONGLY DISAGREE ___ : ___ : ___ : ___ : ___ : ___ : ___ STRONGLY AGREE

20. Having a “joint” would be ideal.

STRONGLY DISAGREE ___ : ___ : ___ : ___ : ___ : ___ : ___ STRONGLY AGREE

21. I do not want to use marijuana right now.

STRONGLY DISAGREE ___ : ___ : ___ : ___ : ___ : ___ : ___ STRONGLY AGREE

22. I would feel less irritable if I could smoke marijuana right now.

STRONGLY DISAGREE ___ : ___ : ___ : ___ : ___ : ___ : ___ STRONGLY AGREE

23. I am thinking of ways to get marijuana.

STRONGLY DISAGREE ___ : ___ : ___ : ___ : ___ : ___ : ___ STRONGLY AGREE

24. All I want to do right now is smoke marijuana.

STRONGLY DISAGREE ___ : ___ : ___ : ___ : ___ : ___ : ___ STRONGLY AGREE

25. It would be difficult to turn down a “joint” right this minute.

STRONGLY DISAGREE ___ : ___ : ___ : ___ : ___ : ___ : ___ STRONGLY AGREE

26. Starting now, I could go without smoking marijuana for a long time.

STRONGLY DISAGREE ___ : ___ : ___ : ___ : ___ : ___ : ___ STRONGLY AGREE

27. Smoking marijuana would be very satisfying right now.

STRONGLY DISAGREE ___ : ___ : ___ : ___ : ___ : ___ : ___ STRONGLY AGREE

28. If I smoked marijuana right now, I would feel more tense.

STRONGLY DISAGREE ___ : ___ : ___ : ___ : ___ : ___ : ___ STRONGLY AGREE

29. I would not enjoy smoking marijuana right now.

STRONGLY DISAGREE ___ : ___ : ___ : ___ : ___ : ___ : ___ STRONGLY AGREE

30. If I had the chance to smoke marijuana, I think I would use it.

STRONGLY DISAGREE ___ : ___ : ___ : ___ : ___ : ___ : ___ STRONGLY AGREE

31. I would not be able to control how much marijuana I smoked if I had some here.

STRONGLY DISAGREE ___ : ___ : ___ : ___ : ___ : ___ : ___ STRONGLY AGREE

32. It would be great to smoke marijuana right now.

STRONGLY DISAGREE ___ : ___ : ___ : ___ : ___ : ___ : ___ STRONGLY AGREE

33. If I had some marijuana right now, I would probably not use it.

STRONGLY DISAGREE ___ : ___ : ___ : ___ : ___ : ___ : ___ STRONGLY AGREE

34. I would feel more restless if I smoked marijuana right now.

STRONGLY DISAGREE ___ : ___ : ___ : ___ : ___ : ___ : ___ STRONGLY AGREE

35. I could easily limit how much marijuana I smoked right now.

STRONGLY DISAGREE ___ : ___ : ___ : ___ : ___ : ___ : ___ STRONGLY AGREE

36. I do not need to smoke marijuana now.

STRONGLY DISAGREE ___ : ___ : ___ : ___ : ___ : ___ : ___ STRONGLY AGREE

37. I will smoke marijuana as soon as I get the chance.

STRONGLY DISAGREE ___ : ___ : ___ : ___ : ___ : ___ : ___ STRONGLY AGREE

38. I have no desire to smoke marijuana right now.

STRONGLY DISAGREE ___ : ___ : ___ : ___ : ___ : ___ : ___ STRONGLY AGREE

39. If I were smoking marijuana right now, I would feel less nervous.

STRONGLY DISAGREE ___ : ___ : ___ : ___ : ___ : ___ : ___ STRONGLY AGREE

40. I have no urge to use marijuana now.

STRONGLY DISAGREE ___ : ___ : ___ : ___ : ___ : ___ : ___ STRONGLY AGREE

41. Smoking marijuana would not make me content.

STRONGLY DISAGREE ___ : ___ : ___ : ___ : ___ : ___ : ___ STRONGLY AGREE

42. I think I could resist smoking marijuana right now.

STRONGLY DISAGREE ___ : ___ : ___ : ___ : ___ : ___ : ___ STRONGLY AGREE

43. It would be easy to pass up the chance to smoke marijuana.

STRONGLY DISAGREE ___ : ___ : ___ : ___ : ___ : ___ : ___ STRONGLY AGREE

44. I crave marijuana right now.

STRONGLY DISAGREE ___ : ___ : ___ : ___ : ___ : ___ : ___ STRONGLY AGREE

45. If I were offered some marijuana, I would use it right away.

STRONGLY DISAGREE ___ : ___ : ___ : ___ : ___ : ___ : ___ STRONGLY AGREE

46. Smoking marijuana would put me in a better mood.

STRONGLY DISAGREE ___ : ___ : ___ : ___ : ___ : ___ : ___ STRONGLY AGREE

47. My desire to smoke marijuana seems overpowering.

STRONGLY DISAGREE ___ : ___ : ___ : ___ : ___ : ___ : ___ STRONGLY AGREE

Scoring of the 47-item Marijuana Craving Questionnaire (MCQ)

Factor analysis of the 47-item MCQ yielded four factors, which we have termed *compulsivity, emotionality, expectancy,* and *purposefulness* (Heishman et al. *Addiction* 96:1023-1034, 2001).

All items are scored on a 1 to 7 scale (Strongly Disagree = 1 and Strongly Agree = 7). Negatively-keyed items (indicated by *) are scored as (8 – raw score). Factor scale scores are obtained by averaging the items within each factor. For General Factor, average all 17 items. Reliability is measured as standardized alpha coefficient.

FACTOR 1 (*Compulsivity,* 7-Items)

Item Numbers: 16, 19, 25, 26*, 31, 35*, 36*
Reliability: 0.82

FACTOR 2 (*Emotionality,* 4-Items)

Item Numbers: 9*, 13*, 28*, 34*
Reliability: 0.78

FACTOR 3 (*Expectancy,* 3-Items)

Item Numbers: 14, 39, 41*
Reliability: 0.55

FACTOR 4 (*Purposefulness*, 3-Items)

Item Numbers: 2*, 12*, 32
Reliability: 0.68

GENERAL FACTOR: 17-items

Item Numbers: 2*, 9*, 12*, 13*, 16, 19, 25, 26*, 14, 28*, 31, 32, 39, 34*, 35*, 36*, 41*
Reliability: 0.81

Source: Heishman, S. J., Singleton, E. G., & Liguori, A. (2001). Marijuana Craving Questionnaire: Development and initial validation of a self-report instrument. *Addiction, 96*(7), 1023–1034. https://doi.org/10.1046/j.1360-0443.2001.967102312.x

APPENDIX 5.9

EMOTIONAL HEALTH SCREENING QUESTIONNAIRE

Below is a list of emotional difficulties that people sometimes experience. For each of the items chosen, the response below that best fits whether you have experienced that particular difficulty.

RESPONSES:

1	2	3	4	5
Strongly Disagree	Disagree	Unsure	Agree	Strongly Agree

EXAMPLE:

__4__ I experience a lot of physical aches and pains on a daily basis.

_____ 1. I feel anxious most days.

_____ 2. I feel anxious or worried that something bad will happen to me.

_____ 3. I feel anxious or fearful about specific things like heights, germs, spiders, etc.

_____ 4. I have had panic attacks where I can't catch my breath.

_____ 5. I feel anxious when I'm around people or in crowds.

_____ 6. I feel anxious when I have to talk to strangers.

_____ 7. I feel sad or down most days.

_____ 8. I often feel guilty about things I've done in the past.

_____ 9. I'm having trouble staying asleep or waking up earlier than I want to.

_____ 10. At times, I feel so depressed that I can't stand it.

_____ 11. Most days, I have no appetite and almost no energy.

_____ 12. I feel that I'm a burden to my family or the people I love and they would be better off without me.

_____ 13. I feel that life is not worth the struggle.

_____ 14. I have or had thoughts of ending my life. If so, how recent_______________?

_____ 15. I've not only had thoughts about ending my life, but also have thought about how I might do it. If so, how recent________________?

_____ 16. I have bursts of energy or excitement that often come on without warning.

_____ 17. During these bursts of energy, I feel I can accomplish just about anything.

_____ 18. Sometimes I have so much energy that I can't fall asleep.

_____ 19. Sometimes when I've had bursts of energy or excitement, I end up doing things I regret later (like spending too much money, gambling, sex with people I don't know or like, or making other horrible decisions).

_____ 20. Sometimes I have strange thoughts that don't make sense.

_____ 21. I've had concerns lately about being forgetful.

_____ 22. I have trouble concentrating.

_____ 23. Sometimes I hear voices that are not my own thoughts.

_____ 24. I feel that I have unusual talents or abilities, like being able read someone's mind.

_____ 25. I feel that people are out to trick me or get over on me.
_____ 26. I feel good about my relationships with others.
_____ 27. I am happy and content most of the time.
_____ 28. I am content with what I've achieved in life so far and feel confident about my abilities to do even more in the future.
_____ 29. There are times when I cannot control my anger.
_____ 30. I've had episodes where I've acted out in anger but couldn't remember it.
_____ 31. There are times when I find it hard to resist the urge to steal something.
_____ 32. There are times when I find it hard to fight the urge to hurt myself.
_____ 33. I have experienced or witnessed traumatic events (like someone being killed or in bad accidents or having fought in combat or having been the victim of a crime or sexual assault).
_____ 34. Sometimes I find it hard to stop thinking about traumatic events I've experienced.
_____ 35. I sometimes have nightmares about traumatic events I've experienced.
_____ 36. If someone has offended me, I find it difficult to let go of.
_____ 37. I have been suspicious of the loyalty or trustworthiness of others.
_____ 38. I tend to be a loner and prefer to do things on my own.
_____ 39. I don't react to things as strongly as others but others think of me as being aloof.
_____ 40. I have difficulty coping with being alone or feeling bored.
_____ 41. When a friendship or love relationship ends, I take it really hard.
_____ 42. I have trouble holding onto friends.
_____ 43. I feel more comfortable letting others make decisions for me.
_____ 44. I'm willing to do or say anything to gain the support or friendship of others.
_____ 45. People sometimes say that I'm a "control freak."
_____ 46. I like to pay attention to details so that things are done correctly.
_____ 47. I often work harder than most other people I know.
_____ 48. People often say that I'm self-centered.
_____ 49. It's important to be admired by others.
_____ 50. I'm more intelligent than most people I know.
_____ 51. I like conning people just to prove how smart I am.
_____ 52. I rarely feel guilty if I've lied or gotten in trouble with the law.
_____ 53. I've done a lot of risky or dangerous things, just for the thrill of it.
_____ 54. I've been in trouble with the law several times.
_____ 55. In grammar school and high school, I had trouble concentrating on my studies.
_____ 56. As I child, I often daydreamed rather than listening to my teachers.
_____ 57. I was often fidgety and restless when I was a child.
_____ 58. I was very accident prone as a child and as a teenager.
_____ 59. In school, math was my worst subject followed by subjects that required memorization.
_____ 60. As an adult, I have trouble focusing on newspaper articles, movies, and TV shows.

Scoring the Emotional Health Screening Questionnaire*

Anxiety Questions: (Items 1 to 6) Scores of 20–30 are indicative of severe anxiety
Scores of 10–19 are indicative of mild to moderate anxiety

Depression Questions: (Items 7 to 11) Scores 25–35 are indicative of severe depression
Scores 15–24 are indicative of mild to moderate depression

Suicide Questions: (Items 11, 12, 13, 14) If any of these items are endorsed with scores of 4 or 5, the client should be referred for a more in-depth suicide assessment by a psychiatrist or psychologist.

Bipolar Questions: (Items 16–20) Scores 20–25 are considered indicative of bipolar traits
Scores 15–19 are considered indicative of mild to moderate bipolar traits

Psychotic or Irrational Thoughts: (Items 20–25) Scores 24–30 are indicative of irrational or psychotic thinking
Scores 18–23 are indicative of possible irrational or psychotic thinking

Overall Satisfaction with Life: (Items 26–28) Scores of 12–15 are indicative of life satisfaction
Scores of 9–11 are indicative of mild life satisfaction

Impulse Control: (Items 29–32) Scores of 16–20 indicate poor impulse control
Scores 8 and below indicate good impulse control

Posttraumatic Stress Disorder: (Items 32–34) Scores of 12–15 are suggestive of PTSD
Scores of 9 and below are nonsuggestive of PTSD

Personality Disorder Questions: (Items 35–50) These items cover the following personality traits:

Paranoid Personality (Items 35–37) scores of 12–15 are significant
Schizoid Personality (Items 38–39) scores of 8–10 are significant
Borderline Personality (Items 40–42) scores of 12–15 are significant
Dependent Personality (Items 43–44) scores of 8–10 are significant
Obsessive-Compulsive Personality (Items 45–47) scores of 12–15 are significant
Narcissistic Personality (Items 48–50) scores of 12–15 are significant
Antisocial Personality (Items 51–54) scores of 16–20 are significant

Attention Deficit Hyperactivity Disorder Questions: (Items 55–60)
Scores of 24–30 indicative of ADHD
Scores 23 are nonindicative of ADHD

*Because reliability and validity of this measure has not been established, it is recommended that any significant findings from this questionnaire be referred to a licensed psychiatrist or clinical psychologist for further examination.

APPENDIX 5.10

SCREENING CASE EXAMPLES UTILIZING *ASAM-3* CRITERIA

CASE EXAMPLE 1

Taylor is a 16-year-old male who currently resides in Baltimore, Maryland, with his grandmother and a younger sister. He was referred for a substance use screening by the County Sheriff's Department after being incarcerated in the county youth detention center. A routine drug screen done upon admission to the detention center revealed that Taylor had a blood alcohol level of .21 and he also tested positive for opioids and cannabis. He told the screening counselor that he has been using opioids intermittently for the past three years and that he drinks and smokes cannabis on a daily basis. Approximately two years ago, Taylor joined a street gang where he started off by watching out for police while other gang members sold drugs on the corner but then moved up to having his own territory to deal drugs (mostly opioids and methamphetamines). Taylor had been incarcerated twice before for possession with intent to distribute charges. He is currently on probation, so his recent arrest also represents a violation of his probation. Taylor's grandmother was contacted to provide additional background information and she states she was "relieved" to hear that Taylor was taken into police custody as she was fearful that he might be killed in a gang-related shooting. Taylor had three high school classmates who have been shot and two of them died of their gunshot wounds. Taylor indicates that he knows he needs to make changes or he risks ending up like his friends who were shot. Taylor's grandmother hopes that he will finally "get the help he needs" so that he will not end up like his mother. Taylor's mother is currently serving a five-year prison sentence on drug possession charges, and Taylor and his sister have been living with their maternal grandmother ever since.

ASAM-3 **Criteria**

Dimension 1 (Intoxication/Withdrawal Potential): Client was intoxicated when seen in the hospital and also tested positive for opioids and cannabis. The high blood alcohol level poses concerns for withdrawal.

Dimension 2 (Medical Conditions/Complications): No known medical conditions or complications.

Dimension 3 (Emotional/Behavioral/Cognitive): No known emotional/cognitive complications Arrests suggest a pattern of antisocial behavior.

Dimension 4 (Readiness to Change): Some indications that client is in Determination stage and ready to change behavior.

Dimension 5 (Relapse/Continued Use Potential): If client refuses help, there is a likelihood of relapse.

Dimension 6 (Recovery/Living Environment): Immediate living situation with grandmother is supportive of client's recovery, however, surrounding neighborhood is dangerous.

CASE EXAMPLE 2

Tiffany is a 23-year-old female who currently works part-time as a hair dresser at a local salon. She was referred for a SUD screening following an incident in which she was arrested for prostitution. Tiffany denies that she soliciting an undercover police officer for sex but does admit that she has been using opioids and cocaine (which was verified by a urine drug screen that Tiffany had submitted as part of this evaluation). She indicates that she has been using prescription opioids (hydromorphone or Dilaudid) which she had obtained from her aunt who had been prescribed the pain medication after being in a car accident. When her mother had discovered that Tiffany had been stealing her aunt's prescription, she threw Tiffany out of the house and since that time, Tiffany has been staying with an older man who supplies her with drugs in exchange for sex. Tiffany's job at the hair salon does not provide her with enough money to get her own apartment. She has applied at other hair salons but has not been able to find work. Tiffany indicates that she has been using hydromorphone daily and has been using it intravenously. Her last use with four hours ago and she reports that she is experiencing some mild withdrawal symptoms, however, she knows she will experience severe withdrawal if she goes without using for another three hours.

ASAM-3 **Criteria**

Dimension 1 (Intoxication/Withdrawal Potential)

Dimension 2 (Medical Conditions/Complications)

Dimension 3 (Emotional/Behavioral/Cognitive)

Dimension 4 (Readiness to Change)

Dimension 5 (Relapse/Continued Use Potential)

Dimension 6 (Recovery/Living Environment)

What is your level of care recommendation for Tiffany given the information you have gathered as part of the *ASAM-3* criteria?

6

INDIVIDUAL COUNSELING TECHNIQUES

LEARNING OBJECTIVES

In this chapter, we will describe the advantages and disadvantages of individual counseling approaches used in treating individuals with substance use disorders (SUDs). In addition, we will also explore a variety of individual counseling approaches and techniques. By the end of this chapter you will be able to:

- describe the advantages and limitations of using individual counseling approaches with SUD clients;
- explain the basic premise of Solution-Focused Therapy (SFT) and how SFT techniques are utilized in treating individuals with SUDs;
- describe how SFT techniques (e.g., the Miracle Question, Scaling Questions, and Finding Exceptions) are utilized when treating individuals with SUDs;
- describe how Rational-Emotive Behavior Therapy (REBT) techniques are especially helpful in treating individuals with SUDs and describe techniques such as Disputing;
- describe how behavioral techniques were developed and how techniques such as behavioral contracting, aversion therapy, and cue exposure therapy (CET) are utilized;
- describe the purpose and goals of 12-Step Facilitated Counseling and how to assess a client's level of involvement with 12-step programs;
- describe how counselors can encourage 12-step participation;
- explain the purpose and techniques associated with existential and Gestalt counseling.

TERMS TO KNOW

SOLUTION-FOCUSED THERAPY

Finding Exceptions an SFT technique whereby clients are asked to recall times when problems with alcohol or drugs were not present in their life

Miracle Question an SFT technique that asks that clients imagine what will be different once the "problem" no longer exists. This technique encourages clients to look to a future in which they are no longer plagued by addiction

Scaling Questions an SFT technique whereby clients are asked to rate the impact of their drinking or drug use or to rate the times when drinking or drug use was not causing problems (e.g., Finding Exceptions) on a scale from 1 to 10

three Ds the three Ds refer to SFT's contention that traditional addiction counseling places too much emphasis on the Disease model, the Dysfunction caused by excessive drinking and/or drug use, and the observation that people who have SUDs often use Denial to avoid admitting to SUD-related problems

RATIONAL-EMOTIVE BEHAVIOR THERAPY

all-or-none thinking tendency to interpret events or behaviors of others in terms of black or white or dichotomous thinking, e.g., interpreting the behavior of others as either totally caring/altruistic or totally evil or mean-spirited

awfulizing tendency to perceive events or comments by others as worse than they really are, tendencies to magnify events as awful

demandingness represented by cognitions or attitudes that come in the form of "shoulds," "oughts," or "musts," e.g., demanding that others should do what one wants them to do

disputing an REBT technique whereby clients challenge irrational beliefs

irrational belief illogical, inconsistent, often unverifiable, and distress-producing cognition attitudes and perceptions pertaining to oneself, others, and the world

minimizing or magnifying tendencies to distort by either downplaying the seriousness of an event or behavior or magnifying it by blowing it out of proportion, e.g., clients may minimize the danger of being contacted by their old drug dealer or may magnify a negative comment by a family member

overgeneralizing tendency to perceive events as "always" happening (or "never" happening) based on limited evidence to support the perception

rational belief logical, consistent, and verifiable cognitions and attitudes, pertaining to oneself, others, or the world

BEHAVIORAL COUNSELING

aversion therapy based on classical conditioning techniques, aversion therapy pairs an aversive/negative stimulus with alcohol or drug use

classical conditioning refers to a learning procedure whereby an unconditioned stimulus such as food is paired with a neutral stimulus (e.g., bell sound) to produce a conditioned response (e.g., salivation) when the bell rings

conditioned stimulus	in the previous example, the bell becomes the conditioned stimulus
conditioned response	in the previous example, the salivation becomes conditioned by the sound of the bell
operant conditioning	is a learning process in which the strength of a particular behavior or its likelihood of occurring in the future is determined by whether that behavior is followed by a positive reward or a punishment
positive reinforcer/ negative reinforcer	both positive and negative reinforcement *increase behavior.* If a particular behavior is followed by a reward, that increases the likelihood of the behavior reoccurring in the future. If an unpleasant situation or feeling is removed (i.e., negative negative reinforcement), then that also increases the likelihood of that behavior reoccurring
punishment	a negative or aversive stimulus that is meant to suppress a behavior from occurring in the future

INTRODUCTION

Although group counseling has been the treatment modality of choice in most substance use disorder (SUD) treatment programs, individual counseling also provides many benefits to clients, especially those who may not be appropriate for a group or who may have co-occurring treatment issues. Individual counseling is also the most prevalent form of counseling in the majority of private practice settings. We will begin by exploring some of the advantages and disadvantages of individual counseling (see Box 6.1).

BOX 6.1

ADVANTAGES AND DISADVANTAGES OF INDIVIDUAL COUNSELING

Advantages

- Allows for more individualized treatment planning
- Allows for better observation of the client
- Client is less able to "hide out"
- Allows for a closer therapeutic bond
- Client may be more willing to reveal embarrassing or distressing life events

Disadvantages

- Client receives only one point of view
- No other feedback
- May increase self-centeredness
- May increase a feeling of uniqueness
- May unintentionally create the erroneous belief that recovery can be attained without having a solid support network!!!

There are certainly unique advantages to individual counseling when compared to disadvantages. When doing individual counseling, counselors only have one client to focus on and not seven or eight as would be the case when facilitating a group. Individual counseling, therefore, affords more time to focus on individualized treatment planning and to address specific goals the client wants to work on. Naturally, it is easier to observe your client's behavior, facial expressions, tone of voice, and pace of their speech in an individual session. Any changes in your client's mood, thought processes, or attitudes will be more readily discerned and affords counselors the opportunity to address these changes in the moment. Imagine a group session, in which one client comes into the session in crisis, and there is not enough time to process the crisis, let alone check in with all the other clients in the group. With individual counseling, all of the counselor's time and attention are devoted to one particular client. Addiction counselors are also better able to note any "dry drunk" behaviors (e.g., impulsivity, irritability, easily frustrated, and judgmental of others) and address those behaviors by expressing concerns. Finally, individual counseling is the mainstay of private office counseling practices, while group counseling is the most-often utilized modality in licensed treatment programs, for example, inpatient-residential, intensive outpatient programs, and halfway houses. For many clients, a combination of both individual and group counseling is the best way to achieve treatment goals.

The Substance Abuse and Mental Health Services Administration (SAMHSA) lists over 96 types of interventions used with SUD clients, for example, relapse prevention therapy, family behavior therapy, motivational interviewing, motivational enhancement therapy, multisystemic therapy, 12-Step Facilitated Therapy, contingency management (CM) therapy, cognitive behavior therapy, rational-emotive therapy, trauma-informed care counseling, and mindfulness counseling. In this chapter, we will be reviewing some of these interventions that lend themselves to individual addictions counseling. This is not to say that group counselors would not be able to use these approaches also; however, some of these treatment approaches are better utilized when tailored to a client's specific needs or goals.

SOLUTION-FOCUSED THERAPY

The first individual counseling approach we will focus on in this chapter is Solution-Focused Therapy (SFT; de Shazer, 1985, 1988; de Shazer & Berg, 1992). What best distinguishes SFT from other counseling approaches is its emphasis on encouraging clients to focus on a future in which SUD problems no longer exist or are no longer problematic. Essentially, SFT believes that people have the answers or solutions to their problems within themselves, and it is the role of the counselor to draw out these solutions through a number of guided therapeutic strategies. SFT critiques other addiction treatment approaches in conceptualizing SUDs as incurable (i.e., chronic) diseases in which denial plays a key role in perpetuating the disease. SFT, therefore, criticizes traditional addiction treatment as being overly focused on what is referred to as the "Three Ds: Disease, Denial, and Dysfunction," which is aligned with the more traditional problem-focused approach to treating SUDs. In using a 3-Ds problem-focused approach, the role of traditional addiction counseling is to first confront clients with their past behaviors in order to have them accept that they have a disease (i.e., a SUD). The second goal is to break down the client's denial of having a SUD and then to encourage clients to admit that their lives had become unmanageable or dysfunctional as a result of their excessive alcohol or drug use. Think about some of the well-known SUD screening measures such as the Michigan Alcoholism Screening Test for Alcohol & Drugs (MAST/AD) or the Alcohol

Use Disorders Identification Test (AUDIT), which focus on "problems" related to alcohol and drug use such as blackouts, family dysfunction, and interference with education or employment. According to an SFT approach, rather than focusing on problems that come about as a result of drinking and/or drug use, SFT prefers to focus on future solutions to these problems.

SFT also embraces the belief that there are different ways to achieve sobriety, whereas the disease model emphasizes both total abstinence and 12-step meeting attendance as the only means by which people can recover from SUDs. Therefore, SFT explores several other paths to recovery such as moderating substance use or harm reduction, especially in the initial phases of treatment. The role of the SFT counselor is to match the client with the best approach toward change. In addition, SFT counselors refer to a recent, growing body of research that points to individuals who attain sobriety and recovery from SUD without accessing any formal intervention or treatment (Curran et al., 1998; Misch, 2007; O'Malley, 2004; Robbins, 1979). This body of research suggests that some individuals are capable of finding their own solutions to SUD problems; therefore, the role of the SFT counselor is to assist clients in discovering those solutions that work best for them.

Similar to Motivational Interviewing, one of the basic tenets of SFT is that clients should be allowed to make choices regarding their treatment rather than having a treatment plan imposed on them. According to Miller and Berg's (1995) findings, the "door to solutions begins with making personal choices" (p. 62), which is a divergence from more traditional addiction-counseling approaches, whereby treatment recommendations regarding abstinence, 12-step group attendance (e.g., "attending 90 meetings in 90 days," "find a sponsor and a home group"), and the need to change people, places, and things in order to maintain sobriety are often nonnegotiable treatment recommendations. SFT uses a gentler approach by asking that clients consider change by first examining how they would like their lives to be in the future. According to Miller and Berg (1995), "Finding the door to solution begins with the choice: I want my life to be different!" (p. 66). They suggest that in order to unlock the door to solutions, there are six key things that need to be considered: (1) make sure the change is important to the client; (2) keep the change small; (3) make the change specific, concrete, and behavioral; (4) the client should be able to state what exactly they will do (i.e., state the change as something that is concrete and observable); (5) the client will state how they will start their journey rather than how they will end it; and (6) the client will be clear about with whom, where, and when these changes will occur. These recommendations are very similar to how counselors collaboratively write treatment plans with their clients. In writing plans, there is a focus on goals that are small and concrete rather than vague or abstract (e.g., improving self-esteem).

Another key aspect to SFT when applied to clients experiencing SUDs is that it utilizes a 5-Step Treatment Model (Berg & Miller, 1991). This model is designed to provide counselors with a framework to help clients find solutions to problems arising from alcohol and/or drug use.

The 5-Step Treatment Model is described as follows:

Step 1: **Working with the Problem Drinker:** Assessing and Building the Therapeutic Relationship.

Step 2: **Negotiating Well-Formed Treatment Goals:** Beginning with the End in mind.

Step 3: **Orienting the Client Toward a Solution:** How to interview for change.

Step 4: **Solution-Focused Intervention:** The Components, Types, and Delivery of Treatment Interventions.

Step 5: **Goal Maintenance:** Strategies for maintaining progress.

The 5-Step Model utilizes many of the techniques that we will be presenting in this chapter. For example, in Step 4, the SFT counselor will introduce various SFT treatment techniques such as the Miracle Question and Finding Exceptions. Scaling Questions would be appropriately used in Step 3 where the counselor is examining the notion of change with the client. These techniques will be described in more depth in the "Solution-Focused Therapy Treatment Techniques" section.

RELEVANCE OF SOLUTION-FOCUSED THERAPY FOR COUNSELORS

SFT begins with an assessment of the client's reasons for entering treatment or what is referred to as the Presenting Complaint (see Box 6.2). The emphasis would be on *what* the client has been experiencing and *why now,* or why the client has chosen this particular point in time to access treatment. The SFT counselor will also focus on what the client has tried in the past to manage or deal with the presenting complaint (including past attempts at counseling or treatment), with an emphasis on what worked as well as what didn't work. SFT counselors are interested in what internal resources the client possesses that can be brought to their current situation in a useful way. What's noteworthy is what the SFT counselor will refrain from focusing on, such as past developmental history (e.g., childhood history, educational history, and family history). They also will refrain from asking about co-occurring mental health or medical problems, as well as social history and social functioning. Some of these areas may be explored, however, only to the extent that they are relevant to the presenting problem. For example, if a client were to bring up that they will usually go on a binge after arguing with their boyfriend or girlfriend, then SFT counselors will explore the history of that relationship.

One of the main reasons for doing a thorough assessment of the problem is that it then allows the counselor and client to formulate treatment goals. Remember, SFT counselors are not interested in performing a more holistic biopsychosocial assessment; rather, SFT

BOX 6.2

PRINCIPLES OF THE SOLUTION-FOCUSED APPROACH

1. No single approach works for everyone.
2. There are many possible solutions
3. The solution and the problem are not necessarily related.
4. The simplest and least invasive approach is frequently the best medicine.
5. People can and do get better quickly.
6. Change is happening all the time.
7. Focus on strengths and resources rather than on weakness and deficits.
8. Focus on the future rather than on the past.

Source: Adapted from Miller, S. D., & Berg, I. K. (1995). *The miracle method: A radically new approach to problem drinking.* W. W. Norton.

counselors focus on assessing the problem (or presenting complaint) that motivated the client to seek help. According to Berg (1992), well-formulated treatment goals would include the points listed in Box 6.3.

Developing treatment goals from an SFT perspective has many of the qualities of good goal-setting (Perkinson, 2017) in that goals are described in simple, measurable, concrete terms rather than something vague like "feeling happier." An example of a simple, concrete goal would be something like "Client will develop positive social supports who support their recovery" or "Client will develop leisure activities that support their recovery."

BOX 6.3

GUIDELINES FOR WELL-FORMED TREATMENT GOALS

1. They are described in social interactional terms.
2. They have contextual or situational features.
3. They are described as including the presence of some behaviors as the start of something rather than the end of something.
4. They are small rather than large.
5. They are salient (important) to the client and, through negotiation, salient to the therapist.
6. They are described in specific, concrete, and behavioral terms.
7. They are described in terms of positive indicators of success rather than as an absence of problems.
8. They are both realistic and achievable.
9. They are perceived by the client as involving "hard work" on their part.

Source: Adapted from Berg, I. K. (1992, June 19–20). *Working briefly with the chemically dependent person: A solution-focused approach.* Workshop booklet. Institute for Advanced Clinical Training.

Solution-Focused Therapy Treatment Techniques

There are three treatment techniques that are central to SFT. The first technique is the *Miracle Question.* The rationale of the Miracle Question is that it encourages clients to explore what the future will look like once their alcohol or drug use is no longer posing problems or difficulties. It is not unusual that when clients enter counseling they do so in hopes that some type of miracle will help bring about the changes they are looking for. This is often because clients have tried everything within their power to change. Here is how the Miracle Question would be posed to the client:

> *Suppose tonight, after you go to bed and while you are sleeping, a miracle happens. The miracle that takes place is that the problem you're struggling with is solved! Just like that! Since you're sleeping, however, you don't know that the miracle has happened. So, when you wake up in the morning, what would be some of the first things that you would notice that would be different and that would let you know that the miracle has taken place and that your problem is solved? (based on Miller & Berg, 1995, p. 38).*

As indicated, the Miracle Question emphasizes what the future will look like when the problem or problems are no longer impacting on the client. The Miracle Question also asks the client to examine what would be their first indications that the miracle took place during the course of the night (i.e., "When you wake up tomorrow morning, *what would be some of the first things* that you would notice that would be different and that would tell you the miracle has happened"). In a videotaped session (Berg, 1990a), Insoo Kim Berg is counseling a woman who has been in recovery from a SUD for several years but has been struggling with being able to lose weight. In the beginning of the session, the client tells Insoo Kim Berg how she was able to lose weight in the past but had regained weight because of the stress of her job, which coincided with her going back to school to finish her bachelor's degree. When Insoo poses the Miracle Question to this client, her whole demeanor changes. The client goes from being very serious and somber to smiling and laughing and becoming fully engaged as she explains how she would know the miracle took place during the course of the night because she would wake up and feel like exercising.

The next technique that is central to Solution-Focused Theory is *Finding Exceptions*. Exceptions are "those times when people do not experience their usual pattern of problem drinking" (Miller & Berg, 1995, p. 79), which would include instances where the client's drinking is greatly reduced and therefore becomes nonproblematic, as well as time periods of total abstinence and participation in treatment and/or 12-step programs. By shining a light on exceptions, it helps to convey a sense of self-efficacy or self-confidence that positive change is possible. It is important to note, however, that not all clients may perceive "exceptions" or instances where they have abstained or reduced their drinking or drug use, other than when they were young. These clients may have only experienced exceptions during times of residential treatment, incarceration, or hospitalization. Once "exception" periods have been identified, the counselor may then ask

> *What was different during those time when you weren't drinking or using drugs?*
> *What are you doing differently during those times of exception?*
> *What would others say you are doing differently during those times?*
> *What happens shortly before or after those times? (Berg, 1992).*

There are also other questions that Miller and Berg (1995) recommend that counselors explore with clients as a means of helping to elucidate how periods of exceptions have come about. For example, counselors would be encouraged to explore with clients how they managed to overcome urges or temptations during the period and what exactly they did that helped them overcome those urges. Similarly, what did the client do the last time they felt they deserved a drink but decided not to indulge? Or what have they done to stay away from situations where they might be more tempted to drink? Finally, how did the client manage to get back on track if they experienced a setback or slip (Berg, 1992)?

LEARNING ACTIVITY 6.1
THE MIRACLE QUESTION

Think about a problem or issue that you are currently experiencing. Imagine if someone were to pose the Miracle Question to you. Assuming a miracle takes place while you are sleeping tonight, how would you know if the miracle took place? What would be different? What would you be feeling? Discuss in small groups or in your chat room.

LEARNING ACTIVITY 6.2
EXCEPTION FINDING

What are some of the things that stand out in the Exception Finding questions that are listed earlier? Why do you think SFT counselors ask clients what their family or loved ones may have to say about periods of exceptions?

The next technique that SFT counselors may utilize with clients is *Scaling Questions.* Scaling Questions is a means for clients to assess exceptions or times when drinking or drug use was not a problem. On a scale from 1–100, clients are asked to estimate the percentage of time that drinking or drug use is problematic. For example, if a client indicates that drinking is problematic 60% of the time, then the counselor would explore with the client what is happening the other 40% of the time when drinking or drug use is nonproblematic. SFT counselors also recommend that clients use graphs to chart the days of the week where exceptions are more likely or less likely to occur in order to help determine days or times of day that are more difficult for them to enact change. Other Scaling Questions counselors might ask would include the following:

Counselor: On a scale from 1 to 10 with 10 meaning you are extremely confident that this problem can be solved and 1 suggesting that you do not have any confidence the problem could be solved, where would you put yourself?

Counselor: On a scale from 1 to 10 with 10 meaning you would do anything to solve this problem and 1 meaning you aren't sure you'll do anything but will probably wait before making changes, where would you put yourself?

Counselor: On a scale from 1 to 10 with 10 meaning you are very confident you can continue to make progress toward change while 1 indicates you lack all confidence, where would you put yourself? (derived from Berg, 1992).

Finally, SFT counselors also offer clients three Change Rules that are designed to help clients come up with new perspectives on change:

Rule 1: If it ain't broken, don't fix it: This rule pertains to instances where a slip or relapse takes place and the tendency of counselors to go back and pick apart the reasons for the lapse or failure. SFT counselors, on the other hand, refrain from "picking apart" the slip as it merely reinforces the client's "problem." This is not to say that there is nothing to be gained by looking at antecedents to slips or relapses, however, not at the expense of reinforcing the problem rather than the solution.

Rule 2: Once you know what works, do more of it: Often there is a tendency to focus on past behaviors that did not work. A well-known colloquial saying that is commonly heard in 12-step meetings goes something like this, "Insanity is when you keep doing the same thing but expect a different result." (This saying is attributed to Albert Einstein!) Often with substance use disorders, people keep repeating the same behaviors (e.g., getting high) but somehow expect that things will end up differently (e.g., "I won't get pulled over for drinking and driving this time" or "I won't fight with my boyfriend or girlfriend this time"). Invariably, however, things turn out the same. Therefore, Rule 2 emphasizes the importance of continuing to do more of what works.

Rule 3: If it doesn't work, don't do it again. Do something different: SFT is often used with families and couples who are experiencing problems in their relationships with one another. When families enter counseling, it is often because they continue to do the same thing over and over again, continue to have the same argument, or continue the same self-defeating behaviors but somehow are "expecting a different result." The purpose of Rule 3 is to try to get clients to begin to try something different with regard to drinking and drug use. By doing so, the hope is that clients will move closer toward a solution.

SFT has many advantages. It is clearly a collaborative approach in which counselor and client work together to find solutions. However, collaborative approaches may be fine when clients enter treatment voluntarily and with some degree of insight into their problems. Solution-Focused approaches may not work as well with clients who are mandated to attend treatment (e.g., court-mandated clients, DUI offender clients, and intimate partner violence perpetrators). Berg (1990b) has developed a list of recommendations for negotiating goals with mandated clients (see Box 6.4).

BOX 6.4

GOAL NEGOTIATION WITH MANDATED CLIENTS

1. Whose idea was it that you need to come here?
2. What makes ______________ think you need to come here?

   What does ______________ think is the reason you have this problem?
3. What would __________ say minimally you need to do different?

   What do you have to do to convince____________ that you don't need to come here?
4. When was the last time you did this? (Finding Exceptions)

   What was different in your life then?

   How did you do this?

   What do you think ______________________ will say he/she noticed different about you then?

   What was helpful in getting you started?
5. What is the first step you need to take to get started this time?

   How confident are you that you can do this again? (Scaling Question)

   What would it take to raise your confidence level?

   What would __________ say the chances are you will do this?
6. What do you suppose___________ would notice different about you when you do this?
7. What difference would it make in your life then?

   What will be going on in your life that is not going on now?
8. How will you know you've done enough?

   What difference would it make in your relationship with those closest with you?

   Who will be the first to notice you've made changes?

Source: Adapted from Berg, I. K. (1990). *Solution-focused therapy: An interview with Insoo Kim Berg.* In J. Carlson & J. A. Lewis (Eds.), *Addiction counseling series* [Videotape series]. Allyn & Bacon.

Goal-setting with mandated clients becomes challenging for most addiction counselors, regardless of their theoretical training or approach. Yet, SFT may prove to be effective with mandated clients if the client is able to identify a goal they wish to work toward. Essentially, SFT is a client-centered approach similar to Carl Rogers' client-centered therapy or Motivational Interviewing in that the counselor is not imposing change on the client, but rather the belief is that the client possesses answers or solutions to their difficulties. Clients may agree that their goal might be to free themselves from the restrictions imposed by the mandate that they attend treatment. In order to do this, changes in behavior and attitudes will need to take place.

Limitations of Solution-Focused Therapy

Obviously, not all SUD clients are appropriate candidates for SFT therapy. For example, clients who are in crisis because of daily substance use resulting in chronic intoxication or withdrawal would best be treated in a residential and/or medically supervised program. Once stabilized, these clients might be more suitable for an SFT approach. Similarly, clients who present with medical complications, health dangers, or major mental health crises (e.g., suicidal or homicidal intent or active psychosis) would also not be appropriate for Solution-Focused approaches until they are stabilized. Another limitation to SFT is that it has a finite number of treatment techniques (i.e., the Miracle Question, Finding Exceptions, Scaling Questions, and others). Although these treatment techniques are powerful tools that really do help clients to look at what future solutions might look like, there are only a limited number of main counseling techniques. It should be pointed out, however, that SFT is not a fully developed counseling theory but rather can be viewed more as a brief therapy type of approach.

CASE EXAMPLE: AMANDA (SOLUTION-FOCUSED THERAPY)

Amanda is a 28-year-old single mother of a 2-year-old daughter who is seeking addiction counseling on an outpatient basis. Amanda indicates that she has been drinking and smoking cannabis since she was in high school and now finds that she is having trouble stopping. She explains that, just about every weekend, she will go out with her friends and they usually end up drinking at a local bar and then will usually go over to one of her friend's apartments where they smoke cannabis. Amanda is quick to point out that she is not foolish enough to drive and instead will take an Uber or Lyft home. She also points out that she does not drink or get high around her 2-year-old daughter, whom she drops off at her parents' when she is going out "partying" on the weekend. Amanda is worried because she feels she is "in a rut" that she cannot get out of and nearly every weekend is spent getting high with her friends, no matter what time of year it is. The following is an excerpt from Amanda's session with a Solution-Focused addictions counselor:

Counselor: Hello Amanda, I'm glad you could make the appointment today. Did you have any problems finding my office?

Amanda: No, the directions you gave me were very helpful.

(*continued*)

The counselor then goes over some basic ground rules with Amanda, such as confidentiality and duty to warn, and she has Amanda sign an Informed Consent form.

Counselor: So, tell me what brings you here today? What would you like to work on?

Amanda: Well, like I mentioned to you on the phone when we set up today's appointment, I've been struggling with trying to stay away from drinking and smoking pot, which I do just about every weekend.

Counselor: You said "just about every weekend," does that mean there are times when you don't drink or smoke pot?

The counselor asks an "Exception Finding" to uncover instances when Amanda doesn't drink or get high on weekends.

Amanda: Yes there have been a few weekends when I didn't go out. Like the weekend of my daughter, Suzie's, birthday. I didn't go out at all that weekend because we had her "kid" party on Saturday and then her relatives/adult party on Sunday.

Counselor: What was that weekend like for you? Did you miss going out with your friends?

Amanda: No, not really. I did enjoy planning Suzie's party and it was so incredible to see her get so excited opening her presents. I felt really good about hosting both parties for her.

Counselor: So, you can go without drinking or drugging when you have something more important or more fun to do?

Amanda: Yeah, I guess so…I didn't think of it that way, but you're right. I really didn't feel like I missed anything. Every weekend when I go out partying, is just like the last one, you know "same old, same old."

Counselor: With the weekend coming up, what do you have planned?

Amanda: I'm supposed to meet up with Cathy and then we're going over to the Roadhouse (a local bar) where her boyfriend's band is playing this Friday night. She wanted everyone to go to help support his band.

Counselor: How are you feeling about going out on Friday?

Amanda: Well I work all week and there are some Fridays when I'm too tired to go out and would just like to stay home.

The counselor asks a "Scaling Question."

Counselor: On a scale from 1 to 10 with 1 being "not important at all" and 10 being "very important," how important would it be for you to go to the Roadside on Friday? Also using the same scale, how important would it be for you to stay home with Suzie on Friday?

Amanda: I would give going out with friends about a 5 and staying home with Suzie this Friday about an 8.

Counselor: So, it sounds like you're leaning more toward staying home with Suzie. What would help to make that a relaxing and fun evening?

(*continued*)

Amanda: Suzie loves pizza, so we would order a pizza and then watch one of her favorite movies.

Here, the counselor introduces the Miracle Question.

Counselor: That sounds like a relaxing evening. I'm going to give you a scenario and then ask you a strange question. This requires creativity and imagination. Are you willing to give this a try?

Amanda: Sure, why not?

Counselor: Okay. You can keep your eyes open or closed, whichever is more comfortable for you. I'd like you to imagine that when you go to bed tonight, during the night, a miracle takes place. The miracle is that all of the conflict that you've been having regarding drinking and smoking pot miraculously disappears, so that when you wake up in the morning, you're no longer troubled by urges to drink or smoke. My question is: when you wake up tomorrow, how would you know the miracle occurred during the night?

Amanda: Wow, that's a tough one. I think the first thing I'd notice is that I'm totally at peace with myself. I'd be thinking clearly, not hungover or dreading going to work. I'd look forward to doing things rather than moping around.

Counselor: Anything else you'd notice?

Amanda: I think I'd really have a different attitude. Like just feeling better about myself. I don't know, like being more at peace with myself.

This brief case illustration provides you with a glimpse into what a Solution-Focused session might look like. Amanda comes into counseling looking for a solution to her dilemma of going out partying with her friends every weekend. She describes her situation as being in a "rut" or being stuck in a pattern of behavior that she is troubled with. SFT is a perfect approach to use with Amanda because she is seeking change.

RATIONAL-EMOTIVE BEHAVIOR THERAPY

Under the framework of cognitive behavioral therapies is Rational-Emotive Behavior Therapy (REBT). Similar to other cognitive behavioral approaches, REBT focuses on helping clients change their cognitions (e.g., beliefs, attitudes, perception of events, and unconscious processes) as a means of lessening their levels of emotional distress. The goal of REBT is not to eliminate the client's emotional responses altogether but rather to diminish their intensity so as to not interfere with recovery. For example, there is a difference between feelings of rage and feelings of annoyance and a difference between feelings of depression and feelings of sadness.

The premise or underlying theory of REBT is derived from an ancient Greek philosopher, Epictetus, who is quoted as saying, "It's not the events of life that make men mad, but rather the view we take of them." Implicit in this statement is the notion that as humans we are not robotic in our reactions to life events; rather our response to those events is determined by how we interpret those particular events. Here is an example: think back to a romantic relationship that ended in a breakup. Most would think of this life event as one that would result in emotional pain, depressive feelings, or perhaps anger or rage. For some, a breakup might even result in despair and suicidal ideas that might emanate from a belief that "I can't live without this person in my life." However, what if you were the person who initiated the breakup? What if you broke off the relationship because your romantic partner had cheated on you with your best friend, or what if your romantic partner was emotionally or physically abusive? Those possible scenarios might lead to completely different emotional reactions. In other words, the breakup could be interpreted entirely differently depending on the circumstances. The example that Albert Ellis (1957a, 1957b, 1958, 1962), the founder of REBT, gives is a situation where you imagine yourself on a crowded elevator. You are standing toward the front of the elevator by the doors when suddenly you are shoved from behind. At first, you ignore being pushed, but then you are shoved again, a little more forcefully. Now you are getting annoyed, and when it happens a third time, you begin to turn around to give this rude, insensitive individual a piece of your mind, but when you turn around, you notice the person shoving you is visually impaired. How would you react? Did your emotional response change? Most would say that they would turn around and not say anything, perhaps even feel a bit guilty for wanting to take this person's head off for shoving them. You have just reinterpreted the situation, or what Ellis refers to as the *Activating Event.* That brings us to the A-B-Cs of emotional response. Most people would conclude that *Activating Events* cause or contribute to our emotional responses or *Consequences.* However, negative life events do not invariably lead to intense emotions. Instead there is the ***interpretation*** of those Activating Events that is based on our beliefs. According to Ellis, our beliefs can either be rational or irrational.

LEARNING ACTIVITY 6.3
BELIEFS THAT SUPPORT ACTIVE ALCOHOL OR DRUG USE

Make a list of beliefs that support or reinforce active alcohol or drug use. For example, "Getting high is the only way I can relax or de-stress after a hard day at work" or "I can't imagine hanging out with my friends and not having a couple of beers." Discuss your list with your classmates.

Beliefs are made up of cognitions, attitudes, thoughts, and self-statements. As described by Ellis et al. (1988), beliefs are not facts, but rather they are hypotheses. Facts are observable and objective, whereas beliefs tend to be subjectively experienced. As indicated earlier, usually irrational beliefs result in intense emotions that are disproportionate to the activating event. Rational beliefs are usually more logical and tend to be consistent, more productive, and less distressing, while irrational beliefs usually have no evidence to support the belief and, therefore, tend to be more illogical or inconsistent and often result in distressing emotions. Ellis et al. (1988) outline several categories of irrational beliefs: (a) demandingness; (b) low frustration tolerance; (c) awfulizing; (d) rating of self and others; and (e) overgeneralizing the future. *Demandingness* refers to irrational beliefs that occur when clients demand that others do what they expect them to do. Often expressed as "shoulds," "oughts," or "musts," these demands that others adhere to how the client feels the other should behave are often unyielding, rigid, and absolute. Low frustration tolerance irrational beliefs are characterized by perceptions of events or life circumstances that clients perceive as "too hard to handle" or adversities that are insurmountable. Clients with low frustration tolerance are often distressed by life circumstances that they perceive as overwhelming and doubt their ability to withstand the circumstances that have created their frustrations. Awfulizing irrational beliefs occurs when clients perceive events as being far worse than they really are. This is true of clients who think pessimistically or live in the "worst case scenario." In AA/NA language, *projection* is similar to awfulizing in that there is a tendency to project ahead to doom and gloom. With ratings of self or others, individuals often hold irrational self-perceptions or perceptions of others as being "bad" or having ill intent toward others. These beliefs also tend to be rigid and absolute, whereby clients judge themselves harshly or hold perfectionistic attitudes toward themselves or others. Finally, overgeneralization refers to irrational tendencies to base their perceptions on one event or limited evidence. Clients often express overgeneralizations with language of "always" or "never." For example, "I'll *always* be a failure so why bother trying," or "You *never* follow through with promises" (Ellis, 1957a, 1957b, 1958, 1962). On the other hand, rational beliefs tend to be more logical, reasonable, and therefore less likely to result in distressing emotional reactions or consequences. The following are examples of Irrational Beliefs and Rational Alternative Beliefs:

IRRATIONAL BELIEFS	RATIONAL BELIEFS
I must be thoroughly adequate, competent, and achieving in all that I do.	It's nice when I do things well, but not everyone is perfect all the time.
The world should be fair and just.	Yes, it's nice when justice prevails, but we know there are a lot of injustices and unfairness in the world.
People should do what I want them to do and live up to my expectations.	We cannot control others, only ourselves.
It's awful when things don't work out the way I want them to.	It's nice when things work out the way we'd like them to, but we can't expect it's going to happen that way all the time.
I need to have immediate gratification, and when I don't get it I'm miserable	We don't always get what we want when we want it.

Source: Adapted from Ellis, A., & Harper, R. A. (1975). *A new guide to rational living.* Wilshire Press.

There are particular irrational beliefs that are common among individuals who have SUDs (Ellis et al., 1988), and the goal of the REBT approach is to help clients to dispute or challenge these irrational beliefs and to adopt more rational, and therefore less emotionally distressing, alternative rational beliefs. Here are some examples:

IRRATIONAL BELIEF	RATIONAL DISPUTE OR ALTERNATIVE
I need a drink to relax	I would like a drink, but there are other ways to relax and I don't have to drink just because I want to.
I deserve to drink. My life/job is so stressful that I deserve a break today!	Yes, jobs and life in general can be stressful, but there are other ways to manage that stress without jeopardizing your health.
It would be too hard to stop drinking. I'd lose all my friends and be bored.	While stopping drinking/drug use will cost me some things, the consequences of continued use will be far worse.

(*continued*)

People who don't drink are doomed to frustration, isolation, and unhappiness.	There's no evidence that people who don't drink are miserable.
The only way to feel comfortable in social situations is to drink or get high.	It's hard at first to learn to be relaxed in social situations, but people do it all the time.
I need more excitement in my life. Sobriety is boring!!!!!	Nobody ever died of boredom. Besides, the price I pay for excitement is harmful and dangerous. There are other ways to manage boredom.
Poor me! Why I can't drink or use drugs like everyone else?	Where's the evidence that you're worthless just because you can't do something? Does drinking really make you feel more valued?

Source: Adapted from Ellis, A., McInerney, J. F., DiGiuseppe, R., & Yeager, R. (1988). *Rational-emotive therapy with alcoholics and substance abusers.* Allyn & Bacon.

These are just a few examples of ways in which REBT counselors will try to get clients to dispute their irrational beliefs surrounding drinking or other substance use. The key is to find out what particular irrational beliefs your client endorses that may put them at greater risk for picking up a drink or drug and then helping them to come up with a rational dispute or alternative such as those described earlier. Here is an example.

CASE EXAMPLE: JACK (REBT)

Jack is 42 years old, is married, and works as a construction foreman. He was self-referred for outpatient counseling after his wife told him to "get help or get out." Jack indicates that he and his wife drank socially for years, wine with dinner, a beer with a pizza on Friday night; however, once Jack was promoted to foreman a few years ago, his drinking increased to where he was consuming about a pint or two of rum every evening and more on weekends. The construction company that Jack works for does large construction jobs, mostly building bridges in and around New York City. These are multibillion-dollar projects that have strict building and safety standards that must be met, as well as deadlines specified in their contracts. Last year, one of Jack's workers fell off a scaffold and drowned in the Hudson River. Jack felt responsible for the worker's death, although an investigation concluded that the worker had failed to connect his safety harness properly. Jack also has a 2-hour commute to and from work each day, which he says just adds to his stress. However, Jack likes living in the suburbs, and every evening (weather permitting), he sits outside in his backyard overlooking the river and drinks, which he indicates helps him to "unwind." Jack also mentions that, because of his stress, he has been smoking on average about two packs of cigarettes a day.

Case Conceptualization: Jack

Jack's alcohol use has progressed, and so too have the problems that Jack is encountering. His wife is especially concerned that, when Jack drinks, he "becomes depressed" and beats himself up for the worker that died a year ago. Using the A-B-C model, the Activating Events that Jack reports are work stress and flashbacks to the worker that died. His irrational Beliefs revolve around his feeling responsible for his employee's death and also that he deserves to drink. Jack perceives his drinking at the end of the day and on weekends as something he deserves given the incredible amount of stress that he is under. The Consequences that Jack experiences are depressive moods and anxiety. As with many SUD clients, Jack perceives his drinking (and smoking cigarettes) as a solution to his stress and problems rather than something that might be exacerbating the problems or creating more stress. His REBT counselor explores Jack's irrational beliefs surrounding his drinking, and at one point Jack states, "I deserve a drink, with the stress of my job, the deadlines, the commute, and then coming home to my wife nagging me all the time, who would not drink?" Jack's counselor introduces REBT principles to Jack and begins to encourage Jack to dispute his irrational beliefs (e.g., "not everyone drinks to deal with stress," "if my wife nags me because of my drinking, drinking more won't eliminate her nagging me"). Once Jack begins to practice disputing his irrational beliefs, he also agrees to find other ways to destress at the end of the day. Jack came up with an interesting alternative. He would get a glass of iced tea or hot tea during cooler weather and would sit outside in the backyard looking at the river. Sometimes his wife would join him, and they would talk about their day.

As described earlier, part of Jack's irrational beliefs revolved around his perception that the only way to manage his stress was to drink and smoke cigarettes. Several years ago, there was a series of important studies that examined the stress-inducing role of cigarette smoking. Given that nicotine is a stimulant, it is reasonable to assume that smoking will increase stress rather than reducing it (Parrott, 1994, 1999). Yet, it is common for smokers to perceive smoking as reducing their stress, and they will often reach for a cigarette when feeling stressed. According to Parrott and Murphy (2012), smokers report greater irritability, stress, and depression than nonsmokers.

LEARNING ACTIVITY 6.4
DISPUTING IRRATIONAL THOUGHTS

If you were Jack's counselor, how might you get him to dispute the Irrational Thoughts that he just expressed in the session? What are some alternative ways for him to cope with his stress?

Remember, as counselors, we can probably agree that Jack is under an incredible amount of stress; however, not everyone manages stress by drinking, smoking, or drug use. Think about ways in which you can manage stress in your daily life.

Limitations of Rational-Emotive Behavior Therapy

Although REBT is adept at providing clients with skills that they can use in everyday life, some clients find difficulty in remembering to utilize these skills and techniques when placed in highly emotional situations. In these instances, counselors will sometimes need to go back to these situations during their sessions with the client to coach them on how to identify irrational beliefs and how to dispute them. Another disadvantage of REBT is that, in certain situations, clients may have difficulty in accepting that they may be catastrophizing an event that at the time they do perceive as catastrophic. For example, if a loved one is hurt or killed in an accident, it might take time before the client might accept that they have the ability to modulate their grief reactions (see Figure 6.1).

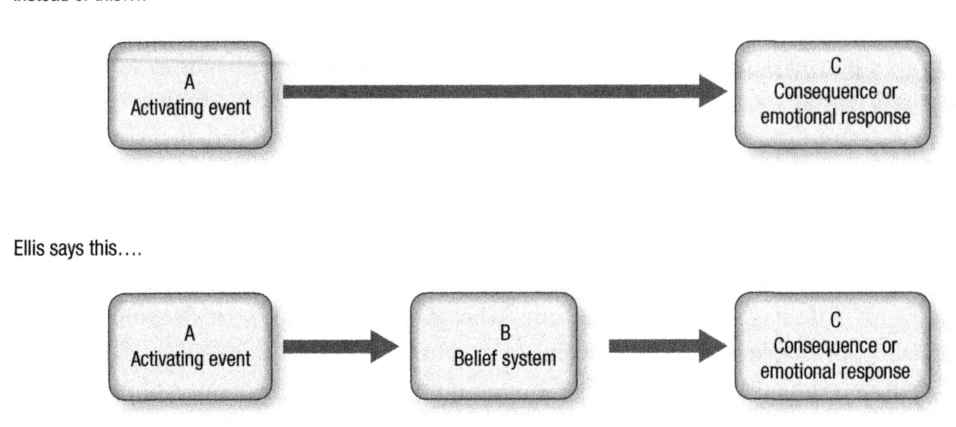

FIGURE 6.1 The A-B-Cs of emotional reactions

BEHAVIORAL COUNSELING

Behavioral Counseling approaches have been used extensively to treat individuals with SUDs for several decades. Based on Classical Conditioning, Operant Conditioning, and Social Learning Theory, the reasoning behind behavioral counseling is that just as drinking and substance use behavior can be learned, so too can these behaviors be unlearned or extinguished. According to behavioral theory, this can occur by one or more techniques: aversion therapy, community reinforcement therapy, CM, and behavioral contracting. Let us begin, however, by reviewing some basics of behaviorism and how those apply to SUDs. Classical conditioning can easily be used to describe how individuals become conditioned to stimuli in their environment when using mood-altering substances. For example, just as Pavlov's dogs did not have to learn to salivate when presented with meat, a person with an alcohol use disorder (AUD) does not have to be taught to respond to the intoxicating effects of alcohol. The physiological response to alcohol is a given or unconditioned stimulus (UCS). However, there are several things that may become paired with drinking alcohol, for example, the visual appearance of a martini glass, the taste of a cold beer, the aroma of the vodka, the sounds of ice cubes, or the music playing in the bar, all of which have the potential to become conditioned stimuli (CS) and therefore all have the potential of becoming very powerful relapse triggers. The same conditioning occurs with substances other than alcohol, for example, the visual appearance of white powder on a mirror, the aroma of cigarette smoke or the sight of a box of cigarettes, the distinct aroma of cannabis or the aroma of crystal meth being "cooked," and the sight of a hypodermic syringe also become CS and potential relapse triggers. A client who was several months in recovery found that he experienced heroin craving when driving through the Lincoln Tunnel. He had not been in New York City since getting clean/sober; however, he realized that he used to go into New York City several times a week to buy heroin when he was actively using. The Lincoln Tunnel had become a conditioned stimulus.

Operant conditioning is associated with Harvard psychologist, B.F. Skinner. By utilizing what became known as a "Skinner box," rats would press a bar in order to receive food pellets.

Here, the food pellet becomes a *positive reinforcement* for bar pressing. Skinner found that he could operantly condition a rat to press the bar numerous times before it would receive a food pellet by varying the time or number of bar presses. This was known as a *reinforcement schedule,* and Skinner discovered that rats would make several bar presses on intermittent or ratio reinforcement schedules. Most students confuse *negative reinforcement* with *punishment;* however, they are very different. The essential difference is that both *positive* and *negative reinforcement* increase behavior. With negative reinforcement, a rat would press a bar in order to escape or avoid a mild electrical shock, whereas *punishment* is used to suppress or reduce behavior; therefore, if bar pressing is followed by a shock (rather than a reward), it would reduce or suppress bar pressing, and the rat would learn to avoid the bar altogether. You might be saying to yourself, "What does all this have to do with SUDs?" to which a behaviorally oriented counselor would reply, "It has everything to do with explaining SUDs!"

Relevance of Behavioral Counseling for Addiction Counselors

Operant conditioning easily applies to SUDs in that many individuals find particular substances positively reinforcing. A person who drinks several beers "to relax" or has a few shots of tequila to "get into a party mood" are descriptions of alcohol as a positive reinforcer. Similarly, many individuals find that smoking cannabis calms them or helps them fall asleep or to appreciate music more or to become more creative. Yet, if a person uses a particular substance to the point where a physiological addiction develops, then as a person develops a tolerance to that substance the use of that substance no longer produces the same high or sense of euphoria. Instead, the person continues to use in order to stop or avoid the discomfort associated with withdrawal, in which case the use of the substance becomes a negative reinforcer (much like the rat who presses the bar to avoid an electrical shock). Remember, both positive and negative reinforcers increase behavior, while punishment suppresses behavior. Therefore, if a person finds that whenever they drink vodka they become nauseous to the point of vomiting, that would be a punishment.

Social Learning Theory (Bandura, 1977) can be applied to our understanding of how SUDs are reinforced; only this time, the factors that influence substance use are found among those in one's social environment. Social Learning Theory examines the influence of role models whom one perceives as being powerful or influential or someone that the person wishes to emulate. This theory explains how one's own substance use will be similar to those role models that individual is exposed to whether it be a parent, an older sibling, schoolmates, or even influential role models such as celebrities. The reason why Social Learning Theory falls under behavioral models is that emulating a powerful role model is perceived by the individual as positively reinforcing, and/or by mimicking that role model the individual is reinforced by those in their social circles.

Behavioral Treatment Techniques

Cue Exposure Therapy

Based on classical conditioning theory, the premise of cue exposure therapy (CET) is that when individuals drink alcohol or use substances, they are constantly being classically conditioned to stimuli in their surroundings (a particular liquor store; the aroma of alcohol or the sight of cocaine; specific people they use with; and events such as sports, concerts, picnics, and weddings) Budney et al. (2013) describe a rather typical situation of a man who comes home after work each day, changes comfortable clothes, sits in his favorite rocking chair on the back porch, puts on his favorite music, and smokes cannabis. In this scenario, there are so many potential cues that have become classically conditioned and are now associated with smoking, that is, his comfortable clothing, his rocking chair, the scenery from his back porch, the music he listens to, and the aroma of the cannabis. If this individual were to seek CET, the session might begin with identifying all of these conditioned cues. The next step would be to plan for systematic exposure to these cues either using imagery or in vivo (live exposure). These exposures would then be repeated over and over again without any opportunity for cannabis use. In an office setting, exposure can take the form of handling drug paraphernalia such as feeling a rolled up "joint" or smelling the aroma of cannabis or handling a spoon, a syringe, rolling papers, a pipe, razor blades, talcum powder on a mirror, a shot glass or bottle of liquor, or particular music associated with alcohol and substance use. The goal of CET is to *extinguish* these CSs. Again, think of Pavlov's dogs. How could he get the dogs stop salivating at the sound of the bell (which had become the conditioned stimulus)? Keep ringing the bell, but do not pair it with meat. When using CET, counselors are presenting the CS to clients (e.g., exposure to paraphernalia, aromas, and sounds) but not allowing it to be paired with substance use with the goal of extinguishing the conditioned response.

Unfortunately, controlled studies that examine the efficacy of CET have not been very encouraging. For example, a meta-analytic study found that, most often, CET was combined with other treatment approaches, so it was difficult to ascertain whether CET made a significant difference (Conklin & Tiffany, 2001). In one study, combining CET with coping-skills training did produce positive outcomes (Loeber et al., 2006).

There are commercially produced cue exposure kits that can be used with clients (see Box 6.5). These would best be used, however, either in residential or inpatient settings where there is a greater likelihood that substance use can be prevented, or if used in outpatient settings, where a responsible, significant other can help monitor the client's response to the CET session afterward.

Aversion Therapy

Aversion therapies are based on classical conditioning principles. By pairing alcohol or other mood-altering substances (the UCS) with a negative or aversive stimulus (the CS),

BOX 6.5

CUE EXTINCTION TRAINING

Sometimes referred to as Exposure Response Prevention (ERP), this approach is based on classical conditioning in that it systematically exposes clients to simulated versions of CS such as drug paraphernalia, aromas, music, and other auditory stimuli associated with substance use. Commercially produced kits are available (e.g., www.killthecraving.com and www.erptherapy.com as well as a book which describes the principles of ERP treatment; Santoro et al., 2001).

Source: Adapted from Santoro, J., DeLetis, R., & Bergman, A. (2001). *Kill the craving: how to control your impulse to use alcohol and drugs*. New Harbinger Publications.

these two stimuli would become paired and would therefore reduce cravings or urges to continue drinking or using substances. The use of aversion therapies has been in existence for quite some time and can be traced back to ancient Rome when physicians would place eels, spiders, and other repulsive items in jugs of wine. Drinking this nauseating combination was thought to prevent future urges to drink (Rackham, 1938). (Apparently, excessive drinking and AUDs were probably quite prevalent in ancient Rome as evidenced by the famous Roman Colosseum placing a two wine-jug limit on spectators. Prior to the two-jug limit, fans were said to have become so intoxicated that they would begin to hurl wine jugs at the gladiators and even at Roman nobility!) Aversion therapy became a more formalized clinical treatment in the 1920s at the Leningrad Psychiatric Hospital in Russia, whereby individuals with AUDs were administered a strong electrical shock when paired with the aroma and sight of alcohol (Kantorovich, 1929). Also, around this same time period, Russian physicians would also pair alcohol with drugs that would induce nausea and vomiting such as ipecac. In the United States, the Schick Shadel Hospital currently uses aversion therapies with individuals with various types of SUDs (Schick Shadel Hospital, 2020). In addition, disulfiram (Antabuse) also works on aversion therapy principles. Taking disulfiram as prescribed on a daily basis will produce profoundly averse reactions if one ingests alcohol. Disulfiram blocks the liver's ability to break down or metabolize acetaldehyde to a nontoxic substance that can be safely eliminated from the body. If an individual drinks alcohol while taking disulfiram, they have essentially poisoned themselves. Also, in order to drink safely with no averse reaction, individuals must stop taking disulfiram for at least a week in advance to avoid this horrendous reaction. The advantage of disulfiram is that it helps to prevent impulsive drinking. Several other chemicals have been used to produce averse reactions following alcohol ingestion including citrated calcium carbamide, lithium carbonate, and apomorphine hydrochloride. The required number of conditioning trials for some of the aforementioned chemicals ranged from five to 10 sessions, which were administered either daily or every other day (Howard & Jenson, 1990; Wiens & Menustik, 1983).

A more practical type of aversion therapy and one that is more conducive to office practice is a technique known as covert sensitization (Cautela, 1967, 1970). In a traditional covert sensitization script, clients are asked to imagine a familiar situation where they would drink or use drugs such as ordering a beer at a local bar. As the bartender pours the beer, the clients are asked to imagine the beer mug and the color and aroma of the beer, but then the client is asked to imagine that they begin to feel nauseous even to the point of vomiting. As the client is beginning to pick the mug up and raise it to their lips, they do begin to vomit into the glass and onto the bar. The client is asked to imagine taking a sip of the beer with the vomit floating in it whereby they would become even more nauseous and vomit again.

This type of scenario is used not only for various types of alcohol but also for cigarette smoking, other substance use, and even for process addictions (e.g., sexual acting out or gambling). The important part of the procedure is that the scene in which alcohol is paired with an aversive stimulus (e.g., vomiting) is repeated over and over again. The research pertaining to the efficacy of covert sensitization is mixed (Lawson & Boudin, 1992; Nathan, 1985; Nathan & Niaura, 1983; O'Leary & Wilson, 1987; Rimmele et al., 1995). The most encouraging study reported increased effectiveness of covert sensitization when the sensitization procedures were clearly defined and conditioned aversion was established and verified (Elkins,

1980, 1991). Unfortunately, research and interest in aversion therapies and covert sensitization treatment approaches has decreased over the past few decades.

Community Reinforcement Approach

The Community Reinforcement Approach (CRA) incorporates several behavioral techniques but is based primarily on the operant conditioning model. CRA is utilized primarily for those with severe AUDs such as those living in group homes or halfway-house living situations (Azrin, 1976; Azrin et al., 1973). In this approach, efforts are first made to establish a healthy living environment in which alcohol and drugs are prohibited. Clients are closely monitored by counselors who work with clients on daily coping skills and also provide clients with access for newspapers, job search materials, and a variety of recreational/social and leisure activities. Clients are also taught ways to identify relapse triggers and how to manage those triggers. Some CRA studies have also incorporated disulfiram into the treatment regimen, and compliance with taking disulfiram was assured by having significant others monitor the client taking the medication (Azrin et al., 1982). The advantage of the CRA approach is that it begins with abstinence and then tries to reinforce client attempts to engage in other prosocial activities (e.g., work, social life, and recreation).

Contingency Management and Voucher Programs

CM approaches utilize operant conditioning principles, especially that of positive reinforcement for desired behaviors (e.g., abstinence). Most CM techniques began to be incorporated into more traditional SUD treatment programs in the 1990s. By utilizing positive rewards such as vouchers for movie tickets, bus/subway or train tickets, gift cards to retail or grocery stores, or opportunities to win prizes for abstinence verified by drug screens, these positive reinforcers often produced increases in abstinence. In other words, attaining the voucher becomes *contingent* on various treatment goals such as substance abstinence or attending a 12-step meeting or attending individual or group counseling sessions. Similarly, in methadone programs, clients would obtain more take-home doses of methadone for each week of verified abstinence from substance use. Positive rewards in the form of vouchers would also be used for other prescribed, positive behaviors such as job searching, finding a job, attending scheduled counseling sessions, completing treatment assignments, or for compliance with medication (e.g., naltrexone; Higgins et al., 1991, 1993, 1994, 2008).

In terms of the efficacy of CM, there have been two meta-analysis studies that provide support for the effectiveness of CM in bringing about positive treatment outcomes for those targeted behaviors such as abstinence, job finding, and improved social interactions (Lussier et al., 2006; Prendergast et al., 2006). In addition, voucher programs have been shown to improve treatment outcomes for cannabis use disorders (Budney et al., 2000) and for individuals participating in opioid treatment programs (Preston et al., 2000).

Behavioral Contracting

Of all the behavioral approaches, contracting is probably the most adaptable one for outpatient programs and private office practices. It is important to first point out, however, that agreements are different from contracts. If a counselor and client set an appointment to meet next Wednesday at 4:00 p.m., that would constitute an agreement. If, however, there is a written contract to meet at 4:00 p.m. next Wednesday, and if the client were to miss that 4:00 p.m. appointment, then the client would be charged $30, that constitutes a contract. Similarly, the contract may also stipulate if the client attends their weekly counseling session on Wednesday as planned and produces a clean drug screen, then they would receive a reward or positive reinforcer such as a gift card. Contracts are used as a means of clearly defining what treatment outcomes are expected and how those positive behaviors will be rewarded. For example, in order to participate in medication-assisted treatment (MAT), such as a methadone-maintenance or buprenorphine (Suboxone, Subutex, or Sublocade) program, abstinence from all other mood-altering substances is required. The following case example provides an illustration of how a behavioral contract (Exhibit 6.1) might be used with a client.

CASE EXAMPLE: MARIA

Maria is a 24-year-old single woman who is currently living with her boyfriend at his mother's house. Maria had been taking classes to become a nurse at a local community college, however, as she and her boyfriend had gotten deeper into their dependence on heroin, Maria stopped going to classes. A few days ago, Maria had nearly overdosed. She knew from the second she injected the heroin that there was "something wrong with it." Her boyfriend's mother called the police and they administered Narcan which reversed the overdose. The emergency medical technicians brought Maria to the ED where she spoke with a substance abuse screener who suggested that Maria be evaluated at the medical center's substance use disorder program. Maria has sought outpatient counseling because the overdose frightened her, and she wants to return to college and "make something of herself." Maria is currently being seen by a counselor in a medication-assisted treatment program who suggests that she begin a methadone detoxification. The counselor describes the program and then recommends that Maria agree to a behavioral contract.

The first step would be to review the contract with the client verbally before presenting the contract in written form as follows:

> Maria, I would like to review the abstinence contract with you before having you sign the written document. Is that okay? Okay, the contract represents an agreement between you and a methadone program that will help you to maintain abstinence from heroin, prescription opioids, and other drugs. Initially, you will be coming to the methadone clinic daily between 7 a.m. and 11 a.m. to receive your prescribed dose. On three of those days, you will be asked to submit a urine drug screen, which will be administered and monitored by one of the female nurses. The screens are given for two reasons; the first is to ensure that you are taking the methadone, and the second is to make sure you are not using any other drugs, as those can be dangerous if mixed with your daily methadone dose. Having you submit the drug screens also becomes a way for us to monitor your progress as you are going through the program. So far does that make sense? Do you have any questions? Okay, so if your drug screens come back negative and you are attending your group and individual counseling sessions regularly, then you will begin to receive take-home doses, which means you do not have to come to the

(*continued*)

clinic every day. Do you have children living or visiting your home? If so, we will supply you with a locked box for you to store your methadone bottles. Children sometimes mistake a methadone bottle for juice, therefore, we want to make sure they do not take your dose by mistake. However, if you come up positive for heroin or other drugs, then that suggests that this may not be the appropriate level of treatment for you, at which point we will make arrangements for you to enter a residential program where you will be safely detoxed, and hopefully will continue in that residential treatment program. Do you have any questions or concerns? If not, I will ask you to sign the written contract. After you sign it, I will witness it and make copies for you.

Exhibit 6.1

BEHAVIORAL CONTRACT

I, Maria Hernandez, agree to adhere to the following contract in order to help ensure my progress in treatment and for my own safety as I move through this program:

1) I agree to remain abstinent from all opioid drugs including heroin and prescription opioids, as well as all mood-altering substances including alcohol. I realize that this is important in protecting my own health and safety.

2) I agree to attend the clinic each morning between 7 a.m. and 11 a.m. in order to receive my daily methadone dose as prescribed by the clinic's medical director. I understand that it is my responsibility to get to the clinic each morning and that, if I miss a dose, it will not be dispensed after the specified dispensing hours.

3) I agree to submit random urine drug screens that will be administered and monitored by one of the program nurses. I understand that if my drug screens are free from opioids and other substances, I will be eligible for take home doses according to the following schedule: 2 weeks of clean screens = 1 take home, 4 weeks of clean screens = 2 take homes per week, and six weeks of clean screens = 4 screens per week. I understand that if any of my drug screens come back positive for any substance (including alcohol), my take homes will revert back to zero.

4) I agree to attend both individual counseling 1× per week for the first three months and group counseling 1× per week for the first six months. I understand that if I miss more than four scheduled counseling sessions, this will result in my termination from the program and referral to a more intensive level of care, for example, intensive outpatient or residential treatment.

I understand the contents of this contract and agree to adhere to these stipulations to the best of my ability. I also understand that if I feel I am being treated unfairly that I have the right to an appeal with the program director, Dr. Paul Ebson, and with the State Division of Addiction Services.

______________________	______________
Maria Hernandez	Date
______________________	______________
Frank Roberts, M.A, LCADC	Date

Behavioral contracting has been effective in both initiating and maintaining behavioral change in a variety of treatment settings, not just in outpatient programs. Contracts can also increase motivation by challenging clients to "put their money where their mouth is" with regard to their stated goals. In one such behavioral contract, a client agreed to send a money order to an organization she despised (e.g., a neo-Nazi party), if she used cocaine again. What made this consequence so poignant was that this client's grandparents had died in the Holocaust, therefore, sending money to support a neo-Nazi organization was so abhorrent to the client that it provided more gravitas to the behavioral contract. Another client contracted that if he drank alcohol, he would turn over his beloved dog to a family member for two weeks. This negative consequence was symbolic of the client's admitting that if he continued to become intoxicated, he would be unable to provide proper care for his dog. Another client contracted that he would give away his prized guitar to a music program that gave music lessons to children living in poor neighborhoods if he continued to smoke cannabis.

Behavioral Skills Training

Skills Training is an outgrowth of behavioral counseling. It is based on the notion that behavioral repertoires can be learned, and therefore are valuable for individuals who are struggling to attain sobriety. For example, as part of a relapse-prevention strategy, counselors can teach their clients *refusal skills* that can be role-played within an individual session and then practiced in vivo. Here is an example of a refusal skills session:

Client: I have to go to my sister's wedding this Saturday and there's no way out of it. Jill told me she'd never speak to me again if I didn't at least show up for the church service and part of the reception.

Counselor: So, Jill is not expecting you to stay for the whole reception correct?

Client: Yes, at least I don't have to stay for the whole thing, that would be way too much.

Counselor: If you felt uncomfortable you could leave, correct?

Client: Yes, my sponsor said he would be around on Saturday and would even pick me up if I felt tense or felt like picking up a drink.

Counselor: What worries you the most?

Client: I know some of my old drinking buddies are going to be there, and the first thing they're going to do is to shove a beer in my face.

Counselor: Okay, I see what you mean, and we did talk about having a club soda in your hands at all times, this way it would lessen the chance of this happening. What about one of these old drinking buddies asking you to have a shot of tequila to celebrate Jill's wedding?

Client: Yeah, I could see that happening, so what do I say?

Counselor: Let's role play the situation, I'll be you, you are one of your buddies.

Client: Okay. Hey Jim, long time no see, where the hell have you been?

Counselor: *I've been working a lot recently, how have you been?*

Client: I'm great, thanks. Hey let's have a shot of tequila to toast the new bride and groom?

Counselor: Thanks, but I promised to drive my sister and her new husband to the airport for their honeymoon. If I get wasted she'll kill me, and she'll probably want to kill you too.

There are a number of ways to help clients develop refusal skills. Some clients are comfortable telling people straight away that they are clean and sober and therefore no longer drinking.

However, other clients are not comfortable announcing their recovery to people they might not know well, so in those instances clients will refuse a drink (or drug), stating that they are taking medication and therefore any alcohol could seriously jeopardize their health. Others might say they are on a diet. The key to refusal skills is to "stick to your guns." In other words, once your client states their refusal, it is just a matter of making the same statement over and over again.

Another type of skills training is teaching clients coping skills. This would usually consist of ways clients can reduce their level of stress or anxiety. Having clients make a list of things they might enjoy doing as diversions from their stress/anxiety is a first step toward developing coping, such as listening to soothing music, going for a walk or hike, playing with a pet, writing in a journal, drawing or painting, reading a book, watching a funny TV show, playing a game, doing yard work, or calling a friend/sponsor. Mindfulness, progressive muscle relaxation, guided imagery, and grounding techniques are also helpful ways to reduce stress that counselors can teach their clients (see Monti et al., 1989).

One of the reasons why young adults drink or use drugs is to help alleviate social anxiety. Interacting especially in social situations with potential romantic interests can often bring about panic levels of anxiety. One way that counselors can help clients is to teach social skills while desensitizing clients by having them use relaxation techniques while envisioning having conversations with an attractive person. Social skills training protocols and ways to increase effective communication are described by Kadden et al. (1992) and Monti et al. (1995). It is often suggested by behavioral counselors that they envision their individual session as consisting of three parts. The first third is where the counselor has their client review their prior week (i.e., going over any difficulties that client may have encountered, any cravings, etc.). In the second third of the session, the counselor teaches the client new skills, and in the third part of the session they plan for the week ahead, which includes any homework assignments the client may be asked to work on before the next session.

Limitations to Behavioral Counseling

Behavioral counseling offers a number of helpful therapeutic tools and techniques that clients can use to help reinforce their commitment to recovery, to avoid relapse, and to learn new ways of coping without the need for substances. However, Behavioral Counseling is not helpful for all clients. For example, a client whose alcohol or substance use is connected to a past history of trauma may benefit more from a trauma-informed approach or from eye movement desensitization response (EMDR) therapy.

OTHER INDIVIDUAL COUNSELING APPROACHES

There are several other counseling techniques that are very adaptive to individual addiction counseling; therefore, we will focus on a few of these approaches, specifically on existential, Gestalt, and mindfulness approaches and techniques.

12-Step Facilitated Counseling

Without doubt, 12-step involvement is a cornerstone of recovery for many individuals who experience SUDs. If you have ever been to an open meeting of Alcoholics Anonymous (AA),

Narcotics Anonymous (NA), or Gamblers Anonymous (GA), you have probably heard speakers credit these 12-step groups for having saved their lives (see Box 6.6). Founded in 1935, AA became the foundation for many other 12-step groups such as NA (founded in 1953) and GA (founded in 1957). Essentially, the goal of 12-Step Facilitated Counseling is to assist clients in establishing a deeper, conscious connection to AA, NA, and GA for the purpose of strengthening and reinforcing one's recovery. One of the main advantages of 12-step groups is that they provide support for one's recovery on a 24/7 basis, 365 days a year. Individuals can readily access meetings in person or online or can reach out to fellow AA, NA, or GA members via Intergroups hotlines. This level of support is far beyond what most counselors or treatment programs can provide with the possible exception of inpatient/residential or hospital-based programs. There are several other advantages to 12-step programs. Most notably, individuals attending meetings learn how to stay sober one day at a time and can receive a great deal of support in achieving this goal. It is often recommended that, in the beginning of one's recovery, they attend 90 meetings in 90 days. The rationale behind this recommendation is twofold: first, if one drank or used drugs on a daily basis, then it is reasonable that they would do something to support their recovery on a daily basis. Second, since meetings differ from one another in terms of size, location, and members, attending different meetings gives a better perspective on the types of meetings available (e.g., open, closed, discussion, and Big Book meetings) Another advantage of 12-step programs is that individuals "work the program" at their own pace. Although there are suggestions regarding

BOX 6.6

DIFFERENT TYPES OF 12-STEP MEETINGS

Open Speakers Meetings: open to both alcoholics and nonalcoholics.

Closed Meetings: open only to alcoholics.

Closed/Open Discussion Meetings: discussion meetings focus on a particular topic introduced by the person leading the group. Topics might include honesty with self or others, letting go of anger, how to live life one day at a time, managing loneliness, and managing cravings.

Step Meetings: each week a different Step is addressed, and members of the group are asked to weigh in on their perspectives on that particular step.

Big Book Meetings: each week a different chapter or passage from the Big Book is discussed (e.g., the Promises of AA). As with other discussion group formats, each group member is asked to weigh in.

Beginners Meetings: these meetings are usually facilitated by AA members with long-term sobriety and are designed for newcomers to AA as a way to introduce important parts of AA.

Women's Meetings: for women only, may be an open or closed meeting and usually allows for discussion.

Men's Meetings: for men only

LGTBQ Meetings: for lesbian, gay, transexual, bisexual, and queer individuals only.

Professionals Group Meetings: groups specifically designed for recovering professionals, e.g., medical doctors, attorneys, psychologists, and counselors. These meetings are usually accessed through state professional organizations.

Institutions and Prison Meetings: usually speaker or discussion meetings led by AA/NA members with long-standing recovery who are brought into prisons, jails, criminal justice halfway houses, psychiatric hospitals, hospitals, and other institutions.

how often one should attend meetings or what types of meetings they attend, there are no hard-and-fast rules regarding how often one attends meetings or at what pace they work the 12 Steps. That is left up to the individual, who hopefully will ask someone with solid recovery to be their sponsor. A sponsor is someone who helps guide individuals in their recovery. A sponsor may also help the individual they are sponsoring to "work the Steps." For example, if someone were to work on the first Step, they might be asked to write out a list of ways in which they were powerless over alcohol, drugs, or gambling (e.g., instances of loss of control or inability to control substance use or gambling) and also instances where that use resulted in major life difficulties or unmanageability. Another advantage of 12-step programs is their ability to model sober behavior as a means of providing hope that people can and do change.

Although the advantages outweigh the disadvantages, as you can see in Box 6.7, there are some disadvantages to 12-step programs. For example, boundaries are often more difficult to define in 12-step groups, as opposed to counselor–client relationships where the National Association for Alcoholism and Drug Abuse Counselors (NAADAC) Code of Ethics goes to great lengths to define the boundaries of therapeutic relationships. It is common for 12-step members to go out for coffee after a meeting or to attend social events together, which would never happen in a counselor–client relationship. And although it is recommended that 12-step members do not become romantically involved with one another, this happens, even though frowned upon. Another disadvantage for some is difficulty with the concept of God or a Higher Power. Although 12-step programs are quick to point out that they are not religious programs and that individuals can determine their own "Higher Power," there are many who struggle with this aspect of 12-step programs. When Bill W., Dr. Bob, and other early AA members

BOX 6.7

ADVANTAGES AND DISADVANTAGES OF THE 12-STEP APPROACH

Advantages to 12-step groups

Learn effective social skills
Explore new style of relating to others
Group setting offers support for new behaviors and healthy connections with others
Facilitates personal growth
Addresses how to stay sober one day at a time
Can work with the program at your own pace
12-step groups are FREE!!!! and ubiquitous!!!

Disadvantages to 12-step groups

No counselor/professional input
Some may become overly dependent on meetings
Boundaries are more difficult
Not everyone is suited for 12-step groups
Some have difficulty with spirituality and Higher Power concept
Gender, race, and ethnicity factors
Working program at one's own pace

were creating the 12 Steps of AA, they borrowed concepts from the Lutheran Church's Oxford Groups, based on the teachings of Rev. Frank Buchman in 1921.

Notice also that "working the program at your own pace" is mentioned as both an advantage and a disadvantage. It is an advantage when taking into account that there are many levels of severity among 12-step group members; therefore, some may need a more intense level of involvement while others may not. Plus, most people do not like being told what to do and when to do it. While sponsors offer "suggestions" to those they sponsor based on the sponsor's own experiences as to what worked for them, remember these are suggestions, not dictates. This is also where 12-step programs differ from traditional counseling, in that counselors usually work from a written treatment plan with goals and objectives that are spelled out and that usually have a time-frame for achieving those goals (see Box 6.8).

BOX 6.8

THE 12 STEPS AND 12 TRADITIONS

Steps

1. Admitted that we were powerless of alcohol and that our lives had become unmanageable.
2. Came to a belief that a Power greater than ourselves could restore us to sanity.
3. Made a decision to turn our will and our lives over to the care of God as we understood Him.
4. Made a searching and fearless moral inventory of ourselves.
5. Admitted to God, to ourselves. and to another human being the exact nature of our wrongs.
6. Were entirely ready to have God remove all these defects of character.
7. Humbly asked Him to remove our shortcomings.
8. Made a list of all persons we had harmed and became willing to make amends to them all.
9. Made direct amends to such people wherever possible, except when to do so would injure them or others.
10. Continued to take personal inventory, and when we were wrong promptly admitted it.
11. Sought through prayer and meditation to improve our conscious contact with God as we understood Him, praying only for knowledge of His will for us and the power to carry that out.
12. Having had a spiritual awakening as a result of these steps, we tried to carry this message to alcoholics and practice these principles in all our daily affairs.

Traditions

1. Our common welfare should be first; personal recovery depends on AA unity.
2. For our group purpose, there is one but ultimate authority—a loving God as He may express Himself in our group conscience. Our leaders are but trusted servants; they do not govern.
3. The only requirement for AA membership is a desire to stop drinking.
4. Each group should be autonomous except in matters affecting other groups or AA as a whole.
5. Each group has but one primary purpose—to carry its message to the alcoholics who still suffer.

(*continued*)

6. An AA group should never endorse, finance, or lend the AA name to any related facility or outside enterprise, lest problems of money, property, and prestige divert us from our primary purpose.
7. Every AA group ought to be fully self-supporting, declining outside contributions.
8. AA should remain forever nonprofessional, but our service centers may employ special works.
9. AA, as such, ought to never be organized, but we may create service boards or committees directly responsible to those we serve.
10. AA has no opinion on outside issues; hence the AA name ought to never be drawn into public controversy.
11. Our public relations policy is based on attraction rather than promotion; we need to always maintain personal anonymity at the level of press, radio, and film.
12. Anonymity is the spiritual foundation of all our traditions, ever reminding us to place principles before personalities.

LEARNING ACTIVITY 6.5
THE "12 AND 12"

Look over the 12 Steps and 12 Traditions. What stands out as you read through the Steps? Some say that the Steps would be a helpful guide for even those who do not have a SUD. Do you agree or disagree? How are the Steps similar to what addiction counselors may focus on when doing individual counseling?

Now look at the 12 Traditions. What were the founders of AA trying to accomplish in creating these Traditions? For example, why was it important for AA to "decline outside contributions," and what do you think the phrase "place principles before personalities" means?

Research indicates that 12-step involvement helps to enhance treatment outcomes (Luborsky et al., 1997; Project MATCH Research Group, 1998) and posttreatment recovery (Laudet & White, 2005). Therefore, 12-step Facilitated Counseling can often encourage clients new to recovery to try meetings as a means to enhance their recovery, or in some instances counselors may assist clients who had gone to some AA or NA meetings but did not continue to explore their reasons for not continuing. Research conducted by Timko and DeBennedetti (2007) indicates that the vast majority of individuals who attend AA end up dropping out within the first year of attendance. Therefore, counselors will encounter many individuals who attended 12-step meetings but who did not continue for a variety of reasons, the most concerning of which is that they relapsed to active alcohol and/or substance use.

Introducing a Recommendation to Attend 12-Step Meetings

Imagine you have begun individual counseling someone new to recovery and you feel that they would benefit from attending AA or NA meetings as a way to help enhance their recovery.

Think about how you, as an addiction counselor, would introduce that recommendation and what you might say to your client. What information would you want to convey to your client that would help make for a successful referral? Here is a way to begin that recommendation; however, think about what you might like to include or exclude from the following:

Counselor: *Nancy, I've been thinking about what you've told me about your drinking and how you've struggled with trying to control how much you drink and when you drink for several years now. I was just wondering if you have thought about going to AA and what you know about 12-step programs.*

Nancy: *It's funny you mention that because a friend of mine whom I confided in about my drinking suggested the same thing. I have to admit that I'm hesitant because of my husband's involvement in state politics and his position on the schoolboard. What if someone sees me at a meeting?*

Counselor: *That's a common concern, and just like your coming here guarantees confidentiality of things we talk about, the same holds true in AA. That's where the "anonymous" part comes in. Everyone is asked to refrain from disclosing the identity of others at the meeting and what's said in the meetings. Plus, by attending an Open meeting, since anyone can attend, it doesn't mean that everyone there is an alcoholic. A family member may attend an Open meeting to find out what meetings are like.*

Nancy: *But if I attend a meeting wouldn't I have to speak or say why I'm there?*

Counselor: *Not by attending an Open Speakers meeting. Here's what you can expect. First, meetings always begin and end on time, so make sure you get there early enough so that you're not searching for a seat once the meeting begins. Chairs will be set up in rows and their may be a lectern or podium. The person leading the meeting will introduce themself and welcome everyone. They will then read a statement regarding the mission of AA and will make a few announcements, perhaps regarding an upcoming anniversary meeting. They will then introduce the first speaker who will share their story of drinking and recovery. There's usually a second and sometimes a third speaker, but rest assured the meeting will only last one hour. At some point, the person leading the meeting will "pass the hat" asking everyone to donate if possible; a dollar or two is the usual donation, and it helps to pay for the coffee and literature that you'll see on a table when you walk in. By the way, although there's a complete list of meetings on AA's webpage, meetings usually have meeting books that also provide listings of meetings in this part of the state. The meeting usually ends with everyone standing, joining hands, and reciting the Lord's Prayer and/or the Serenity Prayer. You will not be asked to speak or say anything. Sometimes the person leading the meeting may ask if this is any one's first time at a meeting. You don't have to raise your hand, but the reason they do this is to offer newcomers a temporary sponsor. Are you familiar with what a sponsor does?*

Nancy: *Is that someone who is like your counselor?*

Counselor: *Not exactly, but it is someone usually has years of sobriety who will help make suggestions about what meetings to attend and how to begin working the Steps. I know a woman who attends the Thursday morning in Riverdale, would you feel more comfortable if I asked her to take you to your first meeting? This way you wouldn't have to walk in alone.*

Nancy: *Yes, I'd like that very much. Will she call me or should I call her?*

It is helpful to have someone who attends AA, NA, or GA accompany someone to their first meeting, and in the vignette described earlier the counselor happens to know someone with solid recovery who can take Nancy to her first meeting. However, if a counselor does not know someone like this to ask, they could suggest that Nancy call AA Intergroup and ask if someone would be able to take her to first meeting. AA Intergroup operates in-state, and it has lists of individuals who go out on "12-step calls" to individuals who are in crisis or who have no way to get to meetings. In some instances, they will provide someone who will accompany the person to their first meeting or meet them outside before the meeting begins.

When presenting 12-Step Facilitated Counseling approaches, it is common for students to sometimes voice confusion over the role of the addictions counselor versus the role of a sponsor. For example, if a client is working on doing their fourth Step (i.e., "fearless moral inventory"), would they go over that with their sponsor or with their counselor, or both? Although the goal of 12-Step Facilitated Counseling is to encourage active participation in 12-step recovery, generally addiction counselors work on different problems that have been identified in the client's treatment plan. Therefore, although a client may wish to address feelings of guilt or shame over past behavior as part of their treatment plan, the fourth Step review would fall under the responsibility of the client's AA/NA/GA sponsor. Also, addiction counselors would use different approaches to help their client let go of past behaviors that have resulted in feelings of guilt and shame such as REBT techniques.

Managing Reluctance to Attend 12-Step Meetings

12-Step Facilitated Counseling also troubleshoots instances where clients may have experienced negative prior reactions to attending 12-step meetings and who may, therefore, be reluctant to returning. In these instances, it may be helpful to first ask a few questions regarding what turned them off to meetings. For example:

"How long did you attend AA/NA, and what types of meetings did you attend?"
"Did you have a sponsor? A home group? Were you involved in doing any service?"
"What did you like and dislike about the meetings you attended?"
"Did you do any Step work, e.g., did you do a first Step? Fourth and fifth Step?"
"What, if anything, might prevent you from returning to AA/NA?"
"What if anything might make you feel more comfortable to return to meetings?"

These questions might help you to gauge what your client's level of involvement in 12-step meetings was like and what their experiences were like. Many 12-step group members make distinctions between those who are truly "in the program" versus those who are "around the program." In other words, distinctions are made between those who truly embrace their recovery by getting involved by setting the room up before a meeting or making coffee, driving those lacking transportation to meetings, going on speaking commitments, and eventually sponsoring newcomers. This is what is referred to as *service*. Those who are "around the program" usually arrive late to meetings and leave early, never make any connections with anyone, never read AA literature, never work the Steps, and do not attend meetings regularly.

Learning Activity 6.7 provides you with an opportunity to think about how you would respond to some common objections to attending 12-step meetings. For example, a client once remarked that he felt "bored" at meetings and was "tired of hearing the same old war stories." In exploring these objections, the client disclosed that he was attending only Open Speakers meetings for several months and had not attended any other type of meeting. He also admitted that he never got a sponsor and did not know what the Steps were or what the Big Book was. No wonder he felt bored and disconnected from the meetings he attended.

Alternatives to Traditional 12-Step Groups

There may be instances where clients have legitimate complaints about feeling marginalized at meetings. For example, gay or lesbian clients may feel disconnected from others at meetings; however, by attending LGBTQ-only 12-step meetings, often there is a feeling of support and connection that one may not feel by attending more traditional 12-step groups. Similarly, individuals who are Jewish may also find the emphasis on Christian teachings objectionable, therefore, connecting Jewish clients with an organization such as J-Recovery may provide a more suitable alternative. A female client commented that she hated going to AA and NA meetings because she was always being "hit on" by men. In this instance, recommendations to attend women-only meetings or Women for Sobriety (WFS) meetings may provide a more helpful alternative. WFS was founded in 1975 on the basis that AA was not always responsive to the needs of women with AUDs. The good news is that there are now an estimated 375 groups in the United States (McCrady & Delaney, 1995), and the bad news is that there are only 375 groups. Unfortunately, there are just not as many WFS groups as there are AA or NA groups (see www.womenforsobriety.org).

There are also instances where people of color may feel marginalized at 12-step meetings that are attended predominantly by White people or are located in White neighborhoods. For example, generally African Americans attend AA less frequently than their White counterparts. AA has literature that addresses these concerns (AA, 2021a, 2021b; see www.aa.org/assets/en_US/p-51_CanAAHelpMeToo.pdf) as well as for Native Americans with AUDs (see www.aa.org/assets/en_US/p-21_aafortheNNA.pdf).

For those who complain that AA or NA are "too religious," there are alternative groups such as SMART Recovery (www.smartrecovery.org). SMART is an acronym that stands for Self-Management and Recovery Training. It is an empowerment-oriented program that

LEARNING ACTIVITY 6.6
LEARNING THE "LANGUAGE OF 12-STEP PROGRAMS"

12-step programs have their own culture or way of doing things. One example is how groups celebrate anniversaries of days, months, or years of recovery. There is also a language or common phrases that are used in 12-step programs. See if you can define some of these common terms or phrases:

- Pigeon
- Big Book
- a "2-Stepper"
- 13th Stepping
- Making amends
- "1st Time Winner"

LEARNING ACTIVITY 6.7
MANAGING RELUCTANCE TO ATTEND 12-STEP MEETINGS

Think about how you would respond to the following comments a client might make pertaining to attending 12-step meetings:

- "AA/NA is too religious" or "AA/NA is a cult"
- "I've been going to a lot of meetings; I'm not getting anything out of them anymore"
- "When I go to meetings I come out feeling more like wanting to drink or use drugs"
- "I saw people using/dealing drugs after a meeting."
- "There were too many _____ people at the meeting"
- "Everyone there smokes"
- "I've been going to meetings, but it is always the same people talking, telling the same war stories"

LEARNING ACTIVITY 6.8
HELPING CLIENTS FIND MEETINGS

For the following case examples, see if you can help these clients find meetings near to where you currently live:

- A 32-year-old Jewish male is looking to attend a self-help meeting that is consistent with his religious beliefs that will help support his recovery from an AUD.
- A 24-year-old lesbian woman is looking to attend an AA meeting with other lesbian women in alcoholism recovery.
- A 17-year-old female has just completed a residential SUD treatment program and is looking to attend NA meetings.
- A 68-year-old woman is looking to attend meetings to help her with her dependence on benzodiazepines.
- A 42-year-old woman is looking to attend meetings with other medical doctors who are recovering from alcohol and prescription opioid use disorders.

utilizes cognitive behavioral approaches to help individuals find alternative paths to recovery. By focusing on self-defeating emotions, cognitions/beliefs, and behaviors, SMART offers assistance to individuals who choose to abstain or who are considering abstinence from alcohol and other substances. However, SMART recovery also focuses on SUDs and behavioral addictions. In addition, SMART offers programs not only to those grappling with addictions but also to family members, professionals, and other special groups (e.g., veterans and youth). According to their website (SMART, n.d.), SMART offers over 3,000 meetings per week (in-person and online); however, there are not as many meetings offered as AA or NA offers weekly. Learning Activity 6.8 asks whether you can help clients find suitable meetings in your area.

Existential Counseling

Existential theory originated in Europe after World War II and grew out of the work done by existential philosophers such as Kierkegaard, Sartre, Heidegger, and Nietzsche. Having experienced two world wars, industrialization, political revolutions, and the overthrow of established monarchies (e.g., Russia), many began to question their own personal value in a world filled with turmoil and often meaninglessness. Existential counseling posits that all individuals have two basic personalities, the *authentic self* and the *inauthentic self*. The authentic individual "realizes fully in his behaviors the core existential assumptions about human nature" (Kobasa & Maddi, 1977, p. 243). The authentic person is able to embrace originality and change and accepts the givens of their past and present with a basic orientation toward the future and the uncertainty that goes with it. And although uncertainty often leads to anxiety, the authentic person is able to accept this anxiety as an integral part of living a full life. The inauthentic person is one who feels inhibited, lacking in choice, and instead views themselves as someone who plays a predetermined social role. In addition, the inauthentic person tends to exploit or manipulate others, is rigidly materialistic, and often feels worthless and insecure. For those working in the addiction treatment profession, these characterizations of the authentic and inauthentic self probably sound similar to the sober self (or authentic self) versus the active addict self (or inauthentic self). Given that existential theory views the need for meaning and purpose in life as a basic need of one's existence, the goals of existential counseling are to help clients realize their authentic self to it is fullest and to assist clients in finding their unique meaning and purpose in life. In order to accomplish these goals, it is necessary that clients come to accept particular existential "givens" or assumptions. For example, as human beings, we will all face unique limitations and challenges throughout our lives. Meaning is found in facing these challenges and limitations rather than avoiding them (Vos et al., 2015). Some of the other existential "givens" include the following: (1) Human life is best understood as a series of decisions (not only concrete decisions but also the generic decisions that tie all the others together); (2) a person is always faced with the choice of the future, and the past which provokes guilt; (3) courage facilitates choosing one's future (because the future provokes anxiety, it is the courageous person who faces these challenges rather than opting for the security of doing nothing); (4) richness of experience stimulates positive development; (5) the authentic self experiences continual change, whereas the inauthentic self tends to remain constant; and (6) in social interactions, the authentic self is oriented toward establishing intimacy, whereas the inauthentic self is oriented toward superficial or contractual relationships. Contractual relationships are sometimes referred to as *exchange relationships* in which favors or services are exchanged between partners. This is quite the opposite of intimate relationships, in which the couple functions for the betterment of one another without keeping a ledger of exchanged services. Existential theorists (e.g., Johnson et al., 1987) also describe four givens of existence: *death, freedom, meaning, and isolation.* The unavoidability of the certainty of death is often at the root cause of everyday anxiety. According to Yalom (1998), the understanding and acceptance of the inevitability of death allows individuals to lead an authentic and purposeful life. For many, the recent coronavirus 2019 (COVID-19) pandemic has resulted in increased death anxiety. One of the most horrifying apprehensions is the thought of dying alone in an intensive care unit without the comfort or solace of close friends and family members. However, existential therapists would be the first to point out that when we die, we die alone. Some react to these apprehensions by becoming more cautious and vigilant about wearing masks and social distancing, while others deny the reality of COVID as a real and present danger and instead view it as part of national conspiracy.

From an existential perspective, *freedom* is conceptualized as one's taking responsibility for shaping the direction and future of their lives. As individuals accept this responsibility, there comes with it a feeling of aloneness given that we are alone in making these choices that will shape our lives. *Isolation* from an existential perspective suggests that, no matter how close we get to others, we are still essentially alone. Therefore, although human beings have an innate drive or motivation to connect to others for contact, support, or warmth, there is also a tension that exists knowing that no matter how close we connect with others we are still essentially alone. As Fernando (2007) explains, we are born into the world alone and we leave the world (i.e., through death) alone. Finally, according to existential theorists, there is also a struggle between finding meaning in one's life or existence or facing meaninglessness. Existential author Viktor Frankl, most known for his work *Man's Search for Meaning* (1992), indicates that an essential drive is for individuals to find *meaning* and purpose in their lives, which results in better overall physical, psychological, and emotional adjustment. Conversely, meaninglessness often results in deviant behavior and pathology (both physical and psychological), which Frankl (1992) describes as an *existential vacuum* that occurs when individuals have lost all sense of meaning in their lives. Again, this concept of an existential vacuum is similar to a state of desperation that results from years of active substance use.

Existential counseling is very applicable to working with individuals with SUDs (Lewis, 2014). As SUDs progress in intensity, most individuals experience increased isolation from others as well as an avoidance of facing the challenges of life that provide individuals with a sense of meaning. Recovery represents a means of attaining connection with others and a way to find one's meaning and purpose in life. As clients become more connected with their counselor, with other group-counseling clients, and with fellow AA and/or NA members, the feelings of loneliness and isolation begin to dissipate. With regard to anxiety resulting from the inevitability of one's death, although substance use may provide momentary relief from death-related anxieties, the paradox of substance use is that its inherent dangers often bring one closer to death. Indeed, some addiction experts view SUDs as a type of "suicide on the installment plan" (especially if we take the recent opioid-related overdose deaths into account). Existential counseling focuses on facing and accepting the inevitability of death by taking responsibility for choosing a life in which one can attain meaning. Leading a fulfilling life serves as a way to buffer death-anxiety (Yalom, 2008). Those who live fulfilling, meaningful lives and who are able to establish intimate connections with others are usually too busy to focus on the apprehensions and anxieties associated with death. Also, many individuals in SUD recovery often experience a profound sense of spirituality (e.g., a belief and trust in a higher power) that also helps to reduce existential anxieties. When faced with life adversities, many in recovery have found peace of mind in being able to turn these adversities over to their higher power.

Gestalt Counseling

At first glance, it seems that Gestalt counseling has very little to do with Gestalt psychology, which was developed by physiological psychologists such as Wertheimer and Kohler who were interesting in describing the nature of perceptual phenomena (e.g., figure-ground relationships and perceptual illusions); however, there are several instances where Gestalt counseling does draw from the early work of Gestalt psychologists. Developed by Frederick (Fritz) and Laura Perls in the 1970s, Gestalt counseling's primary emphasis is on awareness of self. In order to accomplish this goal, Gestalt therapists are concerned with confronting discordant or dissonant views between the client's beliefs/attitudes and their behaviors. Therefore, a Gestalt therapist is very much focused not only on the verbalizations or self-expressions of the client but also on their facial expression and body language. For example, if a client is describing an interaction they had with a loved one, while at the same time they begin to tap their foot, the Gestalt therapist will bring that foot-tapping behavior into focus and question the client vigorously as to why they are tapping their foot. This is done to help bring out some possible discordant emotions or beliefs regarding the loved one that may be expressed by the foot-tapping behavior. In some respects, this is similar to Gestalt psychology in that the foot tapping (which was in the background) is suddenly brought to the foreground (similar to figure-ground perception). The ultimate goal of Gestalt counseling is that the client will cease to experience dissonant or incongruent thoughts or emotions by developing greater self-awareness (Corsini, 1977). Self-awareness is a cornerstone of addiction recovery. Many people in recovery will often comment that, although they feel committed to their sobriety, they often struggle with battles with their "addict self" who tries to tell them "what harm is there is having a drink or two every now and then?" Gestalt counseling may therefore be effective in bringing to awareness these unconscious struggles between the sober self and the addict self.

There are a few Gestalt counseling techniques that are especially useful in addictions counseling. For example, the "empty chair" technique is one of the better-known Gestalt techniques (although it actually originated from Adlerian theory; Lewis, 2014). When using this technique, counselors ask clients to start a dialogue between their old self (e.g., actively substance-using self) and their new sober self. Clients may also be encouraged to actually switch seats as they portray their old and new self. The other way to utilize this technique is to have clients dialogue with significant individuals in their past or current life (e.g., an abusive parent or an exspouse/partner that the client has "unfinished business" with).

"Heightening Awareness" is another Gestalt technique that is designed to help clients develop greater awareness of a particular problem or issue. For example, an addiction counselor may heighten the client's awareness of a decisions they are making that may put them in touch with a past friend they used to get high with. A counselor may also heighten a client's awareness of bodily sensations or physical symptoms they may be experiencing. Finally, counselors may ask clients to "create experiments" in which they transform an issue they have been talking about into a here-and-now action or experiment. An example would be a client experimenting with expressing anger in a calm, assertive way rather than acting out physically by punching a wall or engaging in road-rage behavior. Washton and Zweben (2006) often ask clients to create an experiment with abstinence from all mood-altering substances as a means of heightening awareness of the role alcohol or substances are playing in their lives. In addition, White (1999) has created a seven-stage model that corresponds to Prochaska and DiClemente's Transtheoretical Stages of Change Model (1982) that utilizes a Gestalt model of SUDs that focused on disturbed relationship boundaries, entrenched figure-ground perceptions, and unfinished business with significant others that inhibits healthy movement through the Stages of Change.

NOTES FROM THE FIELD

Erin Murphy, MS, LPC, LCADC

Erin has been working in the addiction treatment field in New Jersey since 2007, and the majority of her work has been as a counselor (and more recently as clinical director) in medication-assisted treatment facilities that treat opioid use disorder clients using methadone. She has been working in medication-assisted treatment for the past twelve-and-a-half years and finds the work challenging. Although she finds there are several benefits to MAT treatment (especially in terms of helping her clients stabilize by allowing them to avoid risky behavior), she find that her clients often are not working and are suffering financially, which impacts on their abilities to attain basic needs (e.g., transportation). One of the frustrations Erin described was that there are often long waiting lists for clients to get into MAT programs. One of the most difficult aspects of Erin's job is that she has to tell her clients that there is nothing that their program can do to help them until their program has an opening. Erin indicates that she utilizes a number of individual counseling approaches in her work with clients, with some approaches being more helpful than others. As a clinical supervisor, Erin feels her counselors are stretched to their limits given their caseloads.

SUMMARY

There are several advantages and disadvantages to individual counseling with SUD clients. However, there are particular circumstances where individual counseling becomes the treatment of choice or may offer a safer, less-threatening entry to counseling and change. There are several individual counseling approaches that are particularly suited to individual counseling. This chapter reviews three of those approaches: SFT, Rational-Emotive Therapy, and Behavioral Therapy. SFT focuses on determining goals that clients want to attain once the problems they experience are no longer impeding their progress or aspirations. Instead of focusing on problems or unmanageability related to substance abuse, the focus is on solutions or how things will be different once the problem no longer exists. Instead of viewing the role of the counselor as needing to break down client denial, counselors work collaboratively on helping clients determine what they would like to change and a future in which the problematic behavior no longer exists. Several useful counseling techniques such as "the Miracle Question," Scaling Questions, and Exception-Finding questions are utilized to assist clients to move toward positive change. REBT focuses on helping clients to examine and change distress-producing irrational beliefs. By disputing the validity or accuracy of these irrational beliefs, clients are then encouraged to adopt rational belief alternatives. Behavioral counseling has yielded a number of treatment techniques that are adapted easily to individual counseling regimens such as CET, aversion therapy, covert sensitization, CM strategies, and behavioral contracting. Finally, 12-Step Facilitated, Existential, and Gestalt counseling approaches all offer additional strategies that counselors can utilize to assist their clients in attaining long-term recovery and/or personal goal attainment.

Before closing, just a few important recommendations for students regarding the individual counseling approaches, techniques, and strategies discussed in this chapter. The first pertains to timing. A therapeutic technique is most effective when offered at a time when the client is most receptive to making changes in their lives. Offering a counseling technique when a client is not receptive will probably result in a lot of frustration for both the client and the counselor. For example, when counseling someone who is in the Pre-Contemplation stage, it is probably not going to be helpful to introduce mindfulness or relaxation training, especially if the client has not identified anxiety as a precursor to their alcohol or substance use. The second word of advice pertains to beginning counselors who sometimes become overly enamored with a particular technique and therefore assume it will work with all of their clients. Over time, skilled counselors develop an intuitive sense as to when and what techniques to offer to a particular client. This is when clinical supervision is most beneficial in assisting beginning counselors in making sound clinical decisions on behalf of their clients.

RESOURCES

Berg, I. K. (1990b). *Goal negotiation with mandated clients*. The Brief Family Therapy Center.

Berg, I. K., & Miller, S. D. (1991). The 5-step treatment model. In *Working with the problem drinker: A Solution-Focused approach*. The Brief Family Therapy Center.

Ellis, A. (1962). *Reason and emotion in psychotherapy*. Citadel Press.

Ellis, A., McInerney, J. F., DiGiuseppe, R., & Yeager, R. (1988). *Rational-emotive therapy with alcoholics and substance abusers*. Allyn & Bacon.

Miller, S. D., & Berg, I. K. (1995). *The miracle method: A radically new approach to problem drinking*. W. W. Norton.

Solomon, R. L. (1980). The opponent process theory of acquired motivation: The costs of pleasure and the benefits of pain. *American Psychologist, 35*(8), 691–712. https://doi.org/10.1037//0003-066x.35.8.691

Washton, A. M., & Zweben, J. E. (2006). *Treating alcohol and drug problems in psychotherapy practice.* Guilford Press.

Wiens, A. N., & Menustik, C. E. (1983). Treatment outcomes and patient characteristics in an aversion therapy program for alcoholism. *American Psychologist, 38*(10), 1089–1096. https://doi.org/10.1037//0003-066x.38.10.1089

Denver Center for Solution-Focused Brief Therapy: This website provide information on trainings, workshops, and SLT books for sale. https://denversolutions.com/Solution-focused-therapy-training-books-by-Teri_Pichot.html

Psychology Tools—Solution-Focused Brief Therapy Worksheets: This website provides several worksheets that can be used with clients, along with a listing of publications. https://www.psychologytools.com/professional/therapies/solution-focused-therapy/

Solution-Focused Brief Therapy Association: This website provides an annual conference and a listing of books, videos and articles for sale. http://www.sfbta.org/

Solution-Focused Brief Therapy Basics: Meet Insoo Kim Berg & Steve de Shazer

Solution-Focused Therapy Role Play with Dr. Todd Grande (YouTube video): https://www.youtube.com/watch?v=gcXENqOwulw

This is a helpful blog that presents basics of SLT along with a brief video of a family therapy session: https://familytherapyblog.com/2015/04/10/solution-focused-brief-therapy-basics-meet-insoo-kim-berg-and-steve-de-shazer/

What Is Solution-Focused Therapy by Dr. Todd Grande (YouTube video): https://www.psychologytools.com/professional/therapies/solution-focused-therapy/

KEY REFERENCES

Only key references appear in the print edition. The full reference list appears in the digital product on Springer Publishing Connect: connect.springerpub.com/content/book/978-0-8261-3586-5/chapter/ch06

Budney, A. J., Brown, P. C., & Stanger, C. (2013). Behavior treatments. In B. S. McCrady & E. E. Epstein (Eds.), *Addiction: A comprehensive guidebook* (2nd ed., pp. 411–433). Oxford University Press.

Budney, A. J., Higgins, S. T., Radonovich, K. J., & Novy, P. L. (2000). Adding voucher-based incentives to coping-skills and motivational enhancement improves outcomes during treatment for marijuana dependence. *Journal of Consulting and Clinical Psychology, 68*(6), 1051–1061. https://doi.org/10.1037//0022-006x.68.6.1051

Ellis, A., & Harper, R. A. (1975). *A new guide to rational living.* Wilshire Press.

Ellis, A., McInerney, J. F., DiGiuseppe, R., & Yeager, R. (1988). *Rational-emotive therapy with alcoholics and substance abusers.* Allyn & Bacon.

Miller, S. D., & Berg, I. K. (1995). *The miracle method: A radically new approach to problem drinking.* W. W. Norton.

Parrott, A. C. (1999). Does cigarette smoking cause stress? *American Psychologist, 54*(10), 817–820. https://doi.org/10.1037/0003-066X.54.10.817

Rimmele, C. T., Howard, M. O., & Hilfrink, M. L. (1995). Aversion therapies. In R. K. Hester, & W. R. Miller (Eds.), *Handbook of alcoholism treatment approaches: Effective alternatives* (2nd ed., pp. 134–147). Allyn & Bacon.

Yalom, I. D. (2008). *Staring at the sun: Overcoming the terror of death.* Jossey-Bass.

7

GROUP COUNSELING TECHNIQUES

LEARNING OBJECTIVES

This chapter provides an introduction to group counseling in the addictions field and reviews pertinent screening and treatment implications. By the end of this chapter, you will be able to:

- describe counseling groups most used in addiction counseling;
- distinguish group therapeutic factors;
- apply group screening and secretion procedures;
- identify developmental stages of group counseling;
- define major theoretical frameworks.

TERMS TO KNOW

closed groups a group format that has a fixed number of clients and does not allow new members to join once the group is initiated

group agreement an agreement document between counselors and clients that outlines responsibilities and expectations for participating in group counseling. This document typically includes confidentiality implications, standards regarding within-group behavior, financial responsibilities, substance use and abstinence rules, and termination procedures

group interventions intentional actions of the group leader that have a goal of facilitating the group process

group process describes the process of how things are taking place in the group, rather than what is taking place (content)

open groups groups that accept new members (who are ready for the experience) on a continuous basis. This format is typical in inpatient settings

psychoeducation groups a group format that has the purpose of educating clients about topics relevant to their substance use

relapse prevention groups	a type of group counseling that is designed to help clients maintain their recovery and reduce the risk of relapse
therapy groups	groups that are focused on resolving important mental health issues in an effort to reduce or eliminate substance use

INTRODUCTION

The Center for Substance Abuse Treatment (CSAT; 2005) characterized substance use treatment and group counseling as "natural allies" (p. xv). This natural fit is based on two primary factors. First, humans are social beings, and we thrive in settings that foster close interpersonal relationships. As a result of this, group counseling has a natural potential to be a powerful influence on clients' recovery (CSAT, 2005). Counseling groups also cultivate an environment that promotes close, genuine connections among members and encourages mutual support and understanding (Corey, 2016; Yalom & Leszcz, 2020). The second factor that contributes to this allyship is that group counseling is among the most commonly used, effective, and economical treatments for substance use disorders (SUDs; Brook, 2015; Brooks & McHenry, 2015; CSAT, 2005). In 2019, 93% of treatment programs for substance abuse reported utilizing group counseling as a part of their treatment structure (Substance Abuse and Mental Health Services Administration [SAMHSA], 2020). Additionally, counseling groups are offered across all treatment levels, including outpatient, intensive outpatient, partial hospitalization, and intensive inpatient settings (Iarussi, 2018).

Group counseling offers many advantages over other formats of addiction treatment (CSAT, 2005). One of the most beneficial factors is that groups help reduce feelings of isolation that are common among persons with substance use issues. In this environment, clients are able to connect with others who share similar struggles and establish a community that is committed to treatment and supportive of their recovery. Also, in counseling groups, clients are able to learn from their peers and observe others who are successfully navigating the recovery process. This peer-to-peer and observational learning is beneficial in terms of tangible gains (e.g., learning coping and trigger-recognition skills), and also it instills hope in clients that they too can overcome substance use issues and reach sustained recovery. Another beneficial factor associated with group counseling is that clients are able to learn and practice skills that will help them navigate challenges beyond addiction treatment. The group environment provides an ideal setting for clients to safely practice newly acquired skills before implementing them in a broader context. Additionally, clients can receive valuable feedback from peers regarding their presentation. This is especially beneficial when it comes to challenging defense mechanisms and harmful behaviors. Group members, based on their common experiences, can effectively confront each other and hold everyone accountable for their own recovery. And finally, group format allows one counselor (or two counselors if the coleadership structure is used) to effectively help a number of clients at the same time. This factor increases the overall economic effectiveness and availability of addiction treatment (CSAT, 2005).

Given the prevalence of group counseling and the effectiveness of this treatment model, it is essential for professional counselors to understand group counseling approaches and to be able to utilize them with clients who struggle with substance use issues. In this chapter, we will explore different types of counseling groups that are used typically in addiction treatment settings, examine the main therapeutic factors that contribute to the effectiveness of this approach, review client screening and group selection procedures, describe developmental stages of group treatment, and discuss theoretical implications, including an example of a group program for co-occurring disorders.

Before we move forward, we have one clarifying note concerning the terminology used in this chapter. The terms "counseling groups" and "psychotherapy groups" sometimes generate confusion for counseling students who are just entering our field. These terms oftentimes are used interchangeably in the literature (and even more among practicing professionals) as they both describe treatment formats that are facilitated by trained professionals and address personal and interpersonal issues. However, in some instances, counseling and psychotherapy groups are differentiated. Sometimes, counseling groups refer to those that are preventative and remedial in nature, while psychotherapy groups are focused on chronic and personality issues (Corey, 2016). In this chapter, we use the term *group counseling* to describe group treatment format that is facilitated by a professional counselor and aims to help clients overcome substance use issues, including factors that are both directly and indirectly impacting their use of substances. Additionally, we want to emphasize that addiction counseling groups also are distinct from 12-step support groups, and these differences will be discussed later in the chapter.

TYPES OF COUNSELING GROUPS IN THE ADDICTION FIELD

There are a number of different counseling groups that are offered to clients who struggle with addiction issues. These groups range from those that are informational in nature to groups that are interpersonal and process-oriented (Yalom & Leszcz, 2020). The CSAT (2005) identified five types of groups that are used effectively in substance abuse treatment settings: (1) *psychoeducational groups*, (2) *skill development groups*, (3) *cognitive-behavioral groups*, (4) *interpersonal process groups*, and (5) *support groups* (see Table 7.1). Although each of the five groups has something unique to offer, and they all are designed to address a portion of clients' needs and aid them in the recovery efforts, it is important to remember that the content covered in each group is not completely exclusive from the others (CSAT, 2005). For example, a differentiating part of the skill development groups is that they focus on the establishment and enhancement of tangible abilities that could be useful in clients' recovery process. However, methods used to develop these skills could be cognitive-behavioral based, and the facilitator could utilize psychoeducational components to accomplish the group objectives.

In the following section, we will explore the five group modalities identified by the CSAT. However, before we examine these specific groups, we will explore briefly two overarching formats that are used to structure counseling groups: closed and open groups (also known as fixed and revolving membership groups).

Closed and Open Groups

Closed and open groups most directly are distinguished by the rules regarding acceptance of new members. Closed groups, once they begin, do not accept new members (i.e., they are closed to new membership). This rule sometimes may be amended by specific group norms

TABLE 7.1 Typical Characteristics of Five Group Types

	CONTENT/ PROCESS FOCUS	SPECIFICITY OF THE AGENDA	LEVEL OF LEADER ACTIVITY	DURATION OF TREAT-MENT	LENGTH OF SESSION
Psychoeducational	Content Focused	Specific	High	Dependent on Program Requirements	15–90 min
Skill Development	Content Focused	Specific	High	Variable	45–90 min
Cognitive-Behavioral	Mixed/ Balanced	Variable	High	Variable	60–90 min
Support	Process Focused	Nonspecific	Low/ Moderate	Variable/Long Term	45–90 min
Interpersonal Process	Process Focused	Nonspecific	Low/ Moderate	Long Term	60–120 min

Source: Adapted from Center for Substance Abuse Treatment. (2005). *Substance abuse treatment: Group therapy. Treatment improvement protocol (TIP) series, No. 41.* Substance Abuse and Mental Health Service Administration.

that allow new members to join during the first few weeks of treatment; however, once this period expires, the group remains closed until termination (Yalom & Leszcz, 2020). Closed groups tend to be more intensive and interpersonal in nature. As a result, these groups tend to be homogenous and typically are centered around a common issue or concern that is relevant for all members. Most closed groups meet weekly, have a predetermined number of sessions, and are relatively short in nature (8 months or less; Yalom & Leszcz, 2020). An example of a closed group would be a trauma-focused group for clients in an inpatient substance abuse treatment program. Depending on the nature of the treatment setting and the availability of eligible clients, membership for this group could be further targeted. For example, group participation could be limited by demographic characteristics (e.g., single-sex groups), relevant treatment issues (e.g., domestic violence), or length of the program (e.g., 20-week treatment program).

Open groups, on the other hand, accept new members continuously; however, there may be some restrictions based on the maximum number of members that the group can accommodate (Yalom & Leszcz, 2020). One of the most unique aspects of open groups is that they often include both clients who are just starting their treatment program as well as clients who may have achieved multiple weeks (or months) of recovery. This environment can be especially helpful in instilling hope and providing guidance for clients who are in early recovery. In terms of organization, open groups often are continuous and typically experience a complete turnover in membership every few months. Additionally, it is not uncommon for open groups to undergo a change in leadership as well. Although leadership change in open groups may be inevitable (due to the nature of this format), Yalom and Leszcz (2020) noted that some consistency in group facilitation is beneficial. They suggested that open groups experiencing leadership changes, especially those that encounter consistent leadership alteration (e.g., groups that are facilitated by counseling trainees and interns), should be co-led by two counselors. Under this model, when one counselor leaves, the second one is able to continue facilitating the group alone until a new cocounselor joins. In addition to a smoother transition in leadership, this approach also ensures the continuity of the group culture and cohesion among members (Yalom & Leszcz, 2020). An example of an open group would be a relapse prevention group for clients who completed an intensive outpatient substance abuse program. This group would be highly flexible, allowing new members to join as they are finishing their programs. Additionally, in this group, clients typically would not have a mandated number of meetings, nor would they have to attend the group every week. Now, let us turn our attention to different types of groups, which can be either open or closed.

Psychoeducational Groups

The primary aims of psychoeducational groups are to (1) help clients gain a better understanding of their substance use issues and factors relevant to their recovery and (2) motivate clients to enter and commit to their addiction treatment program (Martin et al., 1996; Pfeiffer et al., 1991). These groups are designed to help increase clients' awareness and assist them in integrating pertinent information that could benefit their recovery efforts. Psychoeducational groups commonly cover topics that highlight psychological, behavioral, and medical factors associated with substance use issues and the recovery process. Specific instances in which psychoeducational groups are utilized include the following: (1) to help clients who are in precontemplation and contemplation stages recognize the need for substance treatment, (2) to teach clients in early recovery about their disorder and potential barriers to completing treatment, (3) to help family members understand behaviors and decision-making of persons who are using substances, and (4) to assist clients in learning about other resources that could aid their recovery efforts (CSAT, 2005). Consider a group of clients who are in addiction treatment for the first time and trying to understand both the disease of addiction as well as factors associated with recovery. What might be helpful information for group counselors to impart to these clients? Oftentimes, clients benefit from psychoeducation about the neuroscience of addiction (e.g., how drugs of abuse affect the brain), the process of recovery (e.g., the stages of recovery and hallmarks of each stage), and the impact of co-occurring disorders on treatment and recovery (e.g., how to address both addiction and mental illness). Although psychoeducation is a useful aspect of addiction treatment, imparting information alone is insufficient.

LEARNING ACTIVITY 7.1
GROUP PROPOSAL

Small Group Activity: Develop a proposal for an 8-week psychoeducational group on relapse prevention. As a part of your proposal, please (1) determine the group's objectives and goals that clients will attain by completing this group and (2) develop group topics and a detailed outline for each session. Additionally, please determine the treatment setting where you would offer the group as well as the group size and format (open or closed). Please provide a rationale for your decisions.

Skills Development Groups

As we mentioned earlier, skill development groups could rely on methods used in other addiction counseling groups (e.g., psychoeducational or cognitive-behavioral groups). However, a defining characteristic of skill development groups is the establishment and advancement of concrete abilities that are relevant to clients' substance use recovery. These groups ordinarily are focused either on skills that are directly applicable to the cession of substance use or relate to broader areas pertinent to clients' sustained recovery. Groups that directly address clients' substance use emphasize skills that help clients manage cravings, navigate triggering situations, learn replacement behaviors, and develop problem-solving skills, while groups with broader aims address coping strategies, emotion regulation, healthy communication patterns, and grounding and relaxation techniques (CSAT, 2005). A unique advantage of skill development groups is that clients have an opportunity to rehearse skills they are learning. In this setting, clients are able to utilize other group members to practice their skills and receive valuable feedback regarding their progress. For example, consider a skill-building group in which clients are learning drug-refusal skills (e.g., turning down invitations to use drugs of abuse). After learning these skills, one group member may be asked to pretend to offer a drug of abuse to another group member, who would then employ drug-refusal skills. The rest of the group members would watch the interaction and provide feedback as to what went well, what could be improved, and how they might apply what they learned in their unique circumstances.

Cognitive-Behavioral Groups

In rudimentary terms, cognitive-behavioral approaches conceptualize addiction issues as learned behaviors. As such, groups that are based on cognitive-behavioral principles focus on changing these maladaptive behaviors by altering distorted or irrational thinking patterns (Matano et al., 1997; Velasquez et al., 2016). There are several cognitive processes, including clients' thoughts, perceptions, beliefs, and assumptions, that are relevant for substance use treatment, and as such they should be addressed in groups. Clients' maladaptive cognitions (cognitive distortions) could be either directly contributing to clients' continuation of use or could be preventing their attempts at recovery. Examples of thoughts that contribute to clients' use of drugs include, "I need these pills to sleep through the night," "The pain will go away if I am drunk enough," or "I cannot handle all the stress without cigarettes," while cognitions that prevent recovery may present as, "I am not strong enough to quit," "I've failed every time I've tried," or "I do not deserve better than this." Most cognitive-behavioral groups are highly structured, focused on immediate problems, and goal oriented. Additionally, these groups commonly are manualized and require following a specific treatment protocol. Interventions commonly used in these groups include identifying cognitive distortions, engaging in hypothesis testing (i.e., exploring the logic and rationality of thoughts), and implementing more adaptive, rational beliefs. The group setting can be particularly helpful for this type of work as group members can normalize one another's experience (e.g., "Yes, I have had that thought too") as well as supply evidence as to why a thought may be a distortion (e.g., "But there must have been times you have dealt with stress without smoking. What did you do then?").

Interpersonal Process Groups

Interpersonal process groups are probably the most diverse among all groups that are presented here. The emphasis and goals of these groups can vary greatly based on counselors' theoretical orientation. For example, the focus of an interpersonal process group could be on attachment issues, family dynamics, social hierarchy, existential matters, spiritual issues, and so forth. However, despite this theoretical variability, two factors critical to all interpersonal process groups are intrapersonal reflection and interpersonal relatedness. The growth in these groups is primarily driven by members' willingness to reflect on internal processes that are contributing to their substance use (e.g., thoughts, beliefs, values, and insecurities) and honestly share these struggles with the rest of the group. Counselors who are leading process-oriented groups should monitor three factors: (1) individual functioning of each client, (2) interpersonal dynamics and how clients relate to each other, and (3) functioning of the group as a unit (CSAT, 2005).

Unlike psychoeducational or skill-building groups, the focus of interpersonal process groups is not content (e.g., cocaine's effect on neurotransmitters) but rather interactions between group members and the exploration of each group member's inner world. It is in process groups that group members and group counselors can identify psychological defense mechanisms as they arise and bring them to the forefront of group discussion. These defense mechanisms are cognitive strategies that enable individuals to continue their use despite negative consequences. Examples include denial (e.g., "I don't have a problem"), blaming (e.g., "I drink the way I do because of my wife"), minimization (e.g., "I don't use hard stuff like my coworker, Jasper"), and justification (e.g., "Okay, I know I've got to cut back a little, but everyone has a vice, right? It's not like I'm hurting anyone with mine"). One of the benefits of group counseling is that it allows other group members who share similar experiences to identify and provide feedback regarding psychological defense mechanisms. For example, Daniel may say, "I only drink so much because of the stress of my job. Once I get this promotion, I won't need to drink," and Anthony may respond, "I used to rationalize that way too... it turns out there was always another reason for me to drink. I didn't want to see it, but I was finding any excuse I could to explain my behavior, other than the simple fact that I had a disease." Process groups can be powerful mechanisms for increasing self-awareness and insight, as well as connections between group members.

Support Groups

Unlike the rest of the group approaches presented in this section, support group origins are rooted in self-help traditions (CSAT, 2005). Although nowadays some support groups are counselor-led and have explicit goals and objectives, the most defining characteristic of these groups still resides in the comradery and mutual encouragement among group members. An overarching goal of support groups is to create an environment in which members can lower their inhibitions and openly discuss matters related to their recovery. This setting is commonly known for members' honest and open interpersonal interactions, unconditional acceptance, inward reflection, and commitment to change (Cooper, 1987). As a result, support groups are very effective in helping members improve self-confidence and self-esteem (CSAT, 2005). Additionally, these groups are sensitive to members' current needs, and they allow members to help each other in concrete ways. For example, it is common in support groups for members to share advice with each other on topics such as navigating relationships during recovery or access to resources. See Table 7.2 for an outline of the most distinct differences between counseling groups and 12-step support groups.

CASE EXAMPLE: ANDY

Andy is a 32-year-old Asian American male who was referred to treatment by the court. He was given a probation sentence on the condition that he enters a substance use treatment program. During his assessment, he disclosed a history of alcohol and methamphetamine abuse. Andy stated that he started drinking alcohol in high school and that he has been drinking most days since he was 20 years old. Andy disclosed that he initially started using alcohol to cope with the bullying he was experiencing in school. However, he described that, over the years, his alcohol use has intensified. Andy reported that most days he consumes at least one bottle of vodka and that he typically experiences blackouts a couple of times per week. Andy shared that he has been using meth for the last 7 years. He reported that he started using meth when he returned to his hometown (a rural area in central California). Andy said that he does not use meth every day. He disclosed that meth is very accessible in his hometown as a few of his childhood friends are distributing it. Andy acknowledged that meth is "not the best" for him; however, he does not see any issues with his alcohol use. He stated that all his legal issues (multiple assaults and DUI arrests) are connected to his meth use. Andy described that he experiences a rush when he uses meth and that all the anger that has been accumulating over the years comes out. He described alcohol as a calming presence in his life and shared that he just does not "care as much" when he drinks. Andy reported mainly working as a laborer or a construction worker, but he shared that he does not have steady employment. Andy stated that he intends to complete the program in order to avoid going to jail, but he shared that he is not really interested in stopping his alcohol consumption.

LEARNING ACTIVITY 7.2

What are Andy's current treatment needs? What type of counseling group(s) would you recommend for Andy? Please explain why (including your recommendation rationale and desired benefits). What concerns do you have about Andy's participation in group counseling?

THERAPEUTIC FACTORS IN GROUP COUNSELING

Counseling groups are complementary to both individual counseling and 12-step support programs. Each approach, in its own way, contributes to the treatment of SUDs and offers a unique set of advantages (CSAT, 2005; Yalom & Leszcz, 2020). Benefits associated with group counseling are both overt and covert. For example, clients' recovery efforts are supported directly by goals and objectives associated with a particular substance abuse treatment group (e.g., learning relapse prevention and trigger monitoring skills). Additionally, since most clients who enter substance abuse programs struggle with relational issues and isolation (Roth, 2004), the group environment in itself is likely to contribute positively to clients' treatment. Yalom and Leszcz (2020) outlined 11 therapeutic factors, or curative experiences, that serve as pillars of a group environment and account for its therapeutic effectiveness. We will describe the following factors as they relate to substance abuse treatment:

- **Instillation of hope:** Instillation of hope is one of the most critical components in addiction treatment (Miller, 2005). Maladaptive use of substances is a destructive

TABLE 7.2 Difference Between Counseling Groups and 12-Step Support Groups

GROUP CHARACTERISTICS	COUNSELING GROUPS	12-STEP SUPPORT GROUPS
Size	• Limited number of clients (8–20)	• Unlimited number of attendees can join
Attendance	• Only clients who were admitted to the group are able to attend	• Open meetings: Any member of the community is able to attend (even those who do not have issues with substance use) • Closed meetings: Only persons who identify with the group are able to attend (e.g., only persons who identify as having issues with alcohol consumption can attend a closed Alcoholics Anonymous meeting)
Leader	• Led by a trained mental health professional	• Peer led (usually by members who have achieved long-term abstinence and have been a part of the group for an extended period of time)
Sharing and Feedback Norms	• Specific rules and norms exist regarding group participation (e.g., how feedback is given to other members)	• No formal group rules
Length	• 30–90 minutes (depending on the group type)	• Typically 60 minutes
Topics	• A range of topics related to group type	• Topics are typically related to one of the 12 steps
Screening Process	• Formal screening and assessment procedures are used to determine membership	• No screening procedures
Ethics	• Professional ethical standards (e.g., ACA Code of Ethics) are used to facilitate groups	• Guided by the principles of the 12 Traditions

force, and it influences virtually all areas of clients' lives. As a result, clients most commonly enter treatment feeling hopeless. Additionally, the recovery process is challenging and presents many difficulties for clients along the way. Therefore, inciting hope that a better future is possible is exceptionally important during the treatment process. Additionally, interacting with fellow group members who have achieved positive changes in their lives instills hope in clients and shows them that the same is possible for them. Group leaders can contribute to this process as well by treating clients as persons who are capable of changing and motivating them to continue in the recovery process.

- **Universality:** Clients often experience a sense of relief when encountering others who have similar struggles with substance use issues. By participating in counseling groups, clients learn that they are not the only people who are experiencing these difficulties. Additionally, clients realize that their addiction issues are not worse than issues experienced by others (and sometimes, potentially even more important, realize that they as people are not worse than others). Although universality in groups most often develops naturally (as a result of having similar experiences), counselors also can facilitate the experience of universality in groups by creating an environment that is supportive of self-disclosure and encourages members to relate to each other (Yalom & Leszcz, 2020).

- **Imparting information:** In substance use treatment, accessing relevant information is crucial (CSAT, 2005). Clients particularly benefit from learning about the effects of substances on the brain and body, the process of addiction, why it is difficult to stop using drugs, relapse prevention strategies, and so forth. The group counseling setting is beneficial here because clients are able to receive educational content from group leaders, and also they are able to learn from their peers (CSAT, 2005). Peer-to-peer learning could be especially important since clients are able to relate to each other better, and they are able to confront and hold each other more accountable (Milgram & Rubin, 1992).
- **Altruism:** Altruism implies that, in group counseling, clients benefit not only from receiving help from others but also from being helpful to their peers (Yalom & Leszcz, 2020). The relevance of this principle in addiction treatment is that, unfortunately, many clients who struggle with substance use believe that they have nothing valuable to offer. Therefore, when clients participate in group counseling and they are able to help others (or simply support them), their sense of self-esteem and importance improves. These experiences are therapeutic in themselves (Yalom & Leszcz, 2020), and they provide clients with alternative perspectives and contribute to their changing sense of worth (CSAT, 2005).

LEARNING ACTIVITY 7.3 FAMILY ROLES

Reflect on the role you play within your family and your typical behavioral patterns in that environment. Now, think of the few most recent group experiences you had (e.g., friend groups and classes in your counseling program). How similar were your presentations in these settings to the way you interact within your family? How aware were you of these presentations before? What factors do you think influenced your level of awareness?

- **Corrective recapitulation of the primary family group:** The group counseling setting, in many ways, resembles a family unit including authority (parent) and peer (siblings) figures, deep interpersonal relationships, and intimate and competitive/hostile dynamics (Yalom & Leszcz, 2020). For this reason, when clients join counseling groups, they may mimic behaviors that are typical for them when interacting with family members. The benefit of group counseling is that members can become aware of these dynamics, gain a better understanding of them, and engage in corrective experiences (Vannicelli, 1992; Yalom & Leszcz, 2020). Yalom and Leszcz (2020) noted that corrective experiences are critical in this process. The authors cautioned that just simply reliving familial experiences could be hurtful to clients. Therefore, it is important for counselors to stay vigilant of these interactions and facilitate corrective experiences within the group.
- **Development of socializing techniques:** For persons who have substance use issues (especially for those with a long history of substance abuse), social interaction could be closely tied to their substance use, or substances may serve as replacements for missing connections (Lewis, 2014). As a result, social interactions outside of this context could be difficult, and clients may lack confidence and struggle to relate to others. The group counseling setting provides an environment where clients can learn and practice social skills. Additionally, clients are able to observe how others relate socially and learn new skills informally.

- **Imitative behavior:** It is natural for people to learn from others and attempt to imitate persons they deem successful (Bandura, 1994). The same process takes place in addiction counseling groups. Clients are likely to imitate behaviors exhibited by the group leaders and other group members (typically more senior and/or members who are considered successful). This is especially relevant for clients who are in the beginning stages of their treatment. Through the imitating process, clients quickly learn many behaviors that are supportive of their recovery such as attending counseling sessions, going to a meeting, and following treatment center norms. In addition to these naturally occurring events, group leaders also should be intentional in modeling behaviors that would be beneficial to clients and promote their recovery efforts.
- **Interpersonal learning:** Yalom and Leszcz (2020) considered interpersonal learning an essential part of the group process as it provides space for corrective emotional experiences. The group setting provides clients with an opportunity to examine how they relate to others, take responsibility for their actions, and implement desired changes. Within this environment, clients are able to rehearse these changes safely and then further integrate them outside of the group (Yalom & Leszcz, 2020).
- **Group cohesiveness:** Group cohesiveness primarily is characterized by the sense of belonging and feeling of comfort within the group (Toseland & Rivas, 2001; Yalom & Leszcz, 2020). Additionally, clients in groups that have strong cohesion feel valued and supported by other members. These factors, along with strong relationships, are critical in creating an environment that can foster clients' growth and support their recovery. In addition to these direct benefits, group cohesion also impacts clients' ability to utilize other aspects of group counseling (Yalom, 1998). For example, in groups that lack cohesiveness, clients are likely to be reluctant to learn from each other, accept feedback, or exhibit altruistic behaviors (Lewis, 2014).
- **Catharsis:** Catharsis is best described as an emotional release that could occur during group counseling. This process allows group members to genuinely express difficult emotions, such as shame and guilt, that are likely to be associated with their substance abuse. It is important to note that catharsis also entails intentional cognitive processing that follows emotional discharge. This component is essential since unattended disclosures could leave clients feeling too vulnerable and be damaging to them (Brooks & McHenry, 2015; Yalom & Leszcz, 2020). Through this process of emotional sharing and cognitive processing, group members begin to develop new coping strategies that incorporate their emotions (instead of evading them with substance use; Iarussi, 2018).
- **Existential factors:** Addiction issues, at times, may be perceived as unfair or unjust by clients. Afterall, the realities associated with the use of substances oftentimes are exceptionally harsh and contribute to difficult life experiences. However, overemphasis on these perceptions can hinder clients' recovery process (Yalom & Leszcz, 2020). Existential factors refer to the need to accept substance use issues as a reality of life. Through this acceptance, clients can resolve their past use of substances and assume responsibility for their recovery under their given life circumstances (Yalom & Leszcz, 2020).

These 11 factors, individually and cumulatively, represent a foundation of a group environment that fosters growth and development among members. These principles are considered to be universal and tend to be impactful regardless of the group type or the theoretical orientation of group leaders (Lewis, 2014). Intentional engagement across these 11 factors will create an empathic environment that is supportive of clients' recovery and their overall well-being (Johnson et al., 2005). Read the following case example and identify which therapeutic factors are at play in this interaction between group members.

CASE EXAMPLE: GARY

Gary just joined the group and has been silent for the first few sessions. Suddenly, in the middle of another group member's story, Gary beings to sob. He chokes out that he does not think he can "do this" and "nothing has ever been as hard as staying clean." Jonathan, who has two months of sobriety, tells Gary that he felt the same way when he first joined the group, but it does get better with time. Grace also comments that, although she still has her doubts, with a good support network, she seems to be able to get through the day. She tells Gary that what he is feeling now is completely normal and everyone goes through it.

NOTES FROM THE FIELD

Jason Magistro, MA, CPCS, LPC, has been working in the addiction field for 6 years. Specifically, he has experience working in an intake department of a psychiatric emergency room, residential addictions treatment centers, an intensive outpatient program (IOP), and private practice. Since earning his master's degree and license, Jason has worked in almost every level of care for substance use disorders and has provided individual, group, and family counseling.

Jason's approach to addictions counseling is humanistic and existential in nature. He earned his master's degree from the University of West Georgia (with a programmatic emphasis on humanistic/transpersonal studies) as well as a Humanistic Practice Certification. Rather than taking a linear approach to addictions counseling with a focus on behavior change, Jason believes a more holistic perspective is needed. He states, "We are missing the fundamental root of what's going on with the whole person. It's more than just behavior change; you have to consider the bigger, more existential picture." Jason identifies unresolved trauma, unexplored emotions, a lack of meaning, and questions about purpose as contributors to clients' substance use. He notes, "Clients don't know how to fill that void, so they look to substances to give them immediate gratification."

Jason shared that group therapy from an existential perspective is very effective in addictions treatment. He states, "As a group facilitator, I am less of an instructor and more of a mediator. I help clients connect with one another so they know they are not alone." Jason emphasized that an important part of addictions treatment is helping clients form relationships, develop healthy communication patterns, and learn to connect with other people.

Along with reaching and maintaining sobriety, Jason notes that a goal of addictions treatment is to help clients find meaning in their lives and feel a sense of purpose. He shared, "I have former clients reach out to me and tell me that not only have they been sober, they also have been genuinely happy and are enjoying their lives. That is what's most rewarding about this work—hearing that clients are living out their fullest potential."

With regard to challenges working in the addictions field, Jason noted that it can be difficult to work with insurance companies that are unfamiliar with the process of healing. Reaching therapeutic goals often happens in diverse ways and in various amounts of time, which is not congruent with how the insurance companies operate. The lack of insurance coverage poses barriers to treatment among those who really need it.

With regard to recommendations for new counselors, Jason encourages clinicians to work in an inpatient psychiatric environment. He shared that this type of clinical setting gives counselors a broad perspective of presenting concerns and opportunities to see what active addiction really looks like, what active psychosis really looks like, and what active withdrawal really looks like. According to Jason, the driving force for entering the addictions field should be a passion for joining with clients as they pursue recovery. Motives for this type of work cannot be monetary or self-serving. He states, "Remember, working with clients is not about us." Finally, Jason encourages counselors to consult with others, get supervision, and try to avoid working in isolation. He emphasized that it is important for counselors to stay well and healthy in order to provide effective services for their clients.

CLIENT SCREENING AND GROUP SELECTION

Yalom and Leszcz (2020) noted that a good group counseling experience begins with good client screening and group selection procedures. Additionally, the CSAT (2005) stated that every clients' readiness and fit for group counseling should be evaluated before they are placed in a group. When deciding about clients' admittance to a group, counselors should consider several relevant factors, including the nature and format of the group, resources available to the program, clients' prior experiences with group counseling, length of consumption and type of substances used by clients, and associated risk factors (CSAT, 2005). Screening of clients should begin during the initial assessment; however, it is critical for counselors to continuously evaluate clients' fit and potential benefits from the group at least during the first 4–6 weeks of the experience (CSAT, 2005; Yalom & Leszcz, 2020).

The group screening and assessment process could have a significant impact on the overall success of the group. For example, if the group's format and objectives do not match clients' current needs, the group is likely to experience issues with attrition as well as jeopardize clients' individual growth and development (CSAT, 2005). As a result, it is critical for counselors to be intentional when assessing clients and creating counseling groups. Additionally, counselors must consider a wide range of factors when determining clients' readiness and fit for group counseling.

The most comprehensive and effective way for client assessment and group selection is clinical interviewing (CSAT, 2005). Group leaders should meet with each client who is being considered for the group and evaluate their readiness and appropriateness for participation in that setting. This approach provides counselors with the most comprehensive view of clients' needs and allows both counselors and clients to make informed decisions. Several models could be used to facilitate a meaningful assessment interview, but one of the most used and extensive approaches is the American Society for Addiction Medicine (ASAM) Treatment Criteria (ASAM, 2021; CSAT, 2005). This model utilizes a multidimensional assessment for treatment planning and a multilevel continuum of care structure. The treatment planning assessment includes six dimensions: (1) acute intoxication and/or withdrawal potential; (2) biomedical conditions and complications; (3) emotional, behavioral, and cognitive conditions and complications; (4) readiness to change; (5) relapse, continued use, or continued problem potential; and (6) recovery/living environment (ASAM, 2021). The continuum-of-care portion includes the following levels: .5—early intervention, 1—outpatient services, 2—intensive outpatient/partial hospitalization services, 3—residential/inpatient services, and 4—medically managed intensive inpatient service (ASAM, 2021). The most recent revision of the ASAM continuum of care levels introduced additional decimal-number levels. For example, level 3.1—clinically managed low-intensity residential services, and level 3.5—clinically managed population-specific high-intensity residential services were added. However, the beginning (.5) and ending (4) levels have not changed.

Aside from this formal part of the assessment process, counselors also should utilize informal ways of information gathering. For example, counselors who work in an inpatient setting could gather information from clients' case managers and medical staff or by observing clients' interactions with peers. Additionally, counselors could use nonstandardized tools (e.g., Eco-Map; Garvin & Seabury, 1997) to gain a better understanding of clients' needs.

In addition to these selection methods, Yalom and Leszcz (2020) introduced the notion of deselection when determining group membership. The authors argued that this process could be the simplest and the easiest way to determine group membership (although they acknowledge a degree of crudeness in this approach). This principle is important to remember because all clients will not be appropriate and suitable for all groups. And it is counselors' responsibility to make decisions regarding group membership that will be beneficial to each client individually but also valuable to the group as a whole. The CSAT (2005) identified three categories of clients who are not appropriate for group counseling. They noted that clients (1) who do not want to participate, (2) who are not able or refuse to uphold groups agreements, and (3) with acute issues that are not suitable for group counseling (e.g., clients with personality disorders—especially those with limited capacity for empathy) are unlikely to benefit from this process and could be disruptive to other group members (CSAT, 2005). In addition to the criteria identified by the CSAT, it is critical for counselors to consider how each client's presenting issues could impact the rest of the group. Let us examine the case of Tina, which will help us consider the group selection process more closely.

CASE EXAMPLE: TINA

Tina, a 27-year-old Mexican American woman, is a candidate for admission into an inpatient treatment facility. Tina has a history of alcohol, marijuana, and opiate abuse. She stated that she has been drinking alcohol and smoking marijuana since middle school and that she started taking her mother's pain medication in high school. Tina shared that she primarily drinks and smokes marijuana and that she only uses pain medications when she is "really stressed." She reported that she consumes alcohol and marijuana daily. Tina reported that she attempted several times to stop her use but noted that her previous efforts were not successful. She disclosed that she was able to stop using for a few months when she was pregnant, but she relapsed when she entered the third trimester, and her daughter was born with Neonatal Abstinence Syndrome. Tina reported that she entered treatment twice before but that she did not complete the program either time. She shared that the first time she voluntarily terminated her treatment. Tina disclosed that a lot of things were coming up for her at that time, and she "just needed to stop." Tina briefly shared that she has a history of physical and sexual abuse and that being sober brought up a lot of memories for her. The second treatment was terminated involuntarily because Tina violated program rules twice. The first violation was a positive drug screening test and the second was that she had a sexual relationship with her roommate (the program had explicit rules against dating and sexual relationships among program members). Tina disclosed that she is very motivated to stop her use this time as she is pregnant again.

LEARNING ACTIVITY 7.4

What factors would you consider when making a decision regarding the appropriateness of group counseling for Tina?

Please use the ASAM Treatment Criteria to make a recommendation regarding Tina's treatment (please provide the reasoning for your recommendations).

Another important component that could be integrated into the group selection process is preparation of clients for participation in counseling groups (i.e., educating clients how to be "good group members"). As we have discussed in this chapter, the group environment offers myriad therapeutic benefits, and although many of them occur naturally as a result of interpersonal interactions, helping clients understand some of these factors prior to joining the group could be advantageous. For example, a counselor could help clients understand the importance of self-disclosure, vulnerability, awareness of their own feelings and reactions, and willingness to give feedback. Educating clients about the importance of these factors could be beneficial for both the clients' individual growth and the advancement of the group as a whole. Think about other factors you want to discuss with clients prior to them entering a group you are facilitating.

Finally, before we end the section on client screening and group selection, we want to point out an important limitation to all recommendations we made earlier. Depending on the treatment setting and available resources, counselors may not have the ability to independently determine group membership. Rather, the nature and the needs of the organization will supersede intentional group selection and superimpose group membership criteria. For example, in an inpatient treatment center that is funded by a governmental agency (e.g., County Juvenile Justice System), all clients who enter treatment could be required to attend a specific group. In this instance, counselors will not have the ability to manage the membership (beyond blatant violations of group norms that could compel counselors to terminate the offending member) and will have to work on creating an environment that will be helpful for all clients.

DEVELOPMENTAL STAGES OF GROUP TREATMENT

Considering the richness and diversity of human personalities and interactions, coupled with a naturally stressful recovery process, it is reasonable to assume that group counseling is a relatively complex and unpredictable undertaking. However, it is possible to capture and describe established patterns of group behavior and interpersonal dynamics that influence group development and member behavior (Yalom & Leszcz, 2020). Several group development models have been introduced over the years (e.g., Corey, 2000; MacKenzie, 1997; Tuckma & Jensen, 1977); however, most of them describe similar, core processes that take place during group counseling. Yalom and Leszcz (2020) noted that most groups are first focused on interpersonal affiliations and engagement, and then they transition to the emphasis on individual differences, control, power, and status issues. The stage that follows these initial processes is characterized by engagement and intimacy and is often seen as a productive phase. And, finally, the group enters the ending or termination stage (Yalom & Leszcz, 2020). In the following section, we will describe a group development model that is typically used to conceptualize substance use treatment groups:

Initial stage: The beginning of the group counseling process primarily is characterized by exploration and orientation to the group environment (Corey, 2016). Major tasks during this stage include the development of relationships and the establishment of group rules and culture. It is critical for group leaders to be intentional in facilitating connections between them and the group members as well as among the group members themselves (CSAT, 2005). Creating strong interpersonal foundations early will allow deeper and more meaningful group experiences to take place. Additionally, the group leader is responsible for creating the initial structure for the group and initiating a conversation about group rules and norms. It is natural for group leaders to have rules that all members

LEARNING ACTIVITY 7.5
GROUP RULES AND NORMS

Small Group Activity: Using the Association for Specialists in Group Work: Best Practices Guidelines (Thomas & Pender, 2008) and the American Counseling Association (ACA) Code of Ethics (ACA, 2014), please develop a list of group rules and norms that you consider important (please provide a rationale for your choices).

are expected to follow. For example, group leaders are likely to have explicit expectations regarding confidentially, substance use/abstinence, and respectful communication. In addition, Yalom and Leszcz (2020) recommended that therapeutic factors should be a part of group norms as well (e.g., interpersonal learning, altruism, and hope). Finally, group leaders should facilitate a conversation among group members about norms that are important to them. By communicating explicitly and inviting group members to be a part of the conversation, group leaders will not only start creating an open and engaging group culture but also effectively model desirable behaviors.

Transitional stage: Conflict is a natural part of the transition stage as issues regarding ambivalence, reluctance to change, and perceived lack of commitment are likely to emerge (Corey, 2016). Group leaders ordinarily are challenged during this stage as well. Challenges that are common in substance use treatment groups include leaders' knowledge and experience with addiction issues, lack of focus on recovery language, and avoidance of pertinent topics (Lewis, 2014; Vannicelli, 1992). Miller (2005) also suggested that even a struggle for control of the group may take place. The confrontation regarding group control, along with the challenges of leaders' competence, are especially likely to happen if group leaders are not in recovery themselves. Finally, the CSAT (2005) noted that denial is a common occurrence during this stage. It is important for counselors to challenge this denial and to encourage and facilitate group members' confrontation of each other's denial.

Working stage: This stage is considered the most productive, and members accomplish most of the "work" during this stage (CSAT, 2005). The working stage is marked by an increased sense of trust, cohesiveness, investment, and mutually beneficial efforts (Iarussi, 2018; Miller, 2005). These experiences contribute to the group members' willingness to engage in meaningful explorations and emotional disclosures (Yalom & Leszcz, 2020). Additionally, topics that typically caused conflicts in the previous stage are likely to incite appropriate and constructive confrontation in the working stage (Lewis, 2014). During this stage, it is important for group leaders to balance the focus between the content and the process (CSAT, 2005). That is, leaders should be intentional in acknowledging overtly expressed content and feelings as well as in emphasizing the nature of member interaction.

Final stage: At the end of the group counseling process, it is critical to focus on the integration of learning and to prepare for termination. Group leaders should be intentional about facilitating the process of consolidating growth and development that has taken place during the group and consider short- and long-term implications (CSAT, 2005). The CSAT (2005) identified six tasks to be attended to during this stage: (1) facilitating the closure of the group process, (2) examining the impact of the experience on each member, (3) creating space for triggers regarding termination, (4) giving and receiving feedback about each member's role, (5) resolving any unfinished business, and (6) exploring ways of integrating the learning obtained during group. Additionally, it is important to acknowledge that termination can be exceptionally difficult for clients with substance use issues, as many could have experienced significant losses prior to the group counseling experience (Pooler et al., 2014). As a result, counselors should be intentional and account for potential triggers during the termination stage.

THEORETICAL IMPLICATIONS AND FRAMEWORKS

Virtually any theory could be used to develop and structure group treatment for SUDs. If a theoretical framework comprehensively explains the existence of substance abuse, including the development and nature of the issue as well as a path to recovery, then a counseling group could be created based on that premise. However, only a small number of theoretical orientations have been shown to be effective in treating clients who have substance use issues, and even fewer are used to structure counseling groups. In the following section, we will review three theoretical frameworks that are used frequently for substance use group treatment and provide an example of an empirically supported group for co-occurring disorders:

Cognitive Behavioral Therapy

We already reviewed cognitive-behavioral groups (in the "Types of Counseling Groups in the Addiction Field" section) in an effort to acknowledge their prevalence and effectiveness in treating persons who have substance use issues. But we believe it is important to discuss these groups further in this section and provide you with more information regarding the cognitive-behavioral framework for substance abuse treatment. For the purposes of this chapter, we will define cognitive behavioral therapy (CBT) broadly to include both cognitive and behavioral interventions. Although cognitive and behavioral theories are distinct, standalone approaches, most often they are integrated for the purposes of substance use treatment. As a result, we will review them here as a functional unit. Like we mentioned earlier, the CBT approach considers substance use issues to be largely learned behaviors. As people engage in substance use, these substances become powerful behavioral reinforcers, both positive (increasing desirable experiences) and negative (decreasing undesirable experiences), that over time strengthen the influence over one's life (McHugh et al., 2010). Additionally, this model focuses on cognitive, affective, and situational triggers that contribute to substance use (Magill & Ray, 2009). Research evidence has shown that CBT is effective for the treatment of substance use issues and can be applied in both individual and group formats.

In terms of substance use treatment, two primary aims of the CBT approach are to mitigate the reinforcing effects of substances and facilitate rewarding of nondrug activities (McHugh et al., 2010). There are several approaches within CBT that could be used to reach these objectives, but the following five strategies are used most commonly: (1) identifying triggers for relapse (both intrapersonal and interpersonal), (2) increasing coping skills, (3) acquisition of drug-refusal skills, (4) analysis of the role drugs play in clients' lives, and (5) increasing participation in activities that are not drug related (Magill & Ray, 2009). All these strategies are relatively broad and could be tailored to fit clients' particular needs. For example, drug-refusal skills training could include increasing communication skills, assertiveness training, and relaxation techniques. This ability to adapt treatment strategies represents an advantage for group counseling as group leaders are in a position to develop targeted experiences. For example, counselors could develop a specific protocol for a homogeneous group of clients (e.g., pregnant women who have a stimulus use disorder), or they could design a broad objectives group for a heterogeneous set of clients that is flexible and could be adjusted to clients' individual needs.

Dialectical Behavior Therapy

Dialectical behavior therapy (DBT) has an overarching goal of helping clients create a life worth living (Dimeff & Linehan, 2008). Initially, this approach was developed as a specialized application of behavioral therapy for clients who experienced suicidality (Linehan, 1987, 1993); however, it has been adapted for the treatment of clients who struggle with substance use issues (Dimeff & Linehan, 2008). DBT has been shown to be effective with substance use disorders in both individual and group formats (Dimeff & Linehan, 2008; Linehan et al., 1999, 2002).

The term *dialectic* describes a synthesis of two opposing principles that are fundamental to DBT: change and acceptance. Through exploration of these principles and resolution of associated barriers, clients are able to initially envision and pursue their goals and then achieve and sustain meaningful change in their lives (Dimeff & Linehan, 2008). These principles are particularly relevant for substance abuse treatment since many clients experience guilt and shame about their past use and struggle to accept it, and they also have difficulties imagining change in their lives.

DBT treatment is based on the five primary functions: (1) improving clients' motivation, (2) enhancing clients' capabilities, (3) generalizing new behaviors, (4) structuring the environment, and (5) enhancing counselors' capability and motivation (Dimeff & Linehan, 2008). All of these principles could be applied in a group format, and an argument could be made that the group constitutes an ideal setting for many of them. For example, the group environment represents a natural step in the process of behavioral generalization. Within a group context, clients are able to practice their newly acquired skills safely before implementing (generalizing) them on a broader level. Specific treatment objectives for clients who struggle with substance use, according to DBT, are (1) decreasing the use of substances, (2) alleviating physical discomfort and symptoms associated with withdrawal, (3) decreasing craving and temptation to use, (4) avoiding triggering situations, (5) reducing behaviors supportive of drug use, and (6) increasing healthy behaviors and community connections.

Attachment Theory

Attachment theory conceptualizes addiction as both a consequence and cause of poor attachments. In terms of consequences, substance use is seen as a result of insecure attachments and clients' inability to establish and maintain healthy relationships (Flores, 2006). From this perspective, substance use is seen as self-medication and an attempt to find fulfillment and compensate for lacking attachments (Schindler, 2019). The causality component poses that substance use, in addition to being a maladaptive solution to attachment issues, deepens clients' attachment insecurities and contributes to poorer interpersonal connectedness (Flores, 2015). Essentially, substance use becomes a substitute for interpersonal connections and provides clients temporary relief (Flores, 2006). According to this approach, the underlying force that propels substance use is clients' inability to manage relationships (Flores, 2006), and that there is an inverse relationship between substance use disorder and secure interpersonal attachments (Flores, 2001; Walant, 1995).

In terms of treatment, resolving issues related to attachment is critical. Flores (2006) noted that, in order for clients to even be able to establish therapeutic relationships with their peers and counselors (i.e., become attached to treatment), they must be detached from their addictive attachment first. This approach identifies two simple priorities in treatment: (1) to help clients detach from substances and create capacity for treatment and recovery attachments and (2) to help clients learn how to sustain healthy attachments and interpersonal connectedness. Considering its emphasis on interpersonal relationships, Attachment Theory is exceptionally well suited for group counseling. Group counseling provides a rich environment for correcting unhealthy interpersonal relationships (Ormont, 2001; Rice, 2003). Within group format, clients would be able to, first, enact their relational patterns, and then they would be able to create healthy attachments within this safe environment.

Johari Window

Although not a formal theoretical orientation, the Johari Window model is a way of conceptualizing group counseling and informing clinical work in the group setting. Developed by Joseph Luft and Harry Ingram (their first names were joined to create the model's name, "Johari") in the 1950s, the Johari Window is based on principles of self-disclosure and feedback (Armstrong, 2006; Luft, 1963). Specifically, as trust grows in a group, members are more likely to take risks and self-disclose. This self-disclosure leads to group members becoming more known to others. In response to self-disclosure, group members are able to provide feedback, which helps group members become more known to themselves. Group counselors work to create an environment that invites self-disclosure and feedback among group members.

The Johari Window provides a matrix of four quadrants (like panes in a window) that represent information that is either known or unknown to oneself and to others. Quadrant one includes information known to the self and known to others (e.g., open information). In new groups, this quadrant is typically small, yet it grows as trust builds and information is shared among group members. Quadrant two includes information known to others, yet unknown to the self. This could be considered one's "blind spot" and refers to information about one's presentation or characteristics that others observe, yet remain outside of the individual's awareness. This pane gets smaller as group members provide feedback to one another. The third quadrant includes information that is known to self yet unknown to others. Thus, secrets or undisclosed personal information would fit into this quadrant. As group members self-disclose, this quadrant becomes smaller. Finally, quadrant four includes information unknown to others and unknown to the self. This type of information may be aspects of the individual that have not yet been explored, true motives for behaviors, as well as information about the future (Luft, 1963). Group counselors work to facilitate self-disclosure and feedback among group members to expand quadrant one (open information known to

TABLE 7.3 Johari Window Quadrant Examples in an Addictions Counseling Group

JOHARI WINDOW QUADRANT	EXAMPLES OF RELEVANT INFORMATION RELATED TO ADDICTIONS
Quadrant One: Open Information	- Primary drug(s) of abuse - Number of days abstinent - Previous treatment experiences - Demographic information - Negative consequences related to addiction - Goals for treatment
Quadrant Two: Blind Spot	- Personality characteristics - Ways in which the individual is perceived by others - Denial - Rationalizations for use - Defense mechanisms - True function of behaviors (e.g., started a fight with wife to justify having a beer)
Quadrant Three: Hidden Information	- Experiences of cravings that have not been shared - Thoughts of relapse that have not been shared - Using dreams - Feelings of shame - An unfilled prescription for a drug of abuse that has been kept secret
Quadrant Four: Unknown	- Unconscious information - True motives for behaviors - Untapped potential - Unrealized talents or skills - Life in long-term recovery

self and known to others) and reduce quadrants two (blind spots) and three (hidden information). As the group works together toward recovery and better understandings of themselves, quadrant four (unknown) also will reduce in size. See Table 7.3 for examples of information within each quadrant relevant to addictions counseling group members.

Additionally, it is important to note that each group member has different-sized "panes," which can lead to different behaviors within the group. A group member with a larger quadrant three (hidden information) may deflect questions and keep the focus on other group members so as to avoid self-disclosure. Another group member with a large quadrant two (blind spot) may be unaware of their presence in the group or how others experience them. Feedback from others may be particularly helpful to this group member. See Figure 7.1 for examples of group members' Johari Window panes.

Now let us conclude the chapter with an example of a group counseling approach for co-occurring disorders.

An Example: Integrated Group Therapy for Bipolar Disorder and Substance Abuse

Integrated group therapy (IGT) is an evidence-based approach for clients with co-occurring bipolar disorder and SUD (Weiss & Smith Connery, 2011). This treatment is rooted in CBT principles and is focused on addressing maladaptive thoughts and behaviors as well as

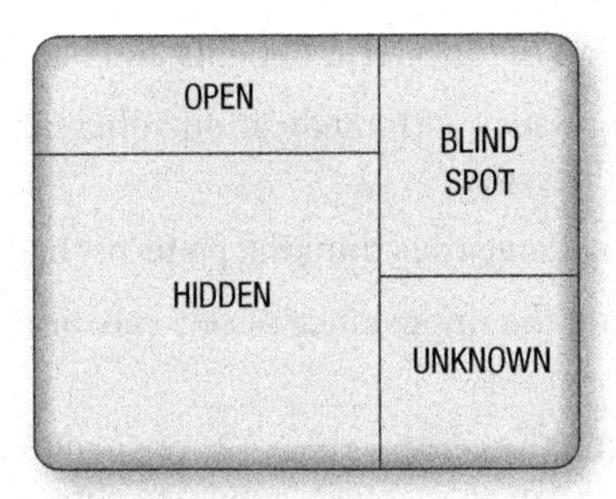

Group Member at the Start of Group Counseling

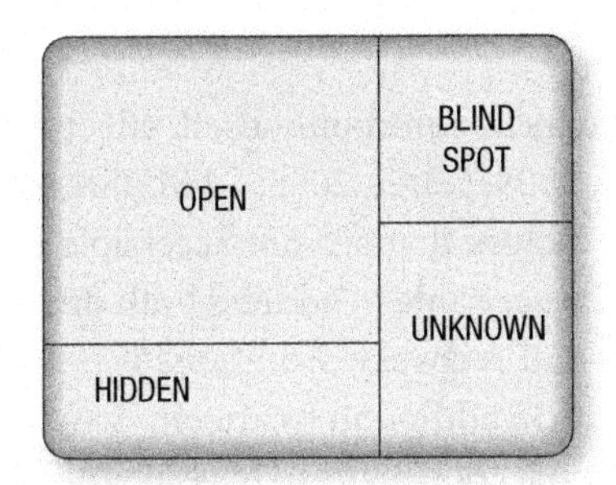

Group Member at the End of Group Counseling

FIGURE 7.1 Changes in Group Members' Johari Window Panes.

preventing relapse of both mood disruptions and substance abuse (Weiss & Smith Connery, 2011). This approach emphasizes the integration of treatment and argues the importance of addressing both mood disorder and substance abuse simultaneously (Weiss & Smith Connery, 2011). The primary goals of IGT are (1) to promote abstinence, (2) to promote adherence to medication treatment, (3) to teach symptom awareness in order to increase mood stability and decrease relapse, (4) skills training, and (5) to improve other relevant life aspects (Weiss & Smith Connery, 2011).

IGT is a manualized model that consists of 12 1-hour-long group sessions. We will briefly outline focal points for each session below:

- Session 1: (1) introducing the topic of "bipolar substance abuse" (p. 51) and (2) learning central rules and treatment routine.
- Session 2: (1) learning to recognize triggers, (2) learning treatment management strategies, and (3) introduction to basic CBT concepts.
- Session 3: (1) exploration of depressive thinking and behaviors and introduction to strategies to combat them.
- Session 4: (1) understanding the impact of family and (2) exploration of the influence of early recovery relationships.
- Session 5: (1) exploration of denial, ambivalence, and acceptance.
- Session 6: (1) learning to recognize warning signs for mood disturbances and substance use relapse and (2) learning symptom monitoring techniques.
- Session 7: (1) learning how to recognize and avoid high-risk situations and (2) learning how to consider long-term consequences of decision-making.

- Session 8: (1) exploration of long-term benefits and barriers of self-help groups.
- Session 9: (1) exploring issues with medication adherence and (2) learning strategies to increase medication adherence.
- Session 10: (1) exploring dangerous thinking patterns that could lead to relapse behaviors.
- Session 11: (1) exploring the importance of self-care and (2) learning strategies to practice self-care.
- Session 12: (1) reviewing the central rules, (2) reviewing the most important experiences in groups, and (3) listing recovery supports outside the group.

SUMMARY

Group counseling is one of the most commonly used, effective, and economical treatments for SUDs (Brooks & McHenry, 2009; CSAT, 2005; SAMHSA, 2020). This environment offers a range of unique therapeutic factors that are not accessible in other treatment modalities. Within counseling groups, clients are able to address both direct and indirect factors that are impacting their substance use and recovery. Additionally, several different types of groups, targeting specific needs of clients in addiction treatment, have been shown to be effective. As a result, it is critical for professional counselors to have an understanding of group counseling and to be able to utilize it effectively as a part of their treatment program.

RESOURCES

Addiction Technology Transfer Center Network: https://attcnetwork.org/
The Association for Specialist in Group Work: https://asgw.org/
Center for Substance Abuse Treatment. (2005). *Substance abuse treatment: Group therapy. Treatment improvement protocol (TIP) series, No. 41*. Substance Abuse and Mental Health Service Administration.
Corey, G. (2016). *Theory and practice of group counseling* (9th ed.). Brooks/Cole-Thomson.
Dimeff, L. A., & Linehan, M. M. (2008). Dialectical behavior therapy for substance abusers. *Addiction Science and Clinical Practice, 4*(2), 39–47. https://doi.org/10.1151/ascp084239
Flores, P. J. (2001). Addiction as an attachment disorder: Implications for group psychotherapy. *International Journal of Group Psychotherapy, 51*(1), 63–81. https://doi.org/10.1521/ijgp.51.1.63.49730
McHugh, R. K., Hearon, B. A., & Otto, M. W. (2010). Cognitive-behavioral therapy for substance use disorders. *Psychiatric Clinics of North America, 33*(3), 511–525. https://doi.org/10.1016/j.psc.2010.04.012
Roth, J. D. (2004). *Group psychotherapy and recovery from addiction: Carrying the message*. Hawthorne Press.
Thomas, V. R., & Pender, V. A. (2008). Association for specialists in group work: Best practices guidelines 2007 revision. *The Journal for Specialists in Group Work, 33*(2), 111–117. https://doi.org/10.1080/01933920801971184
Velasquez, M. M., Crouch, C., Stephens, N. S., & DiClemente, C. C. (2016). *Group treatment for substance abuse: A stages-of-change therapy manual* (2nd ed.). Guilford Press.
Weiss, R. D., & Smith Connery, H, (2011). *Integrated group therapy for bipolar disorder and substance abuse*. Guilford Press.
Yalom, I. D., & Leszcz, M. (2020). *The theory and practice of group psychotherapy* (6th ed.). Basic Books.

KEY REFERENCES

Only key references appear in the print edition. The full reference list appears in the digital product on Springer Publishing Connect: connect.springerpub.com/content/book/978-0-8261-3586-5/chapter/ch07

Center for Substance Abuse Treatment. (2005). *Substance abuse treatment: Group therapy. Treatment improvement protocol (TIP) series, No. 41*. Substance Abuse and Mental Health Service Administration.

Johnson, J. E., Burlingame, G. M., Olsen, J. A., Davies, D. R., & Gleave, R. L. (2005). Group climate, cohesion, alliance, and empathy in group psychotherapy: Multilevel structural equation models. *Journal of Counseling Psychology, 52*(3), 310–321. https://doi.org/10.1037/0022-0167.52.3.310

Matano, R. A., Yalom, I. D., & Schwartz, K. (1997). Interactive group therapy for substance abusers. In J. L. Spira (Ed.), *Group therapy for medically ill patients* (pp. 296–325). Guilford Press.

Pooler, D. K., Qualls, N., Rogers, R., & Johnston, D. (2014). An exploration of cohesion and recovery outcomes in addiction treatment groups. *Social Work with Groups, 37*(4), 314–330. https://doi.org/10.1080/01609513.2014.905217

Thomas, V. R., & Pender, V. A. (2008). Association for specialists in group work: Best practices guidelines 2007 revision. *The Journal for Specialists in Group Work, 33*(2), 111–117. https://doi.org/10.1080/01933920801971184

Velasquez, M. M., Crouch, C., Stephens, N. S., & DiClemente, C. C. (2016). *Group treatment for substance abuse: A stages-of-change therapy manual* (2nd ed.). Guilford Press.

Weiss, R. D., & Smith Connery, H. (2011). *Integrated group therapy for bipolar disorder and substance abuse*. Guilford Press.

Yalom, I. D., & Leszcz, M. (2020). *The theory and practice of group psychotherapy* (6th ed.). Basic Books.

8

FAMILY COUNSELING TECHNIQUES

LEARNING OBJECTIVES

Just as individuals are profoundly impacted by substance use disorders (SUDs), so too are their families, friends, coworkers, and significant others. In this chapter, we will explore how couples and families are impacted by SUDs and will present a variety of treatment models and techniques that are specific to treating couples and families. We will also explore how enabling and codependent behaviors evolve, often as survival roles. By the end of this chapter, you will be able to:

- describe healthy family traits and how SUDs can erode healthy family functioning;
- identify family roles (both spouse-partner and child roles) that are common in SUD families;
- explain how and why SUDs can impact families as well as family progression;
- describe family treatment models (e.g., Family Systems, Structural and Behavioral models) and the treatment techniques that coincide with these models;
- describe the three family treatment entry points;
- describe how families can motivate loved ones who are actively using substances;
- describe family treatment models specific to treating SUDs in adolescents;
- describe the special treatment needs of adult children of alcoholics.

TERMS TO KNOW

alliances unspoken agreements between family members to support one another especially during times of family conflict. Alliances can be supportive and healthy or dysfunctional, e.g., "I'll protect your drinking if you protect mine"

boundaries boundaries are usually physical as well as psychological barriers that exist both within families and with the outside world. Each individual family member may have their own physical or emotional boundary or comfort zone

circular causality	often problems within families do not occur in a linear fashion (e.g., behavior A causes reaction B) but rather in viscous cycles that tend to be self-perpetuating and often self-defeating. If a couple's arguing results in one partner leaving to drink or use drugs, followed by promises to change that are not forthcoming, which results in more arguing, this exemplifies circular causality
collusion	similar to alliances, collusion implies that two family members are colluding or allying together against other family members
differentiation	the ability of a son or daughter to separate from one's family of origin and form new healthy adult relationships
enabling	when family members inadvertently support their loved one's drinking or drug use by providing them with comforts (e.g., money, food, and shelter) or by providing excuses to others for their loved one's aberrant behavior. For example, a husband might enable his wife's drinking by calling her boss to say "she's sick" when in fact she is hungover from drinking the night before
emotional cutoffs	when a family member refuses to communicate with or have contact with another family member or someone outside the family
enmeshment	when family members are overinvolved with one another to the point where healthy differentiation is nearly impossible to achieve. Enmeshed relationships usually lack appropriate boundaries. Enmeshment is similar to "fusion"
family of origin	the family that someone grows up in, usually with biological or adoptive parents or guardians (e.g., grandparents) and sometimes siblings
family of creation	this is a family often composed of friends and parental figures who care for one another. There is often a give-and-take relationship among this group of individuals. A family of creation may include members of one's family of origin as well as individuals who are completely unrelated and perhaps unknown to one another
family roles	it is common for family members in homes impacted by SUDs to take on certain roles. Spouses or partners may take on the role of the enabler or the placater, while children may take on the role of the hero or scapegoat
identified patient (IP)	when families seek treatment, there is usually a person who becomes the symptom-bearer or IP within the family. This may or may not be the individual who is experiencing a SUD, but may be a family member who is experiencing behavioral or emotional adjustment problems

negative feedback loop	circular communication pattern that represents a no-win outcome. For example, a spouse telling their wife, "I drink because you nag me all the time." While the wife may respond with, "If you didn't drink so so much, I wouldn't nag you"
triangulation	when an unstable dyad (like a husband and wife or life partners), as a result of experiencing conflict or instability in their relationship, draw in a third party (e.g., a son or daughter or other family member) who then becomes the target of their conflict

INTRODUCTION

Substance use disorders (SUDs) do not occur in a vacuum, and it is often estimated that for every one individual impacted by a SUD there are, on average, six others who are also affected. This includes family members, spouse/partners, friends, coworkers, and other acquaintances. In this chapter, we will explore the impact of SUDs on families and significant others. Keep in mind that, although it may be common for a client impacted by SUDs to claim that a nagging, demanding spouse or partner or their "pain-in-the-neck kids" drove them to drink (or use drugs), this is more than likely not the case. Many people live in stressful job or family circumstances, but not all cope by relying on mood-altering substances. Yet, what is certain is that years of alcohol and/or substance abuse puts incredible stress and strain on most families and couples' relationships.

Families that are impacted by SUDs tend to share many similarities in terms of how their suffering and dysfunction play out on a day-to-day basis. It is also important to consider when discussing families experiencing SUDs that we are not only referring to families where a parent exhibits an alcohol use disorder (AUD) or SUD but also families where a grandparent or an adolescent/young adult son or daughter is experiencing a SUD. In addition, there are also instances where one or both partners in a couple's relationship is experiencing alcohol and/or drug issues. Therefore, there are a variety of situations where individuals are impacted by SUDs and so are their significant others.

To begin the exploration of families impacted by SUDs, it is important to examine what healthy families look like in order to understand how alcohol or substance abuse erode the very qualities or characteristics that allow families to function in a healthy way. As the famous author Tolstoy remarked in *Anna Karenina*, "All happy families are alike, each unhappy family is unhappy in its own way." So, let us examine some of the traits that characterize healthy families:

1. Healthy family members trust one another.
2. Healthy family members are able to communicate with one another in a clear and direct manner and are able to express loving feelings toward one another.
3. Healthy families value and validate each other's feelings.
4. Healthy family members are invested in the emotional growth of each individual within that particular family.
5. Healthy family members value interdependence (i.e., they can count on one another).

6. Healthy families value independence and autonomy.
7. Healthy families have appropriate rules and boundaries.
8. Healthy families are invested in teaching younger family members.
9. Healthy families value and enjoy leisure time together.
10. Healthy families celebrate holidays, anniversaries, and birthdays via special rituals.
11. Healthy families value connection with extended family members (e.g., grandparents, aunts, uncles, and cousins; adapted from Walsh, 1993).

As mentioned earlier, all of the qualities that allow families to function in healthy ways can be affected and eroded when a family member is actively abusing alcohol or other substances. For example, in healthy families, communication is often clear and direct, whereas in families impacted by SUDs communication suffers and becomes indirect, vague, confusing, or contradictory. Take the following scenario as an example.

LEARNING ACTIVITY 8.1
HEALTHY FAMILY TRAITS

Review the list of healthy family traits and choose the ones that you feel are applicable to your family. Are there traits on the list that you wish were present in your family?

CASE EXAMPLE: JENNA

Jenna is 19 years old and was a sophomore in college and living on campus until being placed on a "disciplinary leave" because of an incident in which she assaulted a fellow student while under the influence. Jenna was so intoxicated when the assault occurred that she was taken to a local ED and had her stomach pumped (her blood alcohol level [BAL] was determined to be .28). Jenna is now back home living with her parents and younger sister, Cara. Jenna's parents are furious that she was asked to leave the university. They had concerns about Jenna's drinking from the time she was in high school; however, they felt she would eventually grow out of her risky behavior. Jenna's parents want her to go to counseling (which is a stipulation of her being readmitted to classes in the fall); however, Jenna states she is thinking of applying to another university anyway "so why bother?" There is constant arguing and tension in the home, and Jenna responds by shutting down any meaningful communication and storming out to go out partying with her friends. Jenna's mother feels that her husband needs to take a more active role in disciplining Jenna by making her get a job and forcing her to go to counseling. Jenna's father is angry both at Jenna and his wife for forcing him to become "the disciplinarian." Whenever Jenna needs money to go out with her friends, she will nag her father because Jenna knows she can usually get him to give in. This makes Jenna's mother even more infuriated at both of them. Jenna states that her mother's "constant nagging" only makes her want to go out more with her friends to "party" to escape all the tension at home. Also, in response to all the tension and family disorder, Jenna's younger sister, Cara, has developed panic attacks.

LEARNING ACTIVITY 8.2 JENNA

Before you read the case conceptualization of Jenna's family, see if you can identify some of the dynamics that characterize Jenna's family (e.g., what are the patterns of communication between family members? What are the power struggles within the family?). Also, see if you can identify any alliances or evidence of collusion. Who is the enabler and how does this person enable? Can you find evidence of a negative feedback loop (as described in the Terms to Know)? Who are the "symptom bearers," and if this family were to present for counseling, who would most likely be the identified patient (IP)? Finally, if you were asked to see Jenna and her family, what would be the most important issues to address?

Case Conceptualization: Jenna

Jenna's family is a good illustration of the type of conflictual communication that occurs in the families where SUDs are present. Problems rarely get talked out or resolved. Instead, Jenna has become quite skilled in being able to pit her parents against one another for her own benefit. Jenna is also resistant to her university discipline committee's recommendation that she seek counseling, even if it means that she will end up transferring to another university. Her mother recognizes that Jenna needs to address her drinking and is therefore reluctant to give Jenna a way of avoiding treatment. This case also provides an example of *triangulation,* as Jenna has been able to pit her parents against one another. The other possibility is that the instability in the parents' relationship is being played out with Jenna taking on the role of the scapegoat in order to take the focus off of the parents' unstable marital relationship. For example, there are dysfunctional communication patterns between the parents, as Jenna's mother feels that Jenna needs to face the consequences of her behavior, while her father seems to be enabling Jenna's attempts to escape these consequences. Also, while Jenna continues to party with her friends who did not go away to college, she claims she does so because her mother nags her "all the time," while her mother feels that she needs to nag Jenna because she drinks most nights and then does nothing during the day. This is an example of a *negative feedback loop* and *circular causality.* Jenna's younger sister, Cara also has become a *symptom-bearer* as she too has developed difficulties in coping within familial stress by developing panic attacks. Life for Jenna and her family has become a far cry from the healthy family traits mentioned earlier. Instead, the dynamics occurring in Jenna's family represent very much the opposite of "healthy family traits." Not surprisingly, research indicates that healthy family traits and dynamics often serve as a protective factor against sons and daughters developing SUDs (Leonard & Homish, 2008).

With regard to communication patterns in families impacted by SUDs, it is often said that there are three "unwritten rules" of living in a home impacted by alcohol or drug addiction, *"Don't trust, Don't talk, and Don't feel"* (Black, 1981). These rules often apply to homes wherein sons or daughters live at home with a parent(s) with active SUDs. Children of alcoholic or addicted parents often learn not to *trust* anyone with family secrets surrounding Mom or Dad's alcohol or drug problem and to refrain from *talking* about anything that goes on at home, behind closed doors. In order to survive in such a dysfunctional system, sons or daughters also learn to suppress or stuff their feelings (*Don't feel).* When feelings are expressed, they usually tend to be invalidated, dismissed, or used against the person who expressed them. It would not be unusual for a son or daughter who is crying because of being

BOX 8.1

TRAITS COMMON TO ADULT CHILDREN OF ALCOHOLICS

- Guess at what normal behavior is.
- Have difficulty following a project through from beginning to end.
- Lie when it would be just as easy to tell the truth.
- Judge themselves without mercy.
- Have difficulty having fun.
- Take themselves very seriously.
- Have difficulty with intimate relationships.
- Overreact to changes over which they have no control.
- Constantly seek approval and affirmation.
- Feel that they are different from other people.
- Are super responsible or super irresponsible.
- Are extremely loyal, even in the face of evidence that the loyalty is undeserved.
- Are impulsive.
- May tend to lock themselves in a course of action without giving serious consideration to alternative behaviors or possible consequences.
- Impulsively can lead to confusion, self-loathing, and loss of control over their environment. In addition, the person spends an excessive amount of energy cleaning up the mess.

Source: Adapted from Woititz, J. G. (1983). *Adult children of alcoholics.* Health Communications.

upset about their parent's being intoxicated to hear, "Stop crying or I'll give you something to cry about!" (Black, 1981, 2003). It is common for children who grow up in homes severely impacted by SUDs to carry dysfunctional communication patterns, problems in establishing intimate relationships, and particular personality difficulties into adulthood. As described by authors such as Janet Woititz (1983), Robert Ackerman (1981), and Claudia Black (1981), adult children of alcoholics (ACOAs) often struggle with the aftereffects of growing up in dysfunctional homes, and not surprisingly these aftereffects often are carried into their adult relationships both at home and at work. Box 8.1 presents a list of common traits of ACOAs as described by Janet Woititz (1983). What addiction counselors will often encounter is that not all ACOAs will manifest all of these traits; rather a few traits often come into focus as being more problematic.

IMPACT OF SUBSTANCE USE DISORDERS ON FAMILIES AND FAMILY PROGRESSION

It is important to point out that families experiencing SUDs vary in the intensity and level of dysfunction they experience. For example, research into alcoholic families concludes that those families who experience less interference with important family rituals (e.g., family dinner time, family vacations, and Christmas holiday rituals) tended to have children who were better adjusted and less likely to become alcoholics as adults (Steinglass, 1979, 1981; Steinglass et al., 1987). Wolin et al. (1980) also found there were three types of ritual patterns in alcoholic families: (1) *intact rituals* were those families that maintained important family rituals in spite of alcoholism; (2) *subsumptive rituals* existed in families that made adjustments or modifications in order to accommodate the drinking; and (3) *disrupted family rituals* were found in those families who were most impacted by their loved one's drinking. Families that managed to maintain *intact rituals* or *subsumptive rituals* tended to have better adjusted children and less likelihood of sons and daughters developing SUDs later in life.

Brown and Lewis (1999) discovered the following traits as being characteristic of families impacted by AUDs: (1) families experience distinct developmental stages as they progress from active drinking to recovery; (2) the environment or context of the drinking family is often traumatic and very harmful to children and adults; (3) the family system of the drinking family is often restrictive, rigid, and closed; and (4) in recovery, the unhealthy family system must collapse (i.e., the defensive structures that maintain the pathology of the entire family must change). In other words, once the alcoholic family member enters recovery, the entire family must also change, and this may be accomplished by abandoning dysfunctional family roles (e.g., enabling behaviors); (5) with the collapse of the unhealthy family system, adults then turn their attention to their own individual recovery (which often takes years); (6) children may be just as neglected or abandoned in early recovery as they were during active drinking especially as parents turn their attention away from the family and onto themselves; (7) families who embark on recovery are on a "dynamic process of difficult change which sometimes takes as a long as 10 years before all the pieces come together: a stable, healthy environment; a secure healthy family system and couple relationship" (adapted from Brown & Lewis, 1999, pp. 17–24). Given that families impacted by SUDs vary in intensity and level of dysfunction, we would be remiss in not pointing out that many studies have noted correlations between child maltreatment, child physical and sexual abuse and neglect particularly in those homes most severely impacted by SUDs. Research also indicates that those children who grow up in severely dysfunctional SUDs homes often are at high risks for developing SUDs as adults (e.g., Halpern et al., 2018; Mandavia et al., 2016).

It is also important for counselors to take into consideration that families impacted by SUDs also experience a progression that often runs parallel to the progression that the alcoholic or addict parent experiences. According to Jackson (1954), families first experience *Denial of the Problem.* In this stage, families attempt to deny that their loved one has a drinking or substance use problem. They may blame external stressors (e.g., job stress and financial stress) for their loved one's drinking or drug use. For example, "Bob drinks every night because he's under so much pressure at work right now." This stage often coincides with the SUD family member's denial that their drinking or drug use is problematic. In the second stage, *Attempts to Eliminate the Problem,* the nonalcoholic spouse or partner begins to isolate from friends and extended family members. Here, the goal is to try to maintain the illusion of having "a happy home" to the outside world. In the third stage, *Disorganization,* the nonalcoholic spouse tries to cope with the ever-increasing tension in the home. This stage often finds frequent arguments, which may result in violence between spouses or partners. This would also be the stage where behavior problems in their children may begin. In the fourth stage, *Attempts to Reorganize in Spite of the Problem,* the nonalcoholic spouse or partner tries to hold everything together by making sure the rent or mortgage is paid, bills are paid, and basic needs are met (e.g., food, shelter, and clothing). Usually in this stage, the alcoholic spouse/partner is ignored based on resentful feelings that they cannot be trusted or counted on to fulfill responsibilities. In the fifth stage, *Efforts to Escape* are characterized by decisions whether to divorce or separate as the nonalcoholic/addicted partner tries to determine whether the marriage and family is salvageable and whether they will be able to sustain the life they have been experiencing. This stage usually corresponds to the person with the AUD "hitting bottom," at which point they may hopefully seek treatment. If this occurs, this leads to the sixth stage, *Recovery and Reorganization of the Whole Family*, as the entire family hopefully will engage in the treatment process (the alcoholic attends treatment and Alcoholics Anonymous [AA], while the nonalcoholic spouse and children also attend counseling and AA and/or Alateen). Even when the alcoholic spouse or partner enters treatment and begins recovery, not all families will engage in their own treatment. The seventh stage occurs if the alcoholic spouse does not "hit bottom" and either separation or divorce is sought. This stage is referred to as *Reorganization of Part of the Family*, referring to the fact that the nonalcoholic spouse and children usually begin to reorganize as a single-parent family.

As mentioned earlier, Brown and Lewis' (1999) research into families impacted by AUDs also found evidence of progressive family stages, which they define as: *Drinking Stage, Transition Stage, Early Recovery,* and *Ongoing Recovery*. During the active *Drinking Stage*, the family is basically in survival mode, as "daily family life becomes dominated by the anxieties, tensions, and chronic trauma of active alcoholism" (Brown & Lewis, 1999, p. 14). Basically, the family is trying its best to cope and to hold things together. As the consequences of drinking become more visible to others and more difficult to resolve (e.g., DUI arrest, medical illness, and physical abuse), there is a growing need for secrecy and isolation from others, which unfortunately cuts the family off from outside sources of help or input from extended family, friends, and the community. As the family moves toward the *Transition stage*, there is a great deal of anxiety, tension, and apprehension as family members move into the "unknowns" of recovery and what will happen next. Brown and Lewis (1999) suggest that the parents need to get a foothold on each of their individual recoveries first before being able to work on their relationship as a couple. Two scenarios are common as couples move into *Transition*. The first is where the couple is in crisis (perhaps due to an arrest, disclosure of an extramarital affair, job loss, etc.), and often anger and hostility permeate the couple's bond with one another. The second scenario is where the couple has a workable, bonded relationship that had included active alcoholism, therefore, this couple is not in crisis as one or both partners move toward recovery. As the alcoholic partner moves toward abstinence, the couple may feel a loss of closeness. In *Early Recovery*, the family also faces many challenges as they experience many "firsts" without alcohol (e.g., first holidays, anniversaries, and birthdays) Couples will begin to find healthier ways to differentiate (separate from one another) as they let go of enabling or controlling dysfunctional roles. Physical and sexual intimacy within the couple's relationship also needs to be addressed and redefined. In addition, parenting roles and responsibilities will need to be redelineated. Sometimes, this is a difficult transition as the nonalcoholic parent had often assumed major responsibility for parenting roles and may resent the newly sober parent's interference in established parenting responsibilities. Finally, in *Ongoing Recovery*, families begin to experience a sense that things have slowed down and calmed down. But this does not happen with the passage of time alone. There are distinctions made between being "dry" versus "sober." An individual with an AUD is considered to be "dry" when they have stopped drinking but have not really embraced recovery, nor have they embraced the need for change. For example, a recovering alcoholic who has been working the 12 Steps of AA has probably begun to look within by making a "fearless moral inventory" of themselves and past alcoholic behavior (as would occur when doing a Fourth Step). Also, they may have made some attempts at "making amends" to their family for their inappropriate or destructive behavior during active addiction (as would occur when doing an Eighth and Ninth Step). A person who is "dry" never even gets close to self-examination or making amends to those family members they may have hurt. Families in ongoing recovery will still experience problems; however, the recovering family now has a framework with which to discuss and resolve problems in a way where every family member can be heard and respected. This would also be the point at which the family can seek treatment. Families in ongoing recovery hopefully can embrace the healthy family traits that were presented at the beginning of this chapter!

LEARNING ACTIVITY 8.3
FAMILY PROGRESSION

Counselors are often become involved in counseling families at various stages in their progression. See if you can identify the challenges that families would be facing in some of these stages (using either Jackson's family progression stages or Brown's stages) and how you as a family counselor might assist families at those particular stages.

TREATMENT ENTRY POINTS

Given the family progression described earlier, it is important that counselors anticipate that there will be particular times when family members will reach out for help or when family counseling may be most helpful. Table 8.1 provides a description of some of these treatment entry points. Note that there are three essential times when families will access counseling for themselves or for their loved ones. The ***First Entry Point*** is when their loved one is actively drinking or using drugs. Here, the family is desperate to get their significant other to seek help for their SUD. Often, families have tried many strategies to get their loved one to accept treatment, so it is important for counselors to find out what the family has attempted and what has not worked or been helpful. It is also important for counselors to understand the varied emotional reactions that family members may have regarding their loved one's substance use. Some family members may be anxious or fearful, while others may feel angry or betrayed. Some family members may be shocked when they first become aware of their loved one's substance use. Counselors need to validate these various emotional reactions as being normal while at the same time attempting to get the family on the same page regarding what steps they need to take next. If the loved one refuses to seek help, there are several approaches that might be utilized to encourage a loved one to enter treatment. Johnsonian Interventions are designed to "confront the loved one with reality in a receivable way." Here, "confrontation" is not done aggressively, but rather in a spirit of love and concern. As described by Vernon Johnson (1973), who originated this technique, family members and loved ones are first gathered together to express their concerns. Family members, friends, and coworkers are then asked to list two or three examples where their loved one's drinking or substance use had caused them concern, in order that these incidents could be presented to their significant other in a loving, concerned manner. The SUD loved one is not included in these meetings. The family members and significant others are then coached as to when and how to present

TABLE 8.1 Family Treatment Entry Points

ENTRY POINT	GOAL
1. When loved one is actively using	To assess current substance use or presenting crisis and to engage family to work on goal encouraging loved one to enter detox or or other treatment
2. When loved one has completed detox or residential treatment	To determine how family can support aftercare and relapse prevention plan. Also encourage family to work on their own growth & refrain from enabling and/or hypervigilant behavior
3. Ongoing recovery	To establish new relationship patterns and healthy family functioning

these concerns to their loved one with the goal that they will agree to enter treatment voluntarily. Counselors sometimes rehearse the intervention prior to actually meeting with the loved one. The intervention approach has been criticized as being coercive because if the loved one refuses help family members are encouraged to impose consequences designed to get their loved one to reconsider treatment. For example, one adult son's "consequence" was that he would call the police if his father continued to drink and drive.

Another less coercive approach that can be used at this entry point is called *ARISE* (A Relational Intervention Sequence for Engagement; Garrett et al., 1997; Landau et al., 2004), which involves three stages designed to encourage their loved one to accept treatment for their SUD. In the First Stage, a concerned significant other or family member contacts a counselor or treatment agency to obtain knowledge about treatment options. Here, the counselor assesses if there is a crisis needing immediate treatment by assessing the severity of the loved one's alcohol and/or drug use and encourages the family member to ask other family members and significant others for assistance. The substance users are asked to join the first in-person meeting. The counselor then proceeds to the Second Stage (only if the substance user has not entered treatment). Here, the counselor will work with the concerned family members and significant others to come up with clear and enforceable consequences for the substance user's continued alcohol or drug use. Stage 2 meetings (up to five sessions) also review efforts that have been attempted in the past, and strategies are developed that encourage the substance users to engage in treatment. Stage 3 is more confrontational, and in some ways is similar to a Johnsonian intervention; however, the expectation is that the substance-using loved one will have entered treatment prior to reaching this stage.

Finally, in some instances where families are at a point of desperation, civil commitment may be the only viable alternative. Presently, 38 states have some form of civil commitment laws that allow family members to petition the courts to commit their SUD loved one into a detox or inpatient-rehab type program (Cavaiola & Dolan, 2016). Based on mental health civil commitment laws that allow the courts to commit individuals deemed to be a danger to themselves or others based on evaluations by licensed psychiatrists and/or psychologists, civil commitments for those with SUDs are also based on the supposition that these individuals are a danger to themselves and others by virtue of the fact that they are not able to make reasonable/rational decisions on their own behalf. The majority of SUD treatment requires individuals to sign themselves into treatment voluntarily; however, can we really expect that someone who has been using alcohol or drugs continuously for several years to make reasonable, rational decisions on their own behalf?

The ***Second Entry Point*** is when the loved has completed a detox or residential treatment program and will be returning home (or may be entering a halfway house or sober-living facility). In each of those instances, it is important that families be involved in the aftercare planning as well as relapse prevention planning. If the loved one is returning home after completing detox or residential treatment, it is important that counselors assist families with the anxiety they are likely to experience now that their loved one is home. Anxieties usually center around whether or not their loved one can be trusted, will they relapse, will they be able and willing to take on responsibilities, will they attend AA or Narcotics Anonymous (NA) meetings, and will they be able to handle the stresses of returning to work or school? Also, it is helpful to have family discussions as to how they can best support their loved one's recovery (e.g., by removing alcohol and prescription medications from the home, by limiting access to large sums of money, and by initially providing transportation to AA or NA meetings and counseling appointments). At the second treatment entry point, it is important that family members keep their expectations realistic. Just because their loved one is abstinent, it does not mean that they will become a caring, loving, empathic individual overnight. This is also not the time to beat the loved one up emotionally for their wrongdoings from the past. The ***Third Entry Point*** occurs when families are looking to work on specific issues pertaining to their loved one's recovery. For example, if family members begin to notice dry drunk behavior (described in Chapter 13, Developmental Issues in Counseling) or if their loved one is not reconnecting with other family members, this may result in families seeking counseling. This may also be a time when family members are entering treatment in order to work through the pain and trauma that occurred as a result of active substance use. It is important for counselors to be aware that not all families are willing or ready to become involved in treatment at these stages. Box 8.2 provides information on when and where to offer alternative treatments to families especially during the aftercare or relapse prevention planning process. Appendix 8.1 provides a sample treatment regimen that might be used in inpatient or intensive outpatient (IOP) programs that offer family treatment services.

Also, counselors need to anticipate that families may present with resistance or ambivalence regarding their willingness to enter family counseling. It is common for counselors to hear, "It's his/her problem not mine, they need to deal with it." In instances such as these, it is helpful for counselors to validate the frustrations that family members have experienced and to hear out what types of struggles they have encountered. Families with a son or daughter experiencing a SUD may feel angry or frustrated by their behavior. Parents might explain how they have had to protect themselves or other family members from negative addictive behaviors as illustrated in the following example.

CASE EXAMPLE: SEAN

When Mr. and Mrs. Prescott's 28-year-old son, Sean, had finally agreed to enter a detox program, his parents were skeptical about his decision to seek help. Their first reaction was that Sean was entering detox only to avoid legal problems or to avoid paying money he owed to his drug dealer. For the past four years, the Prescotts describe their life as "a living hell" in which they had to padlock their bedroom after Sean had stolen his father's watch and his mother's pearl necklace to pawn for drug money. Last Thanksgiving, when the Prescotts hosted a large gathering of grandparents, aunts, uncles, and cousins, Sean

(*continued*)

was up in the bedroom rifling through their guests' purses and coats looking for money and credit cards. Only one of Sean's aunts said anything about the thefts to Mrs. Prescott, who felt humiliated. When Sean's primary counselor called the parents to try to arrange a family counseling session, his parents were angry, frustrated, and wanted no part in Sean's treatment. This had been Sean's third detox within the past year; however, Sean's counselor heard the parent's frustrations and convinced them that, if she was to be of help to Sean, she needed them to be her allies in the process. The Prescotts agreed to come in to discuss an aftercare plan with Sean. Both the parents and the counselor hoped they could convince Sean to go to a long-term residential program followed by a halfway house or, at very least, an intensive outpatient (IOP) program and Oxford House or sober living facility. At one point in the session, Mrs. Prescott said to Sean that she could not go on like this, "feeling like a prisoner" in her own home, adding, "your addiction is sucking the life-blood from me and your father."

BOX 8.2

WHEN AND WHEN NOT TO INVOLVE FAMILIES

Involve family members when...

1. they accept their loved one's SUD as a chronic disease and do not blame themselves;
2. they are willing to be supportive of their loved one's recovery;
3. they accept that, even though there may have been past treatment failures, they need not be cynical or skeptical that recovery cannot be attained;
4. they are willing to let go of enabling behaviors and work on themselves;
5. they are willing to attend AA/NA.;
6. family members are willing to take direction from their loved one regarding what they consider helpful, for example, whether to remove all alcohol or prescription medications from house.

Consider alternative treatment when...

1. the family member(s) are actively using or have an active SUD;
2. the family members are cynical and/or skeptical of their loved one's recovery;
3. the family member views their loved one as manipulative and incapable of change;
4. the family member holds too much anger toward their loved one for past betrayal;
5. the family member blames themselves for their loved one's SUD and are, therefore, unwilling or unable to let go of enabling behavior;
6. the family member remains hypervigilant regarding their loved one's recovery efforts and finds it difficult to allow their loved one to work their own program of recovery;
7. in the instances noted earlier, it will be more helpful to refer family members for their own individual counseling and/or to AA or NA.

Although it is sometime difficult to get families to agree to counseling, it is imperative especially when coming up with a collaborative treatment plan. It is imperative for counselors to remember that, with SUDs, all family members are impacted; therefore, nonaddicted family members and significant others will need to re-examine and re-establish healthier roles and boundaries. Also, keep in mind that family members can either support or sabotage future treatment planning, therefore, it is important they are part of the planning process and have the opportunity to become part of the solution rather than part of the problem (Cavaiola, 2000).

The ability to manage family resistance is an important skill for counselors to possess. There are many instances where families may have had negative experiences with prior treatment providers, and it is important to hear out those complaints in order to work toward collaborative treatment planning (Anderson & Stewart, 1983). Yet, it was also essential for Sean's counselor to validate the parent's feelings of frustration, fear, and skepticism. The Prescotts were clearly overwhelmed and did not know what to do to help Sean accept his SUD and to accept the necessary treatment. Family counseling can provide a helpful environment to explore these feelings and to process them in a useful manner.

FAMILY COUNSELING MODELS AND TECHNIQUES

Just as there are theoretical models and counseling techniques used for helping individuals (e.g., psychoanalytic, behavioral, Gestalt, and cognitive behavioral), there are also models that are more specific to working with couples and families. In this section, we will be presenting four of those family models (Family Systems, Structural Family Therapy, Family Disease Model, and the Behavioral Model) and some of the family counseling techniques that correspond to these various theoretical models.

Family Systems Model

The Family Systems model was originally developed by well-known theorists such as Jay Haley and Murray Bowen. According to Bowen (1978), families are essentially social systems that are bound by a precise and predictable set of rules or dynamics that function throughout the entire family often for up to three generations (Bradshaw, 1995). What is essential to this model when applied to SUDs is that any disturbance to part of the family (or system) will impact all family members, and therefore all members of the family system will react in an attempt to try to maintain balance or *homeostasis.* What's interesting about the concept of homeostasis is that it can occur in healthy family systems as a way to maintain healthy family goals or in dysfunctional family systems as a reaction to changes that may appear as threatening. Here are two scenarios of family homeostasis.

CASE EXAMPLE: JASON

Scenario 1: Jason is 18 years old, a senior in high school, and currently living with his parents and two younger siblings, a 15-year-old brother, Tim, and a 13-year-old sister, Jamie. Jason has been snowboarding since he was 6 years old and began competing when he was 11. Because he was winning local competitions, Jason's coach recommended that he attend a special

(*continued*)

school at one of the ski/snowboard resorts that would provide him with expert coaching and would increase his chances of competing nationally and perhaps even internationally, which would put him on track to compete in the Olympics someday. In order to help make this happen, Jason's parents worked extra hours to bring in more income to pay for their son's school and extra coaching. Jason's father worked in a local factory in Vermont, and his mother worked as an elementary school teacher. Fortunately, both of Jason's siblings were supportive of the extra attention that he was receiving. Tim was also an avid and talented snowboarder, and Jamie was the star of a travelling soccer team, so they appreciated all the time Jason put into improving himself. Jason's entire family was on board with supporting Jason's goals of someday competing in the winter Olympics.

Scenario 2: In the last scheduled competition of the winter snowboarding season, Jason suffered a major injury that required extensive knee surgery. Both Jason and his parents are worried that the injury will jeopardize his scholarship. Jason is anxious that he needs to get back to practicing in order to avoid losing his scholarship. Jason's doctor prescribes an opiate-based analgesic (painkiller) in order to help him with the pain following his surgery. Jason goes through the prescription quickly and asks his doctor for a refill, which she reluctantly prescribes. Within a month, Jason is dependent on the painkillers. His parents are worried that Jason is pushing himself too hard by constantly working out. Within a few months, Jason's doctor refuses to prescribe more painkillers and recommends that he increase his physical therapy sessions. Jason begins to buy prescription opioid pills from a local drug dealer. Also, Jason's father received notice that the factory where he has been employed is closing, and he will need to go on unemployment.

LEARNING ACTIVITY 8.4
ASSESSING FAMILY DYNAMICS

For this Learning Activity, watch any one of the films listed in the "Resources" section at the end of this chapter. See if you can identify the dynamics (i.e., interactional patterns) among the key family members and also identify how these family interactions have been impacted by SUDs.

In the two scenarios described, we see a family struggling to maintain homeostasis. In the first scenario, Jason's family is doing everything to support his goals of attending a special school for snowboarding. This is an example of a healthy homeostasis in which the entire family is supportive of one another and therefore supportive of Jason's goals. Also, in this first scenario, Jason's family embodies many of the healthy family traits described earlier in this chapter. However, in the second scenario, Jason suffers an untimely injury and turns to opiate painkillers, which causes his life to unravel. Compounding the financial woes of the family are worries that Jason's father may be losing his job as his factory may be shutting down soon.

One of the basic principles of the Family Systems model (and a healthy family trait) that Bowen proposes is the concept of differentiation and separation. Healthy families value independence and autonomy, and we see this in the first scenario, where Jason's parents are doing everything possible to prepare to successfully "launch" him off to a specialized school for snowboarding. In ideal circumstances, sons and daughters are encouraged to "leave the nest" as part of their overall development into emerging adulthood. However, think about how SUDs impact on the differentiation process.

The Family Systems model can also be applied to couples. We see this both in active addiction as well as in recovery. During active addiction, couples also experience a need to maintain homeostasis. This usually takes the form of the nonaddicted spouse or partner taking on codependency roles, most often by becoming the enabler or caretaker of their addicted loved one (such as calling their loved one's boss to make excuses for them not being able to make it into work, when in fact they are too hungover). It is common for these homeostatic patterns to exist over the course of many years. Consider a situation in which the addicted partner becomes clean and sober. During active addiction, homeostasis suggests that there will be a certain predictability to how problems are managed. Here, recovery becomes an unknown, and with it comes a great deal of anxiety and apprehension for both partners. The nonaddicted spouse or partner may fear their partner may no longer need them or may fear they may meet someone in AA or NA and fall in love with that person. It is not unusual for the nonaddicted partner to resent their loved one attending AA or NA meetings. A common complaint often voiced by spouses/partners is: "First I lost you to alcohol or drugs and now I've lost you to AA/NA!" In response to these fears, apprehensions, and frustrations, the spouse of a newly sober alcoholic who was attempting to do a "90 in 90" (i.e., attending 90 meetings in 90 days) purchases a monogrammed whiskey flask for her husband for a Christmas present. Although to an outside observer this act seems insane, the purchase of the whiskey flask was actually an attempt to return to the dysfunctional homeostasis that existed prior to the husband getting sober and attending AA.

It is important to consider that there are many instances where both partners are actively using alcohol or drugs. This was the focus on the HBO documentary *Dope Sick Love* (Conte, 2005), which chronicles three couples impacted by SUDs. What becomes obvious is that it is often impossible for couples to recover together. As one partner makes attempts to recover, the other partner often becomes frightened or threatened by this change, and they will pull their partner back into active substance use. Again, this is an example of how powerful dysfunctional homeostasis can be. Cavacuiti (2004) describes the challenges that these couples face when much of their relationship is formed around their substance use. In addition, Cavacuiti found that these couples most often do not fit the classic patterns of codependency (described earlier) and instead finds that their relationships are often complex and varied. He identifies some couples as "concordant couples," referring to those couples whose lives are equally taken over by their drug of preference. Also, Pivnick et al. (1994) studied women participating in methadone programs and found the majority were involved in romantic relationships with men who were also substance users.

Although the Family Systems model was initially developed as a generalist theory, meant to describe all families, it was not until the 1970s that this model began to influence the drug and alcohol treatment field. Steinglass was one of the first researchers to notice repetitious patterns in the family interactions of his clients, which led him to conclude that SUDs had a stabilizing or adaptive function within these families that helped maintain equilibrium (or homeostasis) and also helped solidify family roles and ways in which these families interacted (e.g., expression of emotions and conflicts; see Steinglass, 1979, 1981; Steinglass et al., 1977, 1987) Steinglass also found in instances of active parental alcohol use that these families tended to be more rigid both in terms of family roles and interactions. Therefore, counselors working with families in active addictions may find roles and interactions that are very entrenched and often predictable.

Family Systems Techniques

According to Family Systems theory, substance use may symbolize a maladaptive attempt to maintain a dysfunctional homeostasis. It is not coincidental that problems related to substance use may arise during critical periods in which the family is attempting to negotiate key developmental milestone (e.g., like "launching" an adult son or daughter into the world). As mentioned earlier, in healthy families, differentiation or separation between a young adult son or daughter and their parents is encouraged and supported. However, when a SUD impacts a son or daughter, healthy differentiation becomes impossible and is often replaced by enmeshment (or fusion) as parents find themselves in constant fear of overdose or imprisonment and are convinced their son or daughter will never be able to make a successful transition toward becoming an independent young adult. Because of these tensions and conflicts, this may be a time at which the son or daughter acts out and gets arrested or a DUI. Nothing stops healthy differentiation dead in its tracks like an arrest or some other substance-related crisis. It is at this point when the family often rallies around their son or daughter to try to fend off potential jail or prison time. When family counselors begin to counsel families in the aftermath of an arrest, the therapeutic work must eventually shift the focus away from the arrest and to how the family can address the substance use issues in order to move forward. In order to accomplish this goal, family counselors utilize a few different techniques. The first is *joining*. Here, the family systems counselor is attempting to develop a therapeutic alliance with the family in order to gain their trust and confidence. The counselor joins the family in two ways: first, by supporting the family system and its member (by making a connection with each family member). Joining also involves the family counselor asking each family member what their perception of the problem is. (This is why it is very important to have all family members present, as we have witnessed instances where a younger sibling correctly perceives the dysfunction within the family and speaks the truth, while other family members may be invested in maintaining a dysfunctional homeostasis. For example, after listening intently during a family session, an 8-year-old younger sister finally blurted out "nothing will change as long as Dad and my older brother are drinking buddies." The younger sister was pointing out an unhealthy alliance or collusion between her father and older brother.) Once a connection is made and the family gains trust in the counselor, the counselor then can challenge the family system. The counselor must be able to tell each family member that they understand their perception of the problem and also can state with confidence that there are ways to address the problems (Stanton et al., 1978).

The second technique used by Family Systems counselors is called *restructuring*. Here, the family counselor attempts to challenge the homeostasis by changing the bonding and power alignments among various family members. In order to accomplish these goals, counselors will use techniques such as *contracting* (an agreement to work on particular substance use issues before proceeding to work on other problems), *reframing* (here, the counselor encourages family members to understand how the substance use serves an important function or purpose within the family), and *enactment* (here, the family counselor is asking the family to discuss the substance use problem with one another as they might at home, while the counselor observes the dynamics between family members). Restructuring can be a valuable tool when working with families in that it provides family members an opportunity to experience roles from an entirely different perspective.

CASE EXAMPLE: BRITTANY (FAMILY SYSTEMS)

Brittany is a single woman in her early 20s who is currently living at home with her biological mother and father, her maternal grandmother, and an older brother and two younger sisters in West Virginia. Brittany began using alcohol and marijuana when she was around 13 years old; however, she then progressed to using OxyContin (an opioid analgesic or painkiller), which she ingests orally. There are times when Brittany would "cook" the OxyContin pills down to liquid form in order that she could inject it intravenously. Although Brittany has used other substances in the past eight years, she identifies OxyContin as her current primary drug. Her entire family is aware of her prescription opioid use and are very worried that she will overdose or be harmed when she goes out to buy the drug on the street from drug dealers. Brittany also admits to having used black-tar heroin when OxyContin is unavailable, and she admits to stealing pain medication from her father, who sustained a work-related injury while working as a coal miner.

Case Conceptualization: Brittany

Brittany's opioid use disorder seems to be maintained by several core issues. First, Brittany reports that she was sexually molested by an older, male cousin when she was around 13 years old, which coincides with the initial onset of her using alcohol and marijuana. Brittany was afraid to tell her parents because she worried that they would not believe her. The other core family issue is that when Brittany was 11 years old, her older brother Jon was murdered in a drug deal that had gone bad. This had a devastating impact on Brittany's parents, who blamed themselves for Jon's death because he had been living at home at the time, and the parents felt they could have done more to get Jon into treatment or somehow motivate him to accept help. Now every time Brittany leaves the house, her parents go into "panic mode," as they fear that Brittany will end up being murdered like Jon. Another core issue is that Brittany was raped by three men from whom she had purchased heroin. She has very little recollection of that night and thinks she may have been given a "date rape drug" like gamma hydroxybutyrate (GHB) or Rohypnol. Finally, Brittany admits that the more her parents try to restrict her from going out of the house, the more she rebels by sneaking out of the house at all hours of the day or night.

Brittany's family lives with the trauma of death hanging over them on a daily basis. They never really forgave themselves or grieved Jon's death, and now they live in utter fear that the same thing will happen to Brittany. Brittany's parents had gone into a deep depression after Jon was murdered. As a result of their dread that something may happen to Brittany, Brittany's father rationalizes that if he gives her his painkillers it's better than her going out on the street to buy heroin from a drug dealer who might end up raping or murdering her. This is a family who find themselves in what is sometimes referred to as a "family crucible" in which all members are locked into a pattern of destructive behaviors from which they see no way out. Brittany's siblings very much want her to seek help. Her older brother, Frank, especially feels that his parents have unintentionally become enablers to Brittany's addiction and has concluded that "nothing will change, unless Mom and Dad wake up and begin to make major changes." Brittany's younger sister, Eva, is also very worried about Brittany and constantly fears that something horrible will happen to her. Eva tends to keep these feelings bottled up and binge eats when she feels anxious. A word of caution: we do not want students to assume that everyone suffering with SUDs has experienced several major traumas such as Brittany. As discussed in Chapter 2, An Overview of Etiological Models, there are several possible etiologies or causal factors that may account for why individuals develop SUDs.

There are several ways these Family Systems techniques can be utilized in counseling Brittany's family. Given the murder of Brittany's older brother Jon, Brittany's parents have tried to stabilize the dysfunctional homeostasis created by Brittany's opioid use by focusing all of their efforts on making certain that Brittany does not meet a similar untimely death. Yet, just as Brittany is powerless over her opioid use disorder, so too are her parents and siblings. Because the parents are so focused on Brittany, it is almost as if their other daughter and son are nonexistent.

The real challenge for Brittany's parents and siblings will come once Brittany completes detox and residential treatment and begins to work on her recovery. Often parents and siblings are at a loss as to how to best help their now-recovering loved one, so the tendency is to go back to old roles or ways of relating to one another. This too is an example of homeostasis at work because the family's tendency is to revert to old patterns of interacting because they have no frame of reference of how to interact with Brittany now that she is clean/sober. It is common, therefore, for parents to become hypervigilant, watching their son or daughter's every move, instead of focusing on their own recovery. No wonder that family counselors often refer to this initial period when a loved one comes home from treatment, as *walking on eggshells* because of the tension created by not knowing how to act toward one another in healthier ways. Naturally, this is where counseling becomes vital, especially during these early days/weeks/months of recovery.

Structural Family Model

Structural Family Theory was originated by Salvador Minuchin and his colleagues at the Philadelphia Child Guidance Clinic (PCGC) in the 1980s. Initially, Structural Family Therapy was utilized to treat a number of child/adolescent behavioral problems for everything from bedwetting to eating disorders to fire-setting. Essentially, Structural Family Therapy addresses problems in functioning within a family. In order to bring about change within the family, Structural Family therapists will first "join" with the family in order to understand the invisible rules that govern its functioning. The counselor takes note of how family members relate and interact with one another which is referred to as *mapping*. The family counselor ultimately attempts to change the dysfunctional relationships within the family, causing it to stabilize into healthier patterns.

When Stanton (1979) and Stanton and Todd (1982) joined the PCGC team, it was with the purpose of applying Structural Family Theory and accompanying techniques to counseling heroin-addicted young adults and their families. In their work with families, Stanton and Todd (1982) made several important observations regarding this population. First, they found that although they were often counseling young adult men and women, these individuals often had a great deal of contact with their family of origin (i.e., parents). See Box 8.3. It is often assumed that as one progresses more deeply into their addiction, the more isolated the addicted loved one become from others. However, this

BOX 8.3

FAMILY TIES

It is often assumed in homes that are impacted by SUDs tend to result in disconnections between family members. Such would be the case with adult sons or daughters who are experiencing substance use disorders (SUDs; Chein et al., 1964). However, the majority of research studies and anecdotal clinical accounts suggest very much the opposite, i.e., adult sons and daughters actually do have regular contact and involvement with their parents (Stanton & Todd, 1982; Stanton et al., 1978). Yet, it is also common for these families to have experienced regular family disruptions (e.g., divorce, child abandonment, and separations). Watch any episode of A & E's reality TV show *Intervention* in order to gain an appreciation for the types of family disruptions that are common in SUD families. However, Cervantes et al. (1988) also found that among 98 consecutive admissions to a urban-based methadone maintenance clinic, 67% of the adult clients currently lived with a family member, 26% lived with a parent, and 75% indicated they had close ties with their mothers. Interestingly, in a study of 532 males with opioid use disorder, clients those who reported less frequent weekly heroin use had more frequent contact with their family of origin, their biological parents, and their grandparents (Tseng et al., 2010).

was not the case with families impacted by opioid use disorders (Stanton & Todd, 1982). This finding also holds true with individuals impacted by SUDs other than opioid use disorders especially for individuals younger than 35 years. Here, it was discovered that 60% to 80% of these young adults had contact with one or both parents on a daily basis (e.g., Bekir et al., 1993; Cervantes et al., 1988; Stanton, 1997).

Structural Family Techniques

Stanton and Todd (1982) recommend a six-step structural model for counseling families. This model assumes that an adolescent or adult son or daughter is the IP who presents with a SUD. The six-step model follows the following sequence:

1. Problem Definition & Contracting: In defining the "problem" the "___ism" label (i.e., alcoholism) is not as important as coming up with a behavioral definition of the problem and behavioral change. Counselor approach: (a) establish an alliance with senior family members, (b) assume a nonblaming stance, (c) SUD should be labeled a "family problem" so everyone works toward the goal of abstinence, and (d) disease/genetic model should be explained as a means of reducing guilt/blame/shame.
2. Establish a Context for a Chemical Free Life: Cessation of alcohol or drug use is a prerequisite for further treatment. Discuss how this will occur within the family and how the family can support this context: (a) refer family to 12-step groups such as Alcoholics Anonymous and Narcotics Anonymous, (b) refer couples to spousal support groups, (c) have no expectations of change (e.g., it is too early in the process to expect change to occur), and (d) be prepared to deal with unresolved grief/loss issues.
3. Ceasing Substance Abuse: This becomes the "moment of truth" as the addicted family member realizes that they must choose between their family and SUD: (a) arrange for detox if necessary and (b) continue to support family and their recovery even if the addicted family member refuses further treatment.

4. Managing Crisis & Stabilization: This is often the most frightening stage. Involves dealing with life without substance, changing family roles, and re-establishing trust.
5. Family Reorganization & Recovery: At this stage, the family reorganizes itself as a recovering family with more appropriate boundaries, with parents in charge, and with the beginnings of healthy separation, as the now-recovering son or daughter is able to assume healthy responsibilities in order to become more independent.
6. Follow-Up: The counselor will periodically follow-up with the family to ascertain how they are functioning and to plan how they will manage relapses or any other setbacks.

This six-step model provides a framework by which counselors can assist families to move toward change. Even if the family member with the SUD refuses treatment, it is important to continue to work with the family. There is a saying among family systems counselors, "Work with the part of the family that's workable." In other words, although some family members may want no part of treatment or counseling, counselors can still be helpful to those family members who do desire help and change.

If a family counselor were to utilize Structural Family techniques to working with Brittany's family, the counselor might try to *restructure* the family by placing the older brother in charge of Brittany (e.g., by taking her to NA meetings and helping her to find a job) and giving permission for her parents to focus on themselves by attending NA or AA groups specific to parents and grandparents. The Structural Family counselor might also *contract* with the family to refrain from providing Brittany with money and pain medication. Finally, a family counselor might *reframe* the parent's enabling behavior as being an example of their willingness to do just about anything to keep Brittany alive. When the counselor feels that they have sufficiently joined with this family, she may introduce another "life-saving" approach which would be to seek other forms of intervention even if it means that Brittany will be court-mandated to treatment.

Family Disease Model

The Family Disease Model grew out of AA, the 12-step program which began in the 1950s to assist families and friends of individuals suffering from AUDs. According to folklore, when AA was in its early beginnings, Lois Wilson, the wife of Bill Wilson (one of the cofounders of AA along with Dr. Bob), would meet with the wives and girlfriends of the men attending the AA meeting (which at the time were being held in Bill and Lois's apartment in New York City). The essence of the Family Disease Model is that alcoholism not only impacts the alcoholic but everyone in their immediate social circle (i.e., family and friends). These family members and friends often fall into roles of codependency which is viewed as a "recognizable pattern of personality traits, predictably found within most members of chemically dependent families" (Cermak, 1986, p. 1). Co dependency traits often includes (a) low self-esteem or self-esteem that is based on controlling the alcoholic loved one; (b) feeling responsible for meeting the needs of other's before oneself; (c) experiencing anxiety and boundary issues around intimacy and separation; (d) being enmeshed in relationships with the alcoholic loved one; and (e) having other symptoms such as denial, depression, anxiety, or hypervigilance (Cermak, 1986). The Family Disease Model also hypothesizes that families adopt several different types of codependency roles as coping strategies. These roles are often seen as survival roles in the dysfunctional alcoholic family.

In addition, there is a body of research which has examined the impact of SUDs on family and child functioning (e.g., Collins et al., 1990; Jacob, 1992; Rotunda et al., 1995; West & Prinz, 1987). There are characteristic roles for both the spouse partner and the children as described in Table 8.2.

The aforementioned roles in Table 8.2 represent a variety of codependency roles. For example, the enabler attempts to hold the family together by making excuses when their loved one is unable to make it into work or unable to pay bills. Some parents even supply their addicted sons or daughters with drugs in order to avoid them needing to purchase drugs from dangerous drug dealers. The controller tries to regulate their loved one's substance use by controlling their access to money or transportation to go out to purchase drugs or alcohol. The placater attempts to reduce tension in the home by acquiescing to their loved one's every demand. The placater will do anything to keep the peace within the home. The waiverer, on the other hand, will threaten their loved one with dire consequences (e.g., kicking them out of the house) if they drink or use drugs "one more time," only to acquiesce or cave once the next substance use episode occurs. The waiverer talks a good game but usually does not hold to their threats. The martyr often uses guilt trips in order to get their loved one into stopping their alcohol or drug use. They will usually complain incessantly to others how their life has been ruined by their addicted love one, but rarely, if ever, will do anything about it. What is common in any of the aforementioned spousal or partner roles is that although the behaviors are meant to somehow try to change their loved one, these strategies usually do not work, which then only adds to the already-existing stress levels. It should not be surprising that codependents often are plagued by many stress-related illnesses (Whitfield, 1989).

The child roles are also considered to be survival roles or attempts to cope in a dysfunctional family system that has been ravaged by SUDs. For example, the family hero will try to detract from parental conflicts or tension by calling attention to their latest accolade or award. Family heroes are often the oldest child within the family, and as adults, it is common for them to assume leadership roles or other positions of responsibility or to go into helping professions (e.g., medicine, social services, and counseling). The family scapegoat draws attention to

TABLE 8.2 Spousal/Partner Roles

Enabler	The enabler tries to hold the family together by taking over the responsibilities of their addicted spouse/partner. The enabler encourages or makes possible negative behaviors
Controller	The controller attempts to regulate or limit their loved one's access to money, credit cards, and checkbooks in an effort to prevent him or or from buying alcohol or drugs
Placater	The placater tries to maintain the peace in the family at all costs, by keeping tensions or conflicts from mounting. To accomplish this, the placater gives in or acquiesces to their loved one's every wish
Waiverer	The waiverer vacillates or flip-flops between threatening their loved one with divorce, expulsion from the home, etc., one minute while withdrawing the threat the next minute, as if nothing happened
Martyr	The martyr blames their substance-using significant other for creating all their misery and lot in life. While the martyr is adepts at blame and finger-pointing, they rarely do anything about their plight, other than to complain

themselves by negative acting out behavior that is displayed at school or in the community (which often results in legal difficulties). The scapegoat is particularly adept at getting into trouble at the most inopportune moments which serves to divert attention from parental conflict. If Mom and Dad are fighting at the dinner table, it is the scapegoat who will knock over their milk in order to draw attention away from the argument. The family clown-mascot role is characterized by attempts to diffuse parental conflicts by joking or comic stunts to draw attention away from whatever tension the family may be experiencing at the moment. The lost child is the quiet child, who withdraws from family conflict, hides in their room, and otherwise keeps a low profile. These children tend to internalize family tensions and conflicts. Although these alcoholic family roles are often attributed to Sharon Wegsheider-Cruze (Wegsheider, 1981), they were originally developed by well-known family therapist, Virginia Satir (1988; Satir et al., 1988) who was working with families impacted by cancer. She discovered that children would adopt these roles after one of their parents had been diagnosed with cancer. It is noteworthy that children in stressful family situations will tend to adopt similar survival roles.

Family Disease Model Techniques

Since this model examines how SUDs impact all family members which then results in all family members adopting particular roles in order to cope with the impact of the disease, it is important that counselors first explore how these roles play out with each particular family member without blaming or judging the family. Instead, it is important that counselors empathizes with the family's attempts to cope with the SUD before encouraging them to change these attitudes and behaviors. For example, trying to get a spouse or partner to attend AA or NA will be a difficult task if they do not see a rationale for the recommendation that they attend meetings.

The essential message that would be given to the nonalcoholic, nonaddicted spouses, partners, and/or family members attending AA or NA would be "detach with love, take care of yourself while letting go and allowing your loved one to take care of him or herself." That can be a tall order to someone who has been accustomed to being the caretaker. Therefore, it is important that counselor exercise patience as well as empathy. With children, especially those who have taken on the role of the family hero, it is important for counselors to give them permission to be a child or adolescent and not have to take on the burden and stress of constantly being the overachiever.

With regard to Brittany's family (described earlier), using a Family Disease Model perspective, it becomes clear to the counselor that both Brittany's parents and her siblings have adopted particular roles in response to her opioid use disorder. Her parents have obviously become Brittany's enablers while her older brother Frank has stepped into the "hero" role, shortly after his brother's death, while Brittany's sister, Eva, has become the "lost child" of the family. Frank is usually very outspoken about how "Brittany has ruined the family," while Eva usually does not express her apprehensions. The role of the family counselor would be to try to encourage the family to let go of unhealthy codependent family roles and to adopt healthier roles. For example, rather than enabling Brittany by giving her money and painkillers, they could help her by encouraging treatment. Overall, the message to the family members is "take care of yourself first." This is not dissimilar to AA or NA's recommendation that family and significant others "detach with love."

Behavioral Family Model

Behavioral models examine ways in which families or partners inadvertently or unintentionally reinforce their loved one's drinking or drug use behaviors. There have been several research studies that have determined verbal communication, verbal output, and attention which *increases* around the topic of drinking in couples where there is an alcoholic partner (Becker & Miller, 1976; Billings et al., 1979; Frankenstein et al., 1985; Hersen et al., 1973). Interaction patterns also differed depending on the gender of the person with the AUD. For example, Haber and Jacob (1997) found that when a woman's alcoholic drinking tended to result in more relationship problems whereby these couples experienced more negative interactions than would occur with a male's alcoholic drinking. Generally, men with AUDs experienced fewer negative interactions with their partners when they were drinking. It is also common for spouses to withdraw from their alcoholic spouse when they are drinking believing that this will somehow encourage abstinence, however, research suggests quite the opposite, that is, that assertive and engaged spousal coping was associated with reduced drinking (McCrady et al., 2002; Moos et al., 1990; Orford et al., 1975).

Barbara McCrady has done extensive clinical and research work with couples experiencing SUDs and has developed several techniques for counseling couples where one or both partners are actively using. Her stance is that couples treatment should begin with the very first contact or first session. (The prevalent view in the addictions treatment field for many years was that the addict or alcoholic needed to establish stable and consistent abstinence/recovery first before any couples or family counseling could be initiated.) Working with couples from the onset of treatment, however, provides several advantages. First, it allows both partners to participate in the behavioral change process rather than focusing just on individual partner who has the SUD. Second, couples therapy also allows the couple to reinforce one another (both in session and between sessions) for positive behavior change and to find shared activities that do not revolve around drinking. Third, couples find they are able to communicate more positively with one another, Fourth, couples who participated in couples therapy were better able to identify the role each other plays in maintaining or reinforcing substance use. Fifth, couples therapy allows partner to problem-solve and resolve conflicts together (McCrady et al., 2012, 2013). Here, research indicates that couples who have participated in counseling together had lower rates of domestic violence than those who participated in individual therapy alone (O'Farrell et al., 2004; Schumm et al., 2009). McCrady et al. (2012) discovered that similar to how individuals impacted by SUDs make several key changes as they are going through addictions treatment, so too does the significant others or partners. For example, family members and significant others who participate in couples/family counseling often benefit by

(a) recognizing that their loved one has a SUD that requires change;
(b) understanding and supporting positive behavioral changes in their partner;
(c) increasing awareness of family member's patterns of behaving and thinking; that might trigger substance use in their loved one;
(d) developing emotional, cognitive, and behavioral skills that enhances motivation to change and to support positive changes;
(e) developing expectations of positive behavioral changes (derived from McCrady et al., 2012, 2013)

Behavioral Family Techniques

From a behavioral perspective, family counselors are interested in how the family may be inadvertently *positively reinforcing* alcohol or drug use behaviors. The best example of this is how Brittany's parents would give her money and painkiller medications in order to dissuade her from going down to unsafe neighborhoods to purchase prescription opioids and/or black-tar heroin.

A Behavioral Family counselor would focus on changing the reinforcement patterns such that Brittany would be rewarded for any positive behaviors (e.g., days when Brittany does not use, or when she goes out looking for a job). It is important that Brittany not be given money as a reward because that may be a trigger for her to go and purchase prescription opioids or heroin, so instead it would be recommended that the parents reward Brittany with verbal praise or making her favorite dinner or taking her out for a movie. Behavioral Family counseling would be especially helpful once Brittany detoxes and completes a residential treatment program by helping the family to develop new ways to relate to one another in which the parents could reinforce Brittany's efforts to work on her recovery such as going to NA meetings or talking with her sponsor. Through Behavioral Family and Couples counseling, significant others are taught how to refrain from conflictual communication (which could potentially trigger a relapse) and to focus more on reinforcing positive behaviors. For example, rather than a spouse or parent scolding their loved one for not attending an AA or NA meeting, they would be taught to comment positively when their loved one does attend a meeting by saying something like, "Whenever you come home from a meeting, you seem happy, like a weight's been lifted off your shoulders!"

Community Reinforcement and Family Training

Community Reinforcement and Family Training (CRAFT) was originated by Robert Meyers, PhD (Meyers et al., 2001), for the purpose of helping families cope with a loved one's SUD. CRAFT utilizes several techniques to help families cope. First, CRAFT helps families to refrain from contentious arguing and criticisms and instead to use more positive communication skills and to look for "windows of opportunity" when concerns about alcohol or drug use can be expressed without criticism, anger, or judgment. Instead of "you were drunk and stoned when you came home last night. You're going to end up being a drunk and druggies just like your father," CRAFT would recommend to wait for a more opportune or receptive moment to say something like "I'm concerned because you seemed to have a lot to drink last night." By teaching families how to communicate more positively, they are thereby avoiding critical, name-calling, blaming, and other negative statements. Instead, family members are encouraged to utilize the following communication skills: (1) be brief (i.e., avoid lengthy lectures or preaching, instead make statements brief and to the point); (2) be positive (state what behaviors you want, rather than criticizing, blaming or overgeneralizing); (3) be specific (rather than making vague statements, describe the behaviors you would like to see); (4) describe your feelings in a calm, nonjudgmental, and nonaccusatory way; (5) offer an understanding statement (e.g., express empathy and understanding to your loved one and their struggle with SUDs); (6) accept partial responsibility for your loved one's behavior (family members may cite a small piece of the problem for which they can take responsibility, e.g.,

"I know I've been too lenient and looked the other way, hoping that things would get better, that's my fault."); and (7) offer to help (by asking your loved one, "How can I best help you?" especially in an honest, genuine way; Center for Substance Abuse Treatment [CSAT], 2006; Smith & Meyers, 2004).

CRAFT also emphasizes the use of *natural consequences*. For example, instead of getting the intoxicated loved one into bed when they come home under the influence, it is suggested to leave the person wherever they pass out. This strategy is designed to help stop enabling behaviors. Also, CRAFT utilizes positive reinforcement but finding alternative behaviors or activities that do not involve alcohol or drug use and helping to promote those alternatives. In the HBO video series *Addiction* (Meyers, 2007), there is a segment on CRAFT in which a grandmother is coached on how to utilize CRAFT principles with her young adult grandson, Doug. In coming up with ways to reinforce Doug for nonusing behaviors, the grandmother mentions that Doug used to play the guitar and had expressed interest in playing the drums. The counselor and grandmother then discuss how to use these interests as positive reinforcement for the grandson.

Finally, the CRAFT approach is really about helping family members. Meyers provides a list of *Five Things to Know About Coping With a Loved One's Unhealthy Behavior* which are as follows:

1. Your love has power.
2. You are not alone.
3. You can catch more flies with honey than with vinegar.
4. You have as many tries as you want. Relationships are a process.
5. You can live a happier life whether or not your loved one sobers up (Meyers p. 159 in Hoffman & Froemke, 2007a).

These coping statements are really about empowering family members and providing hope (family members can learn techniques that can help motivate their loved one to recovery) and that they are not alone in their struggles. The emphasis is also on helping family members try new approaches and techniques in order to break old ways of communicating that have become totally ineffective.

There are several advantages and disadvantages to CRAFT. The main advantage is that this approach is considered to be one of the least coercive approaches to help motivate family members or other loved ones to accept treatment. CRAFT also offers several ways to help loved ones communicate concerns about alcohol or drug use. CRAFT is also very advantageous in supporting loved ones and making them aware that they are not alone in their struggle. The main disadvantage is that this approach is not applicable to everyone. For example, in instances where there may be a more immediate danger of overdose or where an inpatient detox is usually the safest choice, there may not be enough time to teach the basics of the CRAFT approach. Although CRAFT is a sound evidenced-based approach when a loved one is actively abusing substances, this is not to say that CRAFT might not be useful in supporting the family once their loved one is in recovery because it really does help to eliminate dysfunctional communication patterns.

CRAFT is also helpful for partners/spouses as it allows them to focus on their own reactions to their loved one's drinking or drug use behavior (Meyers et al., 2001, 2002; Smith et al., 2004). By encouraging family members to alter negative communication/confrontations, by refraining from specific enabling behaviors, and by positively reinforcing non-substance use behaviors, CRAFT assists these spouses/partners to change how they respond to their loved one. Dittrich and Trapold (1984; Dittrich, 1993) developed a brief treatment package that they utilized with a sample of 52 women who were living with a SUD partner. Following this brief group counseling intervention, the women had significantly reduced enabling behaviors and also reported reduced levels of depression and anxiety. In yet another treatment program, Thomas et al. (1994, 1996) were able to identify enabling behavior of 68 spouse living with a SUD partner, and, through a combined approach of psychoeducation and counseling, there were reductions in enabling behaviors.

Considerations Regarding Enabling

Enabling is a particular type of behavior that reinforces drinking and drug use behavior. As defined by Doweiko (2009), enabling is "knowingly behaving in such a way as to make it possible for another person to continue to use chemicals, without having to pay the natural consequences for his or her substance use disorder" (p. 291). In addition, enabling is often based on a set of beliefs that one must tolerate, minimize substance use, or do whatever it takes to support their partner no matter how severe their drinking or drug use is. In some instances, enabling emanates from guilt or fear. Therefore, enabling can easily be viewed from both a behavioral as well as a cognitive-behavioral framework. From a behavioral perspective, specific enabling behaviors are examined while, from a cognitive-behavioral perspective, beliefs that underlie enabling behaviors are examined. A common enabling pattern among parents who have an adolescent or young adult who is active in their SUD and living in their home; is to provide that son or daughter with money or access to credit cards as a means to assuage the parent's guilt for some past transgression (e.g., infidelity, separation/divorce, and past parental substance use). The absolute worst-case scenario is when parents condone substance use or will drink or smoke cannabis with them, rationalizing "what's the harm with having a beer or smoking a joint with my son/daughter. It's better than their shooting up heroin." Nothing positive comes from enabling, yet many parents get caught up in the illusion that enabling behaviors will somehow prevent a worse outcome (e.g., an overdose, injury, or arrest).

Family members often find themselves in a predicament of not knowing how to help their loved one who is struggling with a SUD. There is often a thin line between what is considered *helping* versus that which would be considered *enabling*. In addition, a few decades ago, it was common for counselors to conclude that enabling behaviors on the part of the non alcohol/substance spouse, partner, or parent was evidence of pathological personality traits (e.g., dependent personality disorder or traits) that caused them to engage in irrational enabling behaviors. More recently, however, the prevailing view is that enabling behaviors are normal reactions to the stress caused by a loved one who is experiencing a SUD (Asher & Brissett, 1988; Haaken, 1990; Hands & Dear, 1994; Miller, 1994). Yet, it is also important to keep in mind that not all families exhibit enabling behaviors and some are able to take on an opposite, "tough-love" type of approach. Rotunda and Doman (2001) have advocated that the terms *codependency* and *enabling* stop being used synonymously and that codependency is a pejorative label that should be totally eliminated. As Rotunda and Doman point out, "*having* a problem is not the same as *being* the problem, an implication of extending the disease model to *codependent* family members..." (p. 259). With this in mind, it is important to properly assess and treat enabling behaviors. With regard to assessment, Rotunda (1996) has developed the Behavioral Enabling Scale (BES). The BES is composed of two subscales: the *enabling behaviors subscale* and the *enabling beliefs subscale* (see Appendix 8.2). The *enabling behaviors subscale* consists of 20 items to which participants respond on a 5-point Likert scale (ranging from 1 = not at all, 2 = rarely, 3 = sometimes, 4 = often, and 5 = very often) and contains items related to a variety of enabling behaviors such as giving the partner money to buy alcohol or drugs, making excuses for partner when they were too impaired to execute obligations, and helping the partner by nursing their hangover. The *enabling beliefs scale* consists of 13 items to which participants respond on a 4-point Likert scale ranging from −2 *strongly disagree* to +2 *strongly agree.* The *enabling beliefs subscale* contains items pertaining to one's beliefs regarding enabling, such as it being the nonaddicted partner's responsibility to change their loved one's drinking or drug use or the nonaddicted partner feeling and their responsibility to hold the relationship together, or the belief that their partner cannot get along without their help. Although score interpretation is unspecified, it is assumed that scores on the *enabling behaviors subscale* that fall between 80 and 100 are indicative of extreme enabling behaviors and scores on the *enabling beliefs subscale* that fall between 39 and 52 are indicative of extreme endorsement of enabling beliefs. In a validation study of the BES, Rotunda et al. (2004) found that a higher incidence of enabling beliefs correlated with increased rates of enabling behaviors.

As mentioned earlier, whenever possible it is important that non-SUD family members participate in AA and/or NA in addition to whatever counseling they receive. Be aware that there are some AA and NA meetings that are directed more to spouses and partners, while there are other meetings that are directed more to parents and grandparents. In either instance, the message tends to be similar, that is, "detach with love." See Box 8.4. It is no coincidence that the First Step of AA/NA and AA and NA are the same, that is, "We admitted we are powerless over alcohol/drugs, and our lives had become unmanageable." Enabling behaviors are the exact opposite of "admitting we are powerless" as families/spouses/partners often labor under the false belief that their enabling behavior will somehow protect their loved one and keep them safe. Instead, AA and NA promote that families adopt the 3 Cs: "I didn't Cause it, I can't Control it, I can't Change it." By adopting the 3 Cs, one is essentially admitted they are powerless to change and control their loved one's SUD.

Kasl's 16 Step Approach to Codependency

Dr. Charlotte Kasl (2020) has developed a rather unique approach to treating and managing codependency. Instead of viewing codependency from the lens of addiction (i.e., a loved one being *addicted* to helping someone with a SUD or some other dysfunctional behavior), Kasl put forth a viewpoint that perceives codependency as a form of internalized oppression that can best be viewed within a cultural perspective that takes into account sexism, racism, classism, and homophobia. The 16 Steps that Kasl developed are holistic and fluid in that it evolves as the client is evolving, growing, and changing In some respects, the 16 Steps are based on the 12 Steps of AA, however, they are empowerment-minded and go beyond the traditional 12 Steps. For example, Step 4 of the traditional 12 Steps asks individuals to take

BOX 8.4

DETACHING WITH LOVE

Detaching from a loved one's substance use disorder (SUD) is often easier said than done. Family members, spouses, and partners often struggle to let go of their loved one's substance use laboring under the belief that they can somehow control their use or prevent them from relapsing or that their loved one is incapable of recovering without their hypervigilance and scrutiny. Yet, detachment may appear to someone not familiar with SUD recovery to be selfish or uncaring. Nothing can be further from the truth, as put forth by Beverly Conyers (2015) who has developed a list of recommendations of reasons and ways that nonaddicted family members and significant others can detach. First, Conyers feels that detachment allows "fresh air" into the relationship or an opportunity to let go of unhealthy patterns of interaction such as nagging, crying, scolding, or threatening. Second, detachment allows the addicted loved one to face consequences of their substance use which provides opportunities for learning from these experiences. Often family members or significant others are the one's who suffer the consequences (e.g., when a loved one pays a DUI fine or household bills). Third, detachment helps to save the addicted loved one from the potentially harmful effects of enabling by having the opportunity to face problems themselves. Fourth, detachment empowers the addicted love to take on adult responsibilities, for example, to become financially self-supporting which also allows them to experience the satisfaction of "living life on life's terms" and behaving like a mature adult. Fifth, detachment reduces the shame that the addicted love one often feels for having ruined their lives and from continually disappointing others. Finally, true detachment is truly an expression of unconditional love. It is similar to saying to the loved one, "I believe you have the intelligence, determination and inner strength to recover...you can handle this yourself."

Source: Adapted from Conyers, B. (2015, September 15). *Detaching with love: Eight reasons why detaching is good for your addicted love one*. Hazelden Betty Ford Center.

a "fearless moral inventory," whereas Kasl's Fourth Step suggests, "We examine our beliefs, addictions and dependent behavior in the context of living in a hierarchical, patriarchal culture." Similarly, Kasl's Eighth Step recommends, "We make a list of people we have harmed and people who have harmed us, and take steps to clear out negative energy by making amends and sharing our grievances in a respectful way."

The advantage of Kasl's approach is that it takes a cultural diversity perspective into account when working with clients, rather than pathologizing or judging their behavior as abnormal or aberrant (Kasl, 2020). Therefore, this model seeks to empower clients as they evolve and change codependent behaviors.

Assessing Families

When assessing families, it is important not only to get a thorough history of the family's presenting complaint but also to obtain history of the family or couple and some of the difficulties or adversities they may have faced. In the example of Brittany, the death of her older brother plays a central role in the dynamics of this family. Similarly, consider a father of a teenage son who is smoking cannabis and drinking on weekends who takes a very protective and strict approach toward his son's substance use because the father's brother had died of a drug overdose two years ago. In this instance, family history is very important to gaining a more complete picture of the father's reaction to his son's substance use. Often when addiction counselors are seeing families for the first time, they are seeing them at their lowest or most desperate point. Therefore, it is helpful for counselors to also get a sense of the family's strengths, things they are most proud of, and their hopes for the future. Counselors must also take race, ethnicity, religious, social class, and cultural influences into account, as these factors will certainly shape family values, beliefs, and attitudes. In order for counselors to have an appreciation of the influences of race, ethnicity culture, we highly recommend that you read *Ethnicity and Family Therapy* by McGoldrick et al. (2014) which contains chapters on treating Native Americans, African Americans, Immigrant African families, indigenous Hawaiian families, Latino Americans, Jewish families (including Israeli, Orthodox, and Russian Jewish families), and a variety of European American and Slavic American families. A criticism of examining ethnic-racial-cultural uniqueness is that there may be a danger of stereotyping families. For example, if we were to say that all Latinx families held the same religious or familial values, we would be missing the important nuances between Mexican American, Cuban American, and Puerto Rican families who may be similar in terms of a common language but are different when it comes to culture.

You are probably familiar with the popular expression, "A picture's worth a thousand words." This familiar phrase is very much applicable to the use of genograms as an assessment tool that can be used with families. Family genograms (McGoldrick et al., 2020) are helpful in examining interactional and behavioral patterns within the family milieu. For example, by gathering information about how the family interacts, we may see enabling patterns and other types of dysfunctional behavior. We may see examples of who colludes or allies with whom, or whether there may be enmeshed relationships between a father and teenage daughter or a mother and teenage son. Enmeshed relationships are also ripe for triangulation as "third parties" get unwittingly drawn into conflicts between parents and their teenage sons or daughters. The genogram can also tell us about family roles as we begin to hear which children have taken on roles of hero, scapegoat, clown-mascot, or lost child. Appendix 8.3 provides an example of a four-generation genogram in which the oldest son is the IP and he is experiencing a cocaine use disorder (noted by double lines). Although neither parents of this oldest son are experiencing any substance

LEARNING ACTIVITY 8.5
HELPING VERSUS ENABLING

Imagine a family that has a son or daughter is actively using alcohol and drugs, then develop a list of behaviors that would be examples of helping and a list of behaviors that would be examples of enabling. Also, consider the following scenario: Gina is 25 years old and has just completed a residential treatment program for her Benzodiazepine and alcohol use disorders. She is now back living at home with her parents. Gina was fired from her last job because she was constantly calling in sick (because she was too hung over). Gina's aftercare plan indicates hat she will attend AA and NA meetings and attend an IOP. Unfortunately, Gina had totaled her car (while DUI), so she does not have transportation. She is pressuring her parents to buy her a car so she can get to meetings and IOP. Her mother feels this is a reasonable request for help, however, her father feels this enabling. What are your opinions? Discuss with your classmates.

use issues, it is noted that there is a paternal aunt who is depicted as having an alcohol use disorder and an uncle (on the mother's sides of the family) who is experiencing an opioid use disorder. The format and symbols that are used to compose a genogram are also included at the bottom of Appendix 8.3.

ADOLESCENT FAMILY TREATMENT

Adolescent Family Treatment Models

Adolescents who develop SUDs are especially problematic, and therefore, require specialized treatment. Just as there are various types of inpatient or residential SUD treatment programs for adults, so too there are residential treatment programs specifically for adolescents. Adolescent treatment programs, in general, tend to be more highly structured and activity oriented. In addition, it is imperative that adolescent treatment programs contain a strong family counseling component because without the help and support of the teenager's family, relapse becomes more likely. Through treatment, families can make changes toward becoming part of the solution rather than being part of the problem. The following are a few examples of adolescent family treatment models:

Multisystemic or Multidimensional Family Therapy

This approach is primarily a family-based outpatient, SUD model that requires close collaboration between the adolescent, their family as well as contacts with the adolescent's school and juvenile justice system (if they are mandated to treatment by the courts). The family counselor is responsible for meeting with the adolescent, with the adolescent and their family members, and also with school counselors and juvenile justice officers on an ongoing basis. The goal of these sessions is to provide structure to the adolescent's life by helping to reinforce the family, school, and community's rules and expectations. The other goal is to help prevent the adolescent's SUD from progressing or escalating to a point where residential treatment would become necessary. The HBO video series *Addiction* (Hoffman & Froemke, 2007b) provides a good video illustration of the Multisystemic Family Therapy approach.

Functional Family Therapy

The Functional Family Therapy (FFT) approach was created by therapists Alexander and Parsons (1982) who at the time were working with youth who exhibited a variety of conduct disorders. FFT utilizes a combination of behavioral techniques along with a family systems perspective. From the very onset, FFT family therapists work with both the adolescent and their parents and siblings with the goal of examining how their day-to-day interactions function to regulate their relationships. The behavioral aspect of FFT explores the "payoffs" or reinforcers that maintain or reinforce certain maladaptive behaviors between family members (Waldron & Turner, 2008; Waldron et al., 2001). Alexander and Parsons (1982) describe three behavioral patterns of interaction that are often experienced by families impacted by an adolescent son or daughter's substance use. They are (1) *merging*, which is meant to increase closeness and contact (e.g., even in arguing with one another, family members are engaged or connected to one another); (2) *separating,* which is meant to create distance and autonomy (e.g., an adolescent may have very little interaction with their parents in order to obtain more independence); and (3) *midpointing,* which involves a combination of both merging and separating behaviors (e.g., the adolescent may at one time say, "Pay attention to me, listen to me," while at other times may be saying, "Go away, leave me alone"). According to the FFT model, it is the very nature of these interpersonal family relationships that create problems within the family. The challenge of the FFT approach is to encourage family members to gain a new perspective in which they can look at their own roles in maintaining certain dysfunctional behaviors.

Most of the research on FFT has focused on its impact on acting out or externalizing behaviors (i.e., criminal behaviors); for example, Sexton and Turner (2011) found significant reductions in felony and violent crimes. One study focused specifically on utilized FFT with substance use (Waldron et al., 2001) and found significant reductions in adolescent marijuana use as a result of FFT therapy. Furthermore, the greatest reductions in marijuana use occurred in the families that participated in a combination of both FFT and cognitive behavioral therapy.

NOTES FROM THE FIELD

Carolann Kane, MA, LCADC

Carolann Kane is the Executive Director of the Samaritan Center in Manasquan, NJ, an outpatient mental health and SUD counseling program. The Samaritan Center counselors treat both individuals with SUDs as well as family members who sometimes will seek help because of concerns for their loved one's substance use. The Samaritan Center is designed to provide counseling to family members at various entry points and utilizes supportive counseling and 12-Step Facilitated Counseling (encouraging AA and NA involvement) and other counseling approaches described in this chapter. According to Carolann, the main challenge is helping the family member to detach from their loved one's behavior and to develop strategies that help stop enabling behavior by allowing the substance users to experience natural consequences of their alcohol and/or substance use. Many family members seek counseling feeling guilty and responsible for their loved one's SUD, therefore, it is important that counselors work with them on letting go of these feelings that might prevent them from taking productive steps.

SUMMARY

SUDs do not occur in a vacuum. Not only does the SUD person suffer but so do their families and significant others. Families can often become part of the solution or part of the problem when it comes to SUDs, therefore, it is imperative that families and significant others be involved both in motivating loved ones to enter treatment, also while they are in treatment and then when they return home. This chapter reviews some of the major theoretical models that conceptualize how SUDs impact on family members and how these models can be utilized to help bring about change. In addition to presenting basic conceptualization of Family Systems, Structural Family Theory, the Family Disease Model, and Behavioral/Cognitive Behavioral Theory, we also presented information on the CRAFT approach and Kasl's approach for treating codependency as well as adolescent family treatment approaches.

RESOURCES

Anderson, C. M., & Stewart, S. (1983). *Mastering resistance: A practical guide to family therapy*. Guilford Publications.

Bekir, P., McLellan, T., Childress, A. R., & Gariti, P. (1993). Role reversals in families of substance misusers: A transgenerational phenomenon. *International Journal of Addictions, 28*(7), 613–630. https://doi.org/10.3109/10826089309039652

Brown, S., & Lewis, V. (1999). *The alcoholic family in recovery: A developmental model*. Guilford Press.

Families and Addictions (Website): This website was developed by the Substance Abuse and Mental Health Services Administration (SAMHSA) and lists a number of publications. https://www.samhsa.gov/find-help/national-helpline

Family Behavior Therapy (Website): This guide to behavioral family therapy is presented by the National Institute of Health's (NIH) National Institute on Drug Abuse (NIDA) https://www.drugabuse.gov/publications/principles-drug-addiction-treatment-research-based-guide-third-edition/evidence-based-approaches-to-drug-addiction-treatment/behavioral-5

Family Genogram Programs (Websites): These websites provide programs for writing creating genograms. Some sites provide free samples, others charge usage fees. www.genogramanalytics.com/index.html

How to Make a Genogram (Website): This is from WikiHow.com and provides a step-by-step model for creating a genogram. https://www.wikihow.com/Make-a-Genogram

Introduction to the Genogram: https://www.genopro.com/genogram/

Jackson, J. K. (1954). The adjustment of the family to the crisis of alcoholism. *Quarterly Journal of Studies on Alcohol, 15*(4), 562–586.

Johnson, V. (1973). *I'll quit tomorrow*. Harper & Row.

McCrady, B. S., Owens, M. D., & Brovko, J. M. (2013). Couples and family treatment methods. In B. S. McCrady & E. E. Epstein (Eds.), *Addictions: A comprehensive guidebook* (2nd ed., pp. 454–481). Oxford University Press.

McGoldrick, M., Giordano, J., & Garcia-Preto, N. (2014). *Ethnicity and family therapy* (3rd ed.). Guilford Publications.

Stanton, M. D., & Todd, T. C. (1982). *The family therapy of drug abuse and addiction*. Guilford Press.

Steinglass, P., Bennett, L. A., Wolin, S. J., & Reiss, D. (1987). *The alcoholic family*. Basic Books.

Substance Abuse Treatment and Family Therapy (Website): This one of SAMHSA's Treatment Improvement Protocols which provides in depth information on family therapy. https://www.ncbi.nlm.nih.gov/books/NBK64269/

What is a genogram? (You Tube video): This brief video describes what a genogram is and how it can be used in counseling. https://www.youtube.com/watch?v=MuXvG9tbUMs

Wegsheider, S. (1981). *Another chance: Hope and health for the alcoholic family*. Science & Behavior Books.

Woititz, J. G. (1983). *Adult children of alcoholics*. Health Communications Inc.

KEY REFERENCES

Only key references appear in the print edition. The full reference list appears in the digital product on Springer Publishing Connect: connect.springerpub.com/content/book/978-0-8261-3586-5/chapter/ch08

Ackerman, R. (1981). *Perfect daughters: Adult daughters of alcoholics*. Health Communications.

Anderson, C. M., & Stewart, S. (1983). *Mastering resistance: A practical guide to family therapy*. Guilford Publications.

Brown, S., & Lewis, V. (1999). *The alcoholic family in recovery: A developmental model*. Guilford Press.

Cavaiola, A. (2000). In search of a new metaphor for the impact of drug abuse on families. *Family Therapy, 27*(2), 81–87. https://doi.org/10/1080/08897077.2015.1029207

Halpern, S. C., Schuch, F. B., Scherer, J. N., Sordi, A. O., Pachado, M., Dalbosco, C., Fara, L, Pechansky, F., Kessler, F., & Von Diemen, L. (2018). Child maltreatment and illicit substance abuse: A systematic review and meta-analysis of longitudinal studies. *Child Abuse Review, 27*, 344–360. https://doi.org/10.1002/car.2534

McGoldrick, M., Giordano, J., & Garcia-Preto, N. (2014). *Ethnicity and family therapy* (3rd ed.). Guilford Publications.

Meyers, R. J., Miller, W. R., & Smith, J. E. (2001). Community reinforcement and family training (CRAFT). In R. J. Meyers & W. R. Miller (Eds.), *A community reinforcement approach to addiction treatment* (pp. 147–160). Cambridge University Press.

O'Farrell, T. J., Murphy, C. M., Stephan, S. H., Fals-Stewart, W., & Murphy, M. (2004). Partner violence before and after couples-based alcoholism treatment for male alcoholic patients: The role of treatment involvement and abstinence. *Journal of Consulting and Clinical Psychology, 72*(2), 202–217. https://doi.org/10.1037/0022-006X.72.2.202

Rotunda, R. J., West, L., & O'Farrell, T. J. (2004). Enabling behavior in a clinical sample of alcohol-dependent clients and their partners. *Journal of Substance Abuse Treatment, 26*(4), 269–276. https://doi.org/10.1016/j.jsat.2004.01.007

Stanton, M. D., & Todd, T. C. (1982). *The family therapy of drug abuse and addiction*. Guilford Press.

Stanton, M. D., Todd, T. C., Heard, D. B., Kirshner, S., Kleiman, J. I., Mowatt, D. T., & Vandeusen, J. M. (1978). Heroin addiction as a family phenomena: A new conceptual model. *American Journal of Drug and Alcohol Abuse, 5*(2), 125–150. https://doi.org/10.3109/00952997809027993

Steinglass, P., Bennett, L. A., Wolin, S. J., & Reiss, D. (1987). *The alcoholic family*. Basic Books.

Tseng, K. C., Hemenway, D., Kawachi, I., & Subramanian, S. V. (2010). Family ties and the frequency of heroin use. *Journal of Substance Use, 15*(1), 60–74. https://doi.org/10.3109/14659890903010501

Wolin, S. J., Bennett, L. A., Noonan, D. L., & Teitelbaum, M. A. (1980). Disrupted family rituals: A factor in the intergenerational transmission of alcoholism. *Journal of Studies on Alcohol, 41*(1), 199–214. https://doi.org/10.15288/jsa.1980.41.199

APPENDIX 8.1

FAMILY TREATMENT AGENDA (FOR INPATIENT OR INTENSIVE OUTPATIENT PROGRAM)

Beginning stage: 1–5 weeks
• Commit to treatment.
• Understand that a substance use disorder is a chronic illness.
• Support abstinence.
• Begin to identify and discontinue behaviors that support substance use.
• Learn about the family support groups:
• Al-Anon (www.al-anon.alateen.org)
• Nar-Anon (www.naranon.com)
• Families Anonymous (www.familiesanonymous.org)
Middle stage: 6–20 weeks
• Assess the relationship with the client.
• Develop a realistic perspective on addiction-related behaviors so the family member remains involved with the client but establishes some protective personal distance.
• Work to eliminate behaviors that encourage the client's substance use (i.e., enabling behaviors).
• Move past behaviors that are primarily a response to the client's substance use (i.e., codependence).
• Seek new ways to enrich the family member's life.
• Begin practicing new communication methods.
Advanced stage: 21+ weeks
• Work to develop a healthy, balanced lifestyle that supports the client and addresses personal needs.
• Exercise patience with recovery.
• Evaluate and accept changes, adaptations, and limitations.

Source: Derived in part from the Matrix Center. (1989). *The matrix model of outpatient chemical dependency treatment: Family education guidelines and handouts*. The Matrix Center.

APPENDIX 8.2

BEHAVIORAL ENABLING SCALE (ROTUNDA ET AL., 2004)

1	2	3	4	5
Not at all	Rarely	Sometimes	Often	Very Often

Enabling Behaviors

1. Partner gave money to client to buy alcohol/drugs.
2. Partner purchased alcohol or drugs for client.
3. Partner taken over client's neglected chores because they were drinking/drugging.
4. Partner lied or made excuses to family/friends to hide client's drinking/drugging.
5. Partner drank/used drugs with client or in client's presence.
6. Partner told client it was okay to drink or use drugs on certain days or for special family or social gatherings.
7. Partner borrowed money to pay bills caused by client's drinking/drug use.
8. Partner changed or cancelled family plans or social activities because client was drinking, using drugs, or hung over.
9. Partner had sex with client when really did not want to because they had been drinking or drugging.
10. Partner asked for help from the police, a judge or lawyer, or other professional to get client out of trouble related to drinking or drug use.
11. Partner threatened client with separation because of the drinking or drug use but but later did not follow through with it.
12. Partner paid lawyer or court fees, or bailed client of jail due to drinking or drug-related offense.
13. Partner helped nurse client through a hangover.
14. Partner cleaned up (vomit, urine, etc.) after client got sick.
15. Partner asked or encouraged family members to ignore or be silent about client's drinking or drug use.
16. Partner helped conceal client's drinking or drug use from employers or co-workers.
17. Partner coaxed client up in the morning to go to work when they were hung over.
18. Partner made excuses to others for client's impaired behavior when they were drinking or high.
19. Partner reassured client that his/her drinking or drug use was not that bad.
20. Partner lied or told half-truth to a physician, counselor, probation officer, judge, and police officer about client's alcohol or drug use, or participation in treatment programs.

1	2	3	4
Strongly Disagree	Disagree	Agree	Strongly Agree

Enabling Beliefs

1. It is my duty to take on more responsibility for home and family obligations than my partner in times of stress.
2. I often feel I should take care of my partner regardless of what they do.
3. I can change my partner's drinking or drug use habits and make them stop if I want.
4. I am one of the main reasons my partner has alcohol or drug abuse problems.
5. It is okay that my partner drinks or uses drugs as long as they control how much they use.
6. Sometimes I like when my partner is drinking or high because they are more affectionate and more able to express positive feelings.
7. I miss certain aspects of our daily lifestyle when my partner stops drinking or using drugs (e.g., socializing, entertaining).
8. I need to do whatever it takes to hold my relationship with my partner together.
9. I often do not do or say anything bout my partner's alcohol or drug use because it might make it worse or cause more conflict/tension.
10. I often ignore, deny, or minimize the seriousness of my partner's alcohol or drug use.
11. I tolerate my partner's drinking or drug use as long as they keep working and earning money.
12. I should do my best to protect my partner from the negative consequences of his/her alcohol or drug use.
13. My partner cannot get along without my help.

Source: Adapted from Rotunda, R. J., West, L., & O'Farrell, T. J. (2004). Enabling behavior in a clinical sample of alcohol-dependent clients and their partners. *Journal of Substance Abuse Treatment, 26*, 269–276. Reproduced with permission of Elsevier.

APPENDIX 8.3

FAMILY GENOGRAM

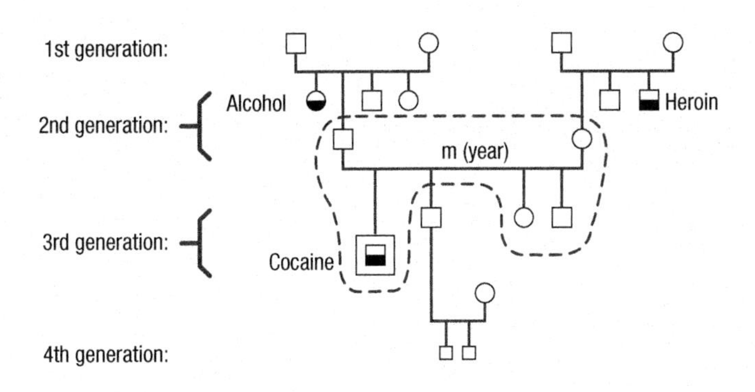

Symbols useful for genograms

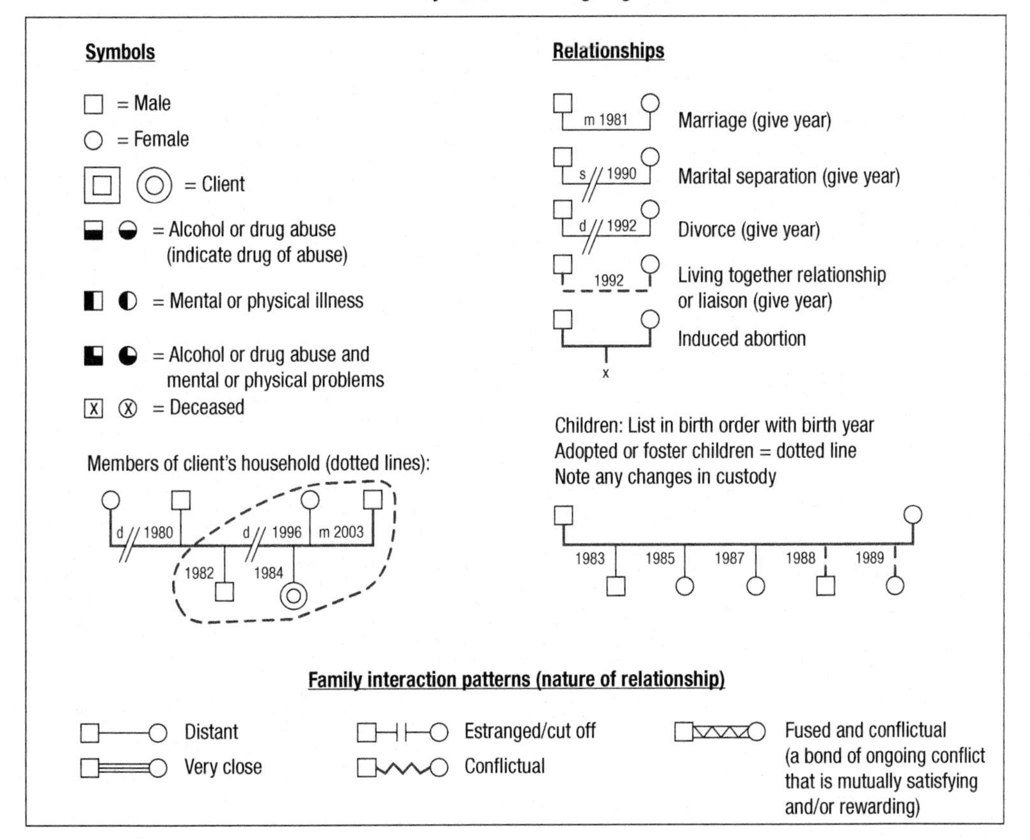

9

MOTIVATIONAL INTERVIEWING

LEARNING OBJECTIVES

This chapter provides an introduction to motivational interviewing (MI), including the spirit of MI, the method of MI, and basic techniques for responding to change talk. Additionally, the Stages of Change Model is reviewed in this chapter. By the end of this chapter, you will be able to:

- identify stages of change;
- describe MI spirit;
- recognize processes that make up the method of MI;
- identity change and sustain talk;
- utilize basic techniques to respond to change talk.

TERMS TO KNOW

acceptance	one of the key aspects of MI spirit that counselors use to communicate affirmation, autonomy support, accurate empathy, and absolute worth
ambivalence	a state in which conflicting motivations for and against change are simultaneously occurring
CAT	commitment, activation, and taking steps—three types of mobilizing change talk
change talk	clients' statements that are supportive of an established change goal
DARN	desire, ability, reason, and need—four types of preparatory change talk
elicit-provide-elicit	a preferred information exchange process in MI that both begins and ends with an exploration of clients' own experiences and perspectives
evocation	one of the central aspects of MI spirit that counselors use to elicit clients' perspectives and motivation for change
expert trap	assuming an expert position and communicating that you, as a counselor, have the best solution to clients' presenting issues
guiding	a communication style that includes elements of directing and following and has the aim of helping clients find their own way

OARS	open question, affirmation, reflection, and summary—four basic skills of client-centered communication
spirit of MI	an underlying set of principles essential to MI: partnership, acceptance, compassion, and evocation

INTRODUCTION

Motivational interviewing (MI) is a collaborative, client- and relationship-oriented approach for initiating and strengthening clients' motivation and commitment to change (Miller, 2000; Miller & Rollnick, 2013). This approach was developed initially in the 1980s as an alternative to traditional methods of addiction treatment that relied primarily on harsh confrontations and aggressive challenges of clients' denial (Miller, 2000). As such, MI is rooted in compassionate connection and meaningful collaboration between counselors and clients. While traditional methods of addiction treatment considered clients' difficulties in achieving change as resistance and denial and deemed it undesirable or detrimental to counseling; MI conceptualized it as *ambivalence* and saw it as an inevitable part of the change process. Essentially, according to MI, the counselor's job is to help clients resolve ambivalence.

MI emphasizes clients' autonomy in the counseling process. Clients' personal choices when making decisions and responsibility for change are seen as critical and are upheld at all times. As a part of MI, counselors are focused on eliciting and strengthening clients' internal motivation, rather than providing clinical expertise and compelling clients to change. MI does consider counselors to be experts on the change process, and it also considers clients to be equally important experts on their own lives. In this collaborative process, clients' motivation and reasons for change are considered key elements for accomplishing desired outcomes, and counselors' role is to assist clients and guide them through this process.

There are many misconceptions about the nature of MI in our field. Some refer to MI as theory, and others see it as a set of skills. In essence, MI is neither, and it is most naturally positioned between those two points (perhaps in the middle). Miller and Rollnick (2009) described MI as a transtheoretical approach that is designed to be used across and in conjunction with many theories. To practice MI, counselors must embody an underlying attitude of care (MI spirit), understand the overall process of change (MI Method), and implement a set of skills (open question, affirmation, reflection, and summary [OARS]) aimed at fostering clients' motivation for change (Miller & Rollnick, 2013).

Additionally, we would like to note that MI is an evidence-based approach. There is a substantial body of literature, including clinical trials and meta-analysis, that indicates MI is effective in treating clients who desire change (Miller & Rollnick, 2013). In addition to the application of MI in the addiction treatment field, this approach was found to be effective across a variety of settings and populations (e.g., medical field; Pietrabissa et al., 2017). However, it is worth noting that the strongest effect size for the use of MI is typically found in addiction treatment settings (Miller & Rollnick, 2013).

In this chapter, we will explore the most essential components of MI and consider how counselors can practice from this perspective and help clients achieve important goals. But before we examine MI deeper, we want to introduce the Stages of Change model (also known as the Transtheoretical Model [TTM]; Prochaska et al., 1992). MI and the Stages of Change model, in many ways, are complimentary of each other, and they are often used together in the addiction treatment field. However, it is important to note that MI and the Stages of Change model are not additions to or extensions of each other; they are separate, standalone approaches. The reason the Stages of Change model is reviewed here is that MI and this model can be used in unison to provide effective care to clients who struggle with addictive disorders. The Stages of Change model helps clinicians understand how and when the change takes place, as well as assess the stage their clients are in, while MI provides a framework for working with clients and increasing their motivation for change.

THE STAGES OF CHANGE MODEL

Stopping the use of substances or altering an addictive behavior usually is not a singular act, but rather, it is a complex process that spans from the point that precedes active consideration of making a change all the way until the attainment of desired goals and achievement of sustainable change. The Stages of Change model (Prochaska et al., 1992) provides a structure to systemically organize this process and help counselors develop treatment plans that are more sensitive to clients' needs and motivations for change. Conceptualizing the process of change in this manner helps counselors understand when and how shifts in clients' attitudes, intentions, and behavior happen. This model emphasizes the need for assessing clients' readiness for change in order to utilize interventions that are responsive to clients' present state. The Stages of Change model describes five distinct stages: (1) *precontemplation,* (2) *contemplation,* (3) *preparation,* (4) *action,* and (5) *maintenance,* through which clients typically progress when attempting to alter their substance use and addictive behaviors (Prochaska & Norcross, 2001). Each stage represents a broad category that encompasses multiple processes that have to be attended for clients to move forward in addressing their problematic behavior.

According to the Stages of Change model, the process of change is progressive but not linear or unidirectional. That is, for clients to achieve a sustainable change, they must progress to the final stage and commit to the newly established patterns, however, clients may begin the change process at any stage (i.e., some clients may start in the precontemplation stage, and others could begin in the preparation stage). Additionally, clients are not expected to make continuous linear progress toward the final stage, but rather, moving forward and backward through stages is considered an inevitable part of the change process. Finally, clients may cycle through the same stage multiple times until the final resolution of ambivalence is achieved. This cycling pattern, or repetitive return to the same stage, should be viewed as a natural part of the change process rather than a failure to adhere to the model. Now, let us review each stage and consider the clinical implications associated with them.

Precontemplation

Clients who are in precontemplation are not considering any changes. This stage is characterized by the lack of awareness for not just a potential solution for the problem but, most often, the existence of the problem in itself. Clients in this stage typically exhibit denial toward having any significant issues and often are annoyed by people in their life (e.g., family, friends, coworkers, and doctors) who may suggest otherwise. Even if the problem is acknowledged in some way, there is no recognition of the need to do anything about it. This stage also includes those clients who wish to make a change but show no intentions of doing anything that would support that wish. Additionally, clients who are referred to counseling as a result of legal or employment issues (e.g., DUI and employee assistance programs), often present in the precontemplation stage. The central theme of clients' presentation in this stage is resistance to recognition or modification of addictive behaviors. Clients in this stage typically are not intending to make any changes within the next 6 months.

CASE EXAMPLE: DAVID—PRECONTEMPLATION

David has been smoking cigarettes for the past 20 years. He started smoking with his friend group when he was 16 years old and has not stopped smoking for a significant period of time since then. David describes himself as a "regular smoker," but when he was asked to specify the amount he smokes, he shared that on a typical day he consumes between one and two packs of cigarettes. During David's last physical exam, his physician expressed serious concerns regarding David's health. David was informed that he was showing signs of early stages of chronic obstructive pulmonary disease, and he is at risk for serious cardiovascular issues. David's initial reaction to the medical news was "All of us will die from something." He also stated that all of his male relatives smoked their whole lives, and many lived into old age. David expressed that he knows smoking is not the best for him but that he never experienced any significant issues as a result of it. He shared that he is able to provide for this family and fulfill all of his duties, and as far as he is concerned there is no need for any changes.

LEARNING ACTIVITY 9.1

What indicators of the precontemplation stage are you able to identify? What questions would you ask David in this stage to incite his contemplation for change?

Contemplation

Awareness that an important problem exists and serious consideration of necessary changes are present in this stage; however, there is a lack of commitment to any concrete action. Clients in this stage consider the pros and cons associated with both maintaining the current behavior and making a change. As a result of this acute awareness of both sides of the argument, clients who are in the contemplation stage experience high levels of ambivalence. Clients are quite prone to being stuck in this stage, and this "stuckness" can persist for long periods of time without initiation of any steps toward change. Two of the main barriers and reasons for clients' difficulty in surpassing this stage are (1) viewing current behavior in a positive light and (2) perceived level of discomfort and energy required for making the desired change. This stage is mostly characterized by meaningful consideration of sustainable problem resolution.

CASE EXAMPLE: DAVID—CONTEMPLATION

David's husband became increasingly worried about David's smoking and started expressing his concerns more often. David's daughter also started frequently commenting on David's yellow fingers and making grimacing facial expressions every time she hugs David when he returns home from work. David shared that since his daughter now is at the age when sports are becoming interesting, it is important for him to be able to teach his daughter and play various sports with her. David expressed disappointment and concern that he is not able to "keep up" with his daughter and husband as much as he expected. David stated that he is starting to recognize the barriers smoking is creating in his life and wants to make a change. However, he expressed doubt in his ability to do it. David described smoking as the most consistent stabilizer of his mood. Also, he added that when he tried stopping a couple of times in the past year, his attempts were unsuccessful, and the process was quite painful.

Preparation

LEARNING ACTIVITY 9.2

What values are the most important in changing David's attitude? What would you say to David to support this change?

This stage is characterized by serious intention to take action and even taking small, preparatory, steps toward change (e.g., removing all alcohol from the household, finding a support group, and asking a partner to be responsible for medication management). Most clients in this stage are planning to make changes within the next month and may have made some unsuccessful steps over the past year. Although typically some action is taken during this stage, a sustainable behavioral modification is not achieved (but clients are showing serious intent to take these steps in the near future). Clients who are in this stage would rank high on both the contemplation and action scales. This stage was called the *decision-making stage* when the model was first introduced.

CASE EXAMPLE: DAVID—PREPARATION

David has informed his family and friends as well as his counselor of his intentions to stop smoking permanently. He also shared his concerns about not succeeding in this task and asked for their support. In addition to the uneasiness and discomfort he fears regarding stopping cigarette smoking, David also is worried about his anxiety and his inability to manage it without cigarettes. He further expressed that he knows he cannot just stop smoking: he stated that he is not a "cold turkey" kind of a person. But he said that he is willing to establish a plan to stop his smoking gradually. He also made an appointment with his physician to explore additional points of support. One of David's friends used nicotine patches to help her quit, and David hopes they have the same effect on him.

LEARNING ACTIVITY 9.3

How would you respond to David's fears about the discomfort associated with stopping his cigarette smoking? What are your thoughts on David's refusal to stop smoking right away?

Action

This stage is marked by concrete behavioral modifications that support the lasting resolution of the clients' identified problems. This stage is the most demanding of clients and requires a significant commitment of time and energy. As a result, the steps taken during this stage are most recognizable and clients are likely to receive external support and recognition for their actions. Clients would be considered to be in the action stage if (1) they reach a previously established criterion of behavior modification (e.g., abstinence from drug use) and (2) they have successfully modified their addictive behavior for a period of time up to 6 months.

CASE EXAMPLE: DAVID—ACTION

Two months after David started decreasing his smoking, he has cut down his nicotine intake to one patch and up to five cigarettes per day. He is proud of his efforts and now believes that he actually can end his smoking completely. David reviewed his initial objectives with the counselor, and they both agreed that the initial plan to completely stop cigarette use at the end of the fourth month was still reasonable. He acknowledges experiencing a lot of physical difficulties when he first started cutting down, but he feels more comfortable now. David also shared that ever since he got promoted at work 2 weeks ago, he is feeling more anxious and is triggered to smoke more. He disclosed that he is able to use some behavior modification techniques he learned in counseling to manage his anxiety, but their effects are short. David stated that he would like to address these issues in a more meaningful and lasting way. He also shared with the counselor that he feels ready to start attending a support group they discussed earlier, and he asked for recommendations. David stated that hearing how others "deal with all of this" would be helpful.

LEARNING ACTIVITY 9.4

What are some risk factors that would be important to consider in David's situation? How would you work with David if he was to relapse during this stage?

Maintenance

Simply put, work in this stage is dedicated to stabilizing achieved changes and preventing relapse. It is important not to consider the maintenance stage as static but rather an active continuation of changes achieved during the previous stage. It is natural for clients to experience cravings and a strong desire to reengage with antecedent behaviors during this stage. Therefore, a commitment toward sustaining achieved changes and a plan for addressing potential barriers must be established. Clients enter this stage when the changes they made are sustained past the 6 months mark.

CASE EXAMPLE: DAVID—MAINTENANCE

Just past the 6-month mark, David has completely stopped smoking, and he has not used a nicotine patch in over 4 weeks. He also disclosed that his husband and daughter feel very proud of him. He shared that now he feels more motivated than ever to maintain the new lifestyle. David expressed a desire to continue his counseling for the time being. He stated that he would like to solidify the progress he made over the last 6 months. He shared that he heard a lot about relapsing and how destructive it could be from people in his support group, and he would like to be better prepared if that happens to him.

Box 9.1 provides a list of questions that could help you better understand clients' position on the Stages of Change Model.

LEARNING ACTIVITY 9.5

What do you think is important to include in David's relapse prevention plan?

BOX 9.1

CONSIDERING THE CLIENT'S POSITION ON THE STAGES OF CHANGE MODEL

1. What are some things you would like to change about yourself?
2. What warning signals would let you know that you need to make changes in your life?
3. What behaviors are you currently engaging in that may have negative consequences on your life?
4. Have you tried to make any changes in the past?
5. What are that reasons that are compelling you to attempt to change now?
6. How would your life benefit from making this change?
7. What is an important step you need to make in order to make this change?
8. What barriers will you have to overcome if you are to achieve this change?
9. How successful are the steps you have been taking?
10. What will you need to maintain this change?

Now that we have a better understanding of the Stages of Change model, we will explore MI principles more closely. We will start this process by examining the MI spirit.

SPIRIT OF MOTIVATIONAL INTERVIEWING

Before considering MI techniques and how they can be used with clients, we must first understand what Miller and Rollnick (2013) called an *underlying spirit* that informs MI practice. The spirit of MI was emphasized particularly in the latest edition of the MI textbook (Miller & Rollnick, 2013) to ensure that MI is utilized only in ways that promote clients' welfare; the authors discouraged the use of MI techniques as means of influencing behavioral changes that are not supportive of these aims. The MI spirit consists of four key components: (1) *partnership,* (2) *acceptance,* (3) *compassion,* and (4) *evocation.* These four elements together form an attitude that is crucial to helping clients increase their motivation and achieve desired goals. Each of these four elements has an experiential and behavioral component. That is, a counselor must understand each one, and also their behavior needs to embody these principles in order to be impactful for the client. If, for example, a counselor experiences acceptance for their client, but their behavior toward the client does not reflect that acceptance, the client is unlikely to receive the benefit.

Partnership

The simplest way of understanding this element is in terms of the counselors' attitude. When practicing MI, counseling is done "with" and "for" a client rather than "to" or "on" a client. A strong commitment to collaboration throughout the counseling relationship is essential. In this relationship, clients are considered to be experts on their lives, and counselors are viewed as experts on the change process. From this perspective, counselors and clients see each other as partners who are joining efforts to address issues and attain goals that are important to clients. Furthermore, in MI, it is important for counselors not to see clients as passive recipients of treatment but as active participants in the counseling process. After all, clients' lives are being changed in this collaboration, and it is necessary for them to assume an active role in order to create lasting results. Although counselors are seen as experts on the change process, they are not to assume the position of having all the right answers. MI frees counselors from this expectation as it would minimize clients' role and undermine the collaborative nature of the relationship. Counselors' primary role is to work on establishing a positive atmosphere that is supportive of clients' goals and is not limiting or coercive.

Acceptance

This aspect highlights the importance of counselors' sincere acceptance of clients and their experiences. Communication of acceptance in MI requires the embodiment of four elements: (1) *absolute worth,* (2) *accurate empathy,* (3) *autonomy,* and (4) *affirmation.* The principle of *absolute worth* requires honoring clients' inherent worth as human beings. It is important to show respect for clients as they are and not expect them to become someone else to gain counselors' respect. Absolute worth also implies that counselors' acceptance of clients cannot be conditioned in any way (e.g., acceptance of clients cannot be tied to their progress in treatment). *Accurate empathy* involves counselors' active investment in understanding clients' presenting issues from their perspective, or, more broadly, an effort toward seeing the world as their clients experience it. *Autonomy* entails upholding clients' rights to make decisions about their life independently. Clients must remain free to be themselves and to choose for themselves. This right must be respected regardless of counselors' (dis)agreement with clients' choices. Finally, the principle of *affirmation* describes intentional acknowledgment of clients' strengths and efforts made toward change. It is important here to note that acceptance does not require approval. Counselors do not need to approve or condone clients' actions (or inactions) in order to communicate acceptance of them as valuable and autonomous human beings.

Compassion

This element involves a genuine commitment to the promotion of clients' well-being. Counselors must consider clients' welfare a priority, and all actions taken during treatment need to be supportive of it. Compassion, however, does not require counselors to personally experience clients' pain or sympathize with their circumstances. To be compassionate involves genuine investment in clients' betterment and promotion of their best interest.

Evocation

To understand evocation, we must consider counseling in a way that is inconsistent with most traditional addiction-treatment modalities. While traditional addiction treatments typically entail assessing what clients are missing and then providing appropriate tools that will allow clients to improve (i.e., deficit-based perspective), MI's position is that clients already have everything they need to create change in their lives (i.e., strength-based perspective). This assumption extends to both skills and knowledge that are required for making a change as well as the motivation necessary to achieve it. Based on this premise, counselors' role is to evoke strengths that clients already possess. In other words, counselors' work should be focused on bringing forward or drawing out clients' unique abilities and experiences that will help them achieve their goals.

NOTES FROM THE FIELD

Marilyn Cornell, MS, LMFT, is a clinical director for a private nonprofit agency that serves homeless veterans. The agency offers a robust, long-term residential treatment program that includes both typical substance use and mental health services (e.g., education programs, individual and group counseling) as well as alternative approaches (e.g., music programs, residential garden, physical fitness program, and equine-assisted therapy). Marilyn began her involvement with the agency over 30 years ago as a volunteer, and for the past 14 years she has worked as a clinical director. In this role, Marilyn oversees the delivery of all treatment services across the agency and supervises counseling interns that are completing their clinical hours.

Marilyn described her work for the agency as a dream job. She shared that she has the privilege of seeing miracles happen every day and is honored to work with veterans who are overcoming addiction issues and are changing their lives. Marilyn is particularly proud that her agency is able to provide a temporary home for their clients and give them the "luxury of time" to rebuild their lives. She expressed appreciation for the courage and dedication clients exhibit when they are entering the program and during the treatment process. Marilyn also shared that she is diligent in keeping track of the "emotional paychecks" that come with every client's success, and she stated that these instances are worth all the work they require.

When reflecting on challenges that are facing the addiction field, Marilyn noted siloed treatment delivery and stigma associated with substance use. Marilyn stated that although our field is getting much better in integrating care for persons who have co-occurring substance use issues, treatment delivery still is isolated, and clients often receive only a portion of the services they need. Additionally, she shared that many providers still have a lot of stigma toward persons who use substances (especially the homeless population), and a number of novice clinicians try to avoid this field as a result of it. Marilyn also noted that homeless clients face additional barriers to receiving treatment. She gave an example of insufficient availability of supervised detoxication centers. Marilyn shared that if clients are unable to have a stable detox process, it is far more difficult for them to break the cycle and actually enter treatment.

(*continued*)

NOTES FROM THE FIELD (*continued*)

In terms of advice for counseling students, Marilyn noted that the most important parts are to be open to learning from future clients and establish good boundaries. Marilyn shared that novice counselors should work on breaking their preconceived notions about addiction issues and embrace their work as a learning experience. Additionally, she stated that counselors must not attach their professional worth to their clients' success and should value their work independently of its immediate impact. Marilyn noted that recovery is a long-term process and not a quick fix. Finally, she stated that it is critical that novice counselors do their own work and address any issues that may be triggering.

METHOD OF MOTIVATIONAL INTERVIEWING

After understanding the underlying principles that form the spirit of MI and inform the overall approach and counselors' attitude, we will explore processes that make up the Method of MI. The MI Method consists of four processes: (1) *engaging*, (2) *focusing*, (3) *evoking*, and (4) *planning*. These four components provide structure and outline a general flow of the change process in MI. Although each of these processes represents a unique stage in clients' quest for change, they should not be considered as exclusive units independent from each other. On the contrary, they are overlapping and mutually beneficial. For example, the client and the counselor are not expected to reach some concrete conclusion of the focusing process in order to move to evoking, but, rather, work on focusing will inform the counselor what values and beliefs are important to the client and could be elicited to help the client strengthen their motivation for change.

The MI method also should be viewed as both sequential and repetitive (as needed). That is, the client and counselor progress from one process to another (e.g., from engaging to focusing), but the return to the previous process is always available and should not be considered a setback. The need to return to the previous stage is considered a natural part of the change process, and it is reflective of an inevitable fluctuation of the client's motivation for change. For example, if the client and counselor are struggling to focus their work and establish a viable direction, it would be beneficial to return to the previous process and work on engagement in order to strengthen their relationship and have a better understanding of what is important to the client. This return to engagement is not a failure (for the client or counselor) but a sensitive response to the client's current needs.

Engaging

The primary goal of this process is the work on establishing a counseling relationship and creating a strong connection with clients. As with other approaches to counseling, building a strong relationship with clients is critical to an effective application of MI. Engagement also is regarded as a necessary first step in MI, and without it the process would not move forward or be helpful to clients. This process should not be considered in terms of length (i.e., number of sessions dedicated to establishing a relationship) but rather in terms of therapeutic alliance and rapport between counselors and clients. Counselors should aim to create a strong connection with clients that will be able to sustain future processes. During the engagement process, counselors should work on genuinely understanding clients' concerns and perspectives, fostering a collaborative partnership, establishing a supportive environment, and increasing clients' comfort. Also, it is important to address internal and external factors that could affect the relationship. That is, to build a strong relationship, counselors and clients must consider interpersonal factors, cultural components, previous experiences with counseling, as well as the systemic and organizational factors.

Another important part of the engaging process is an exploration of clients' goals and values. Having a deeper understanding of what is important to clients is likely to strengthen the relationship between clients and counselors and positively contribute to the aims of the counseling process. Additionally, clients' goals and values could be used later as sources of motivation for clients or to highlight potential discrepancies between clients' behaviors and values. Some questions that counselors could ask to facilitate this exploration are as follows: (1) *What do you care about the most?* (2) *What matters to you?* and (3) *How do you hope your life will be different 10 years from now?* (Miller & Rollnick, 2013).

In addition to aspects that facilitate engagement, Miller and Rollnick (2013) also identified factors that are detrimental to this process. They discerned *six traps* that impede the counseling relationship:

- The *assessment trap* describes an early process that is overly focused on factual information-gathering and disregards, or at least deprioritizes, clients as active participants. This overreliance on assessment could place clients in the role of passive information providers and be detrimental to their motivation for change.
- The *expert trap*, in many ways, represents a natural consequence of the assessment trap. It depicts a relationship in which counselors are expected to have and provide all the right answers. Counselors, as experts, are expected to gather pertinent information and provide solutions that will be effective. However, this method is not effective when it comes to personal change. No amount of information or expertise alone will motivate another person to change, and this method is not inclusive of clients' internal motivators.
- The *premature focusing trap* describes a fallacy of trying to generate a solution before establishing a strong counseling relationship and truly understanding clients' presenting issues. It is important for counselors to have a strong foundation with clients and understand the broader impact of their issues before they move to the next stage.
- The *labeling trap* outlines potential issues associated with the use of diagnostic labels. When counselors are overly focused on clients' diagnoses, they can lose sight of factors that are important to clients (that could either aid or impede the change process) but are outside the diagnostic criteria.
- The *blaming trap* takes place when counselors engage in clients' excessive need to assign blame. An exorbitant amount of time could be spent on determining fault for clients' presenting issues. However, whether these efforts are successful or not, they rarely contribute to clients' overall goals for change.
- The *chat trap* describes a relationship in which counselors and clients spend a significant portion of the time on friendly, aimless conversations. This process could be comfortable (and comforting) for both counselors and clients, but it lacks direction and purpose, and it is unlikely to help clients make desired changes.

Focusing

Once a strong counseling relationship is established, clients and counselors then transition to establishing a clear direction for their work together. This collaborative process includes the development and maintenance of an explicit focus that is supportive of clients' desired goals.

It is important to keep in mind that, although treatment direction needs to be specific, it does not need to be singular. Most presenting issues will involve a complex intersection of potentially competing values and affect multiple areas of clients' lives. As a result, multiple treatment goals may need to be established to capture clients' overall desire for change.

Focusing also is a continuous process in MI. Counseling direction and goals are not just determined in the beginning and then simply followed until the end of the counseling process. Rather, clients and counselors are engaging in an ongoing examination and revision of counseling goals. A useful "tool" that can facilitate this process is establishing an agenda. The agenda, however, should be encompassing of both broad overarching goals clients want to achieve as well as tangible objectives they aim to attain. When establishing an agenda, it is important to be comprehensive and consider clients' desires, values, fears, concerns, and expectations. The treatment agenda should be driven primarily by clients' reasons for seeking counseling, and also it needs to be inclusive of counselors' priorities as well. For example, a client's presenting concern may be the declining relationship with their spouse, and their desire to repair and strengthen the marriage. During the initial stage of counseling, the counselor learned that the client's drinking is a major stumbling block in their marriage. Considering what we know here, in terms of focusing, repairing relationship issues and improving marriage will be at the forefront of the counseling process, and it would be important for the counselor to integrate the client's drinking into the overall agenda. As a part of the focusing process, counselors should consider clients' most important aspirations, how counselors' own desires for clients relate to clients' actual goals, and if treatment direction is clearly established.

Evoking

In addition to being a part of an underlying spirit of MI and an overall attitude toward working with clients, evoking also is a distinct process that is critical to the method of MI. As mentioned earlier, evoking entails eliciting clients' personal reasons for change. Counselors' work is directed to first bring forward, and then strengthen, clients' reasons for *why* they want to change and *how* that process is best achieved. Evoking naturally follows the process of focusing and builds on clients' own motivation.

Counselors' central goal is to incite clients' personal arguments for change. A helpful way to conceptualize the evoking process is to imagine clients having a "committee" in their minds; the "committee" members represent both sides of the change argument (for and against). Counselors' job, from this perspective, is to evoke the reasons and arguments presented by the members of the "committee" who are promoting change (rather than counselors themselves telling clients why they should change). Figure 9.1 illustrates a likely interaction among the mind "committee" members for a client who is considering making a change.

This intentional focus on clients' internal motivators in many ways contradicts most traditional approaches to addiction treatment and may challenge counselors' natural reactions. While other approaches heavily rely on providing clients with compelling reasons for change (e.g., negative health consequences, destructive impact on interpersonal relationships, and financial losses), evoking is dedicated to capturing clients' own motives. For example, let us consider a client who presents for counseling due to substance use related violations of parole conditions. Providing education (i.e., lecturing) about the negative impact of drugs on the client's life, no matter how complete these arguments may be, is unlikely to influence them to make any changes. It is highly probable that the client already is aware of all the factors

It is as if individuals who are ambivalent about change have a committee in their minds giving them reasons both for and against making a change.

FIGURE 9.1 Mind "Committee."

the counselor may provide, and considering that they did not uphold parole conditions these factors were most likely not enough. However, if the counselor is to work on eliciting reasons for change that are based on the client's own values and beliefs and strengthening these reasons in accordance with the client's current desires, the chances of the client making a change increase substantially. After all, people are more likely to make changes based on what is important to them than what is important to others. Miller and Rollnick (2013) noted that an ideal product of evoking would be clients talking themselves into making desired changes.

Planning

The planning process takes place when clients' desire for change is saturated, and there is a need to map out the method of *how* changes will be created and sustained. This is an active process that is dedicated to coherently organizing future efforts and specifying necessary steps that will be supportive of meaningful changes in clients' lives. Planning also should be viewed as an inherently collaborative process. That is, all future strategies that are developed must be consistent with both clients' goals and values as well as inclusive of counselors' priorities. Therefore, for a plan to be considered helpful, (1) it must be agreeable to the client, and they have to be willing and able to implement it, and (2) it has to aid the client in achieving and sustaining desired changes.

Although planning is presented as the last step of the MI method, it should not be viewed as something that happens at the end of the change process. Rather, it is important to consider planning as a versatile process that could be utilized throughout the counseling relationship. For example, intentional planning is helpful when determining initial steps that need to be taken for the client to stop their drug use, as well as in the later stages when the client has achieved desired changes and wants to develop effective relapse-prevention strategies. As a part of the planning process, counselors should consider what would be most helpful for clients to move forward, what barriers clients may encounter, and whether plans are being developed collaboratively.

AMBIVALENCE: CHANGE AND SUSTAIN TALK

Ambivalence describes a conflicted state of being in which clients experience compelling desires that are simultaneously supportive and in opposition to making a change. Typically, clients are cognizant of the pros and cons associated with their choices and most often engage in contemplation of both sides. This position should be viewed as a natural part of the change process that clients are likely to experience when transitioning out of the precontemplation stage. For example, it is normal for the client to experience contention about quitting smoking when the reasons for and against smoking are (potentially equally) enthralling to them. The cessation of cigarette use is likely to involve both the desired health benefits as well as great discomfort that can persist for a prolonged period of time. The client's ability to make a decision about their smoking is further complicated when we consider that the continuation of smoking would entail both poor health outcomes as well as be a source of pleasure and an effective coping tool that the client has reliably used in the past. In this instance, the client essentially is "pulled" in opposing directions by factors that are important to them on both sides.

Ambivalence is a naturally uncomfortable position, and simultaneously it could be a place of safety for clients. As a result of this sense of security, clients may "get stuck" in this state. As the previous example shows, the client is experiencing consistent tension that could become quite intolerable for them (sometimes this discomfort could even be the reason they are seeking counseling). However, ambivalence, as often is the case in the contemplation stage, also provides a sense of safety for the client, since, as long as they stay in this position, all options (for and against change) are still accessible to them. For example, if the client remains in this undecided space, in addition to the discomfort we described earlier, the client still has an equally accessible opportunity to stop and continue smoking. This availability of all options could be valuable to the client and contribute to the perpetuation of ambivalence.

Another factor that could contribute to the client's "stuckness" in ambivalence is that, once they start moving toward one choice, the disadvantages of that side become more relevant, and the advantages of the other side start to be romanticized. That is, when the client is nearing the point of a decision to stop smoking, it is natural for them to focus on both the discomfort that will be involved in that process as well as the appealing aspects that are associated with smoking (the positive aspects of stopping cigarette use and the negative facets of smoking are overshadowed at this time). As a result of this temporarily skewed perception, the client is likely to return to the "middle" and stay in a state of ambivalence.

Miller and Rollnick (2013) identified four different types of ambivalence the client could experience during the change-making process.

- *Approach/Approach:* In this instance, the client is conflicted between two desirable alternatives. Although both options are desirable for the client, the point of contention arises when they move toward one choice, and as a result of that action, the advantages of the other side are highlighted and appear even more appealing, urging the client to reconsider their choices (the same outcome happens when the client moves toward the second option).
- *Avoidance/Avoidance:* Here, the client's choice is between two undesirable options. The client's ambivalence is maintained by the fact that, every time they move toward one side, unpleasant aspects of that choice are accentuated, and the client feels compelled to move back to the "middle."

- *Approach/Avoidance:* Unlike the previous two situations, in this instance, the client is facing only one choice. However, this one option includes both positive and negative factors that are important to the client. When the client leans toward this choice, negative characteristics are highlighted; but when they move away from it, positive aspects become prominent.
- *Double Approach/Avoidance:* In this instance, the client is facing two options, and each side has both compelling positive and negative features. The example we reviewed earlier, of a client deciding to stop smoking, illustrates approach/avoidance conflict. In that situation, when the client considered the decision to stop smoking, primary points of focus were discomfort associated with withdrawal and mood-stabilizing and coping aspects associated with smoking. On the other hand, when the client contemplated the continuation of smoking, the most prominent considerations were the negative health implications of smoking and the positive benefits of stopping cigarette consumption.

Table 9.1 provides a tool that the counselor can use during the session to help the client explore their ambivalence further.

Although ambivalence may be difficult to overcome and could represent an obstacle for clients' desire to make a change, intentional engagement within the counseling relationship, and the promotion of what Miller and Rollnick (2013) call *change talk*, could greatly aid clients in resolving ambivalence and accomplishing their goals.

Change Talk

As we mentioned earlier, clients are commonly aware of positive and negative aspects associated with their choices, and they continuously engage in self-talk that is inclusive of both sides. This nondiscriminate self-talk, however, is likely to contribute to clients' state of ambivalence and prevent them from moving forward. Therefore, in order to help clients reach desired goals, counselors need to be intentional in identifying and helping promote the change side of clients' self-talk.

In the simplest terms, change talk refers to clients' own (expressed) reasons that support the changes they aspire to achieve. It is important to note that, although a common goal in substance use treatment may be cessation of drug use, clients' driving rationales for attaining this goal may vary greatly. When helping clients reach desired changes, counselors have to go beyond this overarching goal of stopping substance use and consider reasons that are motivating clients to move in that direction. For example, a client's primary rationale for wanting to end their substance use may be related to the improvement of interpersonal relationships, legal issues, lifestyle change, and so forth.

TABLE 9.1 Exploring Ambivalence

Benefits of Making a Change	Benefits of Continuing Use
Disadvantages of Making a Change	Disadvantages of Continuing Use

The MI approach emphasizes counselors' need to recognize change talk within clients' narrative and then intentionally engage with them to further these arguments in order to solidify clients' motivation for change. According to MI, clients are far more likely to pursue and achieve goals if the reasons used to motivate them are their own. In a way, MI aims to help clients talk themselves into making wanted changes. To help recognize change talk in clients' narratives, Miller and Rollnick (2013) identified four types of *preparatory change talk: (1) desire, (2) ability, (3) reasons,* and *(4) need* and three types of *mobilizing change talk: (1) commitment, (2), activation,* and *(3) taking steps.* Preparatory change talk signals clients' motives for wanting to change and reveals reasons that are driving clients' intentions for change. If we consider a client who is in a state of ambivalence, preparatory change talk is the language the client expresses that is supportive of making a change. It is important to note that this change talk only indicates that the client is preparing (or, at best, is prepared) to make changes, and in itself does not imply that the changes will take place. Mobilizing change talk, in many ways, builds on preparatory change talk. While in the preparatory change talk, clients express their motivations for change; on the mobilizing side, clients are communicating

TABLE 9.2 Types of Preparatory and Mobilizing Change Talk

TYPE OF CHANGE TALK	DEFINITION	CLIENT STATEMENTS REFLECTIVE OF CHANGE TALK
	PREPARATORY CHANGE TALK	
Desire	Desire refers to the client's expressed wishes or wants for making a change	• I want to stop drinking • I wish to stop using cocaine
Ability	The client communicates this type of change talk when they are confident in their capability to achieve change or they believe that change is possible	• I know I can cut out marijuana from my life • I am able to stop using pain meds
Reason	This change talk identifies the client's recognition that wanted outcomes would follow their decision to change	• I would be able to play sports with my children • It would improve my marriage
Need	Need is expressed in the client's communication that highlights the significance and urgency for a change	• I need to stop taking the pills or I may lose my job • I must end my meth use or I may die
	MOBILIZING CHANGE TALK	
Commitment	This change talk takes place when the client express dedication or promise to making a change	• I promise to stop smoking • I guarantee I will stop using
Activation	Activation change talk is indicative of the client's movement toward change	• I am willing to change what I am doing • I am prepared to stop
Taking Steps	This form of change talk is evident in concrete actions that have been taken by the client and are supportive of wanting changes	• I have removed all alcohol from my house • I told my friends of my goals and have asked for their help

dedication for change. Most often, this change talk is inclusive of clients' statements that clearly indicate movement toward change.

To help remember these different types of change talk, Miller and Rollnick (2013) utilized the acronym DARN CATs. In Table 9.2, we provide brief definitions and give an example of clients' statements that are indicative of each change talk.

LEARNING ACTIVITY 9.6
IDENTIFYING AND RESPONDING TO CHANGE TALK

For each client statement below, please do the following: (1) determine whether change talk is present, (2) using DARN CATs, identify what type(s) of change talk is used, and (3) create a clinical response you would utilize to promote change talk.

1. Since I got out of the hospital, it has been so hard not to smoke. I know I need to stop smoking considering the state of my lungs, but I just feel like I need it all the time. I tried doing a lot of other things to get my mind away from thinking about cigarettes, but it's difficult to do it all day.
   a. Change Talk: Y / N
   b. D A R N C A Ts
   c. Clinical Response:

2. I really wish to end my meth use. I miss my life before I started using.
   a. Change Talk: Y / N
   b. D A R N C A Ts
   c. Clinical Response:

3. My life was so much better before I got hooked on the pills. My family was stable, and I was doing very well at work. I know things could be good again if I could just stop with the pills.
   a. Change Talk: Y / N
   b. D A R N C A Ts
   c. Clinical Response:

4. This time is different, I will make it happen. I went to an Alcoholics Anonymous (AA) meeting every night this week, and I already have a sponsor.
   a. Change Talk: Y / N
   b. D A R N C A Ts
   c. Clinical Response:

5. I know quitting will not be easy, but I promised my husband that I was going to do it. And I have never broken a promise before.
   a. Change Talk: Y / N
   b. D A R N C A Ts
   c. Clinical Response:

Sustain Talk

Sustain talk describes portions of clients' narrative that are against making a change. As we discussed earlier in this section, it is as natural for clients to contemplate reasons against change as it is to think about those that are supportive of that change. Thus, sustain talk is not something to be feared in counseling sessions; rather, it is important for counselors to recognize and acknowledge clients' reasons for opposing the change. The significance of counselors' awareness of sustain talk rest primarily on three factors. First and most apparent is that counselors need to deeply understand clients' presenting concerns and barriers associated with them in order to help clients achieve valuable changes. The second component is that by dismissing or minimizing clients' reasons, counselors would violate the spirit of acceptance we discussed earlier. This violation, in turn, could have a detrimental impact on the counseling relationship and impede clients' progress. And finally, the third factor applies most directly to the dynamics of the change process outlined by MI. According to MI, if counselors consistently overlook or attempt to dispute clients' sustain talk, clients will feel compelled to justify their reasons and emphasize this sustain position further. This form of engagement is likely to reinforce clients' rationale against change and decrease their motivation for change. Sustain talk can be rooted in the same DARN CATs categories that were relevant for the change talk. Going back to Box 9.1, we invite you to consider clients' statements that would be reflective of sustain talk across each category.

CASE EXAMPLE: RESOLVING CONTEMPLATION

Let us consider an example of a client who is contemplating stopping their alcohol use. The client's change talk reveals that the motivation to end drinking is driven primarily by the deteriorating relationship with their children and recent legal issues caused by a DUI violation. The client expressed that family is the most important to them and that they would never want to lose their children's trust. Additionally, the client stated that they are disappointed in themself for putting other people in danger by driving drunk, and that they never want someone to get hurt as a result of their actions. On the other hand, the client's sustain talk identified that drinking is one of the primary means of socializing with their friend group, and that it would be difficult to spend time with friends without drinking. The client also noted that they enjoy being "buzzed" and that alcohol helps them manage the stress and anxiety they experience daily.

In this situation, if the counselor is to dismiss the client's reason for drinking or fall into one of the traps we discussed earlier (e.g., expert trap), the client would be likely to experience the need to justify why they have not stopped drinking yet. To achieve this, the client would have to emphasize how important alcohol is socially and how impactful it is in helping them manage stress and anxiety. Since most of the client's energy in this situation would be dedicated to reasons that are against the change, the change-opposing reasons are likely to stay most prominent for the client and thus decrease their motivation for change and likelihood of achieving it. On the other hand, if the counselor is to acknowledge and empathize with the client's reason for drinking, the need for the client to justify themself would be lower. This would help create an environment where most of the energy could be spent on the reasons that are supportive of change and would positively impact the client's motivation to achieve change.

LEARNING ACTIVITY 9.7

How would you respond to the client's sustain talk in an empathic manner? What skills would you use to promote the client's change talk?

Responding to Change Talk: OARS

Now that we understand the dynamics of change and sustain talk, and we are able to identify different types of change talk, it is time for us to consider clinical responses that would support clients' motivation for change. Miller and Rollnick (2013) identified four foundational skills: (1) *Open question,* (2) *Affirmation,* (3) *Reflection,* and (4) *Summary* (*OARS*) that could be used intentionally to strengthen clients' change talk. These skills are not distinct to MI (Rosengren, 2009), and they are used commonly in many approaches. However, in MI, OARS are utilized intentionally to promote clients' motivation for change. Additionally, they can be used to strengthen the relationship, gain further insight, express empathy, establish a future direction, and so forth.

Let us examine these skills now and see how they can be used to facilitate change talk. We want to note that we will not provide expansive definitions or explanations of OARS skills, as you should be familiar with them from your skills courses already.

LEARNING ACTIVITY 9.8 RESPONDING TO CHANGE TALK USING OARS

For each client statement, please construct a clinical response that is supportive of change talk using one of the OARS skills. For further practice, you can construct a response for each of the OARS skills.

- I am not quite sure if I want to stop smoking marijuana. My partner would be happy if I stopped, but I don't know if I am there yet.
- I know quitting smoking is hard, but I am pretty confident that I could do it. Once I set my mind on something, I don't give up.
- My drinking has led to weight gain. Although I am not sure I want to stop drinking, I know I want to lose weight.
- I wish I didn't need to use the pills to sleep through the night. I have tried a lot of other things to help me sleep, but nothing seems to work as good as the pills.
- I don't care what they say, I know marijuana is not bad for me. But I know that the university tests athletes all the time, and I do not want to lose my scholarship.

- Open question: Open questions create an environment that is most supportive of clients' deeper exploration of change talk. When the change talk is identified, simply asking open questions about those reasons will help clients consider them further. They also allow counselors to elicit clients' values, emotions, thoughts, and so forth. Having a broader understanding of clients' reasons for change and how they influence other areas of clients' lives is likely to increase their motivation. Miller and Rollnick (2013) stated that counselors should always ask an open question to which change talk is an answer.
- Affirmation: Affirmations represent counselors' intentional acknowledgment and support of clients' efforts. When expressing affirmation, it is important that they are direct and specifically acknowledge clients' behaviors, intentions, or personal attributes. Additionally, counselors should avoid using "I" statements when communicating affirmations, as they could be perceived as evaluative or judgmental (Rosengren, 2009).
- Reflection: Reflections were identified as the "mainstay" skill in MI (along with a broader attitude of reflective listening). Miller and Rollnick (2013) stated that if you

reflect change talk, more change talk is likely to come. Reflections include a broad range of responses that differ in complexity (e.g., simple, amplified, double-sided). For example, the counselor could reflect simply on the client's current state, "That frustrated you," all the way to acknowledging more complex implications of the client's values, "It is important for you that your parents are proud of your choices." It is beneficial to remember that the complexity of a reflection is not critical in MI, but rather the most significant part is that the reflections counselors use are supportive of change talk.

- Summary: Summaries are reflective statements that bring together two or more themes that clients expressed in the past (or during a current session). Summaries could be used to simply recap the session and emphasize the most important components, link related ideas that have not been explored before, or transition the focus of a session.

SUMMARY

Change is an inevitable part of the counseling process; however, making a decision to change and reaching desired outcomes is a complex undertaking. Clients may have to navigate a number of reasons that are both supportive and opposing of the changes they wish to attain. This contentious position (i.e., ambivalence) often is uncomfortable for clients. However, also it offers a unique sense of security since, as long as they do not make a decision, all options remain available. MI, as an evidence-based approach, could be used by counselors to assist clients in resolving this conflict and make decisions that are most consistent with their goals. To practice MI, counselors must embody an attitude of care, embrace a method that considers clients to be valuable experts and collaborators, and intentionally employ a set of skills aimed at helping clients resolve their ambivalence and support clients' reasons for change.

RESOURCES

Addiction Technology Transfer Center Network: https://attcnetwork.org/

Fuller, C., & Taylor, P. (2008). *A toolkit of motivational skills: Encouraging and supporting change in individuals* (2nd ed.). Wiley.

Miller, W. R., & Rollnick, S. (2013). *Motivational interviewing: Helping people change* (3rd ed.). Guilford Press.

Motivational Interviewing Network of Trainers: https://motivationalinterviewing.org/

Naar-King, S., & Suarez, M. (2011). *Motivational interviewing with adolescents and young adults.* Guilford Press.

Rosengren, D. B. (2017). *Building motivational interviewing skills: A practitioner workbook* (2nd ed.). Guilford Press.

Stinson, J. D., & Clark, M. D. (2017). *Motivational interviewing with offenders: Engagement, rehabilitation, and reentry.* Guilford Press.

Wagner, C. C., & Ingersoll, K. S. (2013). *Motivational interviewing in groups.* Guilford Press.

Wood, A. (2019). *The motivational interviewing workbook: Exercise to decide what you want and how to get there.* Rockridge Press.

KEY REFERENCES

Only key references appear in the print edition. The full reference list appears in the digital product on Springer Publishing Connect: connect.springerpub.com/content/book/978-0-8261-3586-5/chapter/ch09

Miller, W. R., & Rollnick, S. (2009). The things motivational interviewing is not. *Behavioral and Cognitive Psychotherapy, 37*(2), 129–140. https://doi.org/10.1017/S1352465809005128

Miller, W. R., & Rollnick, S. (2013). *Motivational interviewing: Helping people change* (3rd ed.). Guilford Press.

Prochaska, J. O., DiClemente, C. C., & Norcross, J. C. (1992). In search of how people change: Application to addictive behaviors. *American Psychologist, 47*(9), 1102–1114. https://doi.org/10.1037//0003-066x.47.9.1102

Prochaska, J. O., & Norcross, J. C. (2001). Stages of change. *Psychotherapy: Theory, Research, Practice, Training, 38*(4), 443–448. https://doi.org/10.1037/0033-3204.38.4.443

Rosengren, D. B. (2009). *Building motivational interviewing skills: A practitioner's workbook.* Guilford Press.

10

RELAPSE PREVENTION

LEARNING OBJECTIVES

This chapter describes the experience of relapse among clients with addiction and details several relapse-prevention strategies. By the end of this chapter, you will be able to:

- explain the differences between a lapse, relapse, and prolapse;
- defend the idea that a relapse is not an outcome (i.e., failure) but instead, part of the process toward long-term recovery;
- describe the main tenets of three relapse-prevention strategies: the relapse-prevention model, mindfulness-based relapse prevention, and the Center for Applied Sciences (CENAPS) model;
- summarize the necessity of psychoeducation during relapse-prevention treatment and relevant neuroscience related to relapse;
- predict the effects of various counselor responses to relapse on the therapeutic alliance and counseling outcomes;
- synthesize the transtheoretical model (TTM) and describe the importance of the maintenance stage.

TERMS TO KNOW

abstinence — the cessation of using drugs of abuse or engagement in an addictive behavior

conditioned stimuli — people, places, and things that have been repeatedly paired with substances so that they elicit a craving response even when unaccompanied by alcohol or other drugs

coping skill — a means of navigating difficulty, adversity, or distress. Coping skills can be adaptive or maladaptive, effective or ineffective

craving — a strong cognitive and physical desire to approach a stimulus

lapse — initial return to substance use after a period of abstinence

mindfulness practices — behaviors influenced by the Buddhist tradition in which one takes a curious, kind, and accepting stance of their experience without judgment

prolapse — returning to one's recovery plan and refraining from further use after a lapse

recovery	a way of life in which a person with addiction finds balance and joy without the use of substances
relapse	fully returning to old patterns of use after a period of abstinence
relapse prevention	treatment strategies to avoid, or respond effectively to, a return to use after a period of abstinence
urge surfing	a mindfulness-based strategy in which one becomes aware of and accepts cravings without reacting to them, knowing that the sensation will eventually crest, fall, and pass
warning sign	a cognitive, emotional, or behavioral indicator that an individual is moving away from recovery and towards relapse

INTRODUCTION

Making a change to one's behavior often is an irregular process of starts and stops, rather than a smooth, linear experience. Think about the last time you wanted to change your behavior in some way. Perhaps you wanted to cut back on carbs or fast-food, perhaps you wanted to wake up earlier and stop hitting the snooze button, or perhaps you wanted to start a new exercise regimen or develop a new spiritual practice. When we try to start a new behavior or adjust a current behavior, there will be times in which we do it well and times in which we fall back into old patterns. We need only to consider New Year's resolutions to know this to be true. Research related to New Year's resolutions reveals that only about 55% keep their resolution for 1 month, and only 40% keep their resolution for 6 months (Norcross & Vangarelli, 1988). Therefore, just because a person initiates a behavior change does not mean they will maintain that change indefinitely. In other words, one's intention to change does sufficiently predict actual behavior change (McManus, 2004).

Altering one's substance use or engagement in addictive behaviors is no different than other change processes. It is rare that sustained abstinence (or the cessation of use) occurs on the first try (although these individuals do exist and often are called "one shot wonders" or "first time winners" in Alcoholics Anonymous [AA] meetings). Instead, it often takes time for individuals to learn to manage the disease of addiction and live without substances or compulsive addictive behaviors. There may be periods in which individuals are succeeding in their abstinence goals; then life changes in an unexpected way (e.g., the loss of a loved one), and suddenly they find themselves reverting back to old using patterns. Indeed, it has been suggested that 80% of individuals in recovery will experience a return to use during the first year after treatment (Hunt et al., 1971). In a more

LEARNING ACTIVITY 10.1 NORMALIZING RELAPSE

Consider the last time you wanted to make a change (e.g., to your diet, to your study habits, waking up earlier, starting a new meditation or spiritual practice, exercising, giving up caffeine, not texting while driving, limiting social media use, stop smoking). What were the initial few days and weeks like for you? Did you ever revert to your old behavior? How easy was it to make the change? Did you ever "cheat," "slip up," or willfully ignore your new behavior-change goal?

recent study of 362 individuals with alcohol use disorders (AUDs) who received treatment or attended AA, researchers found that only 62.4% were in remission at a 3-year follow-up (Moos & Moos, 2006). Of those who reached remission at 3 years, 42.9% reported experiencing at least one relapse at a 16-year follow-up (Moos & Moos, 2006). Rather than a failure, however, these returns to old using patterns are part of the process of recovery and provide opportunities for clients to learn which coping responses are lacking or how recovery plans can be improved. Therefore, *relapse-prevention counseling* is an essential part of addictions treatment.

TERMINOLOGY

To understand relapse-prevention strategies, it is important to become familiar with commonly used terminology. For example, the act of not using drugs of abuse is referred to as *abstinence*, yet abstinence is very different from *recovery*. Recovery refers to altering one's way of living in response to the chronic disease of addiction by finding balance and joy without the use of substances (or engagement in addictive behaviors). In many ways, abstinence is easier than recovery, the goal of which is to thrive physically, psychologically, relationally, and spiritually without using substances. Indeed, William Cope Moyers (author of *Broken: My story of addiction and redemption*) noted in an interview, "It's easy to stop using alcohol and other drugs, I did it a thousand times. But it's hard to stay stopped." Thus, relapse-prevention strategies are more than just helping clients refrain from using drugs of abuse; instead, they entail helping clients identify and work toward a variety of wellness goals in addition to altering previous patterns of substance using behavior.

Another important term to clarify is *relapse*. Pause for a moment and ask yourself what thoughts, reactions, and feelings emerge when you read the word "relapse." Oftentimes, it invokes thoughts of failure, feelings of disapproval, and the perception of being betrayed or let down. There are many connotations around the word "relapse" that have been embraced by both clients and counselors. Consider again the words of William Cope Moyers (2012) as he discusses relapse: "Relapse can occur with any chronic illness. Yet the label "relapse" is often associated with addiction to imply that somehow it is caused by the person's lack of will or moral failing. In other words, it's their fault" (p. 148). Moyers goes on to compare relapse among those with addiction to relapse among those with cancer or coronary disease. He posits that when people with other diseases experience relapse, the person is not found guilty for returning to their disease; instead it is the disease that is found guilty for returning to the individual. This perspective, however, often is not afforded to those with the disease of addiction.

Relapse is a common occurrence among a variety of mental and physical illnesses and a frequent experience among anyone who has tried to change their behavior (just ask any dieter!). However, rather than embracing a simple, emotionally neutral definition of relapse, such as, "a breakdown or failure in a person's attempt to change or modify any target behavior" (Marlatt & George, 1984, p. 261), when it comes to addiction, many people associate relapse with a lack of commitment, lack of willpower, or a moral failing. Part of addictions counseling, then, is to help clients destigmatize relapse, yet that requires counselors to destigmatize relapse in their own minds as well. At the conclusion of this chapter, we will discuss counselors' responses to relapse and provide opportunities for you to consider what destigmatizing relapse might look like for you personally.

PSYCHOEDUCATION: A CRITICAL COMPONENT OF RELAPSE PREVENTION

An important component of relapse prevention efforts is *psychoeducation*. Clients are in treatment to learn how to live with the chronic disease of addiction, and the more information they have about that disease, the more apt they will be to manage it throughout their lives. Psychoeducation can occur in group or individual counseling sessions and often is an essential component of family weekends or couples counseling sessions. The more that clients and their loved ones know about the neurological and physiological aspects of addiction, the more confident they will feel in their recovery. Specifically, learning about the neuroscience of cravings and relapse, post-acute withdrawal symptoms, and the Stages of Change model can be extremely helpful for clients with substance use disorders (SUDs).

Neuroscience of Relapse

One place to start when providing psychoeducation to clients in recovery is to discuss the functions of the brain. By learning the basics of neurobiology, clients can understand how the brain responds to drug cues as a way to normalize *cravings* (which are strong cognitive and physical desires to use a substance, often precipitating a relapse). Many clients feel shame when they experience drug cravings, which may result in keeping the cravings a secret or fueling distressing emotional experiences (both of which can increase the risk of relapse). Instead, psychoeducation about the process of *conditioning* can best prepare clients to respond adaptively to cravings and avoid relapse.

When individuals use drugs of abuse, they experience high levels of euphoria and pleasure as a result of the activation of the brain's reward circuitry and the release of specific neurotransmitters like dopamine (Comings & Blum, 2000; Grant et al., 2006; Volkow et al., 2002). Over time, the brain learns which stimuli lead to this experience of reward by remembering the objects, chemicals, or behaviors that have been paired with euphoria and pleasure. Specifically, the amygdala and hippocampus are brain structures involved in the creation and storing of emotional memories that help the brain recall the stimuli that have been associated with pleasure (Koob, 2009; Schultz, 2015; Simpkins & Simpkins, 2013). This process is called *conditioning*. In essence, the brain begins to predict and respond to those cues that have been consistently paired with rewards. With regard to substance use, these cues can entail the neon sign of an individual's favorite bar, a lighter, a pill bottle, a glass crack pipe, or a small spoon. These cues become *conditioned stimuli* and can trigger cravings even in the absence of the drug. This is the reason for the AA slogan, "You have to change old people, places, and things." It is not merely to resist the temptation to fall back into old using patterns, but instead those people, places, and things that have become conditioned stimuli that can trigger cravings due to repeated pairings with drugs of abuse.

For example, if an individual uses heroin intravenously, this person has consistently paired a needle and a syringe with the experience of euphoria (i.e., the high) that accompanies heroin use. The brain learns this pairing and begins to associate needles with the experience of reward. Even in the absence of heroin, the sight of a needle may trigger cravings due to the conditioning that has occurred between the needle and the euphoric response. Therefore, a man who uses heroin may experience a strong craving for the drug when he encounters a needle of any kind (for example, at a doctor's office), which, if not managed, could lead to a relapse. See Figure 10.1.

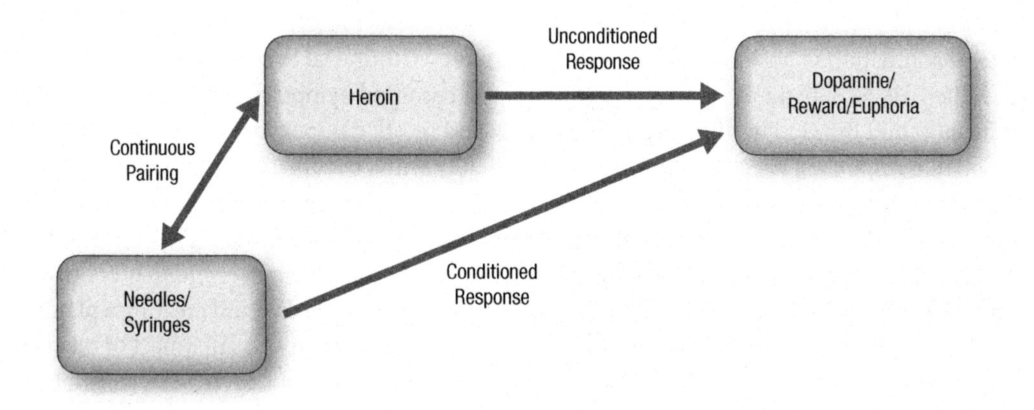

FIGURE 10.1 Conditioning drug cues.

Clients in early recovery can benefit from gaining knowledge about how the brain learns and responds to drug cues. Psychoeducation can explain the predictable pattern in which "one's motivation is to return to the rewards experienced in the past, and to the cues that mark the way to such rewards" (Arias-Carrion et al., 2010, p. 3). Thus, rather than feeling surprised or ashamed by cravings, clients can recognize that the brain has made associations between the people, places, and things that have been paired with their drug use. It is natural, therefore, for the brain to respond with neural firings in anticipation of a reward when the individual encounters one of those conditioned stimuli. Indeed, when a person comes across a sight or smell previously associated with substance use (or even has a using dream while sleeping), they may experience cravings, urges, and motivation to seek out the drug of abuse because the brain is now anticipating a reward (Koob et al., 1998). Relapse-prevention counseling consists of providing this information to clients so they can accurately conceptualize their experience of cravings, gain insight into the neurobiological processes that contribute to cravings, and choose to respond in a way that aligns with their recovery plans. Along with neurobiology, psychoeducation within relapse-prevention counseling should include information related to the body's response to being without a drug of abuse, specifically, post-acute withdrawal.

Post-Acute Withdrawal Syndrome

As a chronic disease, the risk of relapse is ever present among those with addiction; however, there are times in which the risk of relapse is higher than others. One such time is during the first 12 to 18 months of recovery. Chronic substance use leads to *neuroadaptations* or changes in the brain as a result of experience (Blum et al., 2012; Doidge, 2007). In response to chronic ingestion of drugs of abuse and reward circuitry activation, the brain makes changes to restore equilibrium and homeostasis (Blum et al., 2012; Koob, 2009). Specifically, there may be a decrease in the number of dopamine receptors in reward circuitry or a decrease in the natural production of certain neurotransmitters (Blum et al., 2014; Leeman & Potenza, 2013; Wise & Robble, 2020). Once substance use stops, the brain must adjust to the absence of the substance by returning to baseline and healing from the nervous-system damage caused by drug use. Additionally, the body typically goes through acute withdrawal symptoms (the severity of which depends on the specific drug of abuse and use patterns), which can manifest in pain, sickness, insomnia, agitation, depression, or other distressing physical or psychological symptomology.

After acute withdrawal, the collective symptoms that occur in early recovery (12–18 months after the initiation of abstinence) are called Post-Acute Withdrawal Syndrome (PAWS; Gorski & Miller, 1986). Gorski and Miller (1986) outlined common symptoms of PAWS including difficulty thinking clearly, difficulty with memory and recall, dampened emotions or extreme emotional responses, irregular sleep patterns, difficulty with coordination, and amplified sensitivity to stress. While experiencing PAWS symptoms, the risk of relapse is heightened in light of the physical and psychological challenges that occur during this period. PAWS can emerge as early as one to two weeks after an individual has stopped using substances and may continue for up to 24 months (Gorski & Miller, 1986). Preparing clients for PAWS and creating a plan to manage PAWS symptoms without returning to substance use is an important aspect of relapse prevention counseling. Specifically, providing psychoeducation about PAWS can normalize the experience for clients and also correct mistaken beliefs such as, "If recovery feels this bad, I'd rather use!" or "These symptoms are never going to go away!" Learning that there is an end to PAWS as the brain and body heal from drug use can give clients hope and optimism. Additionally, counselors and clients can work together to develop a plan to manage PAWS symptoms until they subside. For example, consider the case of Anna.

CASE EXAMPLE: ANNA

Anna is a 41-year-old female in recovery from an alcohol use disorder. Once she stopped drinking and successfully completed detox, Anna found it incredibly difficult to focus. She felt as though her mind was constantly wondering, and she could not remember to complete the most basic tasks. After learning about Post-Acute Withdrawal Syndrome (PAWS), Anna and her counselor developed a plan to help her get through this period more successfully. Each night before bed, Anna made a list of all the things she needed to complete the next day, including everything from paying a bill and picking up the dry-cleaning to turning in a report to her supervisor and taking her medicine. She entered the to-do list into her smartphone as reminders and received notifications throughout the day to alert her when a task needed to be completed. In this way, Anna was able to fulfill her responsibilities as she navigated the symptoms of PAWS in early recovery.

It is important to note that PAWS symptoms are exacerbated by stress (Gorski & Miller, 1986). Thus, another important aspect of relapse-prevention counseling is to help clients minimize stressful situations to the extent that it is possible (e.g., typically, clients are advised to avoid making major life changes in early recovery such as ending a marriage or getting married, moving, or quitting or starting a new job). For inevitable life adversities, however, clients should be equipped to manage stress in productive ways. By eating nutritious meals, exercising regularly, utilizing relaxation techniques, developing a spiritual life and engaging in spiritual practices, and finding balance among the different realms of life (e.g., work, family, leisure time), clients may be better prepared to face and reduce stress when it emerges (Gorski & Miller, 1986). A final component to the psychoeducation of relapse prevention counseling is teaching clients about the Stages of Change model (Prochaska et al., 1992).

Transtheoretical Model of Change

Many people erroneously believe that the cessation of substance use is the most important and challenging aspect of recovery. This step, however, is only the beginning of the recovery process, which entails much more than abstinence alone. Maintaining behavior change (i.e., continued abstinence) requires another set of skills that often need to be learned, practiced, revised, and reimplemented. The Stages of Change model or Transtheoretical Model (TTM) of change (Prochaska et al., 1992) is an excellent framework for both counselors and clients to use while conceptualizing the change process. According to the TTM, clients start in *precontemplation* (no intention to change), move to *contemplation* (aware of a problem), then *preparation* (begin making small changes), and finally *action* (alter problem behavior).

However, the model does not end with action—instead, the fifth stage is *maintenance*, in which clients work to continue their altered behavior patterns and avoid reverting back to old patterns (i.e., relapse). Sadly, when learning the TTM in counselor-training programs, the maintenance stage often is perceived as an "add on" without receiving much time and consideration (e.g., "And after all this, clients maintain their behavior change indefinitely. That is called the maintenance stage. Now on to our next topic, insurance and billing..."). Yet maintaining new behavior patterns is challenging, thus focusing on the maintenance stage is critical to relapse prevention. Indeed, Prochaska and colleagues (1992) suggested that rather than conceptualizing the TTM as a linear process, it is best to conceptualize it as a spiral in which clients make changes, revert back to previous stages, make changes again, and so on. Prochaska et al. (1992) noted, "As is now well-known, most people taking action to modify addictions do not successfully maintain their gains on their first attempt...relapse and recycling through the stages occur quite frequently as individuals attempt to modify or cease addictive behaviors" (p. 1104).

Therefore, it is imperative that counselors spend time preparing clients for the maintenance stage of change by engaging in relapse-prevention strategies to help them avoid spiraling back through the stages of change and to develop contingency plans in the event that relapse occurs. For example, Connors et al. (2001) noted that in the maintenance stage of change, counselors and clients should identify new positive and negative reinforcers in the client's daily life (apart from drugs of abuse or addictive behaviors), make lifestyle changes that support recovery, increase clients' self-efficacy, and continue to learn and apply new ways of coping. To avoid relapse during the maintenance stage, it also is important that counselors and clients identify and prepare for stimuli or situations that may trigger a return to use. There are many cognitive, affective, and behavioral triggers that can threaten an individual's recovery process; thus, an important part of relapse-prevention counseling is to help clients recognize those triggers and develop appropriate responses to each one. For the remainder of this chapter, we will discuss three prominent relapse-prevention treatment models (i.e., relapse-prevention model, mindfulness-based relapse prevention, and Gorski's Center for Applied Sciences [CENAPS] model), each of which offers unique strategies to help clients identify and respond to relapse triggers (see Table 10.1).

TABLE 10.1 Potential Relapse Triggers

EMOTIONAL TRIGGERS	COGNITIVE TRIGGERS	BEHAVIORAL TRIGGERS
Discontentment or anger	Belief that things are different now and using again will not lead to the same outcomes	Running into old drinking buddies or using friends
Boredom	Belief that substance use can be controlled this time and the individual is an exception or "special"	Isolation and keeping secrets
Sadness or depression	Positive expectations of substance use	Returning to old people, places, and things
Celebration or happiness	Positive memories of substance use (euphoric recall)	Exposure to conditioned stimuli associated with drugs of abuse
Self-loathing	Low self-efficacy and belief that one will not be successful in recovery	Relational conflict
Nostalgia	Belief that recovery is unattainable, too challenging, or not worth the effort	Trauma or tragedy
Craving	Minimization problems caused by drug/alcohol use	Life stressors
Overconfidence	Belief that a drink or drug is "deserved" due to life circumstances	Social pressure

RELAPSE PREVENTION MODEL

The relapse prevention model first emerged in the 1970s as a response to empirical studies investigating antecedents of relapse among clients with AUDs. Marlatt and colleagues found commonalities among the events that triggered relapse and created a model to help counselors and clients conceptualize the process of relapse. Initially depicted as a linear model (Marlatt & George, 1984), the relapse-prevention model is now a dynamic model with interconnected, bidirectional components (Marlatt & Kitkiewitz, 2005). We will briefly review the major tenets of the model, but interested readers are encouraged to consult Marlatt and Donovan (2005).

In order to engage in relapse-prevention counseling, it is of upmost importance to correct clients' misperceptions about relapse. Many people (including both counselors and clients) conceptualize a return to substance use after a period of abstinence as an *outcome*, specifically, a failure (Marlatt & George, 1984). The notion of relapse often is conceptualized in a dichotomous fashion in which a person is either in the "abstinence" box or the "using" box. From this view, the boxes are mutually exclusive, and there is no in-between. When individuals endorse this dichotomous view of relapse, you may hear them say things like, "Well, I guess all that therapy didn't work" or "There go all my abstinence days" or "See? I knew I couldn't make it—I failed." The erroneous belief that individuals are expected to go through addictions treatment and then magically never take a drink or use a drug again is toxic to the recovery process. Inevitably, when a *lapse* occurs (first use of a drink or drug after a period of abstinence), clients feel as though the outcome has been determined—they failed—and thus they have little to no motivation to continue in their recovery efforts. The disappointment, shame, and self-loathing of this failure makes it all too easy to continue drinking or using, thereby leading to a full-blown *relapse*. This predictable sequence of events is called the *abstinence violation effect*, in which an abstinence goal is violated and quickly followed by thoughts of failure and feelings of despair. These thoughts and feelings can fuel an individual into a large-scale, detrimental relapse (Marlatt & George, 1984). Thus, according to the relapse-prevention model, it is important to first reframe the concept of relapse in order to avoid this predicament.

Rather than a dichotomous outcome, Marlatt and George (1984) proposed that relapse is part of the recovery process. The authors made an important distinction between a lapse and a relapse. They noted that a lapse, which is the first use of alcohol or another drug after a period of abstinence, should be perceived as a fork in the road or a choice point, rather than an outcome. The individual who lapses can choose to regroup, rally, and get back on the course of their recovery plan (this is called a *prolapse*), or, alternatively, the individual can sink into despair, concede that all previous efforts were in vain, and continue using substances (which would constitute a full-fledged relapse). The differentiation between a lapse and a relapse, and recognition of choice points along the way, reflects the conceptualization of relapse as part of a continuous *process* rather than an outcome. A lapse does not have to become a relapse, and one way to prevent it from becoming so is to redefine the concept of relapse from a dichotomous outcome to a continuous process. Instead of two mutually exclusive boxes ("using" or "abstaining") with no in-between, a more realistic understanding is to conceptualize recovery as a journey in which periods of abstinence continually get longer while periods of lapses and/or relapses continually get shorter (e.g., 2 drinking days and then a return to sobriety instead of 2 weeks of drinking before returning to sobriety). A client may have three or four relapse episodes after initiating abstinence, but with every lapse therein lies an opportunity to learn what worked and what did not work in the client's recovery plan. As the client learns how to strengthen their recovery efforts, their experiences of abstinence will lengthen until sustained abstinence is obtained. See Figure 10.2 for a visual of the recovery process in which relapse experiences get shorter over time and abstinence experiences get longer.

The understanding of relapse as a complex, dynamic process is the hallmark of the relapse-prevention model (Marlatt & Kitkiewitz, 2005). The model incorporates distal risk factors (such as co-occurring disorders and family history of substance use), cognitive processes (such as motivation and self-efficacy), and cognitive behavioral coping skills (such as self-regulation strategies). When faced with a high-risk situation, individuals respond out of this context of risk factors, cognitions, affective states, and coping behaviors. Thus, according to this model, relapse-prevention counseling can be summarized in three stages: (a) identify high-risk situations and assess the potential risk for relapse, (b) teach clients cognitive and behavioral skills to avoid relapse or reduce the harm should a lapse occur (including

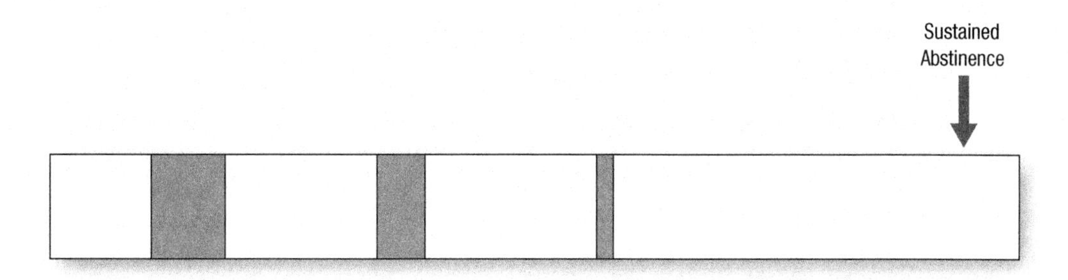

FIGURE 10.2 Progression toward sustained abstinence. White spaces: periods of abstinence (getting longer). Dark spaces: periods of relapse (getting shorter).

lapse-management plans and lifestyle-management plans), and (c) develop relapse roadmaps in anticipation of high-risk scenarios and rehearse appropriate coping responses (Marlatt & Kitkiewitz, 2005). Let's examine each step in more detail.

Identify High-Risk Situations

Identifying and preparing for high-risk situations is central to the relapse-prevention model. According to Witkiewitz and Marlatt (2007), a high-risk situation is "any experience, emotion, setting, thought, or context that presents an increased risk of a person to engage in some transgressive behavior" (p. 5). Early relapse-prevention research identified three key categories of high-risk situations including negative emotional states, interpersonal conflict, and social pressure (Marlatt & George, 1984). Although these are common high-risk situations for many people in recovery, it is important to explore and determine unique high-risk situations for each client (e.g., feelings of loneliness, boredom, conflict with a parent, being invited to get a drink with a romantic partner, positive emotions [such as feelings of accomplishment], cravings and urges, anxiety, or experiencing disappointment at work).

Formal assessments also can be useful in the identification of high-risk situations. For example, the Brief Situational Confidence Questionnaire (BSCQ; Breslin et al., 2000) presents a series of situations and asks clients to report how confident they feel that they could resist using substances in that particular situation. An example item from the BSCQ is, *right now how confident are you that you can resist drinking when you have conflict with others (if you had an argument with a friend, if you were not getting along well with others at work/school)?* Clients then respond on a scale from not at all confident (0%) to totally confident (100%). The BSCQ may be a good starting place to help counselors and clients begin identifying high-risk situations. By becoming aware of scenarios in which they may be most prone to relapse, clients have the opportunity to plan an appropriate response to the situation, rather than reacting impulsively. Once high-risk situations are identified, the next step of the relapse-prevention model is to help clients learn effective cognitive and behavioral coping strategies.

LEARNING ACTIVITY 10.2
IDENTIFYING HIGH-RISK SITUATIONS

Take a moment to reflect on the ways you soothe yourself when you are feeling distressed. What do you do to cope with negative emotions? (Try to remember the last time you were sad, angry, defeated, or disappointed. What did you do?) Some people self-soothe by turning to particular foods, drinking alcohol, or engaging in particular behaviors (e.g., exercise, calling a friend, spiritual practice) or distractions (e.g., scrolling social media, watching TV, gaming). Choose the self-soothing behavior in which you engage that is *least aligned* with your personal wellness goals (for example, eating sugary comfort foods when you are distressed). Now, imagine you were going to abstain from this behavior for 6 months. Which situations may prove to be the most threatening to your abstinence goals? What scenarios may trigger you to reengage in this behavior? Brainstorm as many potential high-risk situations as you can.

Enhancing Cognitive and Behavioral Coping Skills

It is likely that using substances has been the client's primary coping strategy for many years, thus it is important for clients to learn other ways to regulate their emotions and navigate life's adversities without using alcohol or other drugs. To cope successfully means that an individual is able to navigate the inevitable difficulties of life and to tolerate distress in ways that promote their wellness. Cognitive coping strategies include skills like reframing, recognizing and replacing cognitive distortions (e.g., catastrophizing), integrating psychoeducation about craving and urges, and using positive self-statements. Behavioral coping strategies include deep-breathing techniques, progressive muscle relaxation, journaling, spiritual practices, engaging in hobbies, physical activity, and calling a friend for support. There are innumerable potential coping strategies, so it is important for counselors and clients to explore a variety of cognitive and behavioral techniques to determine those that would be most effective (Marlatt & Kitkiewitz, 2005).

In addition to learning coping strategies, counselors and clients also develop *lapse-management strategies* in the event that a client takes a drink or uses a drug (Marlatt & Kitkiewitz, 2005). To prepare for a situation in which a lapse occurs, clients learn how to respond in ways that minimize the abstinence-violation effect and encourage a return to recovery (i.e., prolapse). These strategies may include calling a 12-step sponsor immediately after a lapse occurs, challenging the belief that "all is lost" by reciting or reading a prewritten statement such as, "I don't have to keep drinking. I have a choice. I can stop now and get back on track," or removing oneself from the situation and reaching out to a member of the client's recovery community. It is important that counselors find a balance between preparing clients for the possibility of a lapse without either giving them permission to lapse ("everyone lapses once or twice, so you probably will too") or implying that they are doomed to lapse ("don't expect to get through this without a relapse, it happens to almost everyone"). Instead, it can be helpful to present lapse management plans as a safety measure, just like a fire or tornado drill: you are not implying that the disaster is inevitable, instead, you want the client to feel confident and prepared in the event that the situation occurs (Marlatt & George, 1984; Marlatt & Kitkiewitz, 2005).

A final component of the coping-strategies aspect of the relapse prevention model is to help clients learn skills to decrease the probability that high-risk situations will occur in the first place. Although adversity and difficulty in life is inevitable, clients and counselors can work to minimize the likelihood of high-risk situations. Marlatt and George (1984) posited that the goal for lifestyle changes is to help clients find balance in their lives such that they spend time engaging in both work and play, practice moderation in their activities, and find a sense of harmony within themselves and with others. Thus, along with acute plans to address specific high-risk situations, counselors and clients also can develop general lifestyle plans to achieve greater balance and thereby reduce the risk of relapse.

Relapse Road Maps

Once high-risk situations are identified and potential coping responses are learned, the next step of the relapse-prevention model is to develop concrete plans for maintaining abstinence and other lifestyle changes and to practice those plans. The counselor will not be with the client when they face high-risk situations, thus it is imperative that the counselor and client practice the implementation of the coping responses that will be self-administered by the client (Marlatt & George, 1984). Learning to recognize when there is a heightened risk of relapse and employing a new coping strategy takes time. Thus, it is important that the same amount of time dedicated to helping a client perform the initial behavior change (e.g., to stop using drugs of abuse), is spent helping the client maintain that behavior change (e.g., to continue not using drugs of abuse). Clients and counselors should develop very specific, concrete relapse roadmaps in which they address the following questions: In the event of (insert an identified specific high-risk situation here), what will you do? How will you do it? How successful do you feel you will be in implementing this response? Should a lapse occur, how will you respond? See the case of Aaron for an example.

CASE EXAMPLE: AARON

Aaron is a 34-year-old Caucasian male who has a history of alcohol abuse and marijuana use. After his third driving under the influence (DUI) arrest, Aaron was mandated to professional counseling to address his substance use. For the past six weeks, Aaron has attended an intensive outpatient program comprised of both group and individual counseling. Although Aaron was initially ambivalent about his alcohol and marijuana use (i.e., in the contemplation stage of change), weeks of counseling helped him resolve his ambivalence and make the decision to stop using drugs of abuse. He currently has been clean and sober for 10 days, yet is very concerned about the potential for relapse. In individual counseling, he has been working with his counselor to identify circumstances and situations that may have heightened risk of relapse. Specifically, Aaron said that when he is with his soccer team he tends to drink heavily to "keep up with the guys," when he is alone on the weekends he begins to feel sad about not being in a romantic relationship and often drinks to "get away from his depressing thoughts," and when he scrolls social media at night and sees "everyone else's happy lives," he feels compelled to drink or get high. Aaron and his counselor discuss each high-risk situation in detail to uncover the typical sequence of events (including thoughts, feelings, physical sensations, and actions) that precede his drinking and drug use. Once the high-risk situations are explored, they begin discussing potential ways to cope with these situations rather than drinking alcohol or using marijuana.

Aaron started drinking in high school and began using marijuana in college, so substance use has been his primary coping strategy for more than a decade. At first it was challenging for Aaron to come up with alternative ways to handle stressful situations, but as he and his counselor explored options of effective, adaptive coping strategies (e.g., walking in nature, calling his best friend, physical exercise, journaling, spiritual practices, diaphragmatic breathing, listening to calming music). He seemed to strongly resonate with behavioral coping skills that involved writing. As a journalism major, Aaron has always been gifted with expressing himself through the written word. He decided that when faced with a high-risk situation, his best response would be to engage in some form of writing (e.g., journaling his thoughts, writing out positive self-statements, listing his reasons for not using substances, drafting a gratitude list, writing a letter to his future self). In their individual sessions, Aaron and his counselor engaged in hypothetical high-risk situations (e.g., soccer team inviting him out for a beer, a lonely weekend with no plans, difficulty sleeping and scrolling social media at night) and drafted step-by-step action plans for what Aaron would do to navigate the situation without using alcohol or marijuana. After the plan was devised, Aaron would implement it and report back the follow week as to whether the plan was helpful or to identify areas in need of improvement. Aaron and his counselor would engage in troubleshooting and discuss what would happen if Aaron did take a drink (e.g., how to avoid the abstinence violation effect, steps to resume recovery rather than continue toward a relapse). They also summarized Aaron's past successes (e.g., graduating college) to identify his strengths and increase his sense of self-efficacy. Aaron also shared his relapse road maps with his best friend, his sister, and his AA sponsor to help increase his social support and accountability.

By using the relapse prevention model, clients and counselors can identify high-risk situations and build an arsenal of coping skills to employ in order to avoid relapse. Along with specific action plans for addressing high-risk situations, counselors and clients also develop more general plans for increasing life balance and thus decreasing the probability that high-risk situations will occur. If a client faces a high-risk situation and the planned coping response is ineffective, the counselor and client can use this information to strengthen the relapse road map, enhance self-efficacy, strengthen coping skills, and brainstorm alternative, more effective responses (Marlatt & Witkiewitz, 2005).

MINDFULNESS-BASED RELAPSE PREVENTION

The original relapse prevention model described earlier is still widely used, yet another model also has developed in which elements of mindfulness are interwoven into the existing cognitive-behavioral relapse prevention model. Mindfulness-based relapse prevention (MBRP; Bowen et al., 2011) emerged at a time in which mindfulness was being integrated into various approaches such as Dialectical Behavior Therapy (DBT; Linehan, 1993), Acceptance and Commitment Therapy (ACT; Hayes et al., 2012), mindfulness-based stress reduction (MBSR; Kabat-Zinn, 1990), and mindfulness-based cognitive therapy (MBCT; Segal et al., 2013). MBRP emerged from the work of Marlatt and colleagues after they employed a 10-day meditation course (using Vipassana mediation) with individuals in a minimum-security correctional facility and found decreases in substance use among those who engaged in the course (Bowen et al., 2014). Thus, the benefits of mindfulness meditation as a relapse prevention strategy were realized.

Emergent from the Buddhist tradition, mindfulness is "the awareness that emerges through paying attention on purpose, in the present moment, and nonjudgmentally to the unfolding of experience moment by moment" (Kabat-Zinn, 2003, p. 145). Thus, key mindfulness skills include being present in the here and now, maintaining nonevaluative awareness of one's thoughts, feelings, and sensations, engaging in focused attention, exercising self-compassion, and taking a posture of acceptance rather than judgment. When applied to relapse prevention, mindfulness skills can be an effective means of responding to high-risk situations without relying on alcohol or other drugs. By practicing mindfulness, individuals who face drug cues or triggers can experience the resulting craving with a sense of curiosity and kindness and refrain from self-condemnation or judgment. Additionally, mindfulness teaches individuals how to stay in the present moment (rather than reminiscing about the past or worrying about the future) and how to employ mindfulness meditation strategies (such as focused breathing) as a means of coping (Witkiewitz et al., 2005). In this way, the goal of MBRP is to "develop awareness and acceptance of thoughts, feelings, and sensations through practicing mindfulness; and to utilize these mindfulness skills as an effective coping strategy in the face of high-risk situations" (Witkiewitz et al., 2005, p. 221).

MBRP teaches clients to be aware of triggers, cravings, and urges, to avoid judgment, and to accept these sensations without evaluation (Bowen et al., 2011). Rather than reacting to cravings and urges with despair, anger, or fear, clients can respond with acceptance and create new relationships with these experiences (Bowen et al., 2011). Specifically, clients can learn to observe cravings and accept them without judgment, knowing that they will pass (Witkiewitz et al., 2005). The aim, therefore, is to replace evaluation and judgement with kindness, curiosity, and flexibility. For example, clients are taught to engage in a technique called *urge surfing* in which they take an explorative, curious stance to cravings. As an alternative to reacting to the craving, clients can imagine the craving as a wave in the ocean and themselves surfing on top of the wave as it crests and falls. Clients learn that although cravings may emerge and intensify in response to a drug cue or trigger, they are temporary and will eventually dissipate as the client's internal state returns to baseline. Therefore, by mindfully staying with the craving as it takes its natural course, clients are freed from the compulsion to fight, control, or act upon the craving (Bowen et al., 2011). See Figure 10.3 for an example of how to help clients imagine a craving as a wave.

MBRP is typically facilitated in a group counseling format in early recovery to help clients maintain their behavioral changes and refrain from returning to alcohol and other drug use. Key components of MBRP include enhancing present-focused attention, replacing avoidance behaviors of cravings and triggers with nonjudgmental acceptance, and increasing self-kindness and self-care (Bowen et al., 2014). In addition to the cognitive-behavioral strategies inherent in the original relapse prevention model, MBRP gives clients the opportunity to learn and implement mindfulness meditation practices (Witkiewitz et al., 2005). In this way, clients can increase their self-efficacy as it relates to employing mindfulness strategies (e.g., breathwork, meditation, body scan) when faced with triggers and high-risk situations. Through regular awareness and observation of internal responses to drug cues and triggers, clients can learn to mindfully respond rather than impulsively react. It is important

LEARNING ACTIVITY 10.3
MINDFULNESS MEDITATION

A key aspect of mindfulness practices is to become aware of and accept discomfort, rather than fleeing from it, fighting it, or trying to control it. Given that change is constant, it is true that even feelings of discomfort are not permanent. Therefore, mindfulness allows individuals to become aware of their internal experiences with acceptance and kindness. Take a moment to practice this type of internal, nonevaluative observation. Set a timer for 60 seconds. When you are ready, close your eyes and allow your attention to focus on what is going on inside of you. What are you feeling? Where are you feeling it? What sensations are you aware of? What thoughts are emerging? Don't evaluate anything you find, but take a curious, kind stance to your internal process. Engage in this exercise until you hear your timer go off. What was this activity like for you?

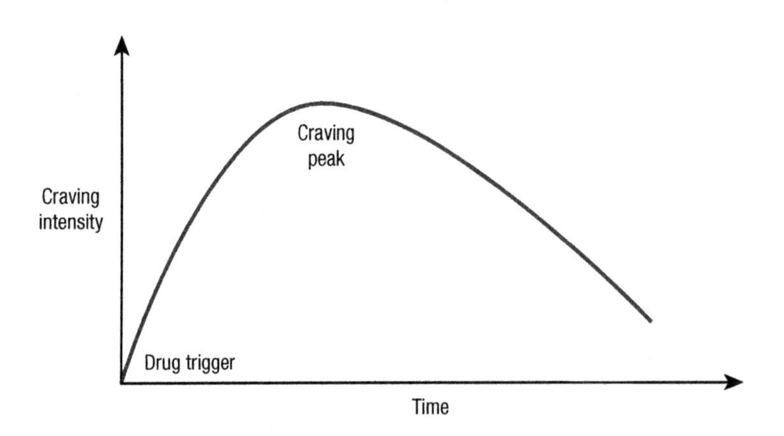

FIGURE 10.3 Craving wave.

to note that counselors who utilize MBRP with clients should engage in their own personal mindfulness practices (Bowen et al., 2014). Specifically, "this program is designed to be facilitated by therapists with an established foundation in mindfulness meditation, an ongoing daily practice, and ideally, formal training in MBRP, MBSR, or MBCT" (Bowen et al., 2011, p. 25).

CENTER FOR APPLIED SCIENCES MODEL

The third relapse prevention model for us to explore is Terence Gorski's CENAPS model, which emerged in the 1970s (Gorski, 1990). In 1982, Gorski founded the CENAPS, and in 1986, he and Merlene Miller published *Staying Sober: A Guide for Relapse Prevention* that is still widely used today. Gorski discussed the importance of recognizing *warning signs*, or indicators that a person in recovery is moving toward relapse. The primary belief of the CENAPS model is that "the relapse process is marked by predictable and identifiable warning signs that begin long before alcohol, other drug use, or collapse occurs" (Gorski, 1990, p. 127). Therefore, the goal of this relapse prevention model is to identify the precipitating thoughts, feelings, behaviors, and contexts that indicate that someone is struggling in their recovery. When warning signs are identified, individuals can interrupt the process of relapse and return to their recovery plan. Like other models, Gorki posited that abstinence is only one part of recovery. In addition to the cessation of substance use, "recovery requires long-term physical, psychological, behavioral, social, and spiritual change" (Gorski & Miller, 1986, pp. 51–52). To help clients make these changes, relapse prevention therapy includes a strong educational component to help individuals learn about the disease of addiction and take appropriate action. Information about addiction can help clients become more prepared to manage life with the chronic disease. The CENAPS model proposes that recovery from addiction progresses in stages, with times of being stuck and times of making movement. The stages include pretreatment, stabilization, early recovery, middle recovery, later recovery, and maintenance. The risk of relapse never completely goes away, thus clients must remain vigilant for signs that they are moving away from recovery and toward substance use. Indeed, Gorski and Miller (1986) wrote, "Recovery from addiction is like walking up a down escalator. It is impossible to stand still. When you stop moving forward, you find yourself moving backwards" (p. 129).

The CENAPS model is built upon a series of nine principles and procedures to help clients learn how to achieve sustained abstinence. Table 10.2 outlines these nine principles and the corresponding procedures. At the heart of the CENAPS model is identifying specific warning signs that indicate a shift toward relapse and subsequently developing a plan for how to manage each warning sign. Importantly, the warning signs can be specific thoughts, types of feelings, or particular actions. According to the CENAPS model, the process of relapse can be conceptualized as endorsing a mistaken belief, followed by addictive thinking, followed by distressing and unmanageable feelings, followed by self-defeating behaviors, followed by contacting old people, places, and things associated with drug use, and finally, culminating in the use of substances (Gorski, 1990). Therefore, warning signs are present along the entire process and clients can learn to identify and manage their unique warning signs. Strategies for coping with warning signs can include challenging maladaptive beliefs, successfully regulating distressing emotions, leaving particular situations, and engaging in drug refusal techniques. To better conceptualize the CENAPS model, consider the case of Roberto.

TABLE 10.2 Center for Applied Sciences Model Summary

PRINCIPLE	PROCEDURE	DESCRIPTION
Self-regulation	Stabilization	Establish a drug and alcohol-free living environment; interrupt using behaviors
Integration	Self-assessment	Take life history and note causes of relapse, self-defeating behaviors, negative patterns, as well as strengths
Understanding	Relapse education	Learn about the biopsychosocial model of addiction and how conditioned stimuli (i.e., people, places, and things paired with substances) can trigger cravings
Self-knowledge	Warning sign identification	Assess thoughts, feelings, and behaviors that precede a relapse, such as boredom, thoughts of invincibility, and euphoric recall
Coping skills	Warning sign management	Develop effective and appropriate responses to warning signs, such as calling members on a 12-step phone list feeling irritable or restless
Change	Recovery planning	Develop recovery activities to engage in when each warning sign emerges, such as working the 12-steps or employing a meditative practice
Awareness	Inventory training	Engage in daily inventories (morning and evening) to plan and review responses to warning signs and identify any new warning signs that emerge each day
Significant others	Involvement of others	Introduce recovery plan to significant others (family members, friends, co-workers, 12-step sponsor) who are supportive and emotionally healthy
Maintenance	Relapse prevention plan updating	Check in with counselor to review recovery plan after six months and adjust, such as adding a new coping skill for newly emerged warning signs

Source: Gorski, T. T. (1990). The CENAPS model of relapse prevention: Basic principles and procedures. *Journal of Psychoactive Drugs, 22*, 125–133. https://doi.org/10.1080/02791072.1990.10472538

CASE EXAMPLE: ROBERTO

Roberto is a 40-year-old Latino male in early recovery from an alcohol use disorder. He is currently in outpatient counseling and his counselor is using the CENAPS model of relapse prevention. After ensuring stabilization and conducting a thorough self-assessment, Roberto and his counselor spend time learning about the recovery process and nature of relapse. Specifically, Roberto learns about Post-Acute Withdrawal Syndrome (PAWS), the concept that relapse as a process, and the importance of developing proactive plans to use in response to relapse warning signs. For several weeks, Roberto and his counselor study and unpack instances in which Roberto relapsed in the past in order to identify warning signs. He develops

(continued)

the following list of warning signs: (1) feeling nostalgic for past using days, (2) stress, (3) conflict with his close friends, (4) the thought that recovery is too hard, (5) restlessness and irritability, (6) starting to isolate, (7) keeping secrets, (8) engaging in risky behaviors (such as gambling large sums of money), (9) picking fights with loved ones, and (10) disengaging from recovery activities like 12-step meetings and group counseling. For each warning sign, Roberto and his counselor develop appropriate coping strategies to employ in the moment. Roberto enjoyed learning how to perceive his thoughts as hypotheses to be tested (rather than indisputable facts) and examining the evidence of their accuracy. He also found using positive and rational self-talk to be a new and refreshing activity. To address his unpleasant feelings, Roberto learned to engage in diaphragmatic breathing and employ a spiritual practice (i.e., prayer) that was important to him. Along with specific coping strategies, Roberto and his counselor developed a concrete plan of recovery activities around which to structure his time (including phone calls with his sponsor, attending 12-step meetings, writing gratitude lists, working the 12-steps, and volunteering at a children's hospital). In continued sessions, Roberto and his counselor will regularly assess whether his coping strategies and recovery activities are effectively managing his identified warning signs and directing him back onto the path of recovery.

The CENAPS model is a structured approach to relapse prevention counseling that provides nine principles and procedures to help counselors and clients strengthen recovery efforts by identifying and managing warning signs. Continued review of coping strategies and opportunities to adjust plans as needed makes this relapse prevention model an evolving process.

NOTES FROM THE FIELD

Heather Bland, MAEd, NCC, LCAS-A, has been a counselor in addiction treatment facilities for over 12 years. She has worked in inpatient, residential, and outpatient settings. Currently, Heather works in an extended treatment program that offers an additional 60 days of residential, level 3 treatment after clients have completed their initial 28 days at the primary facility. Heather notes that the most common substance use disorders she currently sees among clients involve alcohol and opiates.

In her clinical role, Heather provides group counseling, individual counseling, and psychoeducational lectures about the nature of addiction and other topics with her clients. She comments that the most rewarding part of her job is working with clients who are really open and motivated. She contends that clients in recovery from substance use disorders "work harder on any given day than any other client I can think of." Heather says that bearing witness to that type of dedication, openness, and willingness to make difficult changes is very inspiring.

In terms of challenges, Heather notes that observing the sheer power of the disease of addiction can be difficult. She has seen motivated and invested clients unable to attain sustained recovery despite their best efforts. In addition, she said it is challenging to watch clients pick and choose the aspects of treatment in which they will participate, rather than embracing all of them (which, similar to other diseases such as diabetes or hypertension, if patients do not follow treatment protocols, there is a lowered probability of success). Finally, Heather noted that she is frustrated by the difficulties people face in accessing treatment. She longs for addictions counseling services to be more accessible to those who really need it, rather than facing financial barriers preventing those with substance use disorders from getting help.

(*continued*)

NOTES FROM THE FIELD (*continued*)

Finally, Heather reflected upon how important it is that *all* counselors have training in identifying and addressing addiction. She says that she will hear counselors say, "Oh, I don't work with addiction" and her response is, "Yes, you do." In light of the prevalence of substance use disorders, all counselors are working with clients who use substances or are affected by those who use substances. She stated that even counselors working with young children will have child clients who are the symptom bearers of a parent's addiction. Therefore, Heather recommends that all counseling students go to 12-step meetings and doing their own work to develop compassion for those with addiction. She believes it is imperative that counselors who work with substance use disorders are in their own professional counseling in order to provide the best services to clients.

CLINICIANS' RESPONSE TO RELAPSE

A final consideration when providing relapse prevention counseling is the potential effect of a client's relapse on her or his counselor. Consider for a moment that you have been working with a client, Julia, who is dedicated to her recovery and motivated to live clean and sober. After four years of alcohol and cocaine use, Julia entered residential treatment and has since completed the program. She is now working with you in an outpatient clinic and has 90 days of sobriety. You have utilized the relapse prevention model in your work and, together, you and Julia have identified several high-risk situations and have been focusing on strengthening her coping responses. You have seen Julia begin to rebuild the relationships that were damaged by her addiction, including reconnecting with her parents and regaining visitation rights to spend time with her two-year-old daughter (currently in full custody with her ex-boyfriend). It appears as though Julia is doing well and is very committed to her recovery plan, however, one day, Julia misses her scheduled counseling appointment with you. You note that this is unusual behavior, given that she did not call to let you know she would be unable to make the appointment. You call Julia and leave a message, asking her to call you back to reschedule. You do not hear from Julia for seven days, despite leaving another message on her phone. On the eighth day, Julia calls your office and schedules an appointment for the following day. When she arrives, she immediately begins crying and shares that she relapsed by going on a five-day cocaine binge with an ex-boyfriend. Imagine this scenario and reflect on the following questions:

What feelings would come up for you when you learn of Julia's relapse?
What thoughts might you have about Julia?
What thoughts might you have about yourself?
What would you need in that moment?
What would Julia need in that moment?
What would moving forward with Julia in counseling entail?

Relapse is challenging for clients and also can be challenging for counselors. Counselors may take a client's relapse very personally and blame themselves for their client's return to use. Counselors may feel betrayed, disappointed, disillusioned, frustrated, angry, sad, hopeless, or all of these. It is important that counselors who work with clients with substance use disorders have their own spaces and opportunities to process their experiences. It is highly encouraged that counselors are in their own professional counseling so they can explore and discuss their thoughts, feelings, and reactions to their work. In addition, counselors may find it helpful to have a peer supervision group comprised of other clinicians with whom they can consult and process their emotions. Not only is personal counseling and supervision helpful for the well-being of the counselor, these practices also ensure that clients receive the best care. For example, the majority of clients who return to counseling after a relapse are burdened with shame. They have let themselves down and they know that they have let their counselor and group members down. They do not need to be lectured, scolded, or rebuked, and counselors who have not done their own work are at risk of falling into these detrimental patterns. Instead, counselors should keep healthy boundaries with their clients in which they do not take on the responsibility of their client's behavior (i.e., the client's behavior related to drug or alcohol use is not a reflection of the counselor's worth) and thereby do not respond to their client from a place of personal disappointment or betrayal. Instead, counselors are aware that relapse is a hallmark of the disease of addiction and do not take ownership of their client's choices. Rather than a sign that the counselor has failed, relapse indicates a need for adjustments in a client's recovery plan. Counselors can best serve clients by communicating perseverance, hope, and empathy when a relapse occurs.

LEARNING ACTIVITY 10.4
DESTIGMATIZING RELAPSE

You started this chapter with certain beliefs and connotations about the term "relapse." You then read pages of information about relapse and how to engage in relapse prevention counseling with clients. Take a moment to contrast your thoughts/feelings about relapse before you read this chapter to the thoughts/feelings you have about relapse now. Were there any changes? What were your initial thoughts about relapse? To what extent did your initial thoughts about relapse represent the moral model of addiction (i.e., addiction is a personal choice and result of a character flaw or weakness)? What are your thoughts about relapse now? What might a client need from you as you discuss relapse with them? What would be important to communicate?

Counselors should be prepared to respond effectively to clients who have relapsed. There may be time solely dedicated to processing the client's emotions (e.g., shame, despair, hopelessness) as well as time dedicated to correcting irrational beliefs stemming from the abstinence violation effect (e.g., "What's the point of continuing counseling? I'm a loser who can't stay clean."). When the client is in a place to re-engage in relapse prevention counseling, the counselor should have a plan for how to best utilize the relapse as an opportunity to learn. For example, a counselor and client may complete a chart in which they examine the factors that led up to the return to use. As a reminder, relapse is a process with elements that emerge long before the individual actually uses a drug of abuse. Therefore, the counselor and client can examine the client's behaviors, thoughts, and feelings during the weeks leading up to the relapse. In this way, they can reconstruct the chain of events and examine where the client could have interrupted the sequence and what would better prepare the client to respond differently in the future. Counselors should assess clients' motivation and confidence to continue in recovery as well as their level of self-efficacy. The experience of relapse provides an opportunity for counselors and clients to revisit their relapse prevention plans to include additional high-risk situations and warning signs and strengthen existing coping strategies or initiate new ones. In sum, counselors must truly believe that their clients can reach sustained abstinence with continued work and communicate that belief to their clients who may have lost hope.

SUMMARY

Counselors should spend just as much time helping clients maintain their behavior change as they do helping clients initiate their behavior change. There are numerous relapse prevention models that counselors can utilize to help clients learn to live with the chronic disease of addiction without returning to substance use. Clients must be able to find joy and natural rewards in recovery or else it will be very difficult to stay clean and sober. Therefore, part of relapse prevention counseling is helping clients find balance in life, create strong systems of support, and engage in rewarding activities that are aligned with their wellness goals. You may find that in recovery, your client begins engaging in team sports, becomes involved in a faith community, or dedicates themself to a social cause about which they are passionate. Recovery is a time of exploration and discovery of new hobbies, passions, and ways of living. Joy, social support, and balance in recovery are strong protective factors against relapse.

RESOURCES

Bowen, S., Chawla, N., & Marlatt, G. A. (2011). *Mindfulness-based relapse prevention for addictive behaviors: A clinician's guide.* Guilford Press.

Center for Applied Sciences (CENAPS) Model: https://www.cenaps.com/

Connors, G. J., Donovan, D. M., & DiClemente, C. C. (2001). *Substance abuse treatment and the stages of change: Selecting and planning interventions.* Guilford Press.

Copeland, M. E. (1999). *Winning against relapse: A workbook of action plans for recurring heath and emotional problems.* Peach Press.

Gorski, T. T., & Millner, M. (1986). *Staying sober: A guide for relapse prevention.* Herald House/Independence Press.

Marlatt, G. A., & Donovan, D. M. (Eds.). (2005). *Relapse prevention: Maintenance strategies in the treatment of addictive behaviors* (2nd ed.). Guilford Press.

Mindfulness-Based Relapse Prevention: https://mindfulrp.com/

Moyers, W. C. (2006). *Broken: My story of addiction and redemption.* Hazelden.

Moyers, W. C. (2012). *Now what? An insider's guide to addiction and recovery.* Hazelden.

KEY REFERENCES

Only key references appear in the print edition. The full reference list appears in the digital product on Springer Publishing Connect: connect.springerpub.com/content/book/978-0-8261-3586-5/chapter/ch10

Bowen, S., Chawla, N., & Marlatt, G. A. (2011). *Mindfulness-based relapse prevention for addictive behaviors: A clinician's guide.* Guilford Press.

Gorski, T. T. (1990). The CENAPS model of relapse prevention: Basic principles and procedures. *Journal of Psychoactive Drugs, 22*(2), 125–133. https://doi.org/10.1080/02791072.1990.10472538

Gorski, T. T., & Millner, M. (1986). *Staying sober: A guide for relapse prevention.* Herald House/Independence Press.

Kabat-Zinn, J. (2003). Mindfulness-based interventions in context: Past, present, and future. *Clinical Psychology: Science and Practice, 10*(2), 144–156. https://doi.org/10.1093/clipsy/bpg016

Koob, G., F., Sanna, P. P., & Bloom, F. E. (1998). Neuroscience of addiction. *Neuron, 21*(3), 467–476. https://doi.org/10.1016/s0896-6273(00)80557-7

Marlatt, G. A., & George, W. H. (1984). Relapse prevention: Introduction and overview of the model. *British Journal of Addiction, 79*(3), 261–273. https://doi.org/10.1111/j.1360-0443.1984.tb00274.x

Marlatt, G. A., & Witkiewitz, K. (2005). Relapse prevention for alcohol and drug problems. In G. A. Marlatt & D. M. Donovan (Eds.), *Relapse prevention: Maintenance strategies in the treatment of addictive behaviors* (2nd ed., pp. 1–44). Guilford Press.

Prochaska, J. O., DiClemente, C. C., & Norcross, J. C. (1992). In search of how people change: Applications to addictive behaviors. *American Psychologist, 47*(9), 1102–1114. https://doi.org/10.1037//0003-066x.47.9.1102

Wise, R. A., & Robble, M. A. (2020). Dopamine and addiction. *Annual Review of Psychology, 71*, 79–106. https://doi.org/10.1146/annurev-psych-010418-103337

Witkiewitz, K., Marlatt, G. A., & Walker, D. (2005). Mindfulness-based relapse prevention for alcohol and substance use disorders. *Journal of Cognitive Psychotherapy: An International Quarterly, 19*(3), 211–228. https://doi.org/10.1891/jcop.2005.19.3.211

11

TREATING BEHAVIORAL ADDICTIONS

LEARNING OBJECTIVES

Addiction manifests in both the misuse of chemicals and engagement in compulsive behaviors. The purpose of this chapter is to introduce the concept of behavioral addictions and describe four addictive behaviors in detail (gambling, internet gaming, sex, and food). By the end of this chapter, you will be able to:

- apply both the Four Cs of addiction and the Components Model of addiction to your clinical work to help identify behavioral addictions;
- summarize changes to the *Diagnostic and Statistical Manual of Mental Disorders* and *International Classification of Diseases*, accreditation standards, and the definition of addiction to support the recognition of behavioral addictions;
- explain the hallmarks of gambling addiction and considerations related to internet gambling and sports betting;
- differentiate between sex addiction and sex offending;
- describe potential motives for internet gaming and treatment considerations for internet gaming addiction;
- synthesize the relationships among food addiction, eating disorders, and obesity.

TERMS TO KNOW

cybersex engaging in sexually stimulating activities using the internet and/or technology

endogenous chemicals substances produced or originating inside an organism (e.g., dopamine)

eSports competitive gaming in which professional gamers compete in tournaments and organized competitions often with prize money and viewed by spectators

exogenous chemicals substances produced or originating outside an organism (e.g., methamphetamines)

fantasy sports an activity in which users create virtual teams comprised of real athletes and earn points as a result of the athlete's real-life performance

massively multiplayer online games (MMOs)	a type of internet games in which numerous gamers interact within the same virtual world that persists even when individual gamers log off
negative reinforcement	an instance in which something undesirable is removed as a result of engaging in a particular behavior, thereby increasing the probability that the behavior will be repeated
neuroadaptations	changes to neural networks in the brain as a result of experience or exposure to substances
positive reinforcement	an instance in which something desirable is added as a result of engaging in a particular behavior, thereby increasing the probability that the behavior will be repeated
rewards	stimuli that activate the brain's reward circuitry triggering pleasurable or desirable outcomes
reward system	neural circuitry related to the dopamine pathway including structures such as the ventral tegmental area, nucleus accumbens, and prefrontal cortex
self-exclusion	a process by which an individual can place themself on a list prohibiting participation in gambling activities in a particular location or entire state
variable ratio reinforcement schedule	instances in which rewards are distributed in an unpredictable manner after an unknown number of engagements in a particular behavior

INTRODUCTION

Drugs of abuse have addictive properties because they activate the reward circuitry in the brain and are both positively and negatively reinforcing (positively reinforcing because they cause feelings of euphoria and pleasure and negatively reinforcing because they reduce adverse emotional states or undesirable physical sensations such as withdrawal symptoms). *Exogenous chemicals* (substances that originate outside of the body, like heroin) are not the only stimuli that activate the brain's reward circuitry and cause positive and negative reinforcement. In fact, engaging in rewarding behaviors stimulates the release of *endogenous chemicals* (e.g., neurotransmitters that originate inside the body, such as dopamine) that have the same effect on the reward system in the brain. Some activities are *naturally rewarding* and serve to increase the probability of survival and the propagation of the species (e.g., eating high-calorie foods, drinking water, sexual activity), while other activities become *learned rewards* as they are associated with positive outcomes such as financial gain, social approval, or increased social status (e.g., a gambling win, a social media notification, leveling up in an internet game). For individuals with genetic vulnerabilities (e.g., deficiencies in reward-circuitry functioning) or other risk factors (e.g., trauma histories, exposure to addictive behaviors at a young age, access and availability of addictive behaviors, psychological distress), an addiction to a rewarding behavior may develop.

It is important to note that not all behaviors have the potential to become an addiction—only those that activate the brain's reward circuitry and are reinforcing. For example, internet gaming, sex, pornography, food, gambling, and social media all have the potential to become addictive for a minority of individuals, yet no one develops an addiction to folding clothes or mowing the lawn. The difference lies in the effect of the behavior on the individual (i.e., whether or not the behavior is rewarding and reinforcing). Some activities are specifically designed to be highly stimulating and activate reward circuitry in the brain (e.g., playing electronic gambling machines [EGMs], scrolling through social media, playing internet games, using pornography), thus, certain behaviors have higher addiction potential than others.

Along with differences among activities, behavioral addictions develop as a result of differences among individuals. Specifically, not all individuals who engage in potentially addictive behaviors develop an addiction. For example, there are many people who can socially gamble, recreationally play internet games, and occasionally eat high-calorie foods without developing an addiction to these behaviors. However, for a small percentage of people, engagement in these activities becomes compulsive, leads to negative consequences, induces cravings, and becomes out of control. Thus, when assessing the potential of a behavioral addiction, it is important to consider both the nature of the activity (is it rewarding and reinforcing?) as well as the individual's characteristics (do they have risk factors making them more susceptible to behavioral addictions?). A vulnerable individual coupled with a rewarding and reinforcing behavior can lead to a behavioral addiction.

So how can you determine whether a behavioral addiction is present? How do you differentiate between high involvement in an activity (consider a professional athlete or a teenager who games every day with his friends) versus a behavioral addiction? To help with the identification of behavioral addictions, you can utilize two brief screeners, the *Four Cs Model* and the *Components Model*.

Four Cs Model of Behavioral Addictions

A good way to distinguish between behavioral enthusiasts (e.g., triathlete, professional gamer, ambitious employee) and those with addictive behaviors is to examine whether the individual exhibits the *Four Cs Model* of behavioral addictions. Specifically, the Four Cs include the following: the behavior is *compulsive* (the individual feels compelled to engage in the behavior), there is a loss of *control* over the behavior (the individual has difficulty refraining from engaging in the behavior or stopping the behavior once they start), there are negative *consequences* associated with the behavior (the individual continues to engage despite physical, financial, relational, spiritual, or educational/employment problems), and the behavior induces *cravings* or mental preoccupation when it is unavailable (the individual thinks about and has urges for the behavior when they are not engaging). The Four Cs are representative of prominent definitions of addiction and diagnostic criteria of chemical and behavioral addictions (e.g., substance use disorder [SUD], gambling disorder, gaming disorder). If the Four Cs are present, it is a good indication that a behavioral addiction may exist and additional assessment is needed. See the case of Dimitri for an example.

CASE EXAMPLE: DIMITRI

Dimitri is a 15-year-old White, male adolescent who spends between 5 and 8 hours gaming per day. He was introduced to gaming a year ago and found that he was very good at *League of Legends*. When he games, he becomes completely immersed in the virtual world and feels a sense of excitement and pleasure that he does not feel offline. Although unpopular at his high school, he is highly respected in the virtual world and feels very close to his clan. He desires gaming more than anything else and has lost interest in all other activities.

Due to his preoccupation with gaming, Dimitri is experiencing difficulties in multiple areas of his life. As a result of gaming well into the night, Dimitri is not getting enough sleep and is frequently chastised by teachers for falling asleep in class. Additionally, he forgoes homework and household chores in order to game, causing conflict between himself and his parents. His parents also report that Dimitri sometimes will go a week without showering and only does so when his parents threaten to remove all technology from the house. Finally, Dimitri dedicates so much of his time to gaming that he no longer spends time with his friends from school or in his neighborhood.

Dimitri comments that he feels like he *needs* to game. He reports that when he is not gaming, he is thinking about it and feels urges to game that are so strong he will do almost anything to get back to his computer. When he starts gaming, he tells himself it will only be for an hour or two, but he feels unable to stop once he starts and games for much longer than he intends. Sometimes, he will tell himself he is not going to game on a particular day so he can catch up on schoolwork and do a few chores around the house, but he inevitably ends up gaming anyway. He says it feels like he is drawn to the game and reports that nothing is more important to him than gaming.

In the case of Dimitri, it is easy to recognize the Four Cs of behavioral addictions. Rather than being an adolescent who enjoys gaming and is irritated when he has to stop in order to do homework or chores, he demonstrates compulsivity and a loss of control over his gaming behavior. Despite several negative consequences (falling asleep at school, conflict with parents, poor personal hygiene, neglect of former relationships), Dimitri continues to game for many hours each night. When he is not gaming, he reports being mentally preoccupied with gaming and experiencing cravings for the activity. Thus, rather than being a gaming enthusiast, it appears that Dimitri may have a behavioral addiction to internet gaming, warranting further exploration.

The Components Model of Behavioral Addictions

Another way to screen for behavioral addictions is to apply the *Components Model*. Mark Griffiths (1996, 2005) expanded upon the work of Iain Brown (1993) to identify components necessary for an individual's activity to be considered a behavioral addiction (Griffiths, 2019). The six components of the model are: *salience* (the activity becomes paramount in the individual's life), *mood modification* (the activity is used to change an individual's emotional state), *tolerance* (the individual needs more time, intensity, or frequency of engaging in the behavior in order to achieve the desired effect), *withdrawal* (the individual feels adverse emotional or physical states in response to the cessation of the behavior), *conflict* (the individual experiences intrapersonal or interpersonal conflict as a result of engagement in the behavior), and *relapse* (despite periods of abstinence, the individual resumes engagement in the behavior). If all six of these components are present, it is likely that the individual has a behavioral addiction. For example, consider the case of Aisha.

CASE EXAMPLE: AISHA

Aisha is a 27-year-old Black female who lives alone and works full time in banking. Aisha reports that she feels like she is leading two different lives. There is the life that everyone sees, in which she works hard, is responsible, and is active in her church. Aisha states that she also has a secret life, however, in which she spends hours each day in chatrooms engaging in cybersex activities. She was first introduced to the chatrooms by a female friend who said they were exciting and fun, yet Aisha found them to be much more than mere entertainment. She said that online sexual activities made her forget her problems and escape feelings of loneliness and depression. When she is online, she feels invigorated and powerful.

Aisha often finds herself thinking about cybersex throughout the day and counting down the minutes until she is finished with work so she can go home and log on to the chatrooms. Although she used to log on once or twice a week, the amount of time engaging in cybersex has steadily increased to become a daily activity. Recently, however, Aisha has found herself becoming bored with her regular chatrooms and has begun engaging in cybersex activities that are more novel and risky. There are times in which she regrets her online sexual behaviors, yet she feels as though she needs to continue despite the guilt she feels.

Aisha also reports that she often makes excuses as to why she cannot leave her house for activities she used to enjoy (e.g., lunch with friends, choir rehearsal, aerobics class) so she can spend more time engaging in anonymous cybersex. Her friends and family members have commented that they feel disconnected from her, but Aisha says it is because she is putting so much time and energy into her job. Along with putting a strain on relationships that once were important to her, Aisha spends a considerable amount of money on online sexual activities when she should be investing or saving. She also has found herself in some precarious situations (e.g., one online partner wanted to meet offline and became very angry when she refused; another online partner recorded Aisha without her consent or knowledge), and Aisha vowed to quit cybersex altogether. However, she was only able to go 2 weeks before logging on again. Aisha states that when she is not engaging in cybersex she feels irritable, has trouble sleeping, and is restless and agitated. She says that she feels scared knowing that she has lost control.

The six elements of the Components Model are clearly present in the case of Aisha. Cybersex has become the activity around which her life revolves and is more important than her hobbies, work, or offline relationships. Aisha also engages in online sexual activities to change the way she feels and regulate her emotions. She has increased both the frequency and intensity of her cybersex behaviors to achieve the desired effect and reports withdrawal

TABLE 11.1 Characteristics of Behavioral Addictions

FOUR CS MODEL OF BEHAVIORAL ADDICTIONS	COMPONENTS MODEL OF ADDICTIONS
Compulsive	Salience
Loss of control	Relapse
Continued despite negative consequences	Conflict
Cravings or mental preoccupation	Withdrawal
	Tolerance
	Mood modification

symptoms when she is not engaging in the behavior. Aisha has also experienced conflict both with her friends and family as well as within herself as a result of her online sexual activities. Finally, although she tried to limit her behavior, she experienced a relapse after only a few weeks. Given that the six components are present, Aisha may benefit from additional assessment and exploration to see if she has a behavioral addiction.

Therefore, both the Four Cs Model and the Components Model of behavioral addictions are helpful for differentiating between high involvement in an activity and a behavioral addiction (see Table 11.1). While enthusiastic engagement in a behavior can be time consuming, it typically does not come with negative consequences or the loss of control. Additionally, a person who is highly involved in an activity typically does not rely on the behavior as their sole method of emotional regulation. Those with behavioral addictions, however, often report that engagement in their primary addictive behavior is the only way they know how to feel good or stop feeling bad. Thus, the Four Cs Model and the Components Model of behavioral addictions can help mental health professionals explore multiple facets of the individual's relationship with the activity beyond time spent engaging.

RECOGNITION OF BEHAVIORAL ADDICTIONS

Clinicians have been working with behavioral addictions for decades, yet it is only recently that addictive behaviors have been formally recognized in some of the most credible resources in mental health. In the United States and abroad, clinicians rely on diagnostic manuals and classifications of diseases to identify and diagnose psychiatric disorders. Changes to the most recent editions of these manuals reflect the growing acceptance of behavioral addictions among the mental health professional community.

Changes to the *DSM* and *ICD*

Since the 1950s, mental health professionals, particularly in the United States, have relied on the *Diagnostic and Statistical Manual of Mental Disorders* (*DSM*) published by the American Psychiatric Association (APA) to provide criteria for a variety of mental health concerns. The latest edition of the *DSM* (Fifth Edition; *DSM-5*; APA, 2013) made substantial changes to diagnoses related to addictions. Specifically, the *DSM-5* introduced a new chapter titled "Substance-Related and Addictive Disorders," conveying that addictive disorders can exist both with and without substances. The newest edition also includes one behavioral addiction in the chapter, namely, gambling disorder. Moreover, two additional behavioral addictions were included in Section III of the *DSM-5*, which is a section for conditions in need of further empirical investigation. These two behavioral addictions are internet gaming disorder (IGD) and nonsuicidal self-injury disorder. Therefore, the prominent diagnostic manual in the United States now reflects the existence of behavioral addictions (i.e., gambling disorder) with potentially more diagnoses for addictive behaviors to come (APA, 2013).

Although not as frequently utilized in the United States, the *International Classification of Diseases* (*ICD*) published by the World Health Organization (WHO) is a global resource for identifying and diagnosing mental health concerns. The latest revision of the *ICD* (11th Revision; *ICD-11*; WHO, 2018) also demonstrates formal recognition of behavioral addictions. Specifically, the *ICD-11* includes criteria for gambling disorder and gaming disorder in a section titled "Disorders Due to Addictive Behaviours." Furthermore, criteria for compulsive sexual behavior disorder also are included in the *ICD-11*, albeit in the section for impulse-control disorders. Therefore, the most prominent diagnostic classification systems in the world have formally acknowledged behavioral addictions and provided uniform criteria for gambling, gaming, and sex addiction, with proposed criteria for nonsuicidal self-injury disorder (APA, 2013; WHO, 2018).

Finally, it is important to note that the American Society of Addiction Medicine (ASAM; an organization for addiction medical professionals) revised their official definition of addiction in 2011 and again in 2019 to reflect the inclusion of behavioral addictions. Specifically, the current definition notes that both the use of substances and compulsive engagement in behaviors can constitute addiction (ASAM, 2019, p. 1). Furthermore, the authors posited that, along with drugs of abuse, addictive behaviors impact individuals' neurocircuitry and are affected by one's genetic makeup, environment, and experiences. Therefore, given the widespread acceptance of behavioral addictions among addictions professionals, let's consider a few of the most prevalent addictive behaviors, including gambling, sex, internet gaming, and food. Although this chapter provides only a general overview of these behavioral addictions, interested readers are encouraged to consult the resources and websites listed at the end of the chapter for more information.

GAMBLING ADDICTION

Gambling, or wagering something of worth for the chance of winning something of greater value (APA, 2013), has existed for centuries. Currently, there are many different ways to gamble, including casino games, lotteries, horse racing, dog racing, live sports betting, fantasy sports betting, internet gambling, and even day trading or "playing the stock market." Many individuals engage in gambling activities socially or recreationally without experiencing negative consequences, yet some people gamble compulsively, lose control, experience negative consequences, and crave gambling when they are not engaging in the behavior, reflecting a possible gambling addiction.

Gambling can be compelling for a variety of reasons. The most noteworthy among them is the use of *variable ratio reinforcement scheduling*, a concept popularized by behaviorist

B. F. Skinner (1969, 1976). According to behaviorists, behaviors continue when they are reinforced and are extinguished when reinforcements are taken away or punishment occurs. Reinforcements can follow regular schedules (meaning the reinforcements come in a predictable manner) or irregular schedules (meaning reinforcements are unpredictable). One form of an irregular reinforcement schedule is *variable ratio*, in which a person knows a reinforcement is coming but does not know how many times they must engage in the behavior to receive the reinforcement. This type of reinforcement scheduling is the most powerful and most difficult to extinguish. Gambling utilizes variable ratio reinforcement scheduling given that players know that a payout is coming, yet do not know when. They could hit the jackpot on the next round, or the one after that, or the one after that—and this unpredictable reinforcement schedule can keep individuals at gambling machines for hours at a time.

Another factor contributing to the compelling nature of gambling is the introduction of EGMs. The old slot machines with pull-levers and gears have been replaced by electronic machines that operate via computer systems. The graphics and visual effects, sounds, and rapid pace of EGMs have made them a primary form of gambling in casinos, replacing many table games (Schüll, 2012). Beyond casinos, you may find EGMs in the back of gas stations or convenience stores in some states, with men and women fully absorbed in repetitive play. Indeed, many individuals speak of the "zone" or "trance" of playing EGMs, in which the rest of the world fades away and they become immersed in the sights and sounds of the machine (Schüll, 2012). This is an important consideration of gambling addiction; individuals do not become addicted to the payout; instead, they become addicted to *being in action*, or experiencing the trance and thrill of the process of gambling. Specifically, Eades (2003) wrote, "We develop the gambler's trance. Most gambling addicts have periods where they go through depersonalization and derealization. Depersonalization is a psychological term that means the *person* doesn't feel real. Derealization means the *situation* doesn't seem real" (p. 52). This state of depersonalization and derealization, in which nothing else matters but the gambling machine, can be highly rewarding, leading some players to feel compelled to stay in the trance-like state. As gambling machines continue to evolve, it is likely that their rapid speed, sensory stimulation, and reliance on variable ratio reinforcement scheduling may increase the risk of gambling addiction among players.

Internet Gambling

Prior to the 1990s, if a person wanted to gamble, they had to go to a casino or a racetrack. With the rise of internet gambling, however, individuals now can gamble anytime, anywhere, via their computer or smartphone. Internet gambling often occurs by way of offshore websites that vary substantially in how they are regulated (Sulkunen et al., 2019). These websites offer activities like poker, bingo, and other casino games, all from the comfort of one's own home. Internet gambling appears to be growing in popularity; in the study of 117 adults who met criteria for problem gambling, 48.7% had engaged in internet gambling in the previous month (Petry & Gonzalez-Ibanez, 2015). Furthermore, in the study of clients in treatment for pathological gambling, 64.4% reported engaging in internet gambling (Ronzitti et al., 2017). Thus, it is clear that internet gambling has become a global phenomenon and may soon replace the popularity of land-based gambling activities.

Sports Betting

Another recent change to the gambling landscape is the legalization of sports betting. In 2018, the Supreme Court ruled in *Murphy v. National Collegiate Athletic Association* to overturn the previous act that prohibited state-sanctioned sports betting (Melone, 2018). Since the lift of this federal ban, 25 states have legalized sports betting, with more states considering legislation to do the same (American Gaming Association [AGA], 2020). An argument exists as to whether or not sports betting should be considered gambling. Some individuals propose that sports betting requires skill, rather than relying on chance alone, and thus should not be considered gambling. Others, however, argue that, like poker or betting on horse racing, skill may be involved, but the activity still relies heavily on chance, thus constituting gambling.

Along with betting on live sports, another rapidly growing activity is fantasy sports betting. Rather than placing bets on actual sporting events, fantasy sports allow users to create a virtual (i.e., fantasy) team and accrue points as a result of each athlete's actual performance during the season (Nower et al., 2018). Individuals can bet on fantasy teams for the duration of the athletic season or engage in daily betting based on single sporting events (i.e., daily fantasy sports). According to the Fantasy Sports and Gaming Association (FSGA, 2020), 19% of adults in the United States play fantasy sports, and 78% of those players bet on sports. Therefore, when assessing for gambling problems, inquiring about trips to the casino is insufficient. Internet gambling, sports betting, and fantasy sports should be considered and assessed as well.

Gambling Disorder Diagnosis

The diagnosis for gambling addiction has undergone several important changes in recent years. Originally, the condition was labeled "pathological gambling" in the *DSM-III* and classified as an impulse-control disorder (APA, 1980). In the *DSM-5*, however, the diagnosis was renamed "gambling disorder" and classified as an addictive disorder (APA, 2013), highlighting its status as a behavioral addiction. The criteria for gambling disorder include a history of problematic gambling associated with distress or impairment as manifested in at least four of the following: (1) wagering larger amounts of money to achieve the desired effect; (2) experiencing irritability or restlessness as a result of trying to limit or stop gambling; (3) inability to limit or control gambling activities; (4) mental preoccupation with gambling activities; (5) engaging in gambling activities in response to feelings of distress; (6) chasing losses; (7) concealing or lying about gambling behaviors; (8) negative relational, employment, or educational consequences due to gambling; or (9) requiring financial aid (bailouts) from others as a result of gambling losses. If individuals experience four or five of these criteria, their diagnosis is considered mild; if they meet six or seven criteria, it is considered moderate; and meeting eight or nine criteria is considered severe. Importantly, a diagnosis of gambling disorder would not be appropriate for clients who gamble only during manic episodes of bipolar disorder.

Treatment Considerations

There are many clinical considerations when working with clients with gambling addiction. Specifically, it is important to assess for suicidal ideation or suicidal behavior within this population. Given the devastating financial consequences that can occur as a result of gambling addiction (consider losing one's retirement fund, a child's college savings account, or the family home after a gambling binge), the rate of suicidal ideation among problem gamblers is higher than other mental health concerns. Specifically, in the study of 70 people admitted to the hospital as a result of suicidal or self-harm behaviors, researchers found that 17% met criteria for problem gambling (Penfold et al., 2006). Additionally, among 903 clients in treatment for gambling in the United Kingdom, 46.8% reported current suicidal ideation (Ronzitti et al., 2017). Therefore, regular assessment of suicidal ideation or suicidal behavior is an important aspect of treatment. Depending upon the severity of symptoms, as well as the presence of suicidal ideation or co-occurring disorders, it is important to determine whether residential treatment, intensive outpatient treatment, or standard outpatient treatment is most appropriate for clients with gambling addiction.

With regard to clinical approaches, both cognitive behavioral therapy (CBT) and motivational interviewing (MI) have been found to be effective treatment strategies for clients with gambling addiction (Di Nicola et al., 2019; Petry et al., 2017; Raylu & Po Oei, 2010). MI can be an effective clinical strategy for helping clients resolve their ambivalence about behavior change (e.g., whether or not to stop gambling) and increase their own motivation for positive change (Miller & Rollnick, 2013). Additionally, CBT can be particularly helpful for clients with gambling addiction in light of the many cognitive distortions that accompany pathological gambling. For example, individuals with gambling addiction often endorse what is called the *gambler's fallacy*, in which they believe that games of chance are somehow influenced by previous performance (e.g., if you roll a die and get the following numbers: 4, 4, 2, 3, 1, 5, 1, you may erroneously believe you are *due* a 6 because it has yet to be rolled. In actuality, previous rolls of the die do not influence the current roll, which is still fully contingent upon chance). Other cognitive distortions relate to beliefs that players can somehow influence the outcome of games of chance by engaging in certain rituals (e.g., blowing on dice, pressing a button lightly or forcefully, sitting at a certain machine) or that near-misses indicate that a win is coming. A near-miss (e.g., getting two-of-a-kind instead of three-of-a-kind on an EGM) is still a loss, yet it appears to be "close" to a win, thus players erroneously think that they are "making progress," which again is a fallacy in games of chance. The use of CBT can help clients identify cognitive distortions and engage in hypothesis testing (a technique used to assess the extent to which these thoughts are in line with logic and reason) and cognitive restructuring.

A final consideration for treatment for clients with gambling addiction is *self-exclusion*. For some clients, especially those who frequent casinos, a self-exclusion ban may be helpful for their recovery from gambling addiction. The process of self-exclusion entails putting oneself on an exclusion list for either a particular gambling establishment or, if available, a state-wide ban. Some states now offer self-exclusion bans for internet gambling and fantasy sports betting as well. This is a voluntary process in which an individual provides a current photo and completes an application, which

LEARNING ACTIVITY 11.1
SELF-EXCLUSION BANS

Self-exclusion bans vary from state to state. It is important to be aware of self-exclusion policies in the state in which you live and surrounding states. Take a moment to do some research online to discover whether self-exclusion bans exist in your state. Also, review other states' self-exclusion ban policies such as those in New Jersey (www.nj.gov/oag/ge/selfexclusion.html) and New Mexico (www.nmgcb.org/self-exclusion.aspx).

is then shared with casinos in the state (or one casino, depending upon the nature of the ban). With a self-exclusion ban in place, if the individual is seen at a casino, they will be escorted off the premises. Additionally, the individual will be unable to make wagers or collect winnings at casinos, online, or via fantasy sports (again, depending upon the specific exclusion ban in place).

SEX ADDICTION

After a car crash in 2009 with puzzling circumstances, it came to light that pro-golfer Tiger Woods was being accused of having multiple affairs. Weeks later, magazines and tabloids began reporting that Woods checked into a residential treatment facility for *sex addiction*. The public had varying responses to the notion of sex addiction, yet the most prominent opinion was best exemplified by an airplane banner flown over the Augusta National Golf Course while Woods played in the 2010 Masters tournament that read: "Sex addict? Yeah. Right. Sure. Me too."

Sex addiction is less understood than other addictive behaviors. Some equate sex addiction with sexual offending, while others consider it an excuse for poor sexual decisions (such as cheating on a romantic partner). Still others believe that it promotes a sex-negative stance and pathologizes less-common sexual practices.

Although misunderstood by the public at large, clinicians have been working with individuals who have lost control over their sexual activities for decades. Indeed, Patrick Carnes' pioneering work in the area of sex addiction began in the 1980s, and today there are thousands of certified sex addiction therapists, both residential and outpatient treatment facilities dedicated to the treatment of sex addiction, and hundreds of empirical articles providing data related to sex addiction and its treatment. Although Carnes (2005) proposed that up to 6% of the population may have sex addiction, some studies have revealed higher prevalence rates. Indeed, after reviewing available literature, Karila et al. (2014) reported the range of sex addiction to be between 3% and 16.8%. Additionally, in a study of 235 college students, researchers found that 11.1% met criteria for sex addiction (Giordano & Cecil, 2014). Furthermore, among male pornography users, researchers determined that 27.7% had a sex addiction (Kraus et al., 2016). Thus, it appears that compulsive sexual behavior leading to negative consequences and a loss of control is a problem for a notable portion of the population.

Like other potentially addictive behaviors, sex is rewarding (stimulating neurotransmitters like dopamine and endogenous opioids) and both positively and negatively reinforcing. For some individuals, sex becomes the primary means of emotion regulation, meaning they rely on sexual activities to change the way they feel. These individuals crave sexual behaviors when not engaging in them and experience a range of withdrawal symptoms when they attempt to limit or stop compulsive sexual behavior. Additionally, those with sex addiction often find that they need to increase

LEARNING ACTIVITY 11.2 PERSONAL REACTIONS TO SEX ADDICTION

Everyone was raised in families with varying sexual norms and beliefs that impact our current reactions to sex. What comes to mind for you when you read the term "sex addiction"? What are your initial reactions, thoughts, and feelings about individuals with sex addiction? Consider what you learned in your own family of origin about the topic of sex and sexual behaviors. What has influenced your beliefs and understanding about sex? What biases, judgements, or evaluations might emerge in your work with clients with sex addiction?

the frequency, duration, intensity, or novelty of sexual acts to achieve the desired effect. In these ways, sexual addiction is similar to other behavioral addictions, yet differences exist with regard to abstinence and recovery. Some addictions, such as SUDs and gambling disorder, have a clear goal: abstain from the addictive stimulus. For other addictive behaviors, such as sex, food, exercise, internet use, and shopping, it is unrealistic, impossible, or unhealthy to completely abstain from the addictive stimulus. In these instances, the goal is to identify and abstain from those behaviors that have become out of control and compulsive (in sex addiction, these actions are called *acting-out* behaviors) rather than all forms of the behavior. For example, in the instance of sex addiction, a male client may work with his counselor or 12-step sponsor to identify compulsive pornography use and anonymous sexual encounters as his acting-out behaviors. Thus, these are the activities from which he will abstain, while consensual sex within the context of a nurturing, committed relationship may be acceptable (yet often in later stages of recovery. In early recovery, those with sex addiction often abstain from all sexual stimulation in order to give neural networks in the brain a chance to return to baseline).

Some 12-step programs refer to this process of identifying acting-out and acceptable behaviors as the *three circles technique* or *bottom lines, middle lines, and top lines*. Specifically, the inner circle (which also may be called bottom lines) contains acting-out behaviors from which the individual will abstain. The middle circle (or middle lines) consists of behaviors that serve as warning signs that the individual may be nearing acting-out behaviors. Finally, the outer circle (or top lines) is comprised of healthy, aspirational, and encouraged behaviors. See Figure 11.1 for an example of what the three circles activity may look like for a client with sex addiction.

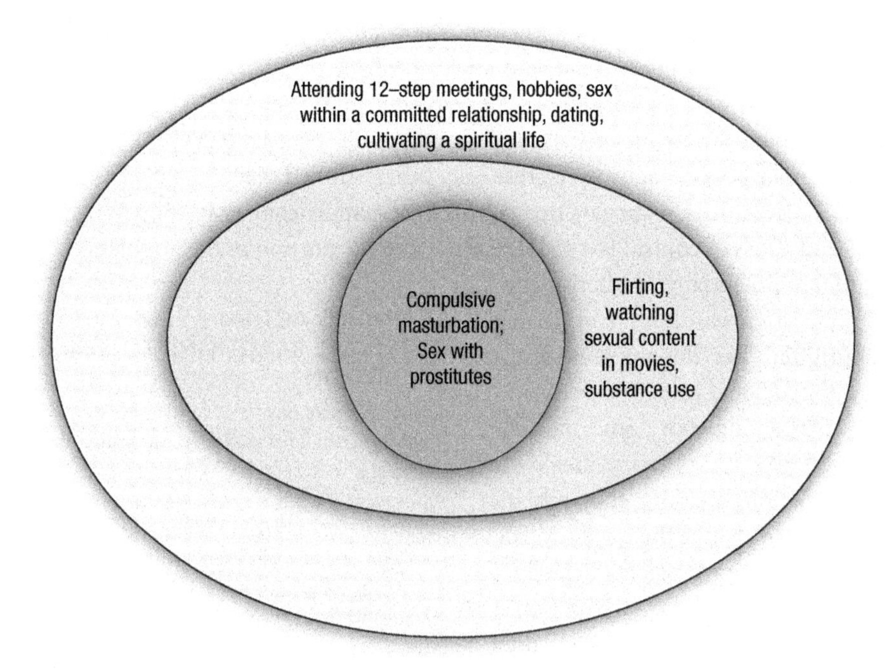

FIGURE 11.1 Example of three circles activity.

Conceptualizing Sex Addiction

It is important to note that sex addiction is not based on the specific type of sexual acts in which an individual engages but rather the role of sexual activity in the person's life and resulting consequences. Specifically, in the early years of sex-addiction research, Goodman (1993) noted, "A behavioral syndrome is designated as an addictive disorder or an addiction, not on the basis of what the behavior is, but on the basis of how the behavior relates to a person's life" (p. 227). Thus, evaluations are not made on the basis of the sexual acts themselves, but on whether those acts are compulsive, out of control, used as the primary means of emotion regulation, result in negative consequences, interfere with life obligations and responsibilities, and cause distress. Indeed, Kafka (2010) proposed criteria for hypersexual disorder (HD) for consideration in the *DSM-5*, which included: (1) substantial time dedicated to sexual acts and fantasies that interfere with other activities, (2) utilizing sex as a response to dysphoria, (3) utilizing sex as a response to stress, (4) difficulty or inability to control sexual acts, and (5) engaging in sexual behaviors despite physical or emotional risk or harm to self or others. Importantly, HD is distinct from paraphilic disorders or sexual activity that occurs only during manic episodes.

Initially, Kafka proposed that if three or more of these criteria were met, HD should be considered. However, the diagnosis was not included in the *DSM-5*, and, after reviewing the feedback, Kafka (2014) raised the threshold to four of the five criteria and added a minimum age of 18 years. The primary reasons for not including HD in the *DSM-5* were reported to be the need for more empirical data and concern regarding the impact of the diagnosis in forensic contexts with regard to sexual offenses (Kafka, 2014).

It is clear that concern and, potentially, confusion exist related to the relationship between sex addiction and sexual offending. The concept of sex addiction stems from the mental health field, while the concept of sexual offending stems from the criminal-justice field (Schneider, 1999). Important distinctions exist between the two constructs, with the main difference related to whether or not an individual's acting-out behavior crosses a legal line to constitute a crime. Many with sex addiction do not engage in illegal acts, and research indicates that less than half of those who commit sexual offenses have sex addiction (Marshall et al., 2008). Delmonico and Griffin (1997) noted the importance of distinguishing between individuals with sex addiction (nonoffenders), individuals who commit sexual offenses (nonaddicted), individuals with sex addiction who commit sexual offenses, and those who have sexual concerns yet do not meet criteria for sex addiction and have not committed a sexual offense. The authors proposed that the motives, emotional experiences, and progression of behaviors differ substantially between these four categories. See Table 11.2 for a summary of these differences.

Treatment Considerations

Carnes (2001) described the cycle of sex addiction, which can be helpful for guiding treatment plans and services. The cycle consists of *preoccupation,* in which individuals become mentally obsessed with sexual thoughts and fantasies. This preoccupation leads to *ritualistic behavior,* in which individuals engage in particular acts in preparation for sexual behavior

TABLE 11.2 Classifications of Individuals With Problematic Sexual Behavior

CLASSIFICATION	COMMON CHARACTERISTICS
Sex Addict (nonoffender)	Individual engages in out-of-control, compulsive acting-out behaviors that do not cross the line of legality; inability to control or stop behaviors despite numerous attempts; feelings of shame and despair follow acting-out behaviors; no illegal acts committed
Sex Offender (nonaddicted)	Individual engages in illegal sexual acts that victimize others; lack of compulsiveness and inability to control behavior; behavior often is intentional or premediated; feelings of hatred, anger, stress, or depression are common; narcissism is common; often low feelings of remorse or guilt for offenses
Sexually Addicted Sex Offender	Individual engages in compulsive sexual acting out behaviors that cross the line of legality; often finds a progression of acting out behaviors from nonoffenses to offenses; sexual offenses often followed by feelings of shame and guilt; acting out behaviors (both legal and illegal) are compulsive and out of control
Sexually Concerned (nonaddicted, nonoffender)	Individual experiences distress related to sexuality although does not meet criteria for sex addiction and has not committed a sexual offense; may experience issues with sexuality; may experience issues with sexual dysfunction; may make poor sexual decisions; sexual behaviors may contradict personal values

Source: Delmonico, D. L., & Griffin, E. (1997). Classifying problematic sexual behavior: A working model. *Sexual Addiction & Compulsivity, 4*, 91–104. https://doi.org/10.1080/10720169708400133

(such as going to a particular location, configuring their surroundings in a specific way, or using drugs of abuse). The next component of the cycle is *acting out,* in which individuals engage in the compulsive, out-of-control sexual activity, followed by *despair,* which is marked by feelings of shame, guilt, self-loathing, and hopelessness (see Figure 11.2).

Treatment for sex addiction involves working with clients to understand each stage of the sex-addiction cycle and intervening effectively. For example, cognitive behavioral strategies may be used to help clients identify and cope with sexual thoughts and cravings and intervene when they begin ritualistic behavior. Alternatively, counselors can help clients respond to the despair they feel after acting out in a way that does not lead to preoccupation of sexual acts (as a way of escaping the despair) and thus interrupt the cycle.

Additionally, attachment work often is a component of sex-addiction treatment given that researchers have consistently found links between insecure attachment styles and sex addiction (Karila et al., 2014; Katehakis, 2009). Thus, addressing early trauma, adverse childhood experiences, and attachment wounds may be necessary in sex-addiction treatment. A psychodynamic or Adlerian approach may be helpful to address family-of-origin issues and resulting private logic. Finally, Riemersma and Sytsma (2013) also proposed that some cases of sex addiction may not involve attachment or family-of-origin issues but instead may

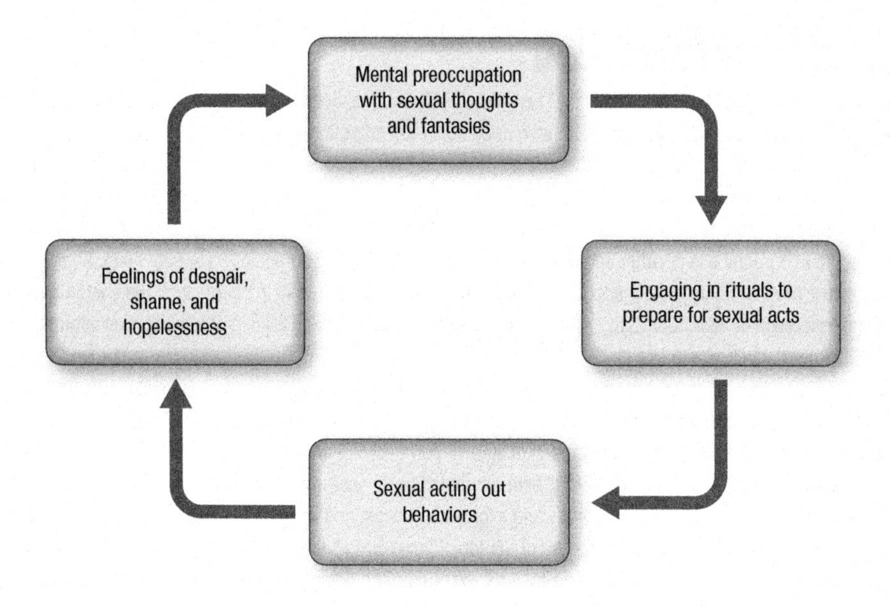

FIGURE 11.2 The cycle of sex addiction.

Source: Carnes, P. (2001). *Out of the shadows: Understanding sexual addiction* (3rd ed.). Hazeldon.

develop as a result of early, chronic exposure to internet pornography. This *contemporary type* of sex addiction (as opposed to the *classic type*) has more to do with *neuroadaptations* resulting from continuous stimulation of the brain's reward circuitry via pornography exposure among adolescents, whose brains are still in the process of developing. Indeed, in the late 1990s, Al Cooper described cybersex as the "Triple A Engine" in that the internet provides sexually stimulating material that is accessible, affordable, and anonymous (Cooper, 1998). For individuals with the contemporary type of sex addiction who do not have histories of trauma or attachment issues, treatment often involves behavioral techniques to eliminate pornography exposure and sexual stimulation so the brain has time to reset and heal from the neuroadaptations caused by chronic stimulation of the reward system. Treatment may also include developing technology plans to help clients use the internet without engaging in pornography use and fostering new ways of regulating emotions and coping with life's adversities.

Another helpful guide for the treatment of sex addiction is Patrick Carnes' (2005) 30 Task Model, which outlines recovery tasks to help individuals reach sexual sobriety (i.e., abstinence from acting-out behaviors). These tasks include actions such as understanding sex addiction, establishing sobriety, becoming involved in a 12-step program (e.g., Sex Addicts Anonymous), enhancing self-care and physical health, working through shame, and building a support system. Rather than days or weeks, recovery from sex addiction often is an extensive process that can take years as individuals learn new ways to manage their emotions, develop alternative coping strategies, address attachment issues, and reestablish healthy and congruent relationships with themselves and others (Carnes, 1991).

NOTES FROM THE FIELD

Sharon Lee, LPC, LMFT, Certified Sex Addiction Therapist (CSAT), is a counselor in private practice who specializes in working with individuals and couples who have been affected by sex addiction. She has over 8 years of experience and received her sex addiction therapist certification (CSAT) through Patrick Carnes' International Institute for Trauma and Addiction Professionals (IITAP).

Sharon decided to pursue training and certification in sex-addiction therapy as a result of working with couples who disclosed pornography use or other addictive behaviors and not feeling fully equipped to help them. Sharon noted, "I became aware of what I didn't know and I didn't like that feeling. I wanted to help people with the shame they were experiencing as a result of their behaviors." After becoming certified, Sharon worked in a group-counseling practice and later began her own private practice.

Sharon identifies the ability to effectively work with trauma as a key to success in counseling clients with sex addiction. She notes that addressing addiction is not enough; instead, counselors also must address the trauma that clients have experienced (even if that trauma is exposure to pornography and subsequent sexual arousal at a young age). Addictive sexual behaviors often are clients' best attempts to self-soothe and cope, and thus they need to process their past traumatic experiences, learn to identify and express emotions, and discover new ways to cope with distress.

When asked about the most rewarding aspect of her job, Sharon stated, "It is extremely fulfilling to help individuals and families break the cycle of addiction. Going to work every day and being a part of a client's change process and accompanying them on this journey is so rewarding." In terms of challenges, Sharon said that counselors entering the addictions field, particularly sex addiction, should be prepared to hear about sexual behaviors that they have not heard of before yet maintain their professional composure. Additionally, Sharon discussed her frustration by the lack of universal acceptance of sex addiction as an addictive disorder. She stated that the pushback from some professionals and questions like, "is this even a real addiction?" are gut-wrenching for her. She wishes that those who question the legitimacy of sex addiction had the opportunity to hear what she hears from clients who say, "I don't want to do this (compulsive sexual behavior) but I cannot stop."

Sharon encourages future counselors to seek training in sex addiction and trauma work and to become educated about 12-step programs in their local areas. She noted that programs such as Sex Addicts Anonymous are pivotal to clients' recovery processes by providing a recovery community to combat shame and call clients out on their "addict-speak" (such as negotiating, justifying, or minimizing compulsive sexual behaviors). The field of counseling needs professional counselors who are equipped to work with clients with sex addiction and their partners and encourages counselors-in-training to do the necessary work to provide effective services for this population.

INTERNET GAMING ADDICTION

Internet gaming has become a multibillion-dollar industry complete with professional gamers, global electronic sports (*eSports*) tournaments, and collegiate eSport associations. Many people engage in online gaming recreationally and enjoy an array of social and personal benefits. For a portion of gamers, however, the behavior can become compulsive and out of control and lead to numerous negative consequences. These individuals may have internet gaming addiction.

The first multiplayer computer games emerged in the 1970s in which players would use text to describe happenings in virtual worlds. These games evolved over time and flourished in the 1990s with the introduction of *massively multiplayer online games* (MMOs). MMOs offer complete immersion experiences into virtual worlds and the chance to engage with other gamers from around the globe. Players create virtual depictions of themselves known as avatars, characters, or champions. Many different types of MMOs exist, including real-time strategy, first-person shooter, role-playing games, and multiplayer online battle arenas. These games can be free-to-play or pay-to-play and can be played alone or with others. Oftentimes, gamers will form clans or guilds with other gamers to compete together in virtual worlds. Additionally, many games continue even after individual gamers have logged off, thus creating a sense of urgency to return to the game and see what has changed within the virtual world.

Internet gaming can be a highly rewarding experience offering compelling sights and sounds, community, the opportunity to advance and achieve, competition, and an escape from offline problems or insecurities. Additionally, like gambling, many games include variable ratio reinforcement schedules in which in-game rewards are unpredictably dispersed (e.g., loot boxes, which may contain objects of value in the game). For some individuals, internet gaming can become the primary means of managing emotions and coping with distress, thereby increasing the risk of addiction. Indeed, scholars have examined motives for gaming and found that some motives are more strongly linked to internet gaming addiction than others. Specifically, in the study of undergraduate students in the United States, researchers found that those participants who played video games to escape anxiety were most at risk for internet gaming addiction (Plante et al., 2019). Additionally, researchers have found that gamers who are primarily motivated by achievement (to excel in the game) and immersion (to escape in the game) also had the strongest link to internet gaming addiction (Carlisle et al., 2019). Rather than assuming that gamers represent a homogenous group, it is important to consider individuals' motives for gaming and the role of gaming in their lives.

LEARNING ACTIVITY 11.3
MOTIVES FOR INTERNET GAMING

Consider a male adolescent who enjoys gaming with friends after school. Why might this adolescent enjoy gaming? What does gaming do for him? (Brainstorm a list of as many potential motives for gaming as possible.) Now consider a teenager who is not very successful in school, yet very skilled within his favorite internet game. What might his motive for gaming be? And how about a person of color, who, when gaming, is represented as a mythical creature without racial features. What motives for gaming might be present?

Proposed Criteria for Internet Gaming Disorder

Although not included in the *DSM* proper, IGD was included in the section of the *DSM-5* designated for conditions in need of further study (APA, 2013). The proposed criteria include: (1) mental obsession or preoccupation with gaming, (2) withdrawal symptomology when not gaming, (3) the need to increase time gaming or frequency of gaming (tolerance), (4) inability to control gaming behaviors, (5) neglect of other hobbies or activities due to gaming, (6) continuing to engage in gaming behaviors despite negative consequences, (7) lying or deceiving others regarding the extent of gaming behaviors, (8) gaming in response to negative emotions or dysphoria, and (9) forfeiting important responsibilities or relationships due to gaming. If five or more criteria are met in a year, in conjunction with distress and/or functional impairment, a diagnosis of IGD may be appropriate (APA, 2013).

Additionally, the *ICD-11* (WHO, 2018) includes an official diagnosis for gaming disorder with similar criteria. Specifically, if an individual has lost control over their gaming behavior, gives gaming priority over other important facets of life, continues gaming behaviors despite negative consequences, and experiences functional impairment, this person may have gaming disorder. The negative consequences associated with internet gaming addiction are varied and may include the neglect of self-care and personal hygiene, sleep deprivation or day-night sleep reversal, financial issues (as a result of spending excessive amounts of money in games for skins [to change the appearance of one's avatar], loot boxes, or other rewards), relational or familial conflict, poor academic performance, loneliness, isolation, excessive anger or rage (due to poor performance in the game or when forced to stop gaming), suicidal ideation, and mental health concerns. The experience of negative consequences as a result of gaming, as well as relying on gaming to alter and manage one's mood, are key indicators that distinguish internet gaming addiction from high involvement in gaming or gaming enthusiasts.

Treatment Considerations

Depending upon the severity of the internet gaming addiction, clients may benefit from either residential or outpatient treatment. For example, reSTART is a residential treatment facility in Washington state for adolescents and adults with behavioral addictions related to technology (e.g., internet games, video games, social media, gambling). As the first residential program for gaming addiction in the United States, reSTART offers clinical services for behavioral addictions and co-occurring disorders (learn more about reSTART by visiting www.netaddictionrecovery.com/). Other individuals with internet gaming addiction may not require the level of care offered by residential treatment and may do well in outpatient group counseling or individual counseling.

Once the appropriate level of care is determined, a variety of clinical approaches can be utilized to help clients with internet gaming addiction. In the review of 30 research studies related to IGD, researchers found that CBT was the most-used approach, in addition to MI and reality therapy (King et al., 2017). Regardless of the clinician's specific theoretical orientation, many individuals with internet gaming addiction (particularly adolescents and young adults) will benefit from learning problem-solving, coping, and social skills to help them navigate the offline world. Moreover, once the function of gaming in the client's life is identified, it may be important to help these clients learn how to meet those needs in alternate, adaptive ways. For example, if a client games to feel competent due to a lack of success in school or relationships, treatment may involve addressing feelings of inadequacy and low self-worth. In addition, behavioral strategies can help clients identify and cope with triggers for gaming (e.g., stress, dysphoria, boredom, relational conflict) and manage withdrawal symptoms when not gaming (e.g., irritability, sleep disturbances, anxiety, anhedonia).

Very practical considerations for internet gaming addiction may be prohibiting access to the internet unless under supervision (at least in early recovery) and helping clients refrain from watching others game (either in person or via live streaming). Clients and their families may choose to make changes to electronic devices to prohibit internet access without passwords and/or delete all gaming apps. Finally, like all addictions, counselors should be aware of the potential for new addictions to develop while individuals abstain from one form of addictive behavior (e.g., while abstaining from internet gaming, a client may begin compulsively using pornography).

FOOD ADDICTION

Another proposed behavioral addiction is food addiction. Like sex, eating is a naturally rewarding behavior necessary for the propagation of the species. For some individuals, however, (specifically those with genetic vulnerabilities), eating can become compulsive and out of control. Moreover, these uncontrolled eating patterns may continue despite a host of negative consequences (e.g., physical, relational, psychological), and individuals may crave food even when they are not hungry. In fact, *hedonic eating*, in which one eats for pleasure rather than in response to hunger, is typical among those with food addiction (Leigh & Morris, 2018).

It is important to note that food addiction differs from obesity, yet obesity may be a negative consequence of food addiction. Food addiction can occur among individuals of any weight or body size and is marked by one's relationship with food, rather than the quantity of food consumed. Specifically, when eating becomes the most utilized means of mood management, is compulsive, is out-of-control, and is both positively and negatively reinforcing, food addiction may be present. Scholars have noted a relationship between obesity and food addiction. In the study of over 200 adults, 7.8% of those of average weight met criteria for food addiction compared to 24.6% of those in the obese range (Gearhardt et al., 2016).

Food Addiction and Eating Disorders

Food addiction also is distinct from eating disorders, although the two conditions can co-occur. The *DSM-5* describes several feeding and eating disorders, yet food addiction seems to overlap most strongly with those that involve *binge eating* (APA, 2013). A binge-eating episode entails two criteria: (1) eating substantially more food in a discrete period of time than others would consume, and (2) feeling out of control while eating (APA, 2013). Both binge eating disorder (BED) and bulimia nervosa (BN) are marked by binge eating, yet BN also involves compensatory behaviors (e.g., purging, laxative misuse, diuretics), which are not present in BED. Importantly, not all individuals with eating disorders have food addiction, and not all individuals with food addiction have an eating disorder. Instead, like other behavioral addictions, "food addiction may be understood as a disorder involving a dysregulated stress response where compulsive overeating functions as a coping mechanism" (Leigh & Morris, 2018, p. 38).

Although the *DSM* does not currently provide criteria for food addiction, the Yale Food Addiction Scale (YFAS) is a commonly utilized assessment instrument to identify and measure food addiction (Gearhardt et al., 2009). Recently updated, the revised YFAS (YFAS 2.0; Gearhardt et al., 2016) assesses the same 11 criteria used to identify SUDs in the *DSM-5* (APA, 2013). The proposed criteria for food addiction include: (1) food consumed in larger amounts and more often than intended; (2) inability to cut down or control consumption of particular foods; (3) substantial time invested in obtaining, consuming, or recovering from eating; (4) experience of cravings for particular foods; (5) eating behaviors result in the neglect of other responsibilities; (6) eating behaviors lead to negative social consequences; (7) previously enjoyed activities are forfeited due to eating behaviors; (8) engaging in eating behaviors in hazardous or risky situations; (9) continuing eating behaviors despite negative physical or psychological consequences; (10) experience of tolerance; and (11) experience of withdrawal (Carr et al., 2017). Depending upon the number of criteria endorsed, food addiction can be classified as mild, moderate, or severe. As a result of being developed from the criteria for SUDs, the characteristics of food addiction differ substantially from the criteria of eating disorders (see Table 11.3). However, some commonalities exist (such as the loss of control), and it is thereby important to assess whether those with food addiction may also have an eating disorder and vice versa.

TABLE 11.3 Summary of Criteria for Eating Disorders and Food Addiction

BULIMIA NERVOSA	ANOREXIA NERVOSA	BINGE EATING DISORDER	FOOD ADDICTION
Binge eating episodes	Restrictive behaviors resulting in low body weight	Binge eating episodes	Consuming more food than intended
Compensatory behaviors	Significant anxiety or fear related to weight gain	Pace of eating is rapid	Loss of control over food consumption
Perception of self disproportionately contingent upon body shape and weight	Perception of self disproportionately contingent upon body shape and weight	Result of binge eating episode is physical discomfort from fullness	Substantial time invested in consuming food or recovering
Frequency of binge eating and compensatory behaviors is at least weekly (for three or more months)	Can occur with or without binge eating episodes and compensatory behaviors	Consuming food in the absence of hunger	Craving for foods
Behaviors are not enacted only during periods meeting criteria for anorexia		Intentionally eating in isolation due to feelings of guilt, shame, or embarrassment	Unable to fulfill responsibilities due to eating behaviors
		Result of binge eating episode is self-loathing, disgust, or depression	Continued eating patterns despite interpersonal issues
		Binge eating episodes lead to significant distress	Former activities forfeited due to eating behaviors
		Binge eating does not occur with compensatory behaviors	Engaging in food consumption in situations that are risky or hazardous
		Binge eating episodes are at least weekly (for three or more months)	Continued eating patterns despite physical or psychological issues
			Tolerance
			Withdrawal

Treatment Considerations

Controversy exists regarding whether or not food addiction is linked to particular foods or ingredients. Specifically, some proponents of food addiction believe that processed foods, especially those high in sugar and fat, are the addictive substances in food addiction (Lerma-Cabrera et al., 2016; Salamone & Correa, 2013). Others, however, do not believe any nutrient or ingredient is addictive in and of itself; instead, any food can be compulsively consumed, thus food addiction is better conceptualized as eating addiction (Coker Ross, 2017). One's stance on whether or not specific foods are more addictive or triggering than others will impact the course of treatment for food addiction. For example, members of the 12-step program Food Addicts in Recovery Anonymous (FA) are charged with abstaining from all foods made with processed flour or processed sugar, due to the perceived addictive nature of those ingredients. The argument is that people do not lose control over their broccoli consumption, but instead highly palatable foods, which are typically made with refined sugar or flour, are the problematic foods.

Along with identifying trigger foods and compulsive, out-of-control eating behaviors from which to abstain, clinicians can work with nutritionists to help clients with food addiction develop nutritional eating plans. Rather than one-size-fits-all, eating plans are unique to the individual and consider their holistic experience and wellness goals. Additionally, a useful component of treatment for food addiction may be enhancing mindfulness practices. Helping clients become aware of their physical cues (e.g., hunger, satiation) and responding intentionally and mindfully can be important skillsets for those who have lost control over their eating behaviors. A mindfulness eating program, such as the Mindfulness-Based Eating Awareness Training (MB-EAT; Kristeller & Wolever, 2014), may be particularly useful in food-addiction treatment.

ADDITIONAL BEHAVIORAL ADDICTIONS

Although beyond the scope of this chapter, several additional behavioral addictions have been proposed by scholars and clinicians including social media use, shopping, exercise, work, love, nonsuicidal self-injury, and even tanning. Over the next several years, as more research is conducted, the mental health profession will gain more knowledge and understanding related to behavioral addictions, including how to better diagnose and treat them. In the meantime, it is important to recognize that rewarding behaviors affect the same regions of the brain as drugs of abuse (Berridge & Kringelbach, 2015; Wise & Robble, 2020) and for individuals with genetic vulnerabilities there exists the risk of developing behavioral addictions.

LEARNING ACTIVITY 11.4
12-STEP PROGRAMS FOR BEHAVIORAL ADDICTIONS

Select a 12-step program from the following list and look up the fellowship online. Read about the mission of the program and a description of the addiction, find the meeting schedule, note if meetings take place in person, virtually, or both, and review the literature/resources of the program on the website.

Computer Gaming Addicts Anonymous
Debtors Anonymous
Food Addicts in Recovery Anonymous
Gamblers Anonymous
Internet and Technology Addicts Anonymous
Overeaters Anonymous
Sex Addicts Anonymous
Sex and Love Addicts Anonymous
Sexaholics Anonymous
Sexual Compulsives Anonymous
Workaholics Anonymous

Along with clinical services, 12-step support groups may be helpful resources for those with behavioral addictions. Following the structure and format of Alcoholics Anonymous, the following 12-step programs are examples of those designed to support the recovery of individuals with specific behavioral addictions: Gamblers Anonymous, Sex Addicts Anonymous, Sex and Love Addicts Anonymous, Overeaters Anonymous, FA, Debtors Anonymous, Workaholics Anonymous, Computer Gaming Addicts Anonymous, and Internet and Technology Addicts Anonymous. These fellowships operate under the principle of recovery in community and encourage meeting attendance, sponsorship, and working the 12-steps. The sheer number of 12-step programs that exist for behavioral addictions provides more evidence for the prevalence of addictive behaviors.

SUMMARY

It has been proposed that addiction is one disorder with many expressions that can be either chemical or behavioral (Hebebrand et al., 2014; Shaffer & Shaffer, 2014). Thus, rather than drawing a definitive line between SUDs and behavioral addictions, it may be more helpful to understand addiction as the misuse of rewards among individuals with genetic vulnerabilities. These rewards can come in the form of exogenous chemicals or behaviors that stimulate endogenous chemicals implicated in reward circuitry in the brain. Although more research is needed to inform diagnostic criteria and treatment protocols, it is clear that some individuals experience compulsivity, a loss of control, negative consequences, and cravings or mental preoccupation as a result of their engagement in rewarding behaviors. These behaviors range from gambling and sex to shopping and eating. Rather than time spent engaging, behavioral addictions are marked by utilizing the rewarding activity as a means of emotion regulation and experiencing both positive and negative reinforcement. Hundreds of books and articles exist related to behavioral addictions, so if you are interested in learning more, consider beginning with the following recommended reading list.

RESOURCES

Carnes, P. (2001). *Out of the shadows: Understanding sexual addiction* (3rd ed.). Hazelden.

Coker Ross, C. (2017). *The food addiction recovery workbook: How to manage cravings, reduce stress, and stop hating your body*. New Harbinger Publications, Inc.

Game Quitters: gamequitters.com

Giordano, A. L. (2022). *A clinical guide to treating behavioral addictions: Conceptualizations, assessments, and clinical strategies*. Springer Publishing Company.

International Association of Eating Disorders Professionals Foundation: http://www.iaedp.com/

National Association of Collegiate Esports: nacesports.org

National Council on Problem Gambling: ncpgambling.org

Roberts, K. (2010). *Cyber junkie: Escape the gaming and internet trap*. Hazelden.

Schreiber, K., & Hausenblas, H. A. (2015). *The truth about exercise addiction: Understanding the dark side of thinspiration*. Rowan & Littlefield.

Schüll, N. D. (2012). *Addiction by design: Machine gambling in Las Vegas*. Princeton University Press.

Stopping Overshopping: https://www.shopaholicnomore.com/

Weiss, R. (2015). *Sex addiction 101: A basic guide to healing from sex, porn, and love addiction*. Health Communications.

Wilson, G. (2014). *Your brain on porn: Internet pornography and the emerging science of addiction*. Commonwealth.

KEY REFERENCES

Only key references appear in the print edition. The full reference list appears in the digital product on Springer Publishing Connect: connect.springerpub.com/content/book/978-0-8261-3586-5/chapter/ch11

American Society of Addiction Medicine. (2019). *Definition of addiction*. https://www.asam.org/Quality-Science/definition-of-addiction

Carnes, P. (2001). *Out of the shadows: Understanding sexual addiction* (3rd ed.). Hazeldon.

Delmonico, D. L., & Griffin, E. (1997). Classifying problematic sexual behavior: A working model. *Sexual Addiction & Compulsivity, 4*(1), 91–104. https://doi.org/10.1080/10720169708400133

Gearhardt, A. N., Corbin, W. R., & Brownell, K. D. (2009). Preliminary validation of the Yale Food Addiction Scale. *Appetite, 52*(2), 430–436. https://doi.org/10.1016/j.appet.2008.12.003

Griffiths, M. D. (2005). A 'components' model of addiction within a biopsychosocial framework. *Journal of Substance Use, 10*(4), 191–197. https://doi.org/10.1080/14659890500114359

Kafka, M. P. (2010). Hypersexual disorder: A proposed diagnosis for *DSM-5*. *Archives of Sexual Behavior, 39*, 377–400. https://doi.org/10.1007/s10508-009-9574-7

Leigh, S. J., & Morris, M. J. (2018). The role of reward circuitry and food addiction in the obesity epidemic: An update. *Biological Psychiatry, 131*, 31–42. https://doi.org/10.1016/j.biopsycho.2016.12.013

Petry, N. M., Ginley, M. K., & Rash, C. J. (2017). A systematic review of treatments for problem gambling. *Psychology of Addictive Behaviors, 31*(8), 951–961. https://doi.org/10.1037/adb0000290

Wise, R. A., & Robble, M. A. (2020). Dopamine and addiction. *Annual Review of Psychology, 71*, 79–106. https://doi.org/10.1146/annurev-psych-010418-103337

12

TREATING CO-OCCURRING DISORDERS

LEARNING OBJECTIVES

This chapter provides an introduction to assessment and treatment of co-occurring substance use and mental health disorders. By the end of this chapter, you will be able to:

- define co-occurring disorders;
- recognize risk factors associated with co-occurring disorders;
- summarize theoretical explanations for the co-occurrence of substance use and mental health disorders;
- describe past and current treatment models commonly used to work with people who have co-occurring disorders;
- recognize important assessment and treatment goals;
- identify main diagnostic features of the most frequently co-occurring disorders.

TERMS TO KNOW

continuing care treatment system that monitors clients' overall progress, supports clients through different stages of treatment (including aftercare), and is responsive to clients' present needs

co-occurring disorders simultaneous occurrence (existence) of substance use and mental health disorders

integrated treatment a model that emphasizes the importance of treating both mental health and substance use disorders at the same time. However, under this approach, unlike the parallel model, treatment is delivered by the same clinician

multiproblem viewpoint a notion that treatment for co-occurring disorders should be multidimensional and address immediate and long-term concerns

No Wrong Door Approach a healthcare system that allows treatment access at any point of entry

parallel treatment	a model that proposes treating both mental health and substance use disorders simultaneously, but treatment for each disorder is conducted by a different clinician (often in different clinical settings)
sequential treatment	a model that proposes a sequential or hierarchical approach to treatment. Under this model, clients presenting issues are treated in order of perceived acuity

INTRODUCTION

Historically, several different terms have been used to describe substance use and mental health disorders that present simultaneously (Substance Abuse and Mental Health Services Administration [SAMHSA], 2015). Initially, following the deinstitutionalization movement of the 1970s, persons who faced substance use and mental health issues were labeled either as chemical abuser mentally ill (CAMI) or mentally ill chemical abuser (MICA), depending on the perceived hierarchy between the two disorders (Scheffler, 2014). However, as our understanding of substance use and mental health disorders progressed and became less stigmatizing, so too did the terminology used to describe people who struggle with these issues. Over time, expressions such as *dual diagnoses*, *dual disorders*, *coexisting disorders*, and *comorbidity* have all been used clinically. However, the term "co-occurring disorders" has "achieved acceptance within the practitioner and scientific community" (SAMHSA, 2015, p. 7) over the last few decades and is most commonly used today.

The evolution and changes related to the terminology used to describe co-occurring disorders are very much representative of the transitions in our overall understanding of these disorders. Initially, our knowledge of co-occurring disorders was scant, and significant questions regarding their existence and validity were prominent. For example, just a few decades ago, most psychiatric textbooks stated that co-occurring disorders were quite rare and did not present a significant clinical concern (Doweiko, 2019). However, our grasp of the complexity of co-occurring disorders and the severity of these issues have improved notably over time, and we now have a better understanding and appreciation of both the commonality of co-occurring disorders and the significant impact they have on clients.

DEFINITION OF CO-OCCURRING DISORDERS

The term *co-occurring disorders* is defined as a synchronous occurrence of a substance use disorder (SUD) and a mental health disorder (SAMHSA, 2020c). Clients with co-occurring disorders have at least one disorder related to the use of substances and at least one disorder related to their mental health. Additionally, a co-occurring diagnosis requires that each disorder is established independently of the other, and that neither disorder is simply a symptom cluster associated with the primary issue (SAMHSA, 2020c). Minkoff (2010) noted that co-occurring diagnosis applies to anyone who has "any combination of any mental health issue and any substance issue, including trauma, gambling and nicotine dependence, whether or not they have already been diagnosed" (p. 11).

CASE EXAMPLE: LISA

Lisa was referred to treatment through her Employee Assistance Program (EAP) following an incident at work. Lisa had an altercation with a coworker that escalated to physical confrontation, and several team members had to get involved to separate them. After the incident, during her conversation with the management team, Lisa was apologetic and disclosed that she was intoxicated.

During your assessment, Lisa shared that she uses cocaine "regularly." She reported that she started using cocaine when she moved to the city after college. Lisa disclosed that the only other substances she uses now are alcohol and tobacco, but she shared that she used "study drugs" while in college (mainly Adderall). When discussing her drug use, Lisa reported that she primarily uses because it alters her mood, it makes her more productive, and it "feels good." Lisa reported that her mood changes significantly and that she experiences a sense of euphoria, high energy, and increased concentration following her use. She also added that these effects can last a long time if she times her hits correctly. She also shared that she is "a bit reckless during those times." Lisa reported that she is likely to max out her credit card when she experiences one of her binges. Also, Lisa stated that she found herself in some "scary situations" during those times.

Additionally, Lisa reported that another reason why she uses cocaine is that she feels "so terrible" when she stops using. Lisa stated that she feels depressed and fatigued when she doesn't use. During the times she did not use, Lisa noted that she did not have an interest in doing "just about anything," and she often fell behind on her duties at work. She stated that these periods can get really bad, and that she was written up at work twice before for poor performance and for not completing her assignments.

THEORETICAL EXPLANATIONS OF CO-OCCURRING DISORDERS

LEARNING ACTIVITY 12.1

Based on the definition of co-occurring disorders, does Lisa have a co-occurring disorder?

What factors did you consider in your decision-making?

What other information would you need/consider to determine Lisa's diagnosis?

Several theories have been offered to explain the existence and development of co-occurring disorders. The first of the possible explanations is the self-medication hypothesis. This theory proposed that co-occurring disorders develop when clients with mental health disorders use substances to self-medicate in order to remedy undesirable symptoms associated with their disorders (Rowland & Marwaha, 2018). An example of substances serving as self-medicaments would be a client who is struggling with depression using stimulants (e.g., cocaine) to offset negative symptoms. Another theoretical explanation proposed that substances are not used to minimize negative symptoms associated with their mental health disorders but rather to maximize desirable effects (Bizzarri et al., 2007). For example, a client who has bipolar disorder (BD) may use methamphetamine to increase and prolong pleasurable effects of mania. In addition to these two hypotheses that conceptualize substance use as a consequence of (or a reaction to) mental health disorders, theories that view substance use as the preceding disorder also have been proposed. These hypotheses generally argue that mental health issues are induced or triggered by drug consumption, and as a result only exist as a consequence of substance use (Swann, 2010).

However, despite these efforts to establish a clear causal relationship between substance use and mental health disorders, co-occurring disorders appear to be far more complex. Researchers from the National Survey on Drug Use and Health (NSDUH; SAMHSA, 2020a) described the relationship between substance use and mental health disorders as bidirectional. That is, the presence of a mental health disorder is likely to contribute to the development and/or exacerbation of a SUD. Similarly, the presence of a SUD will commonly contribute to the development and/or exacerbation of a mental health disorder. Nonetheless, aside from all of these explanations, the most important part for counselors to remember is that co-occurring disorders cause severe functional impairments and a wide range of presenting issues that require intentional treatment planning and interventions (SAMHSA, 2020a).

SCOPE OF THE PROBLEM

National epidemiological surveys consistently indicate that substance use and mental health disorders co-occur commonly. The most recent prevalent data from the NSDUH showed that almost 10 million adults and close to 400,000 adolescents had a co-occurring disorder in 2019 (SAMHSA, 2020a). The co-occurrence of SUDs among persons who have severe mental illnesses also is high, as 3.6 million adults had both a SUD and a severe mental illness in 2019. Co-occurring disorders also are prevalent among clients in substance use treatment facilities (SAMHSA, 2020b). The National Survey of Substance Abuse Treatment Services (N-SSATS) reported that more than half of adult clients in substance use facilities had co-occurring substance use and mental health disorders and that 89% of these facilities reported having clients with diagnosed co-occurring substance use and mental health disorders (SAMHSA, 2020b).

In addition to the high prevalence rates, the epidemiological data also suggests an alarming trend of significant increases in prevalence rates over the last five years. The rates of co-occurring disorders among adults increased by close to 20% since 2015 (just over eight million people had co-occurring substance use and mental health disorders that year), and the co-occurrence of SUDs and severe mental illnesses increased by 56% during the same time period (there were 2.3 million adults with co-occurring substance use and serious mental illness in 2015; SAMHSA, 2020a).

Aside from the high and rising co-occurrence rates, the significance of co-occurring substance use and mental health disorders also is demonstrated by the severity of the impact they have on persons who have these disorders. People with co-occurring disorders commonly have greater levels of psychosocial impairment and are at risk of several negative outcomes, including rapid progression from the initial substance use to the development of a SUD, higher rates of suicide, increased rates of hospitalizations, more frequent medical problems, more likely noncompliance with medications, and higher mortality and morbidity rates (Compton et al., 2007; Hartz et al., 2014; Haviland et al., 2016; Mojtabai et al., 2014; SAMHSA, 2015; Wisner et al., 2013). Also, in terms of treatment issues, clients with co-occurring disorders are less likely to initiate treatment and have low treatment-completion rates, have poorer treatment outcomes, have higher relapse rates, and have higher treatment costs (SAMHSA, 2015). Finally, in addition to challenging clinical issues, co-occurring disorders also are linked with many socioeconomic factors that can impede the recovery process (SAMHSA, 2020b). For example, people who have co-occurring disorders are more likely to face homelessness and unemployment, have higher involvement with the criminal justice system, have increased rates of recidivism, lack social and financial supports, have difficulties in social and family relationships, and face educational issues (Peters et al., 2012; SAMHSA, 2015, 2020b).

LEARNING ACTIVITY 12.2
SYMPTOM DISCRIMINATION

Please read the following scenarios and list all factors that could be influencing clients' symptoms.

1. Denisha's father brought her to counseling due to changes in her behavior. He reports that Denisha has become lethargic, lacks energy, is irritable, and appears "emotionless." She sleeps most of the day and seems to have lost interest in all of her activities. Denisha's symptoms could be related to:
   - Intoxication on the following substances:
   - Withdrawal from the following substances:
   - Having the following mental health concern:
2. Jason reports that he has experienced racing thoughts and excessive speech, is excitable, hyperactive, and goes days without sleeping. Jason's symptoms could be related to:
   - Intoxication on the following substances:
   - Withdrawal from the following substances:
   - Having the following mental health concern:
3. You work at an inpatient community mental health agency. A client was brought in due to psychotic symptoms. He is unable to tell you his name and he appears to be experiencing auditory and visual hallucinations. The client's symptoms could be related to:
   - Intoxication on the following substances:
   - Withdrawal from the following substances:
   - Having the following mental health concern:

ASSESSMENT AND DIAGNOSTIC CONSIDERATIONS

Assessment and diagnosis of co-occurring disorders are complex processes, and a significant number of clients have been misdiagnosed due to inadequate assessment (Atkins, 2014). The intricacy of the assessment procedures and the subsequent diagnostic issues are related to several factors. Some of these impediments are related to the very nature of co-occurring disorders. The simultaneous existence and interaction between substance use and mental health disorders contribute to a great level of complexity and difficulties when it comes to assessment and diagnoses. Also, persons with co-occurring disorders ordinarily have a wide range of presenting issues (Atkins, 2014). This diverse symptomology creates challenges in discriminating among clients' concerns accurately and increases the intricacy of assessment and diagnosis procedures. Additionally, the assessment and diagnostic process is further complicated by the fact that some effects of substance use could distort, mimic, or conceal symptoms of mental health disorders (Atkins, 2014; Brady & Sinha, 2007; Horsfall et al., 2009; Schladweiler et al., 2009). For example, symptoms associated with stimulant use (e.g., methamphetamine or cocaine) could present as BD (mania), including a decreased need for sleep, heightened energy, and increased productivity for a period of time (Ma et al., 2018).

In addition to issues related to the nature of co-occurring disorders, some assessment and diagnostic problems are related to clinical training and treatment structure. In the past, addiction and mental health counselor training were separate, and counselors were trained to address either addiction or mental health disorders, not both (Hagedorn et al., 2012; Merta, 2001). As a result, counselors were not equipped sufficiently to assess (or treat) co-occurring disorders. This has led to the bifurcation of substance use and mental health services, making effective assessment and diagnosis of clients with co-occurring disorders nearly impossible (SAMHSA, 2015). Additionally, assessment of co-occurring disorders is not a part of routine procedures in clinical settings, and as a result these disorders are often underidentified and underdiagnosed (Hiller et al., 2011; Lurigio, 2011; Peters et al., 2012).

The lack of assessment creates a domino effect that ultimately leads to negative health outcomes for persons who have co-occurring disorders (SAMHSA, 2020a). This domino effect starts with the lack of assessment, which leads to the absence of a diagnosis. No diagnosis is then followed by the lack of treatment (or at least of proper treatment). And this ultimately results in reduced chances for long-term recovery and poorer health outcomes for clients with co-occurring disorders (SAMHSA, 2020a). Additionally, insufficient assessment and diagnosis are likely to impede the treatment progress, increase relapse rates, contribute to excessive use of community resources (e.g., crisis care), and exacerbate clients' presenting symptoms (Peterson et al., 2014).

As a result of these factors, it is critical for counselors to be intentional and use thorough assessment and diagnostic procedures when working with clients who have co-occurring disorders (Donovan, 2005; Gil-Rivas et al., 2009; Mazza et al., 2009).

Assessment Recommendations

In order to adequately treat clients with co-occurring disorders, counselors must be able to accurately identify symptoms of each disorder and evaluate their influence on each other. Considering that clients with co-occurring disorders face several complex issues with a multitude of contributing factors, a biopsychosocial approach to assessment is recommended (SAMHSA, 2020c). That is, as a part of the assessment process, counselors should thoroughly examine medical, psychological, and sociocultural factors that are impacting clients' well-being. This approach allows counselors to have the most comprehensive understanding of clients' presenting issues and make the most informed treatment decisions. Also, biopsychosocial assessment is evidence based and is considered to be the standard of care in our profession (SAMHSA, 2020c). An additional point we want to emphasize regarding the assessment of co-occurring disorders is that, in order to distinguish substance-induced and psychiatric symptoms properly, counselors must allow time for intoxication and withdrawal symptoms to dissipate. Standard practice is to wait until the client has been abstinent for 30 days and then reassess them (if symptoms went away during that time, they were likely substance induced).

SAMHSA (2015) has identified eight goals that should guide the assessment of co-occurring substance use and mental health disorders. These goals include:

- Understanding the scope and severity of substance use and mental health issues as well as contextual factors that are influencing them
- Gathering history of previous substance use and mental health disorders and clients' response to treatment
- Gathering family history of substance use and mental health issues
- Determining the level of care needed
- Understanding readiness for treatment and clients' motivation
- Examining individuals' strengths
- Evaluating risk factors

Assessment Tools

The *Structured Clinical Interview for DSM-5* (SCID-5; APA, 2013) is the recommended framework for screening and assessment of clients with co-occurring disorders (SAMHSA, 2015). The SCID-5 provides counselors with a comprehensive plan for evaluation of clients' presenting issues and outlines the *Diagnostic and Statistical Manual of Mental Disorders,* Fifth Edition (*DSM-5*; APA, 2013) diagnostic process. Additionally, SCID-5 could be used as a broader assessment approach, and all assessment tools that we provided in Box 12.1 can be incorporated as a part of this process.

BOX 12.1

ASSESSMENT TOOLS

Depression

- Beck Depression Inventory (BDI)
- Center for Epidemiologic Studies Depression Scale (CES-D)
- EQ-5D
- Hamilton Depression Rating Scale (HAM-D)

(*continued*)

Bipolar Disorder

- Young Mania Rating Scale (YMRS)
- Bech-Rafarlsen Mania Rating Scale (MAS)
- Altman Self-Rating Mania Scale

PTSD

- PTSD Symptom Scale Interview (PSS-I and PSS-I-5)
- Life Events Checklist (LEC-5)
- Clinician-Administered PTSD Scale for *DSM-5* (CAPS-5)
- PTSD Checklist for *DSM-5* (PCL-5)

Personality Disorders

- Minnesota Multiphasic Personality Inventory-II (MMPI-II)
- Millon Clinical Multiaxial Inventory-III (MCMI-III)
- International Personality Disorder Examination (IPDE)
- NEO Five-Factor Inventory

Anxiety Disorders

- Brief Fear of Negative Evaluation Scale (BFNE)
- Depression Anxiety Stress Scales (DASS-21)
- Generalized Anxiety Disorder Questionnaire-IV (GADQ-IV)
- Hamilton Anxiety Rating Scale (HAM-A)

Schizophrenia

- Positive and Negative Symptoms Scale (PANSS)
- Scale for the Assessment of Positive Symptoms (SAPS)
- The Scale for the Assessment of Negative Symptoms (SANS)
- Negative Symptom Assessment-16 (NSA-16)
- Clinical Global Impression Schizophrenia (CGI-SCH)

PTSD, posttraumatic stress disorder.

One final note before we conclude the assessment and diagnosis portion of this chapter: When assessing co-occurring disorders, as with the assessment of any other mental health condition, it is important that counselors utilize a battery of instruments and procedures to gain a thorough understanding of clients' presenting issues and contextual factors that could impact their recovery. For example, counselors should assess the onset, length, and the severity of symptoms related to clients' substance use and mental health issues as well as sociocultural factors that could be influencing clients' presentation. Also, careful consideration should be given to clients' detoxication and the potential impact of withdrawal symptoms before formal assessment and diagnostic decisions (Quello et al., 2005).

TREATMENT IMPLICATIONS

When starting a discussion about treatment for co-occurring disorders, two factors are critical to note. The first one is that co-occurring disorders are treatable conditions (SAMHSA, 2020a). Counselors who work with these disorders can utilize a range of effective treatment strategies that can be adapted across all treatment settings to help clients achieve sustainable recovery (SAMHSA, 2020a). However, the second factor that is important for us to consider is that most clients diagnosed with co-occurring disorders do not receive proper treatment (SAMHSA, 2020c). For instance, the Center for Behavioral Health Statistics and Quality (2019) found that in 2018, only 8% of clients who have co-occurring disorders received comprehensive treatment that addressed both issues. Additionally, nearly half (48.6%) of adults with co-occurring disorders received no treatment (SAMHSA, 2020c). There are several barriers we discussed earlier that limit treatment access; however, one of the factors that has the most direct influence on the delivery of care is treatment models that are used to structure co-occurring treatment delivery. Therefore, before we explore specific treatment recommendations, it is important for us to examine three treatment models that are (were) used to structure client care: (1) sequential treatment, (2) parallel treatment, and (3) integrated treatment.

Sequential Treatment. This model requires the creation of a hierarchical order for treatment. In essence, one disorder is treated first, and then the treatment focus is shifted to the other disorder. The sequence of treatment typically is established according to the acuity of presenting symptoms and perceived disruptive impact on clients' functioning. For example, a client who enters treatment during an active manic episode will receive treatment for BD first, and little time and effort will be dedicated to their substance use until BD is addressed. Similarly, a client who is actively withdrawing from a long-term alcohol use disorder and has a history of delirium tremens will first be treated for the substance use issues, and treatment for their mental health condition will not start until later. Under this model, each disorder is treated exclusively from the other and in order of perceived importance, and it is not uncommon for clients to be referred to another facility for specialized treatment (e.g., inpatient substance use treatment). This approach may appear reasonable in that it addresses the most severe issues first, but functionally, it fails to take into consideration the complex nature of the co-occurrence of these disorders. Another issue with this model could arise in determining the treatment hierarchy. For instance, let's examine the case of Andy who struggles with depression and excessive alcohol and benzodiazepine use. When Andy presented for treatment at a community health center, it was determined that his substance use was more acute than his mental health disorder and that alcohol and benzodiazepine use must be addressed first in order to treat Andy's mental health disorder successfully. Andy, in accordance with the sequential treatment model, was referred to a substance use treatment center. However, when he arrived at this facility, the center clinicians determined that Andy's depression issues were detrimental to successful completion of a substance use program, and they referred Andy to address his depression first.

When we examine Andy's case, it is not difficult to imagine that both sets of clinicians were acting in what they perceive to be Andy's best interest, as they all wanted (what they perceived to be) the most acute issues to be addressed first. However, as a result of the nature of the sequential treatment model, Andy's issues may go unaddressed.

Parallel Treatment. The parallel model entails treating both disorders simultaneously, but treatment for each disorder would be conducted by a different clinician (often in different clinical settings). An example of this model would include a client receiving treatment for generalized anxiety disorder at a community mental health clinic and at the same time attending an addictions recovery clinic for substance use issues. The advantage of this approach would be that (1) clients receive treatment from specialists with expertise in the disorder they are treating, and (2) both disorders are being addressed at the same time. However, a downside of this approach could be that clinicians at each setting may have different theoretical approaches to treatment and in practicing their approach may communicate conflicting information to the client. For example, counselors at a community mental health clinic may perceive substance use issues as an attempt at self-medication with an aim of regulating symptoms of generalized anxiety disorder. But the clinician at the addiction recovery center may conceptualize substance use from the medical disease model and perceive these issues as the primary concern for treatment. These conflicting views may create confusion for the client and ultimately undermine the success of treatment.

Integrated Treatment. This model emphasizes the importance of treating both disorders at the same time. However, under this approach, unlike the parallel model, treatment is delivered by the same clinician. The chief advantage of this model is a comprehensive treatment plan that is sensitive to the complex nature of co-occurring disorders and also responsive to any immediate need clients may have (e.g., presenting with a manic episode, experiencing severe and dangerous withdrawals, etc.). This approach also allows clinicians to examine the relationship between the two disorders and change treatment according to clients' individualized needs. The integrated treatment model, however, demands that clinicians are competent in addressing mental health disorders as well as substance use issues. Considering that one clinician is responsible for addressing substance use and mental health disorders simultaneously, the expectations of clinical "fluency" are higher in this case.

There is substantial evidence to suggest that the integrated model is an effective treatment for co-occurring disorders (SAMHSA, 2020c). Also, national treatment guidelines recommend integrated treatment and argue that both disorders should be treated concurrently (Han et al., 2017; Pettinati et al., 2013; Watkins et al., 2005). This model was shown to be successful in addressing adequately both substance use and mental health issues, including decreased substance use (Drake et al., 2016; Flanagan et al., 2016; Ruglass et al., 2017), increased mental health functioning (Drake et al., 2016; Kelly & Daley, 2013), lowered emergency visits and hospitalizations (Morse & Bride, 2017), and overall life quality and satisfaction (Drake et al., 2016). Additionally, researchers found that this model was effective across different treatment settings (McKee et al., 2013).

Now that we are familiar with the three models that provide an underlining structure for the treatment of co-occurring disorders, we will review specific factors that are relevant for working with clients who have co-occurring disorders.

Guiding Principles for Treatment of Co-Occurring Disorders

The Treatment Improvement Protocol (TIP) panel (SAMHSA, 2020c) developed a set of principles to help guide clinical work with clients who have co-occurring disorders. These principles (titled the "Six Guiding Principles in Treating Clients With Co-Occurring Disorders") described six fundamental guidelines designed to aid counselors in the overall treatment structure and "ideal delivery" (p. 16) of co-occurring disorders services (SAMHSA, 2020c). In the following section, we will review these principles.

Six Guiding Principles in Treating Clients With Co-Occurring Disorders

1. **Recovery perspective:** The recovery perspective requires treatment for co-occurring disorders to be considered as a long-term, multistage process of change (De Leon, 1996; Prochaska et al., 1992; SAMHSA, 2020c). This viewpoint rests on two main assumptions. The first conjecture poses that counselors who work with co-occurring disorders should develop comprehensive treatment plans that ensure continuity of care over time (SAMHSA, 2020c). When developing these plans, in addition to the primary clinical objectives, counselors need to remember that treatment for co-occurring disorders may take place in different settings (e.g., inpatient, intensive outpatient) and that the recovery process may involve factors outside the formal treatment environment (e.g., family and peer support groups, faith community, etc.). Therefore, treatment plans for clients with co-occurring disorders must be inclusive of the primary treatment goals as well as contextual factors that could influence clients' recovery. The second assumption notes that counselors should develop interventions that are sensitive to clients' current needs and target challenges that are specific to each stage of the recovery process (SAMHSA, 2020c). Additionally, interventions that are used during treatment must be considerate of clients' identity and culturally appropriate (SAMHSA, 2020c).
2. **Multiproblem viewpoint:** Clients with co-occurring disorders ordinarily have an array of substance use, mental health, medical, social, and family issues that are significantly impairing their functioning (SAMHSA, 2020c). As a result, the multiproblem notion poses that treatment for co-occurring disorders should be multidimensional and address immediate and long-term concerns. In addition to direct substance use and mental health concerns, counselors also should be cognizant of clients' needs regarding housing, healthcare, work, and support network (SAMHSA, 2020c).
3. **Phase approach to treatment:** Conceptualizing treatment for co-occurring disorders in terms of phases allows counselors to assess clients' needs better, develop more-comprehensive treatment plans, and utilize targeted interventions (SAMHSA, 2020c). Ordinarily, a five-phase approach is used, including client engagement, stabilization, active treatment, continuing care, and relapse prevention (Mueser & Gingerich, 2013; SAMHSA, 2009).
4. **Planning for real-life problems early in treatment:** It is important to recognize that co-occurring disorders exist within clients' lives in a broader context and could contribute to myriad interpersonal and social difficulties. Therefore, counselors must be intentional in addressing these issues early in treatment (SAMHSA, 2020c). In order to maximize clients' recovery efforts, early treatment interventions should incorporate case management as well as services that could assist clients in navigating legal and bureaucratic demands. For example, clients should get assistance regarding legal issues, housing needs, and vocational concerns (Clark et al., 2016; Luciano & Carpenter-Song, 2014; Mueser et al., 2011).
5. **Planning for cognitive and functional impairments:** A significant number of clients with co-occurring disorders will face serious cognitive and functional issues that will impair their ability to engage fully and benefit from the treatment process (Duijkers et al.,

2016). Therefore, it is critical for counselors to adjust their interventions in accordance with clients' needs and level of functioning (SAMHSA, 2020c). For example, counselors should consider adapting the structure and length of their interventions or incorporation of appropriate aids (e.g., visual aids). Even in instances when clients are facing subtle barriers (e.g., mild learning disability), the impact on clients' recovery could be significant, and counselors should be intentional in addressing it early (SAMHSA, 2020c).

6. **Utilizing support systems:** It is vital to realize that counseling, in many ways, is a limited resource. Therefore, it is critical to utilize other support systems (e.g., Dual Recovery Anonymous) to aid clients' recovery efforts (SAMHSA, 2020c). These support systems could be particularly relevant for clients with co-occurring disorders since many of them may have been living in unsupportive environments for decades (SAMHSA, 2020c). Additionally, stigma related to substance use and mental health issues still is very prevalent, and many clients may be ostracized by their families or the entire community. Connecting clients to more sustainable, long-term support systems could be vital to their recovery.

In addition to these principles, the TIP panel identified treatment access and provision of an appropriate level of care as the critical components to effective treatment of clients with co-occurring disorders (SAMHSA, 2020c). Regarding access to services, the TIP panel outlined four main points of contact for persons with co-occurring disorders: (1) routine services for clients who are not in crisis, (2) crisis services for clients who need immediate care or are in a state of an emergency, (3) targeted outreach for high-risk populations (e.g., homeless population) that are unlikely to or cannot access routine or crisis services, and (4) involuntary or mandated services required by the criminal justice system or the child welfare system. Also, the TIP panel recommended the adoption of the "no wrong door" (p. 17) policy that will help expand client access and increase treatment delivery (SAMHSA, 2020c). Box 12.2 provides a brief description of the "no wrong door" policy.

BOX 12.2

NO WRONG DOOR APPROACH

The primary goal of the No Wrong Door Approach is to structure the healthcare system to allow treatment access at any point of entry. This approach rests on the following five principles:

1. Availability of assessment, referral, and treatment planning across healthcare settings
2. A wide availability of creative outreach strategies
3. Flexible treatment programs that are sensitive to clients' individual needs and are able to engage unmotivated clients
4. Client-centered treatment plans that are responsive to clients' transitions through stages of treatment
5. A coordinated system that provides continuity of care

In terms of the appropriate level of care for clients with co-occurring disorders, it is important to consider that, due to the nature of co-occurring disorders, clients entering treatment could have a wide variety of presenting issues. As a result, it is critical that the treatment setting is able to appropriately determine the necessary level of care and adequately meet clients' needs. The American Association of Community Psychiatry (AAPC) developed a standardized way of determining appropriate level of care and treatment intensity. The AAPC's Level of Care Utilization System (LOCUS) helps counselors assess both clients' concerns as well as the treatment center's capacity and resources. In terms of clients' needs, LOCUS outlines six levels of treatment that could be assigned based on clients' presentation and needed level on intensity. The capacity of treatment centers is ranked across three levels based on available service: (1) addiction services only, (2) dual diagnosis capable, and (3) dual diagnosis enhanced. Through this comprehensive assessment, counselors could ensure that clients' presenting issues are addressed appropriately and the treatment resources are maximized.

Additionally, counselors could utilize the Four Quadrants Model originally developed by Ries (1993). This model classifies clients into four groups based on relative symptom severity. Please see Table 12.1 for an illustration of the Four Quadrants Model.

TABLE 12.1 The Four Quadrants Model

III: Less severe mental health disorder—More severe substance use disorder • Recommended Level of Care: Substance use treatment center	IV: More severe mental health disorder—More severe substance use disorder • Recommended Level of Care: High-intensity substance use treatment center or hospitalization
I: Less severe mental health disorder—Less severe substance use disorder • Recommended Level of Care: Primary healthcare setting or community care agency	II: More severe mental health disorder—Less severe substance use disorder • Recommended Level of Care: Mental healthcare setting

CASE EXAMPLE: TOD

Tod is a 35-year-old man who currently works in the service industry and is finishing his bachelor's degree in marketing at a local university. He presented for treatment at the suggestion of his best friend who expressed concerns about Tod's drinking and negativity. Tod also disclosed that his wife has been unhappy "for quite some time now" and that he is afraid if things continue this way, they will divorce.

During the assessment, Tod reported that he first started drinking in high school when he was around 15 years old. He noted that as soon as he started drinking, he was consuming large amounts of liquor. But he noted that drinking was the norm in his friend group, and that he did not see himself as any different from his friends. Tod stated that the only period when his drinking was "somewhat less" was during his time in the army. However, he disclosed that as soon as he got out, his drinking increased significantly. Tod reported that he often blacks out, vomits, and has hangovers as a result of drinking. However, when asked about seizures and delirium tremens, he stated that he never experienced either. Tod disclosed that he had some legal issues related to his drinking. He reported getting a DUI when he was 23 years old and having two other misdemeanor charges in his late 20s. Tod reported that, at the urging of his wife, he went to Alcoholics Anonymous (AA) before, but that he did not find it very helpful. When asked why, Tod noted that "all that talk about giving up control" was not for him.

(*continued*)

In addition to his drinking, Tod also reported consistently feeling down and negative. He stated that he remembers these feelings staring before he even entered high school, and he shared that he feels like that most of the time. Tod shared that he feels tired all the time, and does not feel motivated to do anything. He stated that over the last few years he has become very critical of himself, and that he often feels that he cannot do anything right. Also, he shared that sometimes he contemplates how it would be if he was not alive, but he denied having any active suicidal thoughts.

LEARNING ACTIVITY 12.3

Using the Four Quadrants Model, what quadrant would be the most appropriate for Tod? Please explain why.

In terms of treatment, what recommendations would you make for Tod? Please provide a rationale for your answer.

NOTES FROM THE FIELD

Moneta Sinclair, EdD, LPC, CPCS, MAC, has been a counselor in the addiction treatment field for the past 13 years. During this time, in addition to her clinical role, she also served as a supervisor for masters and doctoral interns as well as an administrator for an addiction counseling program. Currently, she is Director of Addiction Services at a private nonprofit community organization that provides care to the HIV community. The organization offers a number of services for clients with addiction issues including intensive outpatient and continuing care programs, harm reduction and prevention programs, medication-assisted treatment, individual and group counseling, and case management. Additionally, the program works with clients who not only have SUDs, but also struggle with process addictions.

When asked about the parts of her job that she enjoys the most, Moneta noted the variety of services the organization is able to provide. She highlighted that the organization is able to provide necessary care to a wide range of people including clients who need intensive addiction recovery services, those who are transitioning into continuation care programs, as well as persons at risk for developing addiction issues. Additionally, Moneta shared that her favorite event is the Annual Recognition Ceremony where clients get to reflect and share their stories once they successfully complete the program. Moneta disclosed that she is always touched when clients speak of the program as a place that changed their lives, and that these moments serve as reminders of why she is doing this work.

Moneta stated that one of the biggest challenges she faces is accessing all clients who call for help. She shared that often clients call the organization when they are in distress; however, they fail to follow up or utilize services that are offered to them. Moneta noted that they are currently utilizing certified peer specialists to reach out to clients as soon as they contact the organization and actively facilitate the process of connecting clients to their services. She also shared that the organization is in the process of hiring a Community Health Worker who will be able to do more extensive follow ups and address barriers that may prevent clients from accessing care.

Finally, as the most important advice for novice counselors, Moneta identified personal counseling. She stated that doing one's own work and addressing potential personal triggers and barriers to working with this population are critical for being a good counselor. As a continuation of this work, Moneta noted appropriate supervision and additional educational opportunities. Finally, she shared that novice counselors must not overlook serious risk factors associated with addiction issues. Moneta particularly highlighted suicidality and the need for proper assessment and safety planning.

FREQUENTLY CO-OCCURRING DISORDERS

Depressive Disorders

Depressive disorders are one of the most commonly co-occurring disorders among clients with substance use issues (Nunes et al., 2010). In regards to a specific diagnosis, major depressive disorder (MDD) and persistent depressive disorder (PDD) are most likely to present in clients with addiction issues (SAMHSA, 2020c). Prevalence rates of depressive disorders are higher among persons diagnosed with SUD than for the general population (Grant et al., 2016). Nunes and colleagues (2010) estimated that between 20% and 50% of people who seek addiction treatment have experienced at least one episode of major depression during their lifetime, and that up to 20% of clients are experiencing depression when they enter treatment. In addition to the high prevalence rates, clients with co-occurring depressive disorder and SUDs typically experience more severe mood disturbance, lower levels of overall functioning, higher risk of suicide ideation and attempts, more psychiatric comorbidities, and poorer treatment outcomes than people who only have a depressive disorder (Blanco et al., 2012; Gadermann et al., 2012; Nunes et al., 2010).

Main diagnostic criteria: major depressive disorder: MDD can develop at any age, but the highest risk of onset for this disorder is during puberty (American Psychiatric Association [APA], 2013). MDD is primarily characterized by a depressed mood and the loss of interest in pleasurable activities for a period of at least 2 weeks. Depressed mood is commonly experienced as severe sadness, hopelessness, or discouragement. However, for adolescents and children, mood issues may present as irritation rather than sadness. The loss of interest is usually described as a feeling of not caring for anything or as a lack of enjoyment. In addition to mood disturbance and loss of interest, clients must experience at least four of the following symptoms: (1) significant weight change, (2) disturbed sleep hygiene, (3) impaired psychomotor functioning, (4) decreased energy and fatigue, (5) heightened feelings of worthlessness or guilt, (6) difficulties concentrating and impaired decision-making, (7) pervasive thoughts of death and suicidal ideation and attempts. Clients who have MDD will experience these symptoms most of the day (almost every day), and the symptoms will cause significant impairment in clients' lives (APA, 2013).

Persistent depressive disorder: PDD usually is described as a milder and more persistent form of depression (APA, 2013). PDD is most likely to be diagnosed first early in life (at the latest by early adulthood). The most defining aspect of PDD is a depressed mood that presents consistently for at least 2 years (or 1 year for adolescents and children). In addition to depressed mood, clients also will exhibit two of the following symptoms: (1) disturbed appetite and eating patterns, (2) sleep issues, (3) loss of energy, (4) self-esteem issues, (5) inability to concentrate and make decisions, and (6) hopelessness. It is important to note that MDD may precede or occur during PDD. Clients who meet the criteria for both disorders should be diagnosed with MDD and PDD (APA, 2013).

Bipolar Disorder

It is estimated that up to 65% of people with bipolar disorder (BD) have a diagnosed SUD as well (McDermid et al., 2015; SAMHSA, 2016). Also, persons with a bipolar diagnosis have almost six times greater risk of developing substance use issues than people without this disorder (Blanco et al., 2017). Additionally, individuals with SUD are 50% more likely that develop BD than those who do not abuse substances (Grant et al., 2016). Co-occurring bipolar disorder and SUDs also are associated with increased symptom severity (Hunt et al., 2016) and several adverse health, social, and economic consequences (SAMHSA, 2020c). For example, clients with these co-occurring disorders are likely to experience a greater risk of suicide, higher rates of hospitalization, more severe depression and manic episodes, higher rates of mixed episodes, rapid mood cycling, and poorer treatment outcomes (Ma et al., 2018; Swann, 2010; Tolliver & Anton, 2015).

Main diagnostic criteria: BD was commonly known as manic depression (APA, 2013; SAMHSA, 2020c). BD is characterized primarily by mood fluctuations between depressive and manic states (APA, 2013). BD is most likely to be diagnosed in early adulthood; although childhood and later adulthood onsets may also occur. BD is separated into two diagnostic subtypes, Bipolar I (BD-I) and Bipolar II (BD-II). Diagnosis of BD-I requires at least one manic episode that lasts 1 week (or longer) and includes abnormally elevated or irritable mood and persistently high energy. Clients who are experiencing a manic episode commonly describe their mood as euphoric, report feeling enthusiastic, and have increased interpersonal and sexual interactions. Clients who have BD-I could also experience depressive and hypomanic episodes, but they are nonessential for a BD-I diagnosis. In addition to the mood disturbance, clients with BD-I would experience at least three of the following symptoms: (1) feelings of grandiosity and inflated self-esteem, (2) diminished need for sleep, (3) high talkativeness, (4) racing thought, (5) decreased attention, (6) heightened goal-oriented activities or psychomotor agitation, and (7) involvement in high-risk activities (APA, 2013).

The main distinction between BD-I and BD-II is that BD-II requires one or more hypomanic episodes and at least one major depressive episode (APA, 2013). Hypomanic episodes are very similar in presentation to manic episodes. The main differences between the two are that hypomanic episodes are shorter (at least 4 days of persistent symptoms) and the presenting issues are lower in severity. It is important to note that despite these differences in length and severity of symptoms, BD-II is not a "milder" version of BD-I. BD-II is considered a chronic mental health issue and clients with this diagnosis experience longer depressive phases (APA, 2013).

Posttraumatic Stress Disorder

There is a strong association between posttraumatic stress disorder (PTSD) and substance abuse (Grant et al., 2016; Hasin & Kilcoyne, 2012). It is estimated that between 26% and 52% of people with SUDs have a lifetime prevalence of PTSD, and that between 36% and 52% of persons diagnosed with PTSD experience substance use issues during their life (Vujanovic et al., 2016). Additionally, individuals who have PTSD are up to 50% more likely to develop a SUD than people without PTSD (Goldstein et al., 2016). Clients who have co-occurring PTSD and a SUD are likely to have more complex symptom presentation and poorer treatment outcomes (SAMHSA, 2020c). For example, clients diagnosed with these disorders have a higher risk of suicide attempts, greater mortality rates, lower social functioning, and more severe cognitive difficulties (Flanagan et al., 2016; Schumm & Gore, 2016). Additionally, when compared to people who are diagnosed only with PTSD or a SUD, clients with co-occurring disorders reported higher rates of childhood trauma, greater symptom severity, and higher rates of disability (Blanco et al., 2013).

Main diagnostic criteria: Before we examine diagnostic criteria, we want to discuss briefly an important point regarding PTSD. It is critical for counselors to remember that the clinical presentation of clients with PTSD could vary greatly (APA, 2013). For example, clients who have PTSD could present primarily with fear-based reexperiences, dysphoric mood and cognitive disturbances, or arousal and externalizing symptoms (or combination of all, APA, 2013). Therefore, it is important for counselors not to have expectations of "typical" PTSD presentations, as these may bias them and impair their ability to appropriately assess and treat clients.

Regarding diagnosis of PTSD, the most defining characteristics are exposure to one or more traumatic events and significant distress that is experienced as a result of these encounters (APA, 2013). Traumatic events that may lead to PTSD could be caused by (1) directly experiencing a traumatic event, (2) witnessing a traumatic event in person, (3) learning about a traumatic event that happened to a close relative or friend, and (4) repeated exposure to aversive details of a traumatic event (e.g., first responders, professional counselors). Symptoms experienced by clients who have PTSD are separated into four categories (1) intrusive, (2) avoidant, (3) negative cognitive and mood alterations, and (4) arousal and reactivity disturbances (APA, 2013).

Personality Disorders

Research on personality disorders (PDs) and SUDs points to high rates of co-occurrence (SAMHSA, 2020c). It is estimated that between 35% and 65% of clients with SUDs have co-occurring PD (Kock & Walter, 2018). Additionally, persons who have substance use issues are 50% more likely to develop PD than those who do not struggle with substance abuse. Trull and colleagues (2018) also found that co-occurrence of PD and SUDs is especially prevalent in inpatient and residential treatment settings. In addition to high prevalence rates, clients who have these co-occurring disorders also experience more severe mental and substance abuse-related symptoms, more persistent substance use issues, higher mortality rates, increased likelihood of treatment dropout, and higher rates of other co-occurring mental health issues (Kock & Walter, 2018).

Main diagnostic criteria: PDs are marked by maladaptive and inflexible personality traits that cause significant impairments and distress (APA, 2013). Persons diagnosed with PD present a pattern of affective, cognitive, and behavioral presentations that drastically deviate from their cultural norms. Their internal experiences and interpersonal interactions are highly inflexible and contribute to high levels of distress and impairments in social functioning. These patterns of maladaptive presentation ordinarily start during adolescence or young adulthood and are stable over time. PDs are grouped into three clusters based on clients' presentations. Cluster A describes persons who are characterized as eccentric or odd. This cluster includes schizoid, schizotypal, and paranoid PD. Persons who fall into Cluster B would be seen as dramatic, erratic, and emotional. Disorders that make up Cluster B are borderline, antisocial, narcissistic, and histrionic PD. And finally, Cluster C includes individuals who are characterized as fearful and anxious. Cluster C is comprised of avoidant, obsessive compulsive, and dependent PD (APA, 2013).

Anxiety Disorders

In the past, researchers have attempted to determine whether anxiety or substance use is the preceding disorder; however, these efforts produced contradictory findings. For example,

Cheng and colleagues (2004) argued that anxiety disorder generally predated SUD, while Kushner and colleagues (2011) found that at least half of clients with these co-occurring disorders faced substance use issues first. However, regardless of the hierarchical order of onset, researchers have consistently found that anxiety disorders commonly co-occur with SUDs (SAMHSA, 2020c). The presence of 12-month and lifetime SUDs is associated with a significantly higher risk of developing anxiety disorders (Grant et al., 2015, 2016). Additionally, clients with co-occurring anxiety and SUDs experience higher rates of hospitalizations, lower levels of overall functioning, higher symptom severity, increased difficulties in interpersonal relationships, lower treatment outcomes, and poorer health-related life quality (Buckner et al., 2013; Magidson et al., 2012).

Main diagnostic criteria: The *DSM-5* lists 10 specific anxiety disorders. However, a review of each separate disorder is beyond the scope of this chapter, and in this section we will only discuss factors that broadly apply to most anxiety disorders. The essential features of anxiety disorders are excessive levels of anxiety, worry, and fear (APA, 2013). These feelings are typically frequent, long-lasting, and very intense. Also, anxious experiences are not proportional to the actual impact or likelihood of the anticipated event. That is, clients' fears and worries about an event far exceed the potential consequences that could result from that event. Additionally, clients diagnosed with an anxiety disorder commonly worry about everyday life occurrences (e.g., being late to an appointment, completing household chores, etc.). The level of distress caused by these anxious feelings creates significant impairment in clients' overall functioning and causes serious distress.

Attention Deficit Hyperactivity Disorder

SUDs and attention deficit hyperactivity disorder (ADHD) have high rates of co-occurrence (Katzman et al., 2017). It was estimated that almost a quarter of adults who misuse substances meet the diagnostic criteria for ADHD (van Emmerik-van Oortmerssen et al., 2012). Also, Molina and colleagues (2018) reported that children diagnosed with ADHD have a heightened risk of using substances during adolescence, and their use of substances is likely to escalate more quickly. Additionally, daily smoking and cannabis use are more prevalent among persons diagnosed with ADHD than among those who do not have this diagnosis (SAMHSA, 2020c). Clients who have co-occurring SUDs and ADHD are at a higher risk for early onset of SUDs, more severe presenting issues, higher rates of suicide attempts, increased rates of hospitalization, and low treatment adherence rates (Egan et al., 2017; Katzman et al., 2017).

Main diagnostic criteria: The key feature of ADHD is a pervasive pattern of inattention and/or hyperactivity that significantly impacts clients' functioning and development (APA, 2013). The inattention is marked by the presence of six or more of the following symptoms: (1) frequently fails to notice details and give close attention, (2) has difficulties in sustaining attention, (3) often appears not to listen, (4) frequently fails to finish assigned tasks and does not follow instructions, (5) has difficulties with organization, (6) often avoids tasks that require continuous mental effort, (7) frequently loses necessary materials, (8) can be easily distracted, and (9) is forgetful of daily tasks. Diagnostic criteria for hyperactivity require the presence of six or more of the following symptoms: (1) fidgets frequently, (2) often leaves seat when not appropriate, (3) frequently runs and climbs during inappropriate times, (4) is unable to engage in leisure activities quietly, (5) appears to be "on the go," (6) frequently talks excessively,

(7) has difficulties in waiting for their turn, (8) frequently gives answers before questions are completed, and (9) often interrupts others. Symptoms for both inattention and hyperactivity need to be present for at least 6 months in order for one to be diagnosed with ADHD.

Schizophrenia

The co-occurrence rates of schizophrenia and SUDs are high (SAMHSA, 2020c). It is estimated that between 40% and 70% of people diagnosed with schizophrenia will experience a lifetime prevalence of substance abuse (Kerner, 2015; Lybreand & Caroff, 2009). Persons with schizophrenia also are 460% more likely to develop substance use issues than the general population (Doweiko, 2019). Additionally, the co-occurrence of these two disorders has a significant impact on clients' presenting symptoms and treatment outcomes. Clients who are diagnosed with schizophrenia and SUDs have a higher risk of violent and self-destructive behaviors, increased rates of suicide, more housing instability, cognitive dysfunctions, employment issues, poor physical health, unstable social relationships, higher rates of hospitalization and rehospitalizations, and legal issues (Bennett et al., 2017; Jones et al., 2011; Trudeau et al., 2018).

Main diagnostic criteria: One of the main characterizing features of schizophrenia is the heterogeneity of the presenting issues (SAMHSA, 2020c). That is, no single symptom (or symptom cluster) defines this disorder (APA, 2013). Rather a range of emotional, cognitive, and behavioral dysfunctions causes impaired social and occupational functioning. Clients who are diagnosed with schizophrenia present with delusions, hallucinations, or disorganized speech and also have either catatonic or disorganized behavior or experience negative symptoms (e.g., impaired emotional expression). Additionally, clients experience significant impairment in one

LEARNING ACTIVITY 12.4
DIAGNOSTIC IMPLICATIONS

Please read the following diagnostic criteria for schizophrenia and generalized anxiety disorder below. For each disorder, please discuss the following questions:

- Which of the symptoms can also occur due to substance intoxication?
- Which of the symptoms can also occur due to substance withdrawal?

Schizophrenia

At least two of the following symptoms:

- Delusions
- Hallucinations
- Disorganized speech
- Disorganized or catatonic behavior
- Negative symptoms (dampened emotions, loss of interest, decreased speech)

At least one of the symptoms must be the presence of delusions, hallucinations, or disorganized speech.

Continuous signs of the disturbance must persist for at least 6 months.

The disturbance is not due to the direct physiological effects of a substance.

Generalized Anxiety Disorder

Excessive anxiety/worry; causes impairment.

Three or more of the following (6 months):

- Restlessness, feeling keyed up or on edge
- Being easily fatigued
- Difficulty concentrating or mind going blank
- Irritability
- Muscle tension
- Sleep disturbance (difficulty falling or staying asleep or restless sleep)

The disturbance is not attributable to the physiological effects of a substance (e.g., a drug of abuse, a medication) or another medical condition.

of the major life areas (e.g., work, interpersonal relationships, etc.; APA, 2013). Practically, schizophrenia symptoms are divided into positive and negative groups (SAMHSA, 2020c). Symptoms that are associated with an acute course of schizophrenia (e.g., delusions, hallucinations, motor agitation, etc.) are characterized as positive, while symptoms related to the chronic course of schizophrenia (e.g., lack of enjoyment, flat affect, social isolation, lack of emotional expression, etc.) are described as negative (SAMHSA, 2020c).

SUMMARY

The prevalence rates of co-occurring substance use and mental health disorders are high and have increased significantly over the last five years (SAMHSA, 2020a). Additionally, these disorders are likely to have a significant impact on clients' lives and contribute to several severe symptoms. Persons who have co-occurring disorders are likely to face significant issues related to their psychological and social functioning and overall well-being (SAMHSA, 2020b). Although our understanding of these disorders has improved over the years, and we have more effective treatment options, there are still many barriers to treatment, and most clients who have co-occurring disorders do not receive adequate care. As a result of these factors, it is critical for counselors to be aware of the commonality and complexity of these disorders and utilize proper assessment and treatment models to provide appropriate care and help clients overcome these issues.

RESOURCES

Addiction Technology Transfer Center: https://attcnetwork.org/centers/global-attc/products-resources-catalog

Addictions Training Institute: https://addictionstraininginstitute.com/certifications-in-florida/

Department of Veterans Affairs, Veterans Affairs Substance Use Disorder Program Locator: https://www.va.gov/directory/guide/SUD.asp

Integrated Substance Abuse Programs: http://www.uclaisap.org/

Substance Abuse and Mental Health Services Administration. (1999). *Interventions and brief therapies for substance abuse. Treatment Improvement Protocol (TIP) Series, No. 34* (HHS Publication No. [SMA] 12- 3952).

Substance Abuse and Mental Health Services Administration. (2000). *Integrating substance abuse treatment and vocational services. Treatment Improvement Protocol (TIP) Series, No. 38* (HHS Publication No. [SMA] 12-4216).

Substance Abuse and Mental Health Services Administration. (2008). *Managing depressive symptoms in substance abuse clients during early recovery. Treatment Improvement Protocol (TIP) Series 48* (DHHS Publication No. [SMA] 08-4353).

Substance Abuse and Mental Health Services Administration. (2009). *Addressing suicidal thoughts and behaviors in substance abuse treatment. Treatment Improvement Protocol (TIP) Series, No. 50* (HHS Publication No. [SMA] 154381).

Substance Abuse and Mental Health Services Administration. (2020). *Substance use disorder treatment for people with co-occurring disorders. Treatment Improvement Protocol (TIP) Series, No. 42* (SAMHSA Publication No. PEP20-02-01-044).

KEY REFERENCES

Only key references appear in the print edition. The full reference list appears in the digital product on Springer Publishing Connect: connect.springerpub.com/content/book/978-0-8261-3586-5/chapter/ch12

Kelly, T. M., & Daley, D. C. (2013). Integrated treatment of substance use and psychiatric disorders. *Social Work in Public Health, 28*(3–4), 388–406. https://doi.org/10.1080/19371918.2013.774673

Mueser, K. T., & Gingerich, S. (2013). Treatment of co-occurring psychotic and substance use disorders. *Social Work in Public Health, 28*(3–4), 424–439. https://doi.org/10.1080/19371918.2013.774676

Substance Abuse and Mental Health Services Administration. (2009). *Integrated treatment for co-occurring disorders: Training frontline staff* (DHHS Publication No. SMA-08-4366).

Substance Abuse and Mental Health Services Administration. (2015). *Screening and assessment of co-occurring disorders in the justice system* (HHS Publication No. PEP19-SCREEN-CODJS).

Substance Abuse and Mental Health Services Administration. (2016). An introduction to bipolar disorder and co-occurring substance use disorders. *Advisory, 15*(2).

Substance Abuse and Mental Health Services Administration. (2020a). *Key substance use and mental health indicators in the United States: Results from the 2019 National Survey on Drug Use and Health* (HHS Publication No. PEP20-07-01-001, NSDUH Series H-55).

Substance Abuse and Mental Health Services Administration. (2020b). *National Survey of Substance Abuse Treatment Services (N-SSATS): 2019.* Data on Substance Abuse Treatment Facilities.

Substance Abuse and Mental Health Services Administration. (2020c). *Substance use disorder treatment for people with co-occurring disorders. Treatment Improvement Protocol (TIP) Series, No. 42* (SAMHSA Publication No. PEP20-02-01-044).

13

DEVELOPMENTAL ISSUES IN COUNSELING

LEARNING OBJECTIVES

This chapter explores the progression of substance use disorders (SUDs), as well as the progression of recovery. Given the progression of recovery, counselors can often anticipate particular issues that will come up in early, middle, and late recovery. We also will be examining ways in which SUDs impact on normal human development. By the conclusion of this chapter, you will be able to:

- describe the progression of substance use disorders and how substance use impacts on normal development and the attainment of developmental tasks;
- identify Erikson's Psychosocial Stages of Development and be able to explain how SUDs impact on those developmental stages;
- describe the progression of recovery and be able to anticipate particular issues or problems that may arise in early, middle, and late recovery;
- identify and explain Gorski's stages or passage of recovery;
- describe "dry drunk syndrome" and concomitant behaviors and attitudes;
- apply counseling strategies for various developmental stages of recovery.

TERMS TO KNOW

developmental delay a term that describes problems or delays in the normal maturation of an individual that impedes maturity often common in SUD recovery

developmental tasks a main challenge or undertaking that one faces at particular times in their life, such as that a main developmental task of adolescence is one's gaining a sense of identity

dry drunk syndrome a colloquial term used to describe often impulsive or irritable behavior in individuals with established recovery/sobriety, which may signal impending relapse

empty depression/mourning depressive-like symptoms that individuals in early recovery often experience as a result of mourning their preferred substance or their lifestyle during active SUD

Jellinek curve refers to the progression chart used to describe the downward progression or course of an active alcohol use disorder

	and to describe the course or progression often found in recovery
king/queen baby	terms used to describe demanding behaviors often used to control family members or significant others, sometimes found in individuals in early recovery
pink cloud	refers to client attitudes or beliefs that may occur when they complete inpatient SUD treatment that is characterized by having unrealistic expectations of others based upon changes that the client made while in treatment
substitute addiction	a tendency in early recovery to substitute another addiction (often a behavioral addiction) for one's preferred substance

INTRODUCTION

There's a saying that's familiar to most addiction counselors, "Whenever a person's addiction begins, their development stops." Obviously, this saying does not pertain to physical development but rather to cognitive, emotional, and social development. What counselors working in substance use disorder (SUD) treatment programs often observe is that they might be counseling a middle-aged client; however, if that client began using substances in their teen years (e.g., at age 14), then for all intents and purposes, the client is probably functioning at a 14-year-old level cognitively, socially, and emotionally. Counselors would observe these developmental deficits with regard to abilities such as exercising sound judgment, good decision-making skills, the ability to cope with distressing emotions, experiencing empathy toward others, and the capacity to tolerate daily frustrations.

There are two ways to explore development as it pertains to SUDs. First is to explore the impact of SUDs on life span development (i.e., the various stages that people go through from birth to infancy to childhood, to adolescence, young adulthood, middle age, and older adulthood such as those described by Erik Erikson [1963]). Second is to examine development or progression of the SUD from the perspective of the course that one's substance use disorder follows from experimental alcohol or drug use to misuse/abuse and dependence. As with other diseases or disorders that follow a particular progression or course, so too do SUDs. For example, if a person comes down with bronchitis, one can predict with reasonable certainty how long they will feel bronchial symptoms, and it will generally take a week or so before they will begin to feel better. It's also common for SUDs to follow a downward course or progression as the disorder gets worse over time. Many clients are able to describe the downward course of their progression and how that impacted their lives over the course of many years. For example, clients will often describe how they perceived their alcohol or substance use as being a way to relieve stress or a way to relax after a difficult work day, yet over time, they will also begin to describe how they had come to rely on the drink or drug and how they needed more and how their use became more frequent. It's also important that counselors explore the developmental course of recovery (i.e., those changes one might expect to experience as the client gets further away from their active alcohol and/or drug use and move further along in their recovery) and how those changes can help counselors to evaluate their client's quality of commitment to their recovery. The progression of SUDs as well as the progression or course of recovery will greatly depend on whether the individual receives treatment and/or actively participates in a 12-step recovery program (e.g., Alcoholics Anonymous [AA], Narcotics Anonymous [NA] meetings) or has other recovery supports.

IMPACT OF SUBSTANCE USE DISORDERS ON LIFE SPAN DEVELOPMENT AND DEVELOPMENTAL TASKS

Let's begin by taking a look at the some of the most recent epidemiological statistics pertaining to adolescent substance use: According to the Monitoring the Future (MTF) survey (Miech et al., 2019), a number of American adolescents will begin to experiment with alcohol and other substances during their early teen years and into later adolescence. For example, the most recent 2019 MTF survey indicates that 21% of 12th graders, 19% of 10th graders, and 7% of eighth graders reported having engaged in marijuana vaping in the past 12 months. For 12th graders, this represented a 7.7% increase in the past year, which represents the second largest increase in a 12-month time period ever recorded for 12th graders. Interestingly, there were also increases in those who reported daily cannabis use as well as increased LSD use. Other illicit substance use tended to remain steady or constant according to the most recent MTF survey. What makes these findings especially important is that the adolescent brain is still developing and continues to develop up until around age 25. Perhaps this is the reason why addiction counselors see such a profound impact of substance use on teens that often lasts well into adulthood.

Now let's explore Erikson's Psychosocial Stages of Development as outlined in Table 13.1, particularly the tasks of adolescent development where identity formation takes center stage. The key features of identity formation include one's personal sense of self, one's social self (e.g., what it means to be a good friend to others), body image, and one's sense of self in relation to other family members (e.g., what it means to be a good son or daughter or brother or sister). For younger adolescents (13 or 14 years old), life holds limitless possibilities; however, as one matures into older adolescence (17 to 19 years old), there is usually a more realistic sense of what one's strengths and limitations are. For example, if an older adolescent has struggled with math and science, there's a pretty good chance they are not going to be accepted into the engineering program at Stanford, MIT, or Carnegie-Mellon. Now let's explore that happens when we add regular use of alcohol or substances into the mix and how that impacts on identify formation (Cavaiola & Kane-Cavaiola, 1988). Generally, counselors most often find adolescent (as well as adult) clients who never really developed a genuine sense of identity. For example, adolescence is usually a time when dating begins and serves as a foundation for future intimate, loving relationships. However, dating and (often socializing with peers) can be anxiety provoking. Teens who rely on substance use to help lessen their anxiety or who shy away from dating often feel stuck developmentally or experience what Erikson refers to as "role confusion." Developing a sense of self or identity then becomes the prerequisite for moving into young adulthood. Counselors may also see role confusion being expressed by clients who rebel and take on a counter-culture type of identity that also carries over into adulthood.

TABLE 13.1 Erikson's Developmental Stages

STAGE	TRANSITIONAL THEME	DEVELOPMENTAL TASKS
Infancy (0–1 yr)	*Trust vs. Mistrust*	bonding, emotional stability
Toddlerhood (1–2 yrs)	*Autonomy vs. Shame*	beginning to develop independence and doubt
Early Childhood (2–6 yrs)	*Initiative vs. Guilt*	learning motor skills, tasks, and motor control, learning cultural values
Middle Childhood (6–12 yrs)	*Industry vs. Inferiority*	developing learning skills, mastery of academics
Adolescence (12–18 yrs)	*Identity vs. Role Confusion*	adjusting to puberty, exploring social/love relationships, defining one's identity and strengths and weaknesses
Young Adulthood (18–34 yrs)	*Intimacy vs. Isolation*	developing intimate relations, settling down, starting a family, developing parenting skills, occupational development
Middle Adulthood (35–50 yrs)	*Generativity vs. Stagnation*	adjusting to middle age and relationships, adjusting to parenting, dealing with aging parents, increased productivity
Older Adulthood (50–65 yrs)	*Generativity vs. Stagnation*	adjusting to aging, preparing to retire, adjusting to grown children and empty nest
Old Age (65+)	*Ego Integrity vs. Despair*	adjusting to aging, adjusting to retirement, evaluating past achievements, adjusting to loneliness

Source: Erikson, E. (1963). *Childhood and society* (2nd ed.). Norton.

In Erikson's young adulthood stage, the main developmental task revolves around establishing intimate relationships. When this is not achieved, the young adult becomes isolated from others as you'll see illustrated in the case of Kenny described later. Here, we see that Kenny's marriage to Sarah is greatly impacted by his substance use, which has taken precedence over his marriage. Sarah complains that living with Kenny is like "living with a teenager." This type of developmental impairment is unfortunately all too common and supported by longitudinal research studies pertaining to long-term cannabis users (e.g., Brook et al., 2016; Green et al., 2017; Juon et al., 2011; Washburn & Capaldi, 2015), which all point to ways in which cannabis use disorders interfere with the major developmental tasks of young adulthood such as completing an educational program beyond high school, establishing a consistent intimate relationship, and establishing one's self in a career. This is why counselors will often see heavy cannabis users who seem to function more like adolescents in that they are often still living at home with parents, are not involved in stable love relationships, and have not completed college or other educational training programs, which would help put them on course for a career.

According to Erikson, the tasks of middle adulthood revolve around generativity versus stagnation. Middle-aged adults who find themselves content in secure, loving relationships, find fulfillment as parents, or find fulfillment in productivity in their work or careers have achieved this sense of generativity. Those who have difficulty negotiating these tasks of middle adulthood often find themselves feeling stagnant or stuck and feeling unfulfilled with their lot in life. Despair often goes hand-in-hand with these feelings of being unfulfilled. The research reported by Princeton economists Case and Deaton (2020) speaks to these individuals who often fall prey to SUDs. While alcohol or other drug use provides some temporary relief, in the long term such use only exacerbates feelings of despair.

The good news about these developmental tasks, which often become delayed or hampered by alcohol or substance use, is that there are opportunities to resume growth. Counselors see this especially with individuals who work a conscientious and purposeful program of recovery that usually involves a combination of counseling and actively working the 12 Steps. While abstinence is an important starting point, generally we see that abstinence alone is not sufficient for this developmental growth to occur.

CASE EXAMPLE: KENNY

Kenny is a 28-year-old separated father of a 4-year-old son who is seeking counseling at the advice of his divorce attorney. Kenny and Sarah had been married for 6 years and had recently separated, after Sarah had filed a restraining order against Kenny. Approximately 3 weeks ago, Kenny had come home quite late, under the influence of alcohol and cocaine. Sarah was very angry because they had been invited to her parents' home for dinner; however, Kenny had decided to stop "for a drink" after work with his coworkers and ended up staying until closing time. This was not the first time Kenny had not come home on time, and Sarah had run out of patience for this type of behavior. As a result, she went to see a divorce attorney. She feels that her marriage to Kenny is like "living with a teenager." She feels she can't count on him to handle basic responsibilities whether it's helping around the house, paying bills, or helping with childcare for their son.

Kenny began drinking alcohol and smoking cannabis when he was in middle school (around the time he was 13 years old). His substance use progressed to daily use during his junior and senior high school years. Kenny ended up failing most of his classes in his junior year and needed to attend summer school. Kenny barely graduated high school and then went on to take a few courses at a local community college; however, he stopped attending classes because he was too hungover to make it to class. He also had two DUIs and an arrest for possession of cocaine. Kenny states that drinking beer and vaping cannabis are the substances he prefers the most. Kenny's parents are divorced, and since his separation from Sarah Kenny now lives with his mother and younger sister. He does not have much contact with his father, which Kenny attributes to his father "being an alcoholic." Kenny met Sarah when he went to work at his uncle's car dealership. Sarah is the bookkeeper for his uncle's business. Other than his few "drinking buddies" whom he plays video games and gets high with, he has no other social life or friends.

PROGRESSION OF SUBSTANCE USE DISORDERS AND DEVELOPMENTAL ASPECTS OF RECOVERY

When exploring the concept of SUD progression, there are three individuals who have done a great deal of work in this area: E. M. Jellinek (Jellinek & Joliffe, 1940), Terence T. Gorski (1989), and Max Glatt (1969, 1975). Jellinek was responsible for coining the term "the disease concept of alcoholism." Not only was he one of the first researchers to define alcohol use disorder (AUD; i.e., alcoholism) as a disease, he also described four stages that the majority of alcoholics experience during the course of their active AUD. The *pre-alcoholic* or *symptomatic stage* is characterized by "relief drinking" whereby the individual finds themself drinking more often and drinking to manage stress and upsetting emotions. At this stage, drinking becomes more frequent and is essentially a way to cope with current problems. Additionally, drinking at this stage appears to occur more often in social contexts. The second stage described by Jellinek is the *prodromal stage* or *transitional stage*. Here, drinking evolves into a more cyclical pattern. Blackouts (i.e., the inability to recall things said or done while drinking) become more frequent. Also, at this stage the drinker begins to experience problems that result from more frequent and patterned drinking that occur in their occupational, social, or interpersonal life. The third stage is referred to as *crucial* (or *middle*) *stage* in which the drinker is now experiencing more serious problems as a result of drinking. In order to try to manage these drinking problems, the individual may abstain for periods of time only to hastily return to drinking when life becomes too stressful. Other attempts at gaining control may include "geographical cures," for example, moving to another town, changing jobs, or even switching from vodka to scotch as a means of trying to limit or control one's drinking patterns. Here, the person may hide, rationalize, or mask their use, which often contributes to feelings of guilt resulting from embarrassing drinking behaviors. The fourth stage, referred to as the *chronic* (or *late*) *stage* is characterized as the time period in which the individual loses control over their drinking. One drink will invariably result in prolonged periods of intoxication or binges. Also, both mental and physical deterioration are more likely to be noticed by loved ones at the chronic stage. The alcoholic relies on alibis or excuses in order to rationalize the reasons for their drinking. The chronic stage may last for weeks, months, or years (Brande, 2018). The hope is that the alcoholic who "hits bottom" will surrender and ask for help. Unfortunately, many alcoholics die as a result of heavy drinking because of how alcohol impacts on the body physically.

Interestingly, the term *progression* usually provides an account of the downward spiral that many individuals with AUDs endure. Such is the case with the Jellinek stages (i.e., prodromal, chronic, crucial) that describe the downward progression of an alcohol use disorder up until such time that the individual drinker "hits bottom" and hopefully begins their journey into recovery/sobriety. However, a British researcher by the name of Max Glatt (1975) noted deficiencies in Jellinek's progression stages because they only described the harmful progressive nature of AUDs over time. Glatt sought to describe the changes that occur during recovery as the individual progresses in overcoming their AUD. The progression chart depicted in Figure 13.1 is an approximation of the downward progression and recovery progression described by Jellinek and Glatt. While Glatt developed the progression chart you see in Figure 13.1, it is most often referred to as "the Jellinek curve" because it does include Jellinek's crucial and chronic phases.

The developmental models described earlier are extremely helpful to addictions counselors in being able to assess where their client may be in terms of the downward progression so common to many of the SUDs. The course or progression of active SUDs are truly a downward spiral in which individuals tend to get worse over time in a progressive manner. Yet, the developmental models are also helpful in describing what recovery would look like in someone who is truly focusing consciously on their recovery. The disadvantage, however,

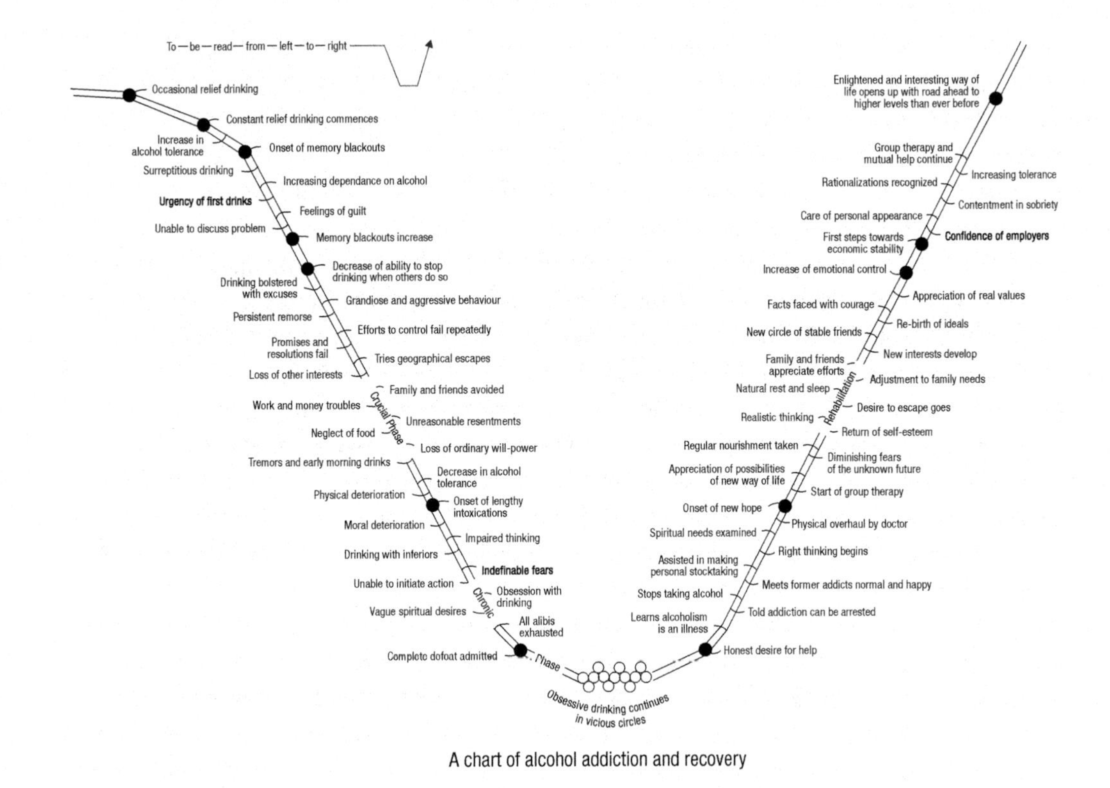

FIGURE 13.1 Progression of alcohol use disorder and recovery.

is that with human growth and development, individuals tend to progress at different rates cognitively, socially, and emotionally.

Gorski (1989) also describes the "progression" or course of recovery in his classic book *Passages Through Recovery.* Similar to Glatt (1975), Gorski felt that there were distinct stages to addiction recovery. He described these stages as follows:

I. Transition (transitioning from active use to abstinence)
II. Stabilization (not drinking a day at a time)
III. Early Recovery (staying stopped/continuous abstinence)
IV. Middle Recovery (achieving lifestyle balance)
V. Late Recovery (building depth & meaning)
VI. Maintenance

In the *Transition* stage, the individual moves from active drinking and/or drug use to abstinence. Even though they want to stop using and may express this goal to family and friends, often they struggle to actually achieve this goal. Therefore, this stage may include a lot of "stops and starts" as the person experiences a couple of days of abstinence, then returns to active drinking for a few days, then returns to abstinence. During Transition, individuals may first make attempts to control use by changing the amount or frequency of drinking or substance use or by changing the type of alcohol/drugs used. Eventually, however, the person in Transition recognizes the need for total abstinence and at that point begins to put together days and then weeks of abstinence. For some, this may require that they enter a detoxification program in order to safely transition from active use to abstinence. For example, individuals who have been using alcohol, benzodiazepines, or opioids on a continual or daily basis for months or years would most likely experience severe withdrawal symptoms if they were to stop using abruptly. Gorski (1989) indicates there are three goals that need to be accomplished during Transition: (1) there is a recognition of a loss of control once alcohol or drug use begins, (2) there is a recognition that loss of control is the result of one's addiction, and (3) one must commit to a program of recovery, which means asking for help.

Once the person completes detoxification, they then move toward *Stabilization*. This period takes place within the first few weeks and months of sobriety or abstinence. Here, the newly abstinent individual is learning how not to pick up a drink or drug "a day at a time" (as is recommended in AA/NA). Having gone through acute withdrawal, the individual now must learn to cope with post-acute withdrawal symptoms (e.g., irritability, anger, depression, anhedonia, etc.). Having social/family support is crucial at this stage because alcohol or drug craving is strongest during the Stabilization stage; however, cravings usually dissipate or lessen over time. Also, during Stabilization, individuals learn to problem-solve without relying on alcohol or drugs (even if a person were to lose their job or face a separation/divorce, the newly sober person learns to face these losses head-on, without retreating into active substance use). Most importantly, as the individual experiences confidence in their ability to abstain, hope and motivation begin to replace the anguish and despair of active addiction.

The *Early Recovery* stage is thought to cover the period beyond Stabilization to the first year of recovery. During this stage, the recovering person is confronting many "firsts" as they learn to manage birthday celebrations, weddings, holidays, and anniversaries without drinking or using substances. As with Stabilization, having a solid support system of family/friends as well as support from an AA/NA sponsor and fellow AA/NA members is crucial to surmounting the challenges of Early Recovery. It's not surprising that research estimates that only 1 in 33 makes it through the first year with their sobriety intact (Timko & DeBennedetti, 2007). In addition to the aforementioned support, it's also crucial that the newly recovering individual is participating in counseling, whether it be individual, group, couples, family counseling or a combination thereof. As Gorski (1989) points out, during Stabilization, the *drinking problem* is addressed, while in Early Recovery the *thinking problem* must be addressed (referring to irrational thoughts, unmanageable emotions, and self-defeating behaviors). For example, it's common for individuals in Early Recovery to "project" negative outcomes by constantly dreading the worst possible scenario. It's also not unusual for early recovering individuals to develop substitute addictions. For example, some may turn to gambling, overeating, sex, or even excessive exercise as a means to experience pleasure derived from dopamine flooding the brain. You may be saying to yourself, "Isn't exercise a good thing?" Exercise is certainly a healthy activity; however, it can become harmful when a person exercises compulsively and excessively to the point of injury. Similarly, eating and sex are also healthy behaviors except when they become compulsive and/or excessive. The main goal of the Early Recovery stage is to put the *sober self* (rather than the *addict self*) in charge. By accomplishing this goal, the Early Recovering individual can begin to take control of their life.

Counseling Clients in Early Recovery

Clients in Early Recovery face many challenges, and our ability to support and encourage clients who are new to sobriety, while at the same time being able to provide feedback to clients regarding risky behaviors or poor judgment, is also a very important part of what counselors provide. This can be a bit of tightrope situation where counselors need to instill a sense of optimism and be encouraging/supportive, yet balance that with constructive feedback when clients become distracted from their recovery or may be making decisions that could put their recovery in jeopardy.

It's important for counselors to be mindful of the pitfalls of Early Recovery, as noted in Box 13.1, that include behaviors and attitudes with which clients often struggle. Empty depression and mourning refers to the type of mourning or grieving (see Chambers & Wallingford, 2017) that clients experience as they move away from active alcohol/substance use and the lifestyle that accompanies it. Early sobriety focuses on changing "people, places, and things"; therefore, clients will often find that they miss the excitement associated with the lifestyle and "friends" associated with past substance use. Usually, individuals in Early Recovery may experience a type of "euphoric recall" whereby the client may remember the positive feelings about getting high or the excitement of obtaining drugs and getting high. The pink cloud is often experienced by clients who have completed a residential program and is based on their having had very positive experiences whereby they really felt love and caring from counselors, staff, and fellow clients. Inpatient programs provide an environment totally removed from the stress and turmoil of everyday life in which clients are able to focus on their recovery and wellness. One very exclusive (and expensive) residential program takes their clients by helicopter to the top of a mountain to do their morning meditation and mindfulness exercises. Yet, residential programs are also the place where clients began to face their demons (e.g., past trauma and character defects), and this is not an easy process, but it is a necessary part of the growth process, which is encapsulated in the adage "No pain, no gain." It's common for clients who have had a positive experience in residential treatment to undergo tremendous growth; however, to assume that the loved ones/significant others have also experienced tremendous growth and change is unrealistic and becomes the essence of being on a pink cloud. As you can imagine, the pink cloud can be a dangerous place, especially if your client gets fired from their job

LEARNING ACTIVITY 13.1
PITFALLS OF EARLY RECOVERY

Can you think of other challenges that face clients who are in Early Recovery in addition to the ones listed in Box 13.1? Write them down and discuss.

BOX 13.1

POTENTIAL PITFALLS COMMONLY FOUND IN EARLY RECOVERY

Empty depression and mourning
The pink cloud
The need for controlling others, i.e., the "king baby–queen baby" syndrome
Pathological narcissism "egomaniacs with inferiority complexes"
Compulsivity—need to make up for "lost time"
Substitute addictions: food, sex, shopping/spending, gambling
Overwhelming guilt over past behavior
Low self-esteem and lack of self-care
Learning the language/culture of 12-step programs

for showing up to work five minutes late or is being harassed by bill collectors or is confronted with angry parents, spouses, partners, or friends who have had to hold things together while your client was away in rehab. Welcome to the real world...goodbye pink cloud.

The king baby/queen baby is characterized by clients who hold onto controlling or demanding behaviors well into their recovery. As described by Tom Cunningham (1986), the king baby is someone who has chronologically reached adulthood without having acquired the necessary maturity to deal with adult life and adult relationships. If the king baby/queen baby does not get their way, look out, because they will think nothing of throwing a tantrum or retaliating. This particular trait is common among individuals who manifest the next trait on the list of pitfalls, pathological narcissism. This particular personality trait is also characterized by excessive egocentricity and self-centeredness. These clients will let you know that they are superior to everyone and, therefore, should be afforded special favors and unconditional praise by others. When caught in a lie or other deceitful behavior, pathological narcissists are masters of placing blame on others for their wrongdoings. The phrase "egomaniacs with inferiority complexes" is often used in AA/NA and depicts the pathological narcissism common in active SUDs and often carried over into Early Recovery. Many personality disorders theorists (e.g., Millon et al., 2004) conclude that narcissistic personality traits are often a means to compensate for feelings of inferiority, hence the colloquial phrase "egomaniacs with inferiority complexes." For a depiction of pathological narcissism, we recommend you watch the film *Flight,* in which Denzel Washington's character accurately portrays a very talented, pathological narcissist. It's important to note that not all clients experience pathological narcissism.

For newly sober clients who suffer from extreme guilt, shame, and low self-esteem, counselors often find that have an unquenchable need to "make up for lost time" or to prove themselves worthy. This belief or attitude often drives one to become compulsive in their jobs or in other major roles (e.g., parenting). While taking a serious approach to one's responsibilities is important, it can become detrimental if one becomes a workaholic or a "clean freak" or a "copter parent." These all represent excessive behaviors that can detract from a newly recovering person's focus on their recovery. The same holds true with substitute addictions, which are also common detractors in Early Recovery. In order to obtain pleasure or excitement, it's not unusual for the newly recovering person to turn to substitute addictions like gambling, sex, food, or even compulsive exercise as a means of finding reward (Washton & Zweben, 2006). Unfortunately, substitute addictions pose the risk of "giving permission" to return to one's drug of preference.

LEARNING ACTIVITY 13.2
GUILT VS SHAME

There's a saying, "Guilt is about what we do, shame is about who we are." Think about examples of guilt versus shame and write them down to discuss in small groups or your chat room. Discuss how you might help a client who is burdened by excessive guilt or shame. Are there ways that guilt might be useful for clients?

CASE EXAMPLE: NICOLE (EARLY RECOVERY)

Nicole is 28 years old and recently completed a 45-day residential treatment program for an alcohol use disorder (AUD) and a stimulant use disorder (methamphetamines). She is currently living with her husband and 2-year-old daughter while she attends an intensive

(*continued*)

outpatient program (IOP) in the evening when her husband gets home from work. Nicole had a difficult time adjusting to life back home with her husband and daughter. Although her husband, Ted, has been very supportive of her recovery, Nicole feels guilty about things she did when she was actively drinking and abusing prescription methamphetamines, such as staying out all night with her single girlfriends and being convicted of a DUI offense. Nicole also finds herself feeling bored being at home all day caring for her daughter and as a result has developed an addiction to bidding on items on eBay, knowing that these are luxury items she can't afford. There have been many instances where Nicole will try to return the items or will sell them, but she is excited every time she wins one of the auctions. Nicole has also been attending Alcoholics Anonymous and Narcotics Anonymous meetings and has a sponsor whom she has developed a positive relationship with. Nicole tries to make meetings in the evenings when she is not in IOP group. Nicole's IOP counselor feels that she is making good progress but is concerned because Nicole seems increasingly depressed and is not really enjoying much of anything other than her eBay shopping. There is no history of depression in Nicole's family, but Nicole indicates that she did go through a period of feeling depressed after a "bad breakup" with her college boyfriend.

Case Conceptualization: Nicole

Nicole is experiencing many of the pitfalls that are common in Early Recovery. She describes "empty depression and mourning" both for her drinking and Adderall use and the lifestyle that went along with her "partying all night." She indicates that she began taking Adderall in college when she had to study for exams or had a term paper to write. Presently, she is experiencing a lot of anhedonic cravings that stem from her feelings of boredom and emptiness. These feelings are exacerbated by the guilt she feels for emotionally abandoning her husband and daughter. In addition, Nicole appears to be developing a substitute addiction to online shopping, which is also a source of both pleasure and guilt, as she is spending money on items she knows she can't afford. With regard to counseling approaches, Nicole's counselor is continuing to work with Nicole on her following through with the relapse-prevention plan that was developed at the time when she was discharged from residential treatment and that has been expanded upon by her IOP counselor. Presently, Nicole feels good about avoiding "people, places and things," she is committed to staying clean and sober a day at a time, and she does have a good rapport with both her counselor and AA/NA sponsor. Her counselor has expressed concerns to Nicole over her guilt and is worried that she is "beating herself up" too much. By helping Nicole to really accept and internalize the disease concept of substance abuse disorders, the counselor is hoping that Nicole will not be too hard on herself and stay focused on "things she can change" such as reestablishing a better relationship with her husband and daughter.

In the *Middle Recovery* stage, the ability to achieve life balance is of utmost importance. Therefore, being able to stay focused on one's recovery while also balancing work, love, and play (or leisure activities) becomes quite a challenge. Take for example, someone who used to play on a softball league during the spring, summer, and fall as their main type of recreation or leisure activity. However, after every softball game, their teammates would break out cases of beer, and many teammates would end up having to call an Uber in order to get home without risking a DUI. In Early and Middle Recovery, it's important to establish new activities that don't revolve around alcohol. Relapse-prevention planning recommends that recovering individuals change "people, places, and things" in order to help ensure sobriety. Changing a leisure activity is an example of changing "things" that may result in a return to drinking or drug use. It's not usual for individuals in Middle Recovery to try to "make up for lost time." Here, the individual realizes how many years they wasted drinking or using drugs, and there's often an internal pressure to regain one's life or career once sober. Yet, this attitude can often result in added pressure or stress, which for some may be a relapse trigger. Of paramount importance during this stage is that individuals learn self-care, which can include going for regular medical and dental check-ups, proper nutrition, sleep, and exercise.

Counseling Clients in Middle Recovery

When clients reach Middle Recovery, they usually have a firm grasp on the concept of staying clean and sober a day at a time and have had many opportunities to practice avoiding relapse situations and both internal and external relapse triggers. Counseling can, therefore, focus on lifestyle balance issues. Someone once asked Sigmund Freud what he considered to be a mentally healthy individual, and those posing the question had figured that he would come up with some esoteric answer in keeping with his theories like "resolving the Oedipal complex" or "being free from distortions of over-reliance on defense mechanisms." Instead, Freud responded with a very pragmatic answer, suggesting that an individual's ability to work, love, and play is evidence of a healthy individual. Implied in Freud's response, however, is the notion that there needs to be a balance between "work, love, and play" because each one could potentially become an addiction in and of itself. Thing about "workaholism" or "sex and love addiction" or individuals who become addicted to leisure activities such as internet gaming, betting on fantasy football, or shopping. So, as counselors, how do we help our clients achieve "lifestyle balance"? Here's a case that illustrates these challenges.

CASE EXAMPLE: VICTOR (MIDDLE RECOVERY)

Victor is 34 years old and currently has been in continuous recovery for the past 4 years. He is a police officer and has been on the police force of a suburban community for the past 9 years. Substance use disorders, especially alcohol use disorders, are common among first responders, which include police officers. Victor began his recovery after having gone through a particularly difficult divorce, which is when he began going out socially with fellow police officers after their shift was over. Following a domestic violence complaint made by Victor's wife around the time of their separation, Victor's captain and lieutenant did an intervention and were able to get him to accept admission into a residential program that specialized in treating law-enforcement personnel. Victor has been doing well since completing rehab. He has an Alcoholics Anonymous (AA) sponsor, attends counseling weekly, and goes to AA meetings about three to four times per week. In order to pay child support, Victor has been working overtime doing security work and has begun to sponsor a few fellow police officers who are new to recovery. Victor has also begun dating again, and this has taken up quite a bit

(*continued*)

of his free time, when he is not having regular visitation with his son. He's also been trying to stay in shape by going to the gym in the morning before work. Victor reports feeling exhausted most of time, and he has become impatient with his coworkers. He recently had a complaint filed against him by someone whom Victor had pulled over for driving under the influence who claimed that Victor had "roughed him up." Victor discussed the incident with his sponsor and counselor.

Case Conceptualization: Victor

Currently, Victor has been continuously clean and sober for the past 4 years and is actively attending AA and meets weekly with his counselor to work on issues pertaining to his divorce, his relationship with his son, and sobriety-related issues. It's also obvious that Victor has been taking on a lot of responsibilities in an effort to maintain his sobriety and keep up with child support obligations, and he is also trying to date. After the aforementioned complaint was filed, Victor's counselor saw the need to address *lifestyle balance* issues. Although Victor wants to date, he is finding this to be very stressful rather than relaxing and fun. Victor appears to have developed two possible substitute addictions, work and exercise, which appear to be interfering with his ability to achieve "lifestyle balance." Although work and exercise are considered positive and commendable activities (e.g., Victor is trying to keep up with his child-support payments and is also trying to stay in shape), these have become compulsive activities that are having a negative impact on Victor's overall functioning. Exercising to the point where it causes physical harm is an example. Working so many hours that it interferes with health or self-care also represents a negative consequence. For Victor, the concern is that his work has become "workaholism." With the urging of his AA sponsor, Victor enters counseling in order to address some of these life balance difficulties. Victor's counselor helps him to prioritize his values and goals in such a way as to determine how he can put his time to better use.

LEARNING ACTIVITY 13.3
SOBRIETY VS MATURITY

As one puts together more time in recovery, hopefully they begin to develop more responsible/mature behaviors or attitudes. Think of examples of traits that characterize a person whom you consider to be mature. Would those traits be similar to that of a sober person in recovery? Also, how do the 12 Steps of AA, NA, and Gamblers Anonymous (GA) promote maturity?

Counseling Clients in Late Recovery

With *Late Recovery* the emphasis is on building depth and meaning in one's recovery. With the difficult days of struggling not to pick up a drink or drug a day at a time behind them, there's now an opportunity to focus on other issues. For example, strengthening relationships that may have been damaged due to years of active substance use or strengthening one's role as a parent or grandparent can become very fulfilling ventures. Individuals in Late Recovery often find ways to free themselves of past family dysfunction or family problems and to let go of rigid behavioral patterns. Some find satisfaction in working on building a new career or business or going back to school to complete a degree or certification that was abandoned due to active alcohol or drug use. The possibilities for personal, spiritual, and intellectual growth are exponential during Late Recovery. While AA/NA (as well as other self-help support groups) provide a solid base for reinforcing recovery, usually in Late Recovery one's role in the program changes as they begin to sponsor others or go out on speaking commitments to other AA/NA groups or provide other types of service. These are activities that are stressed in the 12th Step of AA: "Having had a spiritual awakening as the result of these steps, we tried to carry this message to alcoholics, and to practice these principles in all our daily affairs." Carrying the message to others still suffering is an important aspect of Late Recovery.

Counseling clients in Late Recovery is often similar to counseling clients who seek treatment for general life problems (e.g., to improve partner/spouse relationships, to improve family relationships between parents and children, or to come to grips with family-of-origin issues). However, addiction counselors have a unique advantage in counseling individuals in Late Recovery because they can treat these issues while at the same time keeping the recovery perspective in sight. Take the following case example as an illustration.

CASE EXAMPLE: TOM (LATE RECOVERY)

Tom is a 54-year-old married father of three adult children. Tom has been active in Alcoholics Anonymous (AA) and continually sober for the past 25 years, so he was taken aback a bit when his AA sponsor suggested that he might seek counseling. Tom reports that he had been complaining to his sponsor about his kids and his job and the trouble he was having in controlling his anger toward his daughter and one of his coworkers. As Tom began to describe his frustrations to his counselor, he happened to comment in one of his sessions, "my wife says I'm turning out to be just like my mother." When asked why his wife might have made this comment, Tom explained that his mother had been an active alcoholic for much of his childhood and teen years, but that she got sober and started going to AA when he went off to college. Tom's mother was unusually critical and judgmental, and whenever she had a few cocktails, she would unleash her criticisms to anyone within earshot. Even once she got sober, Tom's wife would still see the remnants of his mother's critical nature. Now she felt that Tom had taken on some of these same characteristics. At first, Tom bristled at the idea that he was "turning into his mother," but after closer exploration with his counselor, he began to see how he was approaching his frustrations with his daughter and coworker the same way his mother would have.

Case Conceptualization: Tom

Counseling in Late Recovery often addresses family-of-origin issues such as Tom's relationship with his mother and his unconscious identification with her critical, judgmental nature. Once Tom began to admit and see these similarities, he was then able to work with his counselor on first making amends for his behavior (as discussed in the eighth and ninth Steps of AA) and then also developing alternate ways to cope with his frustrations using Rational-Emotive Behavior Therapy (REBT) strategies to help him dispute irrational beliefs that others *should* behave the way he wants them to. Tom was eventually able to identify and let go of these behaviors.

In the *Maintenance* stage, the emphasis is on maintenance activities that help to consolidate the progress made and to help insure its continuation into the future. As an analogy, you have to maintain your car (with oil changes, tire rotations, etc.) in order to keep it running. The same holds true with recovery. Developmental psychologist Erik Erikson (1963) said that in later life, people struggle with something he refers to as Generativity versus Stagnation. Generativity is about continued growth and one's ability to give back to others, whether it is the younger generation or those less fortunate. However, those who face stagnation are usually "stuck" in their development and are not really giving to others, nor are they connected to others in a meaningful way. This is why it's important to *maintain* one's recovery by taking a very active approach, one that involves connection with others as well as activities that help promote one's growth.

CASE EXAMPLE: TAMEEKA (LATE RECOVERY/MAINTENANCE)

Tameeka is a 48-year-old married mother of three children (aged 22, 18, and 16) who has been clean and sober for the past 24 years. She began drinking and "smoking weed" back in high school. Tameeka then began working at a state psychiatric hospital as a mental health aide in one of the women's units right after she graduated from high school, at which point Tameeka was offered a scholarship to go to nursing school. She graduated with her RN when she was 20. Tameeka was involved in a relationship with an older guy she knew from her neighborhood, and they would party together after work and on weekends when she wasn't working. In addition to alcohol and cannabis use, Tameeka's boyfriend introduced her to snorting heroin, which quickly became her drug of preference and soon progressed to intravenous use. After overdosing one night where police and emergency medical technicians had to be called, Tameeka went into a residential program, knowing that she might lose her nursing license. Upon successfully completing residential, Tameeka began attending Alcoholics Anonymous (AA) and Narcotics Anonymous (NA) meetings, obtained a sponsor, and broke off the relationship with the guy who introduced her to heroin. Tameeka has since married and had her first child when she was 26 years old. Tameeka decided to enter outpatient counseling at the advice of her AA sponsor because she was feeling increasingly overwhelmed by all the stress in her life. In addition to working long hours in the hospital, Tameeka had also been regularly attending AA and NA meetings. However, recently, her youngest daughter began having unexplained pains throughout her body, and it was suspected that she might have sickle-cell anemia, a very painful condition. Tameeka had stopped calling her sponsor and stopped going to meetings because she was so busy with her daughter's care. After a particularly difficult week, Tameeka found herself in the parking lot of a liquor store and contemplating buying a bottle of vodka. Instead, she drove over to her sponsor's house and talked about her stress and worries about her daughter's condition. Tameeka shared these stresses with her counselor and was able to get back on track with her recovery. Because Tameeka's mother had been addicted to crack cocaine and there was a period of about 8 years when she left Tameeka and her younger sister with their maternal grandmother so that she could party and hang out with men she would get high with, Tameeka swore she would never abandon her children like her mother did. However, instead Tameeka felt she had to be a "super woman" and was reluctant to ask her husband and family for help.

Case Conceptualization: Tameeka

In some ways, Tameeka is dealing with problems similar to Tom (described earlier). They are both several years in recovery but find themselves having to confront issues that seemed to develop during their childhood. Tameeka is clearly overwhelmed and is struggling to maintain her recovery. It seems that the further she got away from attending AA/NA meetings, the more her anger, frustration, and feelings of being overwhelmed worsened. Therefore, her counselor had to encourage Tameeka to get back to attending AA more regularly and to attend meetings that she felt she could get something out of (e.g., closed discussion group meetings or step meetings), as opposed to meetings where Tameeka felt she had to be the "tower of strength" for newcomers to the program. Eventually, Tameeka did work out a reasonable schedule whereby she felt she was maintaining her recovery while asking her husband and other extended family members to help in the care of her daughter.

OTHER RECOVERY MODELS

Stephanie Brown (1985) also outlined stages of recovery. She also conceptualized recovery as a period of personal and emotional growth with each stage having its own developmental tasks and unique relapse risks. The following are Brown's stages of recovery:

Abstinence Stage: This stage begins immediately once the person stops using alcohol and drugs and is said to last for 1 to 2 years of recovery. The developmental tasks that need to be addressed in this stage include: acceptance that one has a SUD, the ability to practice honesty in everyday life, being able to manage cravings, developing coping skills, becoming active in AA or NA, practicing self-care, being able to understand relapse triggers, getting rid of friends who are still using, managing symptoms of post-acute withdrawal, understanding the dangers of substitute addictions and cross-addictions, developing healthy alternatives to alcohol/substance use, and defining oneself as a sober person. Common relapse triggers include being distressed by post-acute withdrawal symptoms and not becoming involved in self-help groups.

Repair Stage: The main challenge of this stage is to repair the damage done by years of active alcohol and/or drug use. Sometimes it's not unusual for clients in this stage to reach a plateau or to feel temporarily worse. This is because clients in this stage need to confront damage done to their loved ones, their careers, finances, and to their self-esteem. Feelings of guilt and shame are often common in this stage. Other developmental tasks include: being able to overcome negative self-labeling and catastrophizing, repairing relationships and being able to make amends when appropriate, improving self-care and being able to take care of oneself, accepting that feeling uncomfortable and distress is part of recovery, developing a balanced lifestyle, and being able to find enjoyable leisure activities. Common causes of relapse at this stage are poor self-care and avoiding going to self-help groups.

Growth Stage: If the Repair stage is about catching up, then the Growth stage is about moving forward (Melemis, 2015). This stage often corresponds to the 3rd to 5th years of recovery and is a time to deal with family-of-origin issues and any past history of trauma. However, in order for clients to be able to deal with these issues in counseling, they must have the necessary coping skills and support systems in place. These are some of the developmental tasks of the Growth stage: being able to identify and manage self-destructive behaviors and negative self-labeling, understanding how dysfunctional family patterns tend to repeat themselves and being able to let go of resentments over these patterns, being able to set healthy boundaries, being able to face and challenge fears, being able to give back to others (e.g., by sponsoring those new to recovery), and being able to periodically self-evaluate oneself.

Finally, author Earnie Larsen (2009) has written extensively on what he refers to as "Stage 2 Recovery." In Stage 1 recovery the substance abusing individual learns how to abstain from alcohol or drugs "a day at a time," while in Stage 2 recovery the goal is rebuilding one's life now that alcohol and drug abstinence has been achieved. Through many years of clinical experience, Larsen finds that individuals in Stage 2 recovery must address their own codependency or self-defeating personality traits which he refers to as "people-pleasers," "tap dancers," "caretakers," "workaholics," "perfectionists," and "martyrs." He finds that by avoiding addressing these dysfunctional roles, individuals tend to get "stuck" in their development as recovering persons. Larsen also emphasizes the importance of building solid intimate relationships and positive social relationships. Similar to Gorski's stages or progression of recovery, Larsen also hypothesizes that there is a progression to one's recovery the longer the individual puts more sober or clean time together and works at improving their life in recovery.

Gorski and Brown's stages are really about continued growth once sobriety or abstinence has been achieved. Think for a second why that's important in recovery. In many ways, sobriety is very similar to how we might define maturity. Mature individuals are able to take on and follow through with day-to-day responsibilities; able to handle difficult emotions like anger, resentment, annoyance or frustrations; and able to let go of things that cannot be changed as alluded to in the Serenity Prayer. Mature/sober individuals are able to express feelings to others, including loving or appreciative feelings. They are able to admit when they've made a mistake and able to take responsibility for an indiscretion or wrongdoing. They are able to deal with conflicts with others and to deal with life's problems in an honest, straightforward manner. These sobriety traits or characteristics are also a good measuring stick for determining one's growth in recovery. After all, sobriety is about change and growth, and someone who is truly working a program of recovery (whether it be in 12-step programs or counseling or both) will invariably show signs of growth. Also, individuals who are truly committed to recovery and exhibit this commitment through the personal work they do both in counseling as well as active participation in 12-step meetings will often exhibit the quality of their recovery in how they handle everyday life. For example, individuals who are able to "live life on life's terms" and do so with honesty and maturity are to be admired for their determination.

Another way to conceptualize the type of growth counselors would expect to see in clients with ongoing recovery is through reviewing what is referred to as The 12 Promises of Alcoholics Anonymous (Alcoholics Anonymous, 1976). In exploring the essence of the Promises listed in Box 13.2, there is an outline or framework for what continuous recovery will look like for someone who had truly embraced sobriety. Here we see individuals who are at peace with themselves and with those around them. Along with that peace comes serenity knowing that personal and financial insecurities and fears no longer take control of them. Self-pity and feelings of worthlessness also dissipate over time with the knowledge that they can be of help to others. In addition, individuals in recovery have come to accept their past behavior without regret while at the same time knowing there is no longer a need to repress those wrongdoings.

BOX 13.2

THE 12 PROMISES OF ALCOHOLICS ANONYMOUS

1. We are going to know a new freedom and a new happiness.
2. We will not regret the past nor wish to shut the door on it.
3. We will comprehend the word serenity.
4. We will know peace.
5. No matter how far down the scale we have gone, we will see how our experience can benefit others.
6. The feeling of uselessness and self-pity will disappear.
7. We will lose interest in selfish things and gain interest in our fellows.
8. Self-seeking will slip away.
9. Our whole attitude and outlook on life will change.
10. Fear of people and economic insecurity will leave us.
11. We will intuitively know how to handle situations which used to baffle us.
12. We will suddenly realize that God is doing for us what we could not do for ourselves.

Source: Alcoholics Anonymous. (1976). *The big book* (3rd ed., pp. 83–84). Alcoholics Anonymous World Services.

DRY VERSUS SOBER: DRY DRUNK SYNDROME

Usually, we think of individuals who are "dry" as those who have given up alcohol or drugs but who have not made other changes in their lives. As Gorski and many other addiction counselors contend, sobriety is about change. There are many instances where someone's family doctor told them to quit drinking or quit drug use, and they followed through with that recommendation. They stopped, but that's all they did. In other words, they didn't go to AA or NA, and they didn't go to rehab or go for counseling. There are probably instances where individuals like this manage well in their daily functioning; however, more often than not, there's a greater likelihood of dry drunk attitudes or behaviors emerging. Several addiction experts have put forth explanations of dry drunk behavior (Hunter & Salomone, 1987). Some of the characteristics include the following:

- Grandiosity
- Arrogance
- Impatience with others
- Becoming frustrated easily
- Intolerance of others
- Denying responsibility for problems
- Judgment
- Indecisiveness
- Dishonesty with self and/or others

- Egotism
- Controlling behavior

Given the aforementioned list of dry drunk behaviors and attitudes, it's easy to see how abstinence alone is not sufficient for growth and change. It's important for counselors to keep in mind that dry drunk behavior can surface at any time in recovery and is most often a sign of an imminent relapse.

LEARNING ACTIVITY 13.4
DRY DRUNK BEHAVIOR

From the descriptions of "dry drunk" behavior and attitudes listed earlier, what are some statements that you might expect to hear from a client that might signal that they are experiencing a "dry drunk"?

NOTES FROM THE FIELD

Robert Lynn, EdD, has worked in the addictions treatment profession for the past 50 years; has held key positions in many clinical settings, employee assistance programs, and state government; and has served on the faculty of several universities including the prestigious Rutgers Institute on Alcohol Studies. He also consults internationally for countries developing addiction treatment delivery systems. He has served as CEO/founder of the Addiction and Behavioral Alliance and as Director of Program Development for the C4 Recovery Solutions, and has also worked with the Navajo Nation's Project K'e. Dr. Lynn also served as one of the field reviewers for the *ASAM-3* and is currently working on a patient placement instrument that is more user-friendly and takes into consideration medication-assisted treatment approaches and harm reduction strategies. He feels that one of the greatest challenges facing the addiction treatment field when he worked as an employee assistance counselor/director was convincing industries that paying for addiction treatment produced a good return on their investment, once employees returned to work after completing addiction treatment programs. Dr. Lynn also describes challenges of counseling clients at various stages of recovery.

SUMMARY

This chapter addresses some of the developmental aspects of recovery both from the perspective of the downward progression of an active SUD as well as the upward progression of recovery. Included are explorations of Gorski's passages of recovery, the dry drunk syndrome, and counseling approaches that can be utilized at various points in recovery. There also is an exploration of how active SUDs can impact on normal human growth and development.

RESOURCES

Alcohol & Drug Addiction Recovery: Dr. David Streem (YouTube Video). This video presents some basic information regarding addiction and progression. https://www.youtube.com/watch?v=J11rcoORHBU

Brown, S. (1985). *Treating the alcoholic: A developmental model of recovery*. Wiley.

Case, A., & Deaton, A. (2020). *Deaths of despair and the future of capitalism*. Princeton University Press.

Earnie Larsen: The Starfish Story (Website-You Tube Video). This website provides a number of videos created by author, Earnie Larsen. https://www.youtube.com/watch?v=BIxvOo077Jo&list=PL4vdI3lR5b1gFZN1xcLvW8mkMYZ2wkPKU

Galen, L. W., Henderson, M. J., & Whitman, R. D. (1997). The utility of novelty-seeking, harm avoidance, and expectancy in the prediction of drinking. *Addictive Behaviors, 22*(1), 93–106. https://doi.org/10.1016/S0306-4603(96)00018-4

Glatt, M. M. (1975). Today's enjoyment—Tomorrow's dependency: The road to rock bottom and the way back. *British Journal of Addiction, 70*(Suppl. 1), 25–34. https://doi.org/10.1111/j.1360-0443.1975.tb01334.x

Gorski, T. T. (1989). *Passages through recovery: An action plan for preventing relapse*. Hazelden.

Nakken, C. (1988). *The addictive personality: Understanding compulsion in our lives*. Hazelden Foundation.

Roadmap to Recovery (Website-Video). This Substance Abuse & Mental Health Services Administration website, provides a look at the recovery progression to maintenance. https://www.youtube.com/watch?v=dkAY8m-uJI0

Sher, K. J., Bartholow, B. D., & Wood, M. D. (2000). Personality and substance use disorders: A perspective study. *Journal of Consulting & Clinical Psychology, 68*(5), 818–829.

Sher, K. J., Trull, T. J., Bartholow, B. D., & Vieth, A. (1999). Personality and alcoholism: Issues, methods, and etiological processes. In K. Leonard & H. Blaine (Eds.), *Psychological theories of drinking and alcoholism* (2nd ed., pp. 54–105). Guilford Press.

Wieczorek, W. F., & Nochajski, T. H. (2005). Characteristics of persistent drinking drivers: Comparisons of First, Second and Multiple Offenders. In D. A. Hennessy & D. L. Wiesenthal (Eds.), *Contemporary issues in road user behavior and traffic safety* (pp. 153–166). Nova Science Publishers.

KEY REFERENCES

Only key references appear in the print edition. The full reference list appears in the digital product on Springer Publishing Connect: connect.springerpub.com/content/book/978-0-8261-3586-5/chapter/ch13

Brook, J. S., Zhang, C., Leukefeld, C. G., & Brook, D. W. (2016). Marijuana use from adolescence to adulthood: Developmental trajectories and their outcomes. *Social Psychiatry and Psychiatric Epidemiology, 51*, 1405–1415. https://doi.org/10.1007/s00127-016-1229-0

Brown, S. (1985). *Treating the alcoholic: A developmental model of recovery.* Wiley.

Erikson, E. H. (1963). *Childhood and society* (2nd ed.). Norton.

Galen, L. W., Henderson, M. J., & Whitman, R. D. (1997). The utility of novelty-seeking, harm avoidance, and expectancy in the prediction of drinking. *Addictive Behaviors, 22*(1), 93–106. https://doi.org/10.1016/s0306-4603(96)00018-4

Glatt, M. M. (1969). *The alcoholic and the help he needs.* Priory Press Ltd.

Glatt, M. M. (1975). Today's enjoyment—Tomorrow's dependency: The road to rock bottom and the way back. *British Journal of Addiction, 70*(Suppl. 1), 25–34. https://doi.org/10.1111/j.1360-0443.1975.tb01334.x

Gorski, T. T. (1989). *Passages through recovery: An action plan for preventing relapse.* Hazelden.

Hunter, T. A., & Salomone, P. R. (1987). Dry drunk symptoms and alcoholic relapse. *Journal of Applied Rehabilitation Counseling, 18*(1), 22–25. https://doi.org/10.1891/0047-2220.18.1.22

Ilgen, M., McKellar, J., & Tiet, Q. (2005). Abstinence self-efficacy and abstinence 1 year after substance use disorder treatment. *Journal of Consulting and Clinical Psychology, 73*(6), 1175–1180. https://doi.org/10.1037/0022-006X.73.6.1175

Larsen, E. (2009). *Stage 2 recovery: Life beyond addiction.* Harper One.

Sher, K. J., Trull, T. J., Bartholow, B. D., & Vieth, A. (1999). Personality and alcoholism: Issues, methods, and etiological processes. In K. Leonard & H. Blaine (Eds.), *Psychological theories of drinking and alcoholism* (2nd ed., pp. 54–105). Guilford Press.

14

MULTICULTURAL CONSIDERATIONS IN ADDICTION TREATMENT

LEARNING OBJECTIVES

The purpose of this chapter is to describe multicultural considerations in both the conceptualization and treatment of addiction. By the end of this chapter, you will be able to:

- recognize the impact of your own cultural identities and associated privilege and oppression on your clinical work;
- synthesize the racial implications of the emergence of drug laws and more recent "war on drugs";
- demonstrate an understanding of the four domains of the Multicultural and Social Justice Counseling Competencies;
- describe the associations among substance use and minority stress, race-based traumatic stress, acculturative stress, and generational trauma;
- develop plans to partner with community leaders and engage in holistic treatment;
- assess whether addiction treatment strategies are culturally sensitive and ensure interventions are appropriate for diverse clients.

TERMS TO KNOW

acculturation changes resulting from contact between members of different cultural groups

acculturative stress psychological strain caused by the process of adjusting to a new culture

cultural appropriation when members of one culture take an aspect of another culture (e.g., art, dress, religious practices, intellectual property) and present it as their own while stripping it of its original meaning and intent, to the detriment of the culture from which it originated

culture membership in a particular group marked by shared beliefs, norms, values, traditions, worldviews, ideologies, and experiences

discrimination unjust or unfair treatment of an individual or population based on their cultural group membership

minority stress	psychological and emotional pain resulting from stigmatization associated with one's marginalized status within a society
oppression	systemic devaluing accompanied by undeserved challenges and disadvantages as a result of one's cultural group membership
privilege	systemic valuing accompanied by unearned benefits and advantages as a result of one's cultural group membership
race-based traumatic stress	psychological pain and distress as a result of existing within a racist society
racism	a system of dominance and power in which members of particular racial and ethnic groups are oppressed and devalued due to their racial/ethnic group membership

INTRODUCTION

Despite commonalities among drug-using behaviors and withdrawal symptoms, addiction counseling is not "one-size-fits-all." Instead, counselors must consider cultural factors in their conceptualization and treatment of addiction. The American Counseling Association (ACA, 2014) defines *culture* as "membership in a socially constructed way of living, which incorporates collective values, beliefs, norms, boundaries, and lifestyles that are cocreated with others who share similar worldviews comprising biological, psychosocial, historical, psychological, and other factors" (p. 20). Therefore, culture encompasses a variety of factors such as gender, age, race, ethnicity, social class, religion and/or spirituality, sexual orientation, ability status, nationality, and immigration or refugee status. The unique composition of a client's cultural identities should be explored and considered when providing addictions counseling services. Additionally, the unique composition of a counselor's cultural identities should be acknowledged and considered when providing addictions counseling services. In fact, all of the information provided in this textbook should be synthesized and applied within the context of culture, including historical contexts, norms, traditions, values, beliefs, and the experience of marginalization, privilege, and oppression. In this chapter, we highlight important multicultural considerations for both the conceptualization and treatment of addictive behaviors, which are essential for providing ethical and competent care.

MULTICULTURALLY COMPETENT COUNSELING

People exist within contexts of social systems, which are marked by hierarchies of power, social norms, dominant and counter narratives, and culture-bound values. To fully understand clients and provide effective services, counselors must acknowledge these contexts and consider clients' unique cultural identities in their work. In fact, the development of a strong therapeutic alliance, the accurate conceptualization of a client's presenting concern, the implementation of effective interventions, and engagement in meaningful advocacy efforts all hinge on considerations of clients' cultural identities. The Multicultural and Social

Justice Counseling Competencies (MSJCC; Ratts et al., 2016) provide a helpful framework for how counselors can attend to cultural dimensions in clinical practice. Specifically, the MSJCC are made up of four domains: counselor self-awareness, client worldview, the counseling relationship, and counseling and advocacy interventions.

To provide multiculturally competent services aligned with social justice, counselors must first be aware of their own cultural identities and the privilege and/or oppression associated with those identities. *Privilege* refers to power or status resulting from membership in a cultural group that is valued by society (Johnson, 2006; McIntosh, 1990, 2015). With this systemic valuing comes certain advantages, unearned benefits and assets, access to resources, and opportunities. In the United States, privileged cultural groups include the male gender, White race, heterosexual orientation, middle and upper socioeconomic status, American citizenship, and able-bodied status, among others. In contrast, *oppression* refers to disempowerment resulting from membership in a cultural group that is devalued by society. This systemic devaluing comes with challenges, undeserved difficulties, limited access to resources, and restricted opportunities. In the United States, oppressed or marginalized groups include female or transgender individuals, people of color, members of the LGBQIA+ community, individuals of lower socioeconomic status, immigrants and refugees, and those with disabilities, among others (Johnson, 2006; McIntosh, 1990, 2015).

It does not take long to learn which cultural groups are valued in a particular society. Indeed, Samuel Ortiz, a Hispanic male, noted, "As a child you understand intuitively what and whom society values...by the age of 5, I knew I was living in a society where I looked and sounded different from most other people and that this was not a good thing" (1999, p. 10). Thus, even children are aware of systemic valuing (privilege) and devaluing (oppression) in the culture in which they reside. The origins of systemic privilege and oppression in the United States are beyond the scope of this chapter, but for readers who are considering these topics for the first time, it is imperative that you gain knowledge and awareness in this area to better understand your own cultural identities and how those attributes will impact your clinical work. For now, take a moment to complete Learning Activity 14.1 to begin the process of considering yourself as a cultural being and contemplating

LEARNING ACTIVITY 14.1
MY CULTURAL IDENTITIES

We all have a unique constellation of cultural identities that make us who we are. Go through the following list and note your cultural identities. As a reminder, race differs from ethnicity in that race is characterized by physical attributes such as skin color, hair texture, eye shape, etc. Ethnicity, on the other hand, refers to heritage and belonging to a particular group defined by beliefs, values, and norms. Therefore, a person's race may be "White" and their ethnicity may be "German and Italian." Additionally, ability-status refers to whether or not you are able-bodied or have a physical or mental disability.

What is your:

Age ____________________

Race ____________________

Ethnicity ____________________

Gender ____________________

Sexual orientation ____________________

Social class ____________________

Ability-status ____________________

Religion/spirituality ____________________

Nationality ____________________

Immigration or refugee status ____________________

All of these elements make up your unique cultural identity. Consider the privilege or oppression associated with each element of your cultural identity in modern society. What are your reactions to this activity?

the privilege or oppression associated with each aspect of your identity (note, individuals can simultaneously be members of both privileged and oppressed groups. Consider a White, gay male who experiences White privilege and male privilege, yet experiences oppression due to his sexual minority status).

Along with understanding your own cultural identities (i.e., counselor self-awareness), the second domain of the MSJCC calls counselors to understand their clients' unique worldviews. It is imperative that counselors who work with addictions (or any other presenting concern) consider their clients' age, gender, race, ethnicity, ability-status, socioeconomic status, religion or spirituality, sexual orientation, nationality, and immigration or refugee status and how these factors impact the way in which the client operates in the world. Counselors consider questions like: what are the client's cultural norms? In what ways has the client experienced privilege? In what ways has the client experienced oppression? What are the client's beliefs and values? What is the historical context of the client's cultural identities? How might the client be experiencing the counselor and the counseling process? What are the client's strengths? Multiculturally competent counselors recognize the unique worldview of their clients in their clinical work. Unfortunately, some addictions counselors fall into the trap of conceptualizing their clients based on their drug of abuse (e.g., "Ok, this client is another heroin user"). Multiculturally competent counselors resist this myopic view and consider their client's multifaceted identities and the context in which the alcohol or other drug use occurs.

The third domain of the MSJCC refers to the counseling relationship and encourages counselors to consider how their unique cultural identities and the cultural identities of their clients may affect the therapeutic alliance. Each counselor-client dyad is distinct and influenced by the cultural identities of both the counselor and the client. For example, the way in which a 55-year-old Latina, female counselor forms a therapeutic alliance with a Latina client may differ from the way in which a 25-year-old Black, male counselor forms a therapeutic alliance with the same Latina client. Similarly, a White, heterosexual, male counselor's relationship with a White, bisexual client may look different from his relationship with a Middle Eastern, heterosexual female. Both the counselor and client's unique cultural identities, and experiences of privilege and oppression, will influence the counseling relationship, and multiculturally competent counselors are called to recognize these effects.

Finally, the fourth domain of the MSJCC refers to counseling and advocacy interventions. Depending upon clients' unique cultural identities, counselors determine (and coconstruct with clients) appropriate clinical goals and treatment plans. Rather than rigidly applying interventions in the same manner with each client, counselors can culturally adapt evidence-based treatments (EBTs) to enhance cultural sensitivity and treatment effectiveness (Burlew et al., 2013). Indeed, Resnicow et al. (2000) described the *cultural sensitivity framework* in which counselors incorporate clients' cultural identities into their work and modify or tailor their treatment approaches accordingly. The authors described two dimensions of the cultural sensitivity framework: *surface structure* (adapting the intervention's message and materials to be relevant to a client's culture) and *deep structure* (adapting the intervention itself to align with the norms, values, and practices of a client's culture; Resnicow et al., 2000). By culturally adapting interventions, counselors ensure that their clinical work is relevant and respectful of clients' cultural identities, thereby increasing clinical effectiveness. For example, Lee et al. (2013) developed and applied a culturally adapted version of motivational interviewing

(MI) for Latino clients who engaged in problematic alcohol use. The researchers found that clients who received the culturally adapted MI intervention (which addressed acculturation stress, the social contexts of alcohol consumption, and cultural values) demonstrated fewer heavy drinking days and fewer negative consequences of drinking than clients in the unadapted MI intervention (Lee et al., 2013).

Additionally, the fourth domain of the MSJCC ensures that counselors are cognizant of opportunities for advocacy efforts at the individual, community, and public level (Toporek & Daniels, 2018; Toporek et al., 2009). When counselors become aware of injustice, discrimination, or oppression experienced by their clients, they can act *with* or *on behalf* of clients to remove obstacles to their wellness (O'Hara et al., 2016). For example, a counselor who becomes aware of racially driven targeting practices of alcohol and tobacco companies in a particular community may choose to raise awareness about these unjust practices and implore city leaders to engage in more regulation of alcohol and tobacco ads.

Given the vast diversity of clients with substance use disorders (SUDs), it is imperative that counselors consider and become competent in these dimensions of the MSJCC. Let us now explore multicultural considerations in the conceptualization of addiction that can increase counselors' cultural competence. Specifically, the information in the following sections can help counselors better understand their clients' worldview (domain two of the MSJCC), the counselor and client relationship (domain three), and appropriate interventions and advocacy work (domain four). Additionally, your reactions to the information in the following sections can illuminate your own beliefs, preconceptions, and biases related to various cultural groups and addictive behaviors, which is an essential step in counselor self-awareness (domain one).

MULTICULTURAL CONSIDERATIONS IN CONCEPTUALIZING ADDICTION

It is clear that differences exist among cultural groups with regard to substance using behaviors. Before examining these statistics, it is important to emphasize the need for nuance and attention to within-group differences, rather than considering between-group differences alone (e.g., the variance within a cultural group [e.g., Asian] is just as important as the variance between cultural groups [e.g., Asian and White]). Although it can be helpful to look at general trends related to substance use according to cultural identities, it is harmful to assume that all members of a particular cultural group perceive, use, and respond to substances in the same way. Trends and statistics have their purpose, yet forgoing nuance and failing to consider within-group differences could lead to harmful, inaccurate applications of these data. For example, there are 574 federally recognized Native American tribes and villages in the United States (Bureau of Indian Affairs, n.d.) with great variance in substance using behaviors at the community and individual level. To assume that all Native Americans have the same relationship with substance use is a grave error, and, in fact, the "drunken Indian" stereotype is a product of this misperception and has done substantial damage to the Native community (Dunbar-Ortiz & Gilio-Whitaker, 2016; Giordano et al., 2020; Westermeyer, 1974). Decades ago, Westermeyer (1974) described the variance among Native tribes, subgroups, and individuals with regard to alcohol use. He concluded, "Thus statements about Indians and alcohol should specify which Indians, in what place, during what period, and under what circumstances" (Westermeyer, 1974, p. 36). The same is true for the substance use statistics of all cultural groups. These data should be understood within the appropriate current and historical context, aspects of which we will examine in the chapter.

With that in mind, we know that variance exists among racial and ethnic groups with regard to substance use. According to the National Survey on Drug Use and Health (NSDUH), in the past year, the percentage of adults in each racial and ethnic group with a substance use disorder were as follows: Native American/Alaskan Native, 12.7%; Latino(a)(x), 8.6%; Hawaiian/Pacific Islander, 7.7%; Black, 7.6%; Asian, 4.0%; and a national average of 8.1% (Substance Abuse and Mental Health Services Administration [SAMHSA], 2017). Rates of illicit drug use in the past year were as follows: Native American/Alaskan Native, 23.7%; Black, 21.0%; Hawaiian/Pacific Islander, 19.5%; Latino(a)(x), 17.0%; Asian, 9.3%; and a national average of 17.9% (SAMHSA, 2017). According to the 2019 NSDUH survey, past-month illicit drug use rates among Americans aged 12 and older by racial and ethnic group were: Multiracial, 22.5%; Black, 14.6%; Native American/Alaskan Native, 14.5%; White, 13.6%; Hawaiian/Pacific Islander, 11.1%; Latino(a)(x), 11.1%; and Asian, 5.6% (SAMHSA, 2020).

In addition to racial/ethnic differences, data also reveal gender differences in substance use. For example, data indicate that men are admitted to addictions treatment more frequently than women (66.9% and 33.1% of admissions, respectively; Center for Behavioral Health Statistics and Quality, 2014), and illicit drug use in the past month was higher among men (12.8%) compared to women (8.5%; Center for Behavioral Health Statistics and Quality, 2017). See Table 14.1 for more data regarding racial/ethnic and gender differences in substance use.

Furthermore, with regard to sexual orientation, the NSDUH found that individuals identifying as sexual minorities (i.e., bisexual, gay, lesbian) had higher illicit drug use in the past year (40.3%), higher binge drinking in the past month (36.2%), and more reported substance use disorders in the past year (16.4%) compared to the national average (18.0%, 26.5%, and 7.9% respectively; SAMHSA, 2018). Additionally, individuals identifying as sexual minorities had higher rates of past year use among 10 illicit drugs compared to individuals identifying as heterosexual (Medley et al., 2016). There are many ways to interpret these numbers, and the remainder of this section is dedicated to examining important considerations for the conceptualization of addiction among diverse populations.

History of Drug Laws and Drug Exposure

When conceptualizing addiction, it is important for clinicians to be aware of the history of drug laws and the context in which they emerged. Rather than the creation of laws driven by the nature of the addictive substances themselves, antidrug laws were more often created in response to the demographics of those who were using the substance (Loue, 2003). For example, in the 1850s, the United States saw a rise in Chinese immigrants, who quickly became the scapegoat for myriad problems in the country, particularly on the West Coast (Mark, 1975). The anti-Chinese movement was augmented by anti-opium laws (which first emerged in California in the 1880s) and thrived on the exaggerated claims that Chinese immigrants were overwhelmingly addicted to opium and the inflation of potential negative consequences that could emerge from continued opium use within this community (Mark, 1975). Additionally, the use of marijuana among the growing Mexican immigrant population

TABLE 14.1 Substance Use Percentages by Demographic Factors

	MALE	FEMALE	ASIAN	BLACK	LATINO	NATIVE AMERICAN	WHITE	REFERENCE
Eighth grade illicit drug use (annual)	13.2	13.3		13.1	15.5		1.3	Johnston et al. (2019)
10th grade illicit drug use (annual)	29.5	30.2		36.4	31.0		27.7	Johnston et al. (2019)
12th grade illicit drug use (annual)	39.7	36.8		38.8	37.2		39.5	Johnston et al. (2019)
12th grade daily marijuana use	7.2	3.4		5.9	4.3		5.8	Johnston et al. (2019)
Lifetime cannabis use disorder (adults)	8.4	4.3	3.1	7.2	4.5	11.5	6.7	Hasin et al. (2016)
Last year symptomatic high-risk drinker (adults)	9.5	7.8		7.0	9.4		9.0	Fan et al. (2019)
Past year persistent alcohol use disorder (adults)	35.6	32.1		48.6	43.0		31.1	Fan et al. (2019)
Binge drinking in past month (adults)			15.0	25.7	28.7	26.8		SAMHSA (2017)
Past year illicit drug use (12 years and older)			10.0	21.9	19.1	25.1	21.7	SAMHSA (2020)

led to claims that the drug made Mexicans violent, which led to the Marijuana Tax Act of 1937 (Reinarman & Levine, 1997). In the same way, the first anti-cocaine drug laws emerged in response to the use of cocaine among Black laborers in Southern states (despite the fact that White employers often gave cocaine to their Black employees to increase productivity; Hogan, 2009). The public's reaction to opium use among the Chinese, marijuana use among Mexicans, and cocaine use among Black people was very different from their reaction to morphine and barbiturate use among middle- and upper-class White people (which also was prevalent during the same time periods). Substance use among people of color was conceptualized by a narrative of fear and danger, while substance use among White populations was ignored, minimized, or justified.

A common thread among the first drug laws was the impact on marginalized group members (who were the primary focus of the law) and privileged group members (who influenced the creation and implementation of the law). Specifically, since marginalized racial and ethnic groups were portrayed as "threats" (such as threats to job security for White Americans and/or threats to the status quo and social order; Hogan, 2009), antidrug laws became a way to control these populations. Laws that targeted substances used by marginalized groups were, in part, an effort to discourage these individuals from coming or staying in America and a way to police those who did (Mark, 1975).

In addition to understanding drug laws, it is imperative to understand the history of exposure to substances among cultural groups. For example, prior to colonization, Native American tribes utilized a variety of substances for medicinal or ceremonial purposes (e.g., tobacco, peyote, kava; Coyhis & White, 2006). Some tribes used alcohol, largely in rituals and ceremonies, without incurring problems like abuse and addiction. When Europeans arrived, however, Native people were introduced to large quantities of distilled alcohol, which was often brought to treaty and trade meetings by White men. The use of alcohol among Native groups began to grow, as did rates of intoxication. Although many Native leaders tried to reduce the spread of alcohol among Native people and limit the amount of alcohol used in trade agreements, alcohol became a weapon used by non-Natives to facilitate dependence, manipulation, and control of Native people (Coyhis & White, 2006). In fact, the intoxication among Native people gave rise to the idea that Native Americans are biologically predisposed to seek and consume alcohol, which contributed to the idea of racial inferiority (although genetic vulnerabilities may exist among people and families, there is no evidence that all members of a particular racial or ethnic group are more or less susceptible to addiction). Therefore, addiction rates among particular cultural groups must be conceptualized in light of the history of drug laws and initial drug exposure. Along with this history, it is important for counselors to understand the current status of drug laws, including the "war on drugs."

War on Drugs

In the early 1970s, under the Nixon administration, the U.S. government began its crusade against drugs of abuse by identifying illegal drugs as "public enemy number one" (Alexander, 2012, p. 48). Later, in 1982, Reagan declared a "war on drugs," and the resulting policies and laws were dramatic. In 1981 the annual federal budget for anti-drug initiatives was $2 billion, yet by 1993, the budget had jumped to $12 billion, with most funding dedicated to prisons and law enforcement (Reinarman & Levine, 1997). Additionally, the number of incarcerated Americans went from 300,000 in 1980 to approximately two million in 2000, with drug arrests as the primary reason for this striking increase (Alexander, 2012). After Reagan, the Bush Sr. and Clinton administrations continued the "tough on crime" and "hard on drugs" political platforms and increased funding, policies, and laws to support the drug war (Alexander, 2012). The notion that drug use and possession was a crime, rather than a public health issue, became firmly entrenched in American society.

What does the history of the "war on drugs" have to do with multicultural considerations in the conceptualization of addiction? Rather than impacting all Americans who use substances at equal rates, the "war on drugs" has had tremendously detrimental consequences on members of racial and ethnic marginalized groups in this country. Indeed, the "war on drugs" began as a reaction to the "crack scare" in the 1980s, which resulted from crack cocaine use (a cheaper way to use cocaine) in poorer urban communities that were disproportionately comprised of Black and Latino individuals (Reinarman & Levine, 1997). Once cocaine use spread to the urban poor, "politicians and the media focused on crack—and the drug scare began—when cocaine smoking became visible among a 'dangerous group'" (Reinarman & Levine, 1997, p. 19). Thus, the very emergence of the "war on drugs" had racial/ethnic implications.

As the drug war continued, it became apparent that the laws against drug use and possession were not being equally enforced among members of various racial/ethnic and socioeconomic status groups. Although rates of drug possession and selling occur among all racial and ethnic groups at similar rates, almost 75% of those imprisoned for drug crimes are people of color (Alexander, 2011). How does one make sense of this discrepancy? There are a few possible reasons: (a) people of color and poorer communities are searched and raided more frequently than White individuals or those in more affluent communities (consider the frequency of drug raids in poor urban communities compared to prestigious college campuses), and (b) when found with an illegal drug, some individuals are ushered directly into the criminal justice system while other individuals are ushered into rehabilitation programs and treatment facilities. Thus, variance exists in the enforcement of drug laws. Ethan Nadelmann (2013), founder of the Drug Policy Alliance, described the process of drug use criminalization and how the enforcement of specific laws is linked to privilege and oppression in society. Specifically, he noted that drug laws "are not typically going to be enforced against the Whiter and wealthier and more affluent or middle class members of society. Inevitably those laws will be disproportionately enforced against the poor and younger and darker-skinned members of society" (2013, para 10–11).

Alexander (2011, 2012) proposed that the war on drugs and resulting mass incarceration of people of color represents a new caste system similar to the mechanisms of control utilized during the Jim Crow era. Specifically, once people of color are arrested for drug charges and labeled

LEARNING ACTIVITY 14.2
TRUTH ABOUT THE WAR ON DRUGS

Prior to reading this section, what were your thoughts related to the war on drugs and mass incarceration related to drug offenses? Had you considered these phenomena in terms of racial justice? In her book *The New Jim Crow,* Michelle Alexander wrote, "Nothing has contributed more to the systematic mass incarceration of people of color in the United States than the War on Drugs" (Alexander, 2012, p. 60). What are your thoughts about the influence of race on the war on drugs? What might it take to shift the public narrative from one of punishment (criminalization) for drug use to rehabilitation (treatment)?

as felons, they lose many rights such as serving on a jury, voting, access to food stamps, and opportunities for public housing (Alexander, 2012). To examine the effects of felony drug charges, Pager (2007) conducted a field experiment to assess employment opportunities among those who have been incarcerated. Using Black and White testers (actors) with fictitious resumes, Pager found that the White tester with no drug charge received 34% of the callbacks for job interviews at entry-level jobs. The White tester with a felony drug charge received only 17% of the callbacks. Alarmingly, the Black tester with no criminal record received only 14% of the callbacks, while the Black tester with a drug charge received only 5% of the callbacks for entry-level positions. Therefore, Pager (2007) found that having a felony drug charge substantially decreased employment opportunities, especially among people of color.

Additionally, the "war on drugs" came with the Anti-Drug Abuse Act of 1986, which established mandatory minimum sentences for possession of certain quantities of drugs (Bjerk, 2017). These thresholds for triggering mandatory minimum sentences varied among different drugs of abuse, and those differences again revealed racial bias. For example, prior to the Fair Sentencing Act of 2010, the amount of powder cocaine needed to trigger mandatory minimum sentences and the amount of crack cocaine needed to trigger mandatory minimum sentences differed substantially. Specifically, possession of .005 kg of crack cocaine would lead to a mandatory minimum sentence of 5 years for a first offense, yet it took .5 kg of powder cocaine to trigger the same mandatory minimum sentence. That means only .005 kg of crack would result in the same consequences as .5 kg of powder cocaine (a difference of 100:1). Why such a discrepancy? At the time these laws were created, 80% of crack users were Black, while powder cocaine (which was more expensive) was used primarily by White individuals. The Fair Sentencing Act of 2010 sought to reduce the disparity of charges between crack and powder cocaine possession, and resulted in changing the triggering quantity of crack cocaine from .005 kg to .028 kg. Thus, although disparity still exists, the difference is approximately 20:1 rather than 100:1 (Bjerk, 2017). In sum, the "war on drugs" and its rippling effects has led to the mass imprisonment of people of color, a phenomenon that counselors should acknowledge in their work with addiction.

Media Portrayal of Drug Use

Along with disparities in drug laws and the enforcement of those laws, the narratives in mass media related to substance use among various cultural groups create divergent public perceptions. Indeed, some researchers claim that the media is aiding in the creation of "narcotic apartheid" (Netherland & Hansen, 2016, p. 666) in which drug use is conceptualized very differently based on the race of the user. An empirical examination of popular media stories related to heroin and prescription opioid use in 2001 and 2011 revealed significant differences in the messages, language, and depictions of substance use based on the racial composition of the associated community. For example, stories related to substance use in primarily White settings were depicted as surprising and unexpected, and the etiology of use and personal stories of users were explored at length leading to sympathetic and humanizing descriptions. Oftentimes, the focus of the story was on the overdose or death of the user (Netherland & Hansen, 2016).

On the other hand, stories related to substance use in primarily Black and Latino settings communicated that drug use was expected in those areas, and the reports omitted personal stories of the users and etiology of use, leading to dehumanizing effects (Netherland & Hansen, 2016). Among Black and Latino communities, the focus of the story did not include conditions that led to substance use (which was common stories of drug use in White settings) but rather emphasized the criminality of the behaviors. In light of these disparities in media coverage of substance use, the researchers noted that the study "points to the crucial role of racialized imagery and narratives in generating public support for disparate policy response in drug control" (Netherland & Hansen, 2016, p. 681).

The way in which the mass media describes drug use, individuals who use drugs, and communities in which drug use takes place affects public perception of these issues. Consider the following two fictitious news headlines and note the potential implications of the messages:

Headline 1: White college hopeful dies tragically from heroin overdose to the shock of his family and friends.

Headline 2: Deceased Black male found in possession of large quantities of heroin, most likely with intent to distribute.

Narratives and messaging related to substance use and addictive behaviors are powerful. Thus, it is imperative that counselors (and the public at large) are critical consumers of the media and able to identify evidence of prejudice and oppression. Now let's turn our attention to specific risk factors of substance use that are relevant to diverse cultural groups and can aid in the conceptualization of addiction.

Racial/Ethnic Discrimination and Race-Based Traumatic Stress

Drugs of abuse stimulate the reward system in the brain causing the release of neurotransmitters and subsequent feelings of pleasure, euphoria, calm, or other mood-altering reactions. Therefore, drugs of abuse and rewarding behaviors (e.g., gambling, internet gaming, sex) often are utilized by individuals as a means of *changing how they feel*. Albeit maladaptive, drugs of abuse and addictive behaviors can become an individual's primary means of coping with negative emotions. Hence, risk factors for addiction include experiences and situations that can lead to negative emotional states such as stress, fear, depression, anger, despair, anxiety, and hopelessness. There are many situations that can lead to these negative reactions, including *racial/ethnic discrimination*. Thus, experiences of discrimination can serve as a risk factor for substance use among people of color by increasing the probability of coping through drugs of abuse. For example, in the study of 505 people of color, Rose et al. (2019) found that perceived discrimination significantly increased the odds of substance use (i.e., cigarette, alcohol, marijuana) among participants. Furthermore, a study of youth from the Cherokee Nation revealed that higher frequencies of racial discrimination were associated with elevated levels of substance use (Garrett et al., 2017). Finally, among Latino adults in the United States, researchers found that experiences of discrimination were related to increased risks of SUDs (Otiniano Verissimo et al., 2014).

In addition to experiences of discrimination, members of marginalized racial and ethnic groups are subject to *race-based traumatic stress*. Racism differs from discrimination as it is a system of dominance resulting from historical patterns of injustice toward members of marginalized groups (Harrell, 2000). The emotional states that accompany living in a racist society can include hypervigilance, a persistent sense of danger, anger, sadness, and vulnerability (Harrell, 2000). Indeed, many scholars have asserted that racism is a form of trauma and can lead to traumatic stress (Bryant-Davis, 2007; Carter, 2007; Kirkinis et al., 2021). Therefore, just like experiences of discrimination, race-based traumatic stress can heighten individuals' risk of coping through the use of substances or addictive behaviors.

It is important to note that not all members of marginalized racial and ethnic groups respond to discrimination and race-based traumatic stress by using substances (Giordano et al., 2021). Indeed, many people of color cope through social support, religious/spiritual practices, and advocacy. However, when conceptualizing addiction, it is important to recognize that these systemic stressors increase the risk of maladaptive coping responses (e.g., substance use) among marginalized populations to a greater extent than privileged populations. Consider the following case of Devon. How do you conceptualize his substance use? What risk factors is he experiencing? If you were his counselor, what would you want to explore with Devon?

CASE EXAMPLE: DEVON

Devon is a 19-year-old Black, heterosexual male, who is a sophomore at a public liberal arts University in the Southeast. He was referred to the college counseling center from the student academic services office as a result of failing two courses and being put on academic probation. Additionally, Devon received three underage drinking tickets for consuming alcohol in his dorm room, and the Resident Assistant found him using marijuana on two occasions. Since he began college, Devon has been taking a full course load as well as working part-time as a cashier in the University dining hall to help pay for school. When asked about his experience at the University, Devon quickly stated that he "hates it here." He noted that he does not "fit in" and he is tired of being the only Black male in his classes. Devon reported that he often is asked to "share the Black perspective" by his professors, and when he is at work, he is the subject of derogatory racial slurs from other students. He noted that one night he came home from work and found the door to his dorm room covered in offensive, discriminatory language and symbols. Devon said he started drinking regularly a few months ago as a way to "calm down," and he finds that marijuana relaxes him. In session, Devon appears somber and avoids eye-contact with the counselor. When asked what he wants to get out of counseling Devon says, "Nothing. I'll figure it out myself."

Generational Trauma

Another form of trauma that poses as a risk factor for self-soothing via drugs of abuse is *generational trauma*. Generational trauma, or historical trauma, is unique in that it refers to a collective traumatic experience causing psychological pain that is passed down to subsequent generations and linked to poor mental and physical outcomes (Brave Heart, 2004; Conching &

Thayer, 2019). Examples of these collective traumatic events can include genocide, war, poverty, discrimination, terrorism, internment, colonization, and massacres. Rather than only psychological, it is proposed that traumatic experiences have a biological impact and can alter gene expression, the study of which is known as *epigenetics* (Deans & Maggert, 2015; Siegel, 2012; van der Kolk, 2014).

In this burgeoning research field, preliminary evidence suggests that stressful or traumatic events can alter the expression or behavior of particular genes in one's offspring without changing the structure of their DNA (Deans & Maggert, 2015). Therefore, parental experiences of trauma can lead to changes in the epigenome (or gene expression) of their children, which can lead to poorer psychological and/or physical health outcomes. These detrimental outcomes resulting from epigenetic changes may predispose some individuals toward addiction (Conching & Thayer, 2019). The Holocaust, Japanese interment, transatlantic slave trade of Africans, and lynching and acts of terrorism against Black Americans all constitute examples of collective traumas that may have repercussions on subsequent generations.

In the instance of Native Americans, a history of genocide, war, broken treaties, displacement, forced assimilation through boarding schools, lost land, lost language, spiritual oppression, poverty, systemic oppression, and the criminalization of Native practices were traumatic events that affected all Native people in the United States (Brave Heart, 2004; Nutton & Fast, 2015). The use of substances among certain Native American subgroups may reflect a *historical trauma response*, in which individuals attempt to soothe the psychological pain associated with generational trauma (Brave Heart, 2004). Along with substance use, historical trauma responses can consist of suicidal thoughts, nonsuicidal self-injury, emotion dysregulation, depression, anger, anxiety, and unresolved grief (Brave Heart, 2004). Thus, it is necessary for counselors to consider the function of substance use (e.g., coping with generational trauma) among diverse clients. Indeed, Giordano et al. (2020) noted, "Culturally competent counselors should recognize that substance use and mental health concerns are understandable outcomes of generational trauma, historic and current oppression, stereotyping, and multilevel injustice toward Native people" (p. 168). The consideration of generational trauma, particularly among members of marginalized cultural groups, is imperative in the conceptualization of addiction.

LEARNING ACTIVITY 14.3 GAINING KNOWLEDGE ABOUT HISTORICAL TRAUMA

The only way for counselors to consider and explore the effects of generational trauma in clinical practice is to be aware of historical traumas pertinent to various cultural groups. There are many aspects of Native American history, including collective traumas, that are not well known by the general public. Select one of the following topics and search online for a reputable source to learn more about the event. How might this information grow your understanding of generational trauma?

- Native American boarding schools and forced assimilation
- Indian Removal Act
- Pueblo Revolt of 1680
- 1851 Indian Appropriations Act
- The Long Walk of the Navajo
- The Trail of Tears
- 1883 Code of Indian Offenses
- The Dawes Act
- Massacre at Wounded Knee
- Dakota Access Pipeline

Acculturative Stress

Another risk factor for substance use that has particular relevance to marginalized racial and ethnic group members is *acculturative stress*. Acculturation is defined as "those phenomena which result when groups of individuals having different cultures come into continuous first-hand contact, with subsequent changes in the original cultural patterns of either or both" (Redfield et al., 1936, p. 149). The process of acculturation is common among individuals who leave their home country to reside in a host country for a duration of time and can affect individuals in myriad ways. Berry (1997) described four acculturation strategies including *assimilation* (adopting the culture of the host country), *separation* (maintaining the culture of one's country of origin), *integration* (maintaining the culture of one's country of origin and adopting cultural aspects of the host country), and *marginalization* (foregoing the culture of the host country and one's country of origin). See Figure 14.1.

For some individuals, the emotional and psychological effects of adjusting to a new culture can be distressing and can have negative effects on the individual's physical health, decision-making processes, occupational functioning, and relationships (Smart & Smart, 1995). This experience is called *acculturative stress*. Sam and Berry (2006) noted that the acculturation process can trigger depression as individuals experience the loss associated with foregoing aspects of their culture of origin, as well as anxiety in the face of uncertainty related to living within the new host culture (Sam & Berry, 2006).

In light of the potential detrimental outcomes of acculturative stress, it is not surprising that researchers have found associations between acculturative stress and substance use

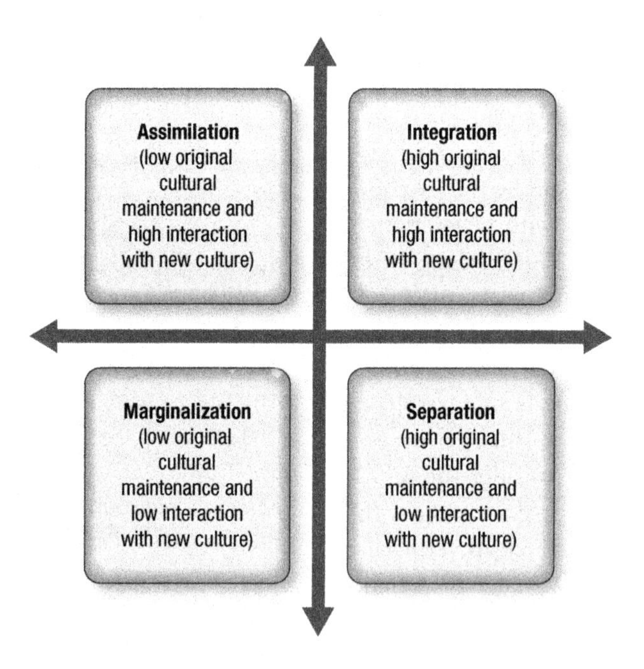

FIGURE 14.1 Acculturation strategies.

Source: Berry, J. W. (1997). Immigration, acculturation, and adaptation. *Applied Psychology: An International Review, 46*, 5–34. https://doi.org/10.1080/026999497378467

among various cultural groups. For example, in the study of Asian Americans, researchers found that acculturative stress among Vietnamese participants and family cultural conflict among Chinese participants significantly predicted increased alcohol consumption (Park et al., 2014). Additionally, among a sample of international students, researchers found a direct relationship between acculturative stress and alcohol-related consequences (Hunt et al., 2017). Like other stressors, the process of acculturation may, for some individuals, increase the risk of coping through substance use.

Minority Stress

Minority stress is another risk factor for substance use among marginalized populations. Specifically, research consistently reveals higher rates of substance use among marginalized sexual orientation group members including bisexual, gay, and lesbian individuals. For instance, in the study of past-year SUDs, researchers found that White, Black, and Hispanic sexual minorities had higher rates of alcohol use disorder, nicotine use disorder, and cannabis use disorder compared to their heterosexual counterparts (Rodriguez-Seijas et al., 2019). Additionally, a study of over 3,000 adolescents revealed that sexual minority youth had higher odds of tobacco, marijuana, alcohol, and prescription drug use compared to their heterosexual counterparts (Mereish et al., 2017). One potential factor influencing these disparities is minority stress.

The construct of minority stress emerged as a way to conceptualize the conflict faced by gay men with regard to their personal values and the values of the dominant culture (Meyer, 1995). Specifically, minority stress is defined as "excess stress to which individuals from stigmatized social categories are exposed as a result of their social, often a minority, position" (Meyer, 2013, p. 4). The proposed processes of minority stress for sexual minority individuals include: (a) stressful or negative events (acts of violence or discrimination), (b) expectations of stressful or negative events (presumption of stigma and prejudice), (c) internalized homophobia, and (d) concealment of sexual minority status (Meyer, 1995, 2013).

The stigmatization of having a sexual minority status and accompanying expected or experienced negative encounters can lead to a state of stress among sexual minority individuals. It is hypothesized that individuals experiencing minority stress may employ maladaptive coping strategies, such as substance use, as a means of managing their psychological distress (Anhalt & Morris, 2003). Some empirical evidence supports this hypothesis. For example, in a meta-analysis of risk factors of minority stress among lesbian, gay, and bisexual adolescents, researchers found that negative reactions to sexual minority disclosure, psychological stress, victimization, and a lack of adult support were significantly correlated with substance use among participants (Goldbach et al., 2014). Additionally, with regard to gender diversity, researchers examined minority stress and substance use among a sample of transgender adults (Gonzalez et al., 2017). The authors found that some characteristics of minority stress (i.e., internalized stigma) were associated with an increased likelihood of excessive alcohol use among transgender men and cannabis use among transgender women (Gonzalez et al., 2017). As counselors work with sexual minority clients who use substances, it may be helpful to consider and explore experiences of minority stress.

Targeting Practices

A final multicultural consideration in the conceptualization of addiction is the acknowledgment of targeting practices related to alcohol and tobacco use. The location of stores that sell alcohol and tobacco products, as well as marketing and advertising practices, are important considerations with regard to exposure and accessibility of substances. Research indicates that people of color and poorer communities are targeted more heavily by alcohol and tobacco organizations to advertise and sell products (Lee et al., 2018; Primack et al., 2007; Rose et al., 2019). For example, researchers found that Black young adults were exposed to more tobacco and alcohol advertising, and Hispanic young adults were exposed to more alcohol advertising, than their White counterparts (Rose et al., 2019). Furthermore, this increased exposure to alcohol and tobacco marketing was associated with increased likelihood of cigarette use and risky alcohol use (Rose et al., 2019). Additionally, Primack and colleagues (2007) examined 11 studies of pro-tobacco advertisements and found that pro-tobacco messaging was denser and more concentrated in predominantly Black areas compared to predominantly White areas. Specifically, the researchers found that the odds of an advertisement being tobacco-related were 70% higher in Black communities as compared to White communities (Primack et al., 2007). This data coupled with the existence of border towns, which house multiple liquor stores and bars in close proximity to dry Native American reservations, illuminates targeting practices of tobacco and alcohol companies (Lee et al., 2018). Specifically, these practices make alcohol and tobacco products more available and marketed more heavily in and around poor communities and/or communities of color.

It is incumbent upon counselors to consider the holistic experience of their clients when conceptualizing addiction. Multiculturally competent counselors should reflect upon the potential impact of risk factors such as systemic oppression, racial bias, race-based traumatic stress, generational trauma, acculturative stress, minority stress, and targeting practices as it relates to their clients' experiences with addictive behaviors. Ignoring these factors can lead to incomplete or inaccurate client conceptualizations. In addition to multicultural considerations in conceptualizing addiction, it is important to consider culturally sensitive treatment practices. Let's now turn our attention to multicultural considerations in clinical work with addictions.

MULTICULTURAL CONSIDERATIONS IN TREATING ADDICTION

The third domain of the MSJCC emphasizes the importance of considering both the counselor and client's unique cultural identities in the development of the therapeutic relationship. Additionally, the fourth domain of the MSJCC charges counselors to consider their clients' cultural identities when selecting and implementing clinical interventions and treatment approaches. Therefore, rather than a box to check or an "add-on" to counseling, cultural considerations should influence every aspect of the therapeutic process. One of the first steps toward engaging in multiculturally competent practice is to create a space where clients and counselors discuss their cultural identities and ways in which those identities may influence the counseling process. This practice is known as *broaching* (Day-Vines et al., 2007). Jones and Welfare (2017) noted, "Broaching describes a process by which counselors can bring cultural characteristics of the client and the counselor into the room and invite clients to explore the relevance of those characteristics" (p. 49). Thus, for example, a White, female counselor may say to her Asian, male client: "Our cultural identities are central to who we are and acknowledging them is an important part of the counseling process. I identify as a White, heterosexual, Italian American female. I am curious as to how you would describe your culture." And after the client responds, the counselor may go on to say, "And what comes up for you as you think about working with a White, female counselor?" The tone of broaching is one of genuine curiosity and a sincere interest in understanding the client's worldview.

Broaching is an important practice for counselors working with all presenting concerns; and it also is an essential component of addictions counseling. Specifically, counselors can engage in broaching by: (a) inquiring as to the influence of the cultural identities of both the counselor and the client on the therapeutic relationship, and (b) exploring ways in which the client's culture and related experiences may be relevant to their addictive behaviors (e.g., alcohol used as a means of coping with racial discrimination). In a qualitative study of broaching behaviors among licensed professional counselors conducting intake sessions with clients with addiction, researchers found that counselors used a range of broaching styles from direct to indirect, yet some did not engage in broaching at all during the intake session (Jones & Welfare, 2017). One barrier to broaching identified by participants was the administrative tasks necessary during the first session of addictions counseling, which did not allow time to discuss multicultural factors. The researchers noted that advocating for different administrative structures to create time for broaching can improve the counseling relationship (Jones & Welfare, 2017).

LEARNING ACTIVITY 14.4 BROACHING PRACTICE

Anita is a Latina female in her early 30s who voluntarily entered an intensive outpatient program (IOP) due to her alcohol and prescription medication (benzodiazepines) use. In her first individual session with you, Anita states that she started drinking heavily and using Xanax more than prescribed after her older brother died in a car accident. Anita was very close with her brother and states, "I keep picking up the phone to call him and remember all over again that he is gone." She states that her Catholic faith teaches her that her brother is in a better place now, but she is having a very hard time managing her pain and grief.

Envision that Anita is your client. How might you engage in broaching with Anita? Consider how you would broach cultural differences between yourself and Anita. Additionally, how might you broach the relevance of multicultural factors to Anita's presenting concern? What comes up for you when you consider the practice of broaching?

By broaching early in addictions counseling, counselors are communicating to clients that they recognize the importance of culture and are open to discussing multicultural topics throughout the counseling process. This work is imperative given that research suggests clients of color are less likely to complete addictions treatment compared to White clients. For example, researchers found that among veterans in an opiate substitution program (i.e., methadone or levo-alpha-acetyl-methadol [LAAM] treatment), race was a significant predictor of attrition; specifically, Black participants had lower retention rates than White participants (Mancino et al., 2010). Additionally, Mennis and Stahler (2016) investigated completion rates among a national sample of over 400,000 adult clients in outpatient SUD treatment programs and found that White clients are almost 1.5 times more likely to complete treatment than

Black clients. Additionally, Hispanic clients also were found to have lower completion rates than White clients (Mennis & Stahler, 2016). These racial and ethnic disparities in retention and completion rates may be due, at least in part, to the degree of multicultural competence among counselors and cultural relevance of the treatment programs themselves.

Culturally Sensitive Practice

Multiculturally competent counselors consider clients' unique cultural identities when implementing clinical interventions and treatment plans. This means that it is incumbent upon counselors to tailor interventions to align with their clients' culture, rather than rigidly implementing the same interventions in the same way with all clients. Cultural adaptations of treatment approaches require consideration of clients' racial and ethnic cultural norms and histories, religious and spiritual values and beliefs, socioeconomic status realities, gender roles and norms, and experiences associated with ability-status, age, and sexual orientation. To culturally adapt treatment approaches, counselors are encouraged to consult with members of various cultural groups, review existing literature, and converse with experts (Burlew et al., 2013). With regard to substance use treatment, ensuring that materials and messages are congruent with the client's culture (surface structure) and that the programs themselves are reflective of the client's cultural values and worldviews (deep structure) is necessary for engaging in culturally sensitive practice (Resnicow et al., 2000). Indeed, "understanding ethnic and cultural differences in the predictors and determinants of substance use is an essential element in developing culturally sensitive ATOD [alcohol, tobacco, and other drug] interventions" (Resnicow et al., 2000, p. 277). Thus, cultural adaptations in addiction counseling require that counselors consider the following questions:

- How might risk factors of addiction differ across cultural groups?
- How might protective factors of addiction differ across cultural groups?
- Could differences exist among cultural groups with regard to the *function* or *purpose* of using drugs of abuse?
- What societal or environmental forces affect substance use among cultural groups?

These questions, and others like these, should influence the creation and implementation of SUD treatment programs.

The efficacy of culturally sensitive addictions treatment is well known in light of empirical research projects investigating the impact of culturally sensitive practices (Guerrero et al., 2012; Lee et al., 2013; Patchell et al., 2015). For example, researchers examined the treatment effectiveness of a culturally adapted substance abuse prevention intervention with Native American adolescents who were at-risk for substance abuse (Patchell et al., 2015). The culturally adapted intervention called the Native Talking Circle was based on the Cherokee Talking Circle intervention but tailored for Plains Indians. The intervention spanned 8.5 weeks, totaled 10 hours, and was led by a Native American facilitator. The Native Talking Circle reflected traditional cultural values and beliefs and emphasized connectedness, belonging, responsibility, tribal stories, tribal history, and the strengthening of Native cultural identities. Among 44 Native American adolescents (who all identified as Plains Indians), the intervention led to significantly higher levels of self-reliance and significantly lower levels of substance use (Patchell et al., 2015). Additionally, Guerrero and colleagues (2012) studied over

5,000 Latino clients in addictions treatment to determine factors that contributed to treatment completion. The researchers found the use of language translators and offering program materials in Spanish were significantly associated with treatment completion among Latino clients (Guerrero et al., 2012).

Another example of a culturally adapted treatment program includes the Red Road to Wellbriety. This program was crafted by and for Native Americans and integrates features of the 12 Steps of Alcoholics Anonymous with Native traditions, beliefs, values, and practices (e.g., Medicine Wheel, Talking Circles, the Sacred, Four Laws of Change; White Bison Inc., 2002). Rather than asking Native clients to participate in treatment programs that largely were created by and for White men, the Red Road to Wellbriety is a means of aligning addictions treatment approaches (e.g., the 12 Steps) with the Native way. With regard to addictions treatment for Asian Indians in the United States, Rastogi and Wadhwa (2006) noted that programs should incorporate clients' unique experiences and values such as the process of acculturation, collectivism, religious diversity, cultural norms of shame and honor, and environmental stressors (e.g., prejudice). Finally, Yu and colleagues (2009) presented a case study in which they adapted a substance abuse intervention for Asian Americans. Specifically, an addiction screening tool was translated into seven Asian languages, and the practitioners went into communities to meet with clients. Clients were given small incentives as well as prepared information packages to take home that were translated into their native languages (Yu et al., 2009). These are but a few examples of culturally adapted treatment approaches for diverse clients, yet there are numerous ways in which counselors can engage in culturally sensitive addictions practices. Another important multicultural consideration in addictions treatment is partnering with community leaders.

Partnering With Community Leaders

Providing culturally sensitive treatment for addiction among diverse clients also means relinquishing the idea that services must be delivered in a particular location, in a particular way. Not all members of cultural groups believe that formal addictions treatment in a professional treatment facility is the best way to address substance use. For example, there is some evidence to suggest that before seeking addictions treatment from a mental health professional, members of the Black community may first seek help from religious or spiritual leaders or clergy (SAMHSA, 2014). Additionally, Native American individuals may prefer to approach members of their tribe or community (Giordano et al., 2020) or traditional healers (Goodkind et al., 2010) for assistance with substance use. Rather than imposing a one-size-fits-all approach to addictions treatment, counselors should consider partnering with community leaders (e.g., spiritual leaders, tribal leaders, educators, doctors) to create innovative ways of delivering services to community members with SUDs. This may mean equipping community leaders to recognize and address addiction among members of their own communities.

By partnering with community leaders, counselor can avoid *cultural appropriation*, or taking something from another culture and presenting it as one's own to the detriment of the originating culture and to the benefit of the borrowing culture (Young & Brunk, 2009). Appropriation can occur with regard to many cultural aspects including art, dress, intellectual property, human remains, and religious/spiritual beliefs and practices (Young & Brunk,

2009). The harm of cultural appropriation is that by commandeering a cultural object, practice, belief, or artifact from the original cultural context, it can be stripped of its original meaning, applied in a way that is incongruent with its original purposes, and thereby dishonor or discredit the culture from which it came. Thus, rather than taking and applying practices from other cultures (e.g., Talking Circles or Sweat Lodge Ceremonies), addictions counselors should partner with members of the originating culture and allow them to lead, facilitate, and control their cultural practices.

NOTES FROM THE FIELD

Angela Dainas, MEd, LMFT, worked in the addictions field for 5 years and currently works with eating disorder populations. She served as the clinical director of a residential treatment facility with a detoxification unit, as well as a partial hospitalization program (PHP) and intensive outpatient program (IOP). Angela provided individual, group, and family counseling services and developed programming to fit the curriculum used in her programs.

Although Angela had previous experience working primarily with eating disorders, her move to working primarily with substance use disorders proved to be a significant shift. She noted that she had to address the addiction head-on, rather than addressing co-occurring mental health issues in the hope that once they were addressed the addictive behaviors would subside.

Angela's approach to working with addiction is very systemic in nature. She notes that family members are key components of addictions treatment as they increase accountability and provide multiple perspectives on client issues. Angela described, "I am a huge proponent that denial keeps people sick—you can rationalize or minimize anything. Working with the client's family helps provide multiple perspectives on the issues and holds the client accountable to their goals." From a systemic perspective, counselors can conceptualize treatment as involving the entire family, which Angela posits is necessary in addictions counseling. It is important to consider the client in light of the systems of which they are a part.

When it comes to advice for upcoming counselors, Angela was quick to note the importance of being able to recognize addiction among clients. She stated, "If you don't recognize addiction, your clients aren't going to get better, but you won't know why." She encouraged counselors to add addictions knowledge to their foundation of counseling skills training in order to provide effective services.

Angela noted that it is important for counselors to recognize that their job is not to "save" their clients. Instead, the client has the power to make change, and counselors join with the client to develop a plan to help them reach their goals. She described addictions counseling as holistic, systemic, and very relational. Angela said she enjoyed working in the addictions field because she "loves watching people get better." Specifically, as clients learn how to experience and manage emotions without substances, they would "come back online" and begin to be active participants in their own life stories. Angela said it was important for her clients to hear, "You are not broken—you are sick, and you just need to learn to manage it." Counselors play the crucial role of helping clients manage their addiction and embark on the road to recovery.

Providing Holistic Treatment

According to the Association for Addiction Professionals (NAADAC) *Code of Ethics* (2021), addictions professionals should: (a) be aware of diverse cultures, (b) work from a posture of cultural humility, (c) understand their own cultural identities, (d) respect the family and community structures relevant to a client's culture, (e) use clinical practices that are evidence based and relevant to the cultural groups being served, (f) advocate for diverse clients, and (g) engage in counseling styles that are meaningful to the unique clients they serve (thereby acknowledging that conventional counseling practices may not be the best option for all clients). The fulfillment of these ethical codes requires addictions counselors to provide *holistic* care for their clients by considering cultural, environmental, neurobiological, physical, spiritual, and psychological factors. To focus on one factor to the neglect of others is an incomplete and, potentially, harmful way to practice counseling. For example, evidence suggests that Black clients seeking addictions treatment may be less likely to be assessed and treated for co-occurring disorders (SAMHSA, 2014). This reality reflects both racial bias as well as a myopic view of addictions counseling, which will be limited in its effectiveness. Specifically, if co-occurring mental health concerns are left undetected and untreated, the client is less likely to reach their recovery goals. Instead, counselors should approach clients holistically and provide integrated care.

Another example pertains to the relationship between adverse childhood experiences (ACEs) and substance use. It is well documented that clients with more ACEs have higher rates of alcohol and other drug use (Dube et al., 2002, 2003; Felitti et al., 1998). Holistic counseling would thereby include an assessment of childhood trauma and the integration of trauma-informed care into addictions counseling when appropriate (e.g., Seeking Safety, Trauma Recovery Empowerment Model, Addictions and Trauma Integration Model). In sum, clients cannot be compartmentalized; rather, addictions counselors should consider their client's unique cultural identities, past experiences, and current realities as they engage in clinical work.

SUMMARY

Culture is an essential component of who we are, and all counselors are charged with demonstrating multicultural competence and engaging in culturally sensitive practice. Specifically, counselors should be aware of their own cultural identities, recognize and understand their clients' worldviews, be mindful of how their culture and the culture of their clients will affect the counseling relationship, and utilize counseling interventions and advocacy techniques that are aligned with the client's culture (Ratts et al., 2016). When engaging in culturally sensitive practice, the client's unique cultural identities should be considered in order to inform both the surface and deep structures of clinical work (Resnicow et al., 2000). In addition, when working with clients with addiction, counselors should consider myriad factors such as the history of drug laws, current drug policy and enforcement, media portrayal of drug use, race-based traumatic stress, generational trauma, minority stress, acculturative stress, and targeting practices. Addictions counseling does not occur in a vacuum and is not one-size-fits-all. Instead, effective services require that counselors address their clients holistically and infuse multicultural considerations in both the conceptualization and treatment of addiction.

RESOURCES

Alexander, M. (2012). *The new Jim Crow: Mass incarceration in the age of colorblindness*. The New Press.

Association for Multicultural Counseling and Development: https://multiculturalcounselingdevelopment.org/

Coyhis, D. L., & White, W. L. (2006). *Alcohol problems in Native America: The untold story of resistance and recovery—"The truth about the lie."* White Bison, Inc.

Johnson, A. G. (2006). *Privilege, power, and difference* (2nd ed.). McGraw-Hill.

National Survey on Drug Use and Health. *Race and ethnicity*. https://www.samhsa.gov/data/report/2015-national-survey-drug-use-and-health-race-and-ethnicity-summary-sheets
Pager, D. (2007). *Marked: Race, crime, and finding work in an era of mass incarceration*. University of Chicago Press.
Reinarman, C., & Levine, H. G. (1997). *Crack in America: Demon drugs and social justice*. University of California Press.
Substance Abuse and Mental Health Services Administration. (n.d.). *Improving cultural competence*. https://store.samhsa.gov/sites/default/files/d7/priv/sma14-4849.pdf
Wellbriety Movement website: http://www.wellbriety.com/
White Bison, Inc. (2002). *The red road to Wellbriety: In the Native American way*. Author.

KEY REFERENCES

Only key references appear in the print edition. The full reference list appears in the digital product on Springer Publishing Connect: connect.springerpub.com/content/book/978-0-8261-3586-5/chapter/ch14

Alexander, M. (2012). *The new Jim Crow: Mass incarceration in the age of colorblindness*. The New Press.
Center for Behavioral Health Statistics and Quality. (2017). *2016 National Survey on Drug Use and Health: Detailed tables*. Substance Abuse and Mental Health Services Administration.
Coyhis, D. L., & White, W. L. (2006). *Alcohol problems in Native America: The untold story of resistance and recovery—"The truth about the lie."* White Bison, Inc.
Day-Vines, N. L., Wood, S. M., Grothaus, T., Craigen, L., Holman, A., Dotson-Blake, K., & Douglass, M. J. (2007). Broaching the subjects of race, ethnicity, and culture during the counseling process. *Journal of Counseling & Development, 85*(4), 401–409. https://doi.org/10.1002/j.1556-6678.2007.tb00608.x
Dunbar-Ortiz, R., & Gilio-Whitaker, D. (2016). *"All the real Indians died off" and 20 other myths about Native Americans*. Beacon Press.
Felitti, V. J., Anda, R. F., Nordenberg, D., Williamson, D. F., Spitz, A. M., Edwards, V., Koss, M. P., & Marks, J. S. (1998). Relationship of childhood abuse and household dysfunction to many of the leading causes of death in adults: The adverse childhood experiences (ACE) study. *American Journal of Preventive Medicine, 14*(4), 245–258. https://doi.org/10.1016/s0749-3797(98)00017-8
Goldbach, J., Tanner-Smith, E., Bagwell, M., & Dunlap, S. (2014). Minority stress and substance use in sexual minority adolescents: A meta-analysis. *Prevention Science, 15*, 350–363. https://doi.org/10.1007/s11121-013-0393-7
Hunt, E. N., Martens, M. P., Wang, K. T., & Yan, G. C. (2017). Acculturative stress as a moderator for international student drinking behaviors and alcohol use consequences. *Journal of Ethnicity in Substance Abuse, 16*(3), 263–275. https://doi.org/10.1080/15332640.2016.1185656
Johnston, L. D., Miech, R. A., O'Malley, P. M., Bachman, J. G., Schulenberg, J. E., & Patrick, M. E. (2019). *Demographic subgroup trends among adolescents in the use of various licit and illicit drugs, 1975–2018 (Monitoring the Future Occasional Paper No. 92)*. Institute for Social Research, The University of Michigan.
Lee, C. S., Lopez, S. R., Colby, S. M., Rohsenow, D., Hernandez, L., Borrelli, B., & Caetano, R. (2013). Culturally adapted motivational interviewing for Latino heavy drinkers: Results from a randomized clinical trial. *Journal of Ethnicity in Substance Abuse, 12*(4), 356–373. https://doi.org/10.1080/15332640.2013.836730
Mark, G. Y. (1975). Racial, economic, and political factors in the development of America's first drug laws. *Issues in Criminology, 10*(1), 49–72.
Mereish, E. H., Goldbach, J. T., Burgess, C., & DiBello, A. M. (2017). Sexual orientation, minority stress, social norms, and substance use among racially diverse adolescents. *Drug and Alcohol Dependence, 178*, 49–56. https://doi.org/10.1016/j.drugalcdep.2017.04.013
Netherland, J., & Hansen, H. B. (2016). The war on dugs that wasn't: Wasted Whiteness, "dirty doctors" and race in media coverage of prescription opioid misuse. *Culture, Medicine, and Psychiatry, 40*, 664–86. https://doi.org/10.1007/s11013-016-9496-5
Pager, D. (2007). *Marked: Race, crime, and finding work in an era of mass incarceration*. University of Chicago Press.

Primack, B. A., Bost, J. E., Land, S. R., & Fine, M. J. (2007). Volume of tobacco advertising in African American markets: Systemic review and meta-analysis. *Public Health Reports, 122*(5), 607–615. https://doi.org/10.1177/003335490712200508

Reinarman, C., & Levine, H. G. (1997). *Crack in America: Demon drugs and social justice.* University of California Press.

Rose, S. W., Mayo, A., Ganz, O., Perreras, L., D'Silva, J., & Cohn, A. (2019). Perceived racial/ethnic discrimination, marketing, and substance use among young adults. *Journal of Ethnicity in Substance Abuse, 18*(4), 558–577. https://doi.org/10.1080/15332640.2018.1425949

Substance Abuse and Mental Health Services Administration. (2017). *2015 National Survey on Drug Use and Health: Race and ethnicity summary sheets.* https://www.samhsa.gov/data/report/2015-national-survey-drug-use-and-health-race-and-ethnicity-summary-sheets

Westermeyer, J. (1974). "The drunken Indian": Myths and realities. *Psychiatric Annals, 4*(11), 29–36. https://doi.org/10.3928/0048-5713-19741101-07

15

ADVOCATING FOR ADDICTED POPULATIONS

LEARNING OBJECTIVES

Advocacy is an essential component of a counselor's role. There are many ways in which counselors can advocate on behalf of clients with addiction at the individual, community, and public levels. By the end of this chapter, you will be able to:

- defend the claim that all counselors are advocates and should be competent in advocacy interventions and strategies;
- describe the six domains of counselor advocacy and provide examples of advocacy efforts for individuals with addiction within each domain;
- synthesize the history of advocacy efforts for addicted populations including the development of grass-roots organizations, recovery schools, and collegiate recovery programs;
- explain the impact of several legislative actions aimed to advocate for individuals with addiction;
- compare and contrast acute versus long-term care for individuals with addiction;
- summarize the most prominent barriers to treatment for individuals with addiction including stigma, lack of treatment access, and poor treatment quality.

TERMS TO KNOW

acute care model providing brief, isolated interventions for substance use without long-term, posttreatment continuing care options

advocacy actively working to remove barriers or obstacles that hinder the wellness of groups or individuals

biopsychosocial model holistic conceptualization of addiction as emerging from the unique interplay of biological, psychological, and social factors

collegiate recovery program organized continuing care and support for students in recovery from addiction who are attending institutions of higher education

moral model belief that addiction is a condition that is chosen and caused by an individual due to a character flaw or moral deficiency

recovery community organizations	peer-led nonprofit organizations that provide recovery support for members of the local community
recovery school	a sober educational environment exclusively designed to support students in recovery from addiction
stigma	a socially defined difference linked to undesirable traits
sustained recovery management	offering long-term continuing posttreatment care to support clients' recovery from the chronic disease of addiction

INTRODUCTION

The positioning of this chapter at the end of your textbook should not give the impression that it is the least important. Instead, after increasing knowledge and awareness related to addiction by reading the preceding chapters, the next logical question is, "What can we do about it?" This chapter provides details related to advocacy efforts for individuals with addiction in hopes of motivating readers to join the movement and engage in their own advocacy efforts.

COUNSELORS AS ADVOCATES

LEARNING ACTIVITY 15.1 THINKING LIKE AN ADVOCATE

Advocacy simply means removing barriers to a person's wellness. Think about your own life. Have you ever spoken on behalf of someone who was being treated unfairly? Have you ever acted on behalf of someone with less power? Have you ever become aware of an injustice or act of oppression and done something about it? Now ask yourself, is there a particular humanitarian issue or cause that you feel strongly about? Is there a particular oppressed group that you feel passionate about? If you could work to improve the lives of a specific group or population, who would it be and why?

Counselors and other mental health professionals have multifaceted roles: they offer individual, group, and family counseling services; they aid in programming in schools and colleges; and they serve as *advocates*. Specifically, counselors are agents of change and work to improve the lives of their clients, communities, and the public-at-large. But what exactly is advocacy? When you read that word, what comes to mind? Many students immediately think of lobbying on Capitol Hill or writing letters to senators, and certainly, that is part of it. But advocacy happens in myriad ways at different levels. At its core, "advocacy involves breaking down barriers to wellness, acting to dismantle systems of privilege and oppression, and working for and with marginalized populations to effect change and promote development" (O'Hara et al., 2016, p. 2). The charge to break down barriers to wellness and dismantle systems of oppression is a key component of counselors' job descriptions. Indeed, counselors advocate by raising awareness about privilege and oppression, seeking to affect social change, working to eradicate injustice, fighting against oppressive systems, and pursuing equal access, opportunity, and treatment for all persons. The role of advocacy is not an "add-on" to a counselor's responsibilities; instead, it is at the heart of what we do. And, it is very likely that you have engaged in advocacy efforts before, whether or not you called it "advocacy." Review Learning Activity 15.1 to explore your history of advocacy activities.

ADVOCACY COMPETENCIES

In 2003, the American Counseling Association (ACA) endorsed competencies to guide counselors' advocacy efforts. Specifically, "advocacy competence can be thought of as the ability, understanding, and knowledge to carry out advocacy ethically and effectively" (Toporek et al., 2009). These advocacy competencies described effective ways to advocate *with* and *on behalf of* clients/groups at three different levels: individual, community, and public arena. The competencies were updated in 2018 to describe six domains in which advocacy can occur: (1) client/student empowerment (supporting a client's self-advocacy skills), (2) client/student advocacy (acting on behalf of a client), (3) community collaboration (supporting a group's efforts to address an injustice), (4) systems advocacy (acting on behalf of a group to address an injustice), (5) collective action (supporting a population in their efforts to address an injustice), and (6) social/political advocacy (acting on behalf of a population to address an injustice; Toporek & Daniels, 2018). Therefore, counselors can come alongside a client, group, or population as an ally to support their advocacy efforts (acting with), or counselors can use their power and influence to address issues faced by a client, group, or population (acting on behalf of). Table 15.1 provides examples of each advocacy domain. What comes up for you as you read through this table? Can you think of other examples?

TABLE 15.1 Advocacy Domains

DOMAIN	DESCRIPTION	EXAMPLE
Client/Student Empowerment	Supporting a client or student in their use of self-advocacy skills (counselor as ally)	Help client construct a concrete plan for what advocacy will entail and discuss potential positive and negative outcomes
Client/Student Advocacy	Acting on behalf of a client or student who is facing a barrier or injustice (counselor as change agent)	Speak to individuals in leadership positions about an injustice faced by a client or student
Community Collaboration	Supporting a group in the community as they work to address a barrier or injustice (counselor as ally)	Help group members develop specific goals and advocacy action plans, while considering potential positive and negative outcomes
Systems Advocacy	Acting on behalf of a group in the community that is experiencing oppression or injustice (counselor as change agent)	Speak to local government representatives about an injustice faced by a group in the community
Collective Action	Supporting a population as they work to eradicate an injustice or act of oppression on a large scale (counselor as ally)	Help members of a population access a means to spread their message
Social/Political Advocacy	Acting on behalf of marginalized or oppressed populations to bring about systemic change on a large scale (counselor as change agent)	Appear on a news program or mass media source to raise public awareness about an injustice faced by a marginalized population

Source: Adapted from Advocacy Competencies (Toporek, R. L., & Daniels, J. (2018). *2018 update: American Counseling Association advocacy competencies*. https://www.counseling.org/docs/default-source/competencies/aca-advocacy-competencies-updated-may-2020.pdf?sfvrsn=f410212c_4; Toporek, R. L., Lewis, J. A., & Crethar, H. C. (2009). Promoting systemic change through the ACA advocacy competencies. *Journal of Counseling & Development, 87*, 260–268. https://doi.org/10.1002/j.1556-6678.2009.tb00105.x)

It is important for students to consider their reactions to the charge to be advocates. Green and colleagues (2008) noted, "Students in counselor education programs must be made aware that effective interventions when working with oppressed and disenfranchised clients will be conducted outside of their offices and in the community" (p. 15). Therefore, a counselor's work will not take place strictly in counseling rooms. Instead, counselors often will be out in the community using their skills to bring about systemic change and dismantle systems of oppression that impede their clients' development and growth. As counselors become aware of barriers, injustices, and acts of oppression (typically by listening to and empathizing with clients), they are moved to act and influence change (Lewis et al., 2011). Ratts and Greenleaf (2018) noted, "As advocates, helping professionals use their positions to influence policy and work with community leaders to change oppressive systemic barriers" (p. 84). Counselors are uniquely poised to be effective advocates given their interpersonal skills, ability to empathize, and use of communication styles that elicit understanding rather than defensiveness.

Advocacy also is a natural outgrowth of cultural humility and multicultural competence. Ratts et al. (2016) noted that a counselor's attitudes and beliefs, knowledge, skill, and action related to advocacy are aspects of multiculturally competent counseling. Specifically, the Multicultural and Social Justice Counseling Competencies (MSJCC) state, "privileged and marginalized counselors intervene with, and on behalf of, clients at the intrapersonal, interpersonal, institutional, community, public policy, and international/global levels" (Ratts et al., 2016, p. 11). Thus, as counselors grow in their cultural competence and humility, they will naturally enhance their advocacy skills and ability to influence change at multiple levels. Take a look at Table 15.2 and engage in a quick self-evaluation. Which advocacy skills do you already possess? In which skills are you most strong? Which skills would you like to improve?

TABLE 15.2 Advocacy Skills

Effective communication	Strategic planning	Organization
Collaboration	Empathy	Developing a message
Collect data	Examine research	Create strong relationships with others
Think critically	Ingenuity	Consider multiple perspectives
Seek out information	Cultural humility	Self-awareness
Motivate others	Leadership	Creativity
Persistence	Resilience	Delegate tasks
Strong writing skills	Question the status quo	Educate others
Troubleshooting	Foster partnerships with organizations	Consultation
Modeling desired behavior	Professionalism	Teachability

ADVOCACY FOR INDIVIDUALS WITH ADDICTION

There are many groups and causes for which counselors can and should advocate. In this chapter, we focus specifically on advocating for individuals with addiction. You may be asking, "What barriers to wellness do these individuals face?" Let's pause so you can take a moment to complete Learning Activity 15.2 and consider potential answers to that question.

LEARNING ACTIVITY 15.2
BARRIERS FACED BY INDIVIDUALS WITH ADDICTION

Reread the definition of advocacy provided by O'Hara et al. (2016). Now consider an individual with a substance use disorder. This person has a history of multiple addiction treatment experiences and is an active member of Alcoholics Anonymous. What barriers to wellness might this individual face? What obstacles might stand in the way of this person's growth, development, and achievement of personal goals? Write down as many as you can think of in multiple realms of life (e.g., relational, occupational, societal, spiritual, physical, financial, etc.).

As you hopefully ascertained from your learning activity, many obstacles exist for individuals with addiction such as: limited availability of treatment, high cost of treatment, ineffective interventions, public stigma, inaccurate information related to addiction, inadequate training of mental health professionals in the treatment of addictions, acute rather than long-term care, and the criminalization of individuals with addiction (rather than rehabilitation). Although there is much advocacy work to do for those with addiction, it is important to consider the work that has already been done, which has led to substantial gains for this community. Let's consider the history and work of the New Recovery Advocacy Movement.

New Recovery Advocacy Movement

In the 1990s and early 2000s, small, grass-roots recovery organizations began developing across the United States (White, 2014; White et al., 2012). In an effort to organize individual recovery organizations, the Alliance Project formed in the late 1990s with the goal of giving voice to the recovery community at large. The Alliance Project organized a Recovery Summit in 2001 in Minnesota, which gave rise to a new advocacy organization, Faces & Voices of Recovery (White, 2014). Specifically, Faces & Voices of Recovery has the mission of "changing the way addiction and recovery are understood and embraced through advocacy, education and leadership" (Faces & Voices of Recovery, n.d.-a, para 1). By dismantling stigma, discrimination, and injustice against individuals with addiction, this organization seeks to help the recovery community thrive in the United States. Faces & Voices of Recovery has three primary goals: (a) to influence policies and laws to promote recovery, (b) mobilize communities to support recovery, and (c) increase addictions treatment quality and access (Faces & Voices of Recovery, n.d.-a, para 4). The organization has made great gains in affecting public policy and public perception, developing recovery centers in communities across the nation, increasing recovery support programs, and raising awareness related to recovery through media, music, and art (Faces & Voices of Recovery, n.d.-b, para 4). Thus, since the early 2000s, the New Recovery Advocacy Movement has worked to shift public perception regarding the nature of addiction and experience of those in recovery from addictive behaviors (White, 2007, 2014). The specific goals and strategies of this advocacy movement are listed in Table 15.3. Read through the table and consider why each goal and strategy is important and how each may influence American culture.

TABLE 15.3 Goals and Strategies of New Recovery Advocacy Movement

Change the narrative around addiction to present it as a disease with viable solutions	Ensure representation of individuals in recovery (and their family members) at all levels of policy-making
Increase the visibility of those in long-term recovery to demonstrate the efficacy of solutions to addiction	Assess community needs related to addictions treatment and recovery support
Draw attention to and correct the dehumanization or vilification of individuals with addiction	Provide education related to the success of recovery and multiple pathways to achieve long-term recovery
Increase availability of quality addiction treatment and recovery support	Increase public support and volunteers for recovery support and advocacy
Influence public policy and laws to support recovery	Make community recovery centers more visible and create more opportunities for peer-based recovery support and activities
Change the narrative around addiction from the moral model (e.g., individual with addiction is bad) to the biopsychosocial model (e.g., individual with addiction has a disease for which there are solutions)	Develop public events that celebrate recovery and draw attention to the success of those in long-term recovery
Change public perception about addictions treatment (e.g., it works, even if an individual needs several rounds of treatment)	Conduct and support research that provides data related to the effectiveness of addictions treatment and pathways to long-term recovery
Encourage individuals in long-term recovery to share their story and perspective	Foster grassroots recovery organizations to join national movement

Source: White, W. L. (2007). The new recovery advocacy movement in America. *Addiction, 102*, 696–703. https://doi.org/10.1111/j.1360-0443.2007.01808.x

For over two decades, the recovery community has been developing, organizing, and advocating for changes in the American narrative related to addiction by creating a new recovery paradigm. Rather than a single program, the advocacy movement is working to develop a robust culture of recovery. Specifically, White (2014) described recovery homes, community organizations, schools, ministries, and industries as part of the new recovery culture. Let us consider a few elements of this emerging recovery culture to better understand the results of the New Recovery Advocacy Movement.

Legislation

One of the most noteworthy forms of advocacy for individuals with addiction came with the passing and implementation of new legislation. The Wellstone and Domenici Mental Health Parity and Addiction Equality Act (MHPAEA) of 2008 (which took effect in 2010) called for parity of insurance coverage for mental health and addiction treatment. This legislation required insurance benefits for mental health and addiction treatment to be comparable, or no more restrictive, than benefits for other medical treatment procedures (Mulvaney-Day et al., 2019). The MHPAEA expanded the previous parity act (Mental Health Parity Act) of

1996 by including substance use disorder (SUD) treatment (Busch et al., 2014). This act was a huge victory for advocates of those with addiction, given that it was the first federal parity law that included addictions treatment (Mulvaney-Day et al., 2019). In fact, Edmond et al. (2016) noted, "the MHPAEA has the potential to positively influence treatment on a national scale for a disorder that is remarkably undertreated" (p. 81). Researchers have found that access to substance use treatment among employee-sponsored insurance enrollees increased from .8% on average pre-parity legislation to 1.2% on average after parity legislation (Mulvaney-Day et al., 2019). Thus, more individuals are accessing addictions treatment as a result of the implementation of the MHPAEA.

More recently, the Comprehensive Addiction Recovery Act (CARA) was signed into law in 2016 in response to the opioid epidemic in the United States. This legislation created robust support for addiction prevention, education, treatment, and recovery programming (Community Anti-Drug Coalitions of America [CADCA], n.d.). Specifically, the CARA gave nurse practitioners and physician assistants the ability to prescribe medication to individuals with opioid use disorder (e.g., buprenorphine) to aid in their treatment. Additionally, the legislation raised the cap of patients receiving medication-assisted treatment from 100 to 275 among eligible physicians. Furthermore, CARA increased disposal sites of prescription opioids, increased the availability of naloxone to first responders (which can reverse an opioid overdose), and increased support for prescription monitoring programs. In sum, the enactment of CARA provided more funding for grants, treatment, and prevention programs in response to the opioid epidemic (CADCA, n.d.).

Finally, the 2018 Eliminating Kickbacks in Recovery Act (EKRA; part of the Substance Use Disorder Prevention that Promotes Opioid Recovery and Treatment for Patients and Communities [SUPPORT] act) is another important piece of legislation that advocates on behalf of individuals with addiction. Specifically, the act deems "patient brokering," or giving/receiving compensation for referring patients to a treatment facility or laboratory, a criminal offense (Harris, 2019). EKRA applies to both private and publicly funded programs (Ouellette & Rose, 2020), therefore, various agencies within the field of addictions treatment can face criminal penalties (e.g., fines, imprisonment) for soliciting or receiving payments for referrals to their treatment or recovery facilities. For example, an individual was found guilty of violating EKRA in 2020 for receiving kickbacks from a clinical toxicology lab in exchange for her referrals to the laboratory for drug testing (Ouellette & Rose, 2020). This bill is a step toward ensuring that client welfare, rather than profit, is the motivation for referrals to treatment and recovery centers. It is important to note that all of the legislation described in this section resulted from years of effort and dedication from professionals advocating for individuals with addictions. More legislation is needed, but great headway has been made in recent years.

Recovery Schools

Another recovery support structure that has been influenced by the New Recovery Advocacy Movement is the formation of recovery high schools. These schools first emerged in 1979 and are designed exclusively to support students in recovery from addiction (White, 2014). According to the Association of Recovery Schools (ARS, 2021), recovery high schools have the following goals: (a) provide education for students in recovery, (b) align with all state requirements for earning a secondary school diploma, (c) ensure all students are working a recovery program, and (d) be available to any secondary school students in recovery who meet eligibility requirements. Many students who attend recovery schools have a history of addictions treatment, thus the schools are an important component of continuing care (White, 2014).

LEARNING ACTIVITY 15.3
RECOVERY SCHOOLS

Reflect back to your own experience in high school. What was the culture like in terms of alcohol and drug use? To what extent were alcohol and other drugs available? What programs can you recall that addressed alcohol and other drug use at your school? Now envision that you are a 15-year-old high school student in recovery. What might you need from a recovery high school to support you in your recovery efforts? What activities, programs, or characteristics of a recovery high school might aid in your academic success, identity development, and recovery?

At the time of writing of this textbook, there are 43 recovery high schools in the United States as reported by the ARS. In a study of 17 recovery high schools, the average enrollment in the school was found to be 24.5 students, with a range of 6 to 50 students (Finch et al., 2014). The schools offered a variety of therapeutic services (e.g., counseling, addiction psychoeducation, drug testing, family support) yet "a primary aim of all schools was to provide a safe and sober environment in which students could pursue their education" (Finch et al., 2014, p. 123). The researchers concluded that the recovery schools faced several challenges, with funding as the most substantial. Fifteen of the schools received public funds, and two schools relied on tuition payments, grants, and donations (Finch et al., 2014). Although research is still burgeoning, there is some empirical support for the effectiveness of recovery schools. A longitudinal study assessed the efficacy of recovery high schools among students who enrolled after addictions treatment (n = 134) as compared to students who completed addictions treatment but did not enroll (n = 60; Finch et al., 2018). The researchers found that students who completed at least one month in recovery high schools were more likely to be abstinent from alcohol, marijuana, and other drugs and demonstrated less absenteeism at follow-up than students at nonrecovery high schools (Finch et al., 2018). Thus, advocates for individuals with addiction may seek to help secure funding for recovery schools and aid in the development of more recovery schools across the nation.

Collegiate Recovery Programs

In addition to recovery support at the secondary school level, the recovery advocacy movement has influenced the development of Collegiate Recovery Programs (CRPs), which emerged in the 1980s. College environments are known for being hostile to recovery. Consider your own undergraduate experience: what was/is the culture related to drug and alcohol use? How available were/are drugs and alcohol? To what extent were/are drugs and alcohol part of social norms?

To help support students' recovery while in college, CRPs have developed. Laudet and colleagues (2014) noted, "The goal of CRPs is to allow recovery students to extend their participation in a continuing care program without having to postpone or surrender achieving their educational goals" (p. 89). Currently, there are 133 CRPs in the United

States (Association of Recovery in Higher Education [ARHE], 2019) with common features such as sober housing options, on-campus 12-step meetings, professional counseling services, peer support, sober activities and social events, physical spaces for gatherings, and professional staff (Bugbee et al., 2016; Laudet et al., 2014). Many programs also encourage students to sign behavioral or sobriety contracts while they participate in the CRP (Laudet et al., 2014). Researchers have sought to learn more about students who enroll in CRPs. A national survey of 29 CRPs and 486 participating students revealed that most students began regularly using substances in midadolescence (15.9 mean age for alcohol; 15.3 mean age for marijuana; Laudet et al., 2015). Among those students who had received professional addictions treatment (82.5%), the mean age of treatment initiation was 20.6 years old. Additionally, the researchers found that among the sample of students in CRPs, 76.1% had a history of mental health treatment, 10.9% had a secondary issue of an eating disorder, and 12.8% had a secondary issue of sex/love addiction (Laudet et al., 2015).

LEARNING ACTIVITY 15.4
COLLEGIATE RECOVERY PROGRAMS

One of the pioneering CRPs is housed within Texas Tech (Center for Collegiate Recovery Communities established in 1986). Visit the program's website at www.depts.ttu.edu/hs/csa/ and explore their mission, values, events, and resources. In your opinion, what would make a CRP successful? In addition to recovery support, what might be beneficial for students enrolled in the program while in college?

The exact nature of CRPs varies between universities, yet according to the ARHE (2019) there are eight standards for CRPs: (1) recovery should be abstinence based; (2) there should be a physical space associated with CRP for students to gather; (3) the CRP should be comprised of students supporting each other in a collegiate recovery community; (4) CRPs should have a variety of recovery support activities and programs available; (5) a paid, qualified professional should support the students of a CRP; (6) CRPs should be nonprofit organizations; (7) CRPs should be associated with higher education institutions; and (8) CRPs should have on- and off-campus partners and collaborators. A qualitative study of CRP directors revealed several common components of successful programs including: community and relationship formation, access to campus resources (e.g., mental health support, academic advisors), clear program expectations, sober events, opportunities for student leadership, and advocacy at the university level (e.g., increase awareness of addiction and normalize recovery; Watts et al., 2019). As CRPs continue to emerge and develop within American universities, more empirical research will help identify those elements that are most effective in supporting collegiate students in recovery.

BARRIERS FACED BY INDIVIDUALS WITH ADDICTION

Although substantial progress has been made with regard to advocacy, barriers and obstacles continue to impede individuals with addiction in their pursuit of wellness. Counselors are uniquely positioned to help address these obstacles to support clients with addiction. As you read, consider ways in which you could join advocacy efforts to dismantle these barriers.

Stigma

Decades of misperceptions about addiction have led to firmly entrenched stigma about the condition. *Stigma* refers to an occurrence in which a person is labeled due to a difference and, subsequently, "dominant cultural beliefs link labeled persons to undesirable characteristics" (Link & Phelan, 2001, p. 367). Thus, a person with addiction is seen as different and labeled an "addict." Then the label of "addict" is associated with a host of undesirable characteristics (e.g., criminal, lazy, selfish, immoral, deviant, untrustworthy). Societal stigma can lead to *internalized stigma* in which "people endorse prejudice and stereotypes associated with a stigmatized status and apply them to the self" (Earnshaw, 2020, p. 1303). The consequence of internalized stigma is *shame*, which can lead individuals to isolate, hide, and potentially cope through maladaptive behaviors (Earnshaw, 2020; Wiechelt, 2007). Indeed, both social and internalized stigma can inhibit help-seeking behaviors among those with addiction by fostering shame and embarrassment. According to the 2015 National Survey on Drug Use and Health, the national average of American adults with a SUD in the last year was 8.1%, yet the average percentage of those who sought addictions treatment in the last year was .6% (Substance Abuse and Mental Health Services Administration [SAMHSA], 2017). The discrepancies in those numbers can be attributed, at least in part, to stigma and shame. Thus, the insidious nature of societal and internalized stigma can impede treatment seeking and increase the risk of engagement in addictive behaviors. See Figure 15.1.

Societal stigma associated with addiction has been fueled by the *moral model of addiction,* which purports that individuals choose addiction due to a personal moral failing or character flaw like selfishness, weakness, or antisocial personality traits (Brickman et al., 1982; Lassiter & Spivey, 2018). Indeed, McGinty and Barry (2020) stated, "Stigma is persistent, pervasive, and rooted in the belief that addiction is a personal choice reflecting a lack of willpower and a moral failing" (p. 1291). Additionally, the symptoms of the disease of addiction often violate social norms and can hurt other people (e.g., theft, betrayal, aggressive behavior, drunk driving), thus, unlike other diseases, it often is challenging for the public to show compassion for those with addiction (Volkow, 2020). Instead, stigma and prejudice (fueled by the moral model) are commonly experienced by individuals with addiction.

Counselors can advocate for individuals with addiction by working to change public perception regarding the disease and decrease stigma. Counter to the moral model, counselors can introduce the *biopsychosocial model* (Marlatt & Baer, 1988) and inform clients, families, and the public about the biological, psychological, and social etiological factors related to addiction (e.g., genetic predisposition, childhood trauma, modeling, social learning). Rather than a moral failing, recent neuroscience and empirical data illuminate the role of genetic factors and environmental risk factors that contribute to the development of addiction. Additionally, the biopsychosocial model underscores the necessity of professional treatment to

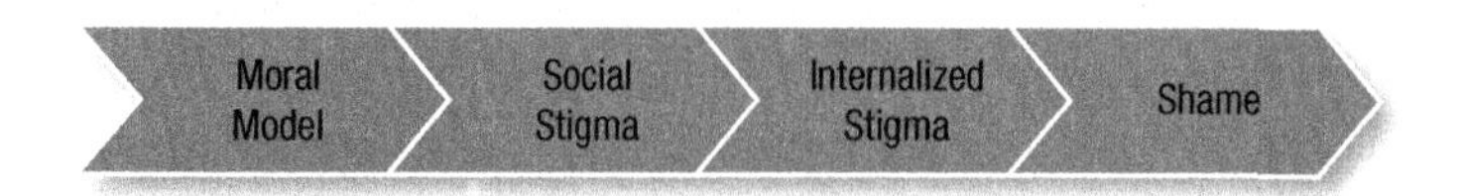

FIGURE 15.1 Stigma and shame.

help individuals with SUDs reach sustained abstinence, rather than relying on sheer willpower. Leshner (2001) noted, "It is essential to understand when dealing with addicts that we are dealing with individuals whose brains have been altered by drug use. They need drug addiction treatment" (p. 78).

Thus, although the moral model is pervasive, counselors can combat stigma by correcting and replacing moralistic beliefs with more accurate neuroscience related to the disease of addiction. To accomplish this task, counselors can disseminate current research findings to the general public, share the latest neuroscience with policy-makers, and openly discuss the benefits of rehabilitation treatment (which corresponds to the biopsychosocial model) over criminalization (which corresponds with the moral model; Polcin, 2014). Earnshaw (2020) recommended that mental health professionals write articles for newspapers and other media outlets, utilize social media platforms, and engage in conversations with members of their community to educate and correct the public perception of addiction. In addition, counselors can help combat stigma by using person-first language (e.g., "individual with a substance use disorder" rather than "addict"; Broyles et al., 2014; Heit & Gourlay, 2009; Warren, 2007) and presenting stories of individuals with addiction who are in long-term recovery (in order to humanize individuals with the disease and demonstrate that recovery is possible; Earnshaw, 2020; Polcin, 2014). Indeed, as the general public begins to understand addiction as a disease that can be treated by professionals (like other mental health and physical illnesses), the stigma associated with addiction will begin to decrease.

Treatment Quality and Access

Along with stigma, another primary barrier faced by individuals with addiction is access to quality treatment. In 2017, 19.7 million (7.2%) Americans aged 12 and older had a SUD in the previous year (SAMHSA, 2018). Only 4.0 million people, however, received any treatment for addiction in the previous year. Thus, approximately 15.7 million people aged 12 and older in the United States had a SUD yet did not receive any form of treatment (SAMHSA, 2018). What are the barriers that preclude individuals with addiction from accessing treatment? Researchers have investigated this question and found myriad obstacles at both the individual level (e.g., belief that one does not need treatment) and systemic level (e.g., geographic proximity to a treatment center). With regard to systemic issues, barriers to treatment can include admissions difficulties and transportation concerns (Owens et al., 2018), lack of coverage to pay for treatment (SAMHSA, 2018), and lack of childcare, especially for women with SUDs (Taylor, 2010).

Additionally, Priester and colleagues (2016) conducted a review of 36 articles and found two primary barriers to treatment among those with co-occurring SUDs and mental health concerns: personal barriers and structural barriers. Among the structural barriers, the researchers identified lack of service availability (particularly in rural areas), limited training in co-occurring disorders among professionals, excessive waitlists, lack of cultural competence among professionals, lack of childcare, and high costs of services (Priester et al., 2016). These barriers to treatment for co-occurring disorders are significant given that 8.5 million adults and 345,000 adolescents had co-occurring mental health concerns and SUDs in 2017 (SAMHSA, 2018).

Even when treatment is available, the type and quality of treatment for SUDs varies considerably. Indeed, Abraham et al. (2013) investigated differences between publicly funded and privately funded SUD programs in the United States. Using a sample of 595 programs, the researchers found that privately funded programs were more likely to have a physician on staff, prescribe medications for SUDs (e.g., buprenorphine), be accredited, have master's level counselors, and utilize 12-step modalities compared to publicly funded programs (Abraham et al., 2013). The lack of access to a physician and medication can be major limitations to SUD treatment, especially for those seeking medication management for opioid use disorders. Thus, the quality of treatment can vary depending upon available funding sources (public or private funding; Abraham et al., 2013). Advocacy is needed to ensure that all individuals with addiction have access to quality treatment services. Despite how daunting this goal may seem, equity and social justice require that all individuals—whether homeless veterans, rural single mothers, or formerly incarcerated men—are able to access services that can support their recovery. The development of more treatment and recovery centers, increased transportation and childcare options, and ensuring high-quality training of mental health professionals to work with clients with addiction are all forms of advocacy that can make a large impact in the treatment of this population.

NOTES FROM THE FIELD

Sharon DeEsch, LPC, MAC, has been working in the addictions field for 38 years. Her expansive career has included a variety of professional positions to serve individuals with addiction including counselor, educator, contractor, director, and interventionist. Sharon has worked in private practice, in behavioral health settings, and in psychiatric hospitals; taught DWI classes; taught at a community college; and established and directed intensive outpatient programs (IOPs).

Sharon's passion for working in the addictions field stems from her own recovery journey. She began volunteering with individuals with addiction and went back to school to get her training and education. Throughout her career, Sharon has learned that "not all clients are the same and not all clients get sober in the same way." Thus, she has received numerous trainings and worked with a variety of populations in order to gain expertise in the field of addictions. For example, Sharon received the Love First training to become a Love First Interventionist. In this role, Sharon helps organize and prepare interventions so friends and family members can help get their loved one into addictions treatment. The interventions are built upon love, care, and concern for the individual with addiction and can be the pivotal moment in which they decide to enter treatment. Sharon noted that an interventionist is not an entry-level job; instead, after years of learning about the addictions field and addictions treatment (including family systems and advanced counseling experiences), some professionals may choose to move into the role of interventionist to help clients get into treatment.

After 38 years in the field, Sharon says what she finds most rewarding is seeing people get better and "getting their lives back." She advised not to let businesses or insurance companies define what success is for our clients; success does not mean never relapsing, and that is not the expectation we have for any other chronic illness. Instead, success is working toward sustained recovery and learning how to thrive. With regard to challenges, Sharon noted the grief that comes with attending former client funerals. Although recovery is possible for those with addiction, there are many who die from the disease, and that can be heavy and difficult for counselors.

In terms of advocacy, Sharon noted that all professionals who work with the public need to be educated about addiction. It is a pervasive issue, and she asserted that we need more competence, training, and resources so that those with addiction can be identified and helped. Sharon stated, "All counselors will work with clients with substance use disorders or who are in relationship with individuals with substance use disorder. They have to know how to detect, identify, and address addiction." Sharon believes that in order to advance the field of addictions treatment all communities need treatment facilities, and there should not be a city or town without access to a detoxification center or treatment center. She also believes that more intervention teams in hospitals and treatment programs can help clients enter treatment and start their recovery journeys.

Acute Versus Long-Term Care

Another substantial barrier faced by individuals with addiction is the prevalence of acute care models versus long-term care models (White, 2014). Although addiction is known to be a chronic disease, treatment services often are acute in nature and may not provide aftercare, posttreatment monitoring, or clinical follow-ups (Scott et al., 2004). Instead, the acute care model is marked by reliance on independent, separate, brief interventions (such as detoxification), a perspective that recovery should be attained after a single treatment experience, and minimal (if any) emphasis on posttreatment care (Scott et al., 2004). In opposition to the acute care model is the model of *sustained recovery management*, which responds to addiction like any other chronic medical or psychological illness that requires continuing care. Indeed, long-term care, or sustained recovery management, provides continuing posttreatment care, aftercare planning, regular follow-up appointments, and connects clients to recovery support programs in the community.

Rather than the acute care model (e.g., stabilization in a hospital for five days without follow-up), long-term care models often provide a step-down plan to help clients receive continuing care at lower levels to support treatment gains. For example, a client who attends a 90-day residential treatment program for an alcohol use disorder may step down to an intensive outpatient program for 12 weeks, followed by stepping down to outpatient weekly counseling for 8 weeks. At the termination of her weekly outpatient counseling, she may continue attending Alcoholics Anonymous and have 6-month check-in appointments with her counselor to ensure she is meeting her maintenance and recovery goals. The client may also become involved in a community recovery center and participate in monthly group meetings for recovery support. This example demonstrates continuous care and long-term recovery support, rather than acute care.

Although historically the acute care model has been prevalent in addictions treatment, recent research suggests that the paradigm may be shifting toward long-term, sustained recovery maintenance. In a qualitative analysis of 18 addictions treatment providers and probation professionals, researchers found that program practices and ideals were more aligned with long-term recovery support than the acute care model (Conner & Anderson, 2020). Continued advocacy efforts should emphasize the need for long-term recovery maintenance (comparable to other chronic illnesses) and discontinue the use of the acute care model in the treatment of addictions. Consider the following case of Adrienne. What obstacles does she face?

CASE EXAMPLE: ADRIENNE

Adrienne is a single mother of two children aged three and five. She works part time as a server at a local restaurant and part-time as an administrative assistant at a dentist's office. While she is at work, Adrienne's children stay with a neighbor who runs a daycare out of her apartment. Adrienne recently slipped and fell at the restaurant where she works and hurt her back. She went to the doctor and was prescribed hydrocodone for the pain. Over the last several months, Adrienne has started taking the medication more than prescribed and has visited several other pain clinics to get additional prescriptions. She claims the pain from her fall has gotten worse and she needs the medication to continue working, but

(*continued*)

secretly she knows she has started to crave the medication and needs more to feel its calming effects. Adrienne lives in a small rural town without a prescription monitoring system in place to assess how many opioid prescriptions are being filled. Therefore, Adrienne is able to get many prescriptions (e.g., oxycodone, hydrocodone) from many different physicians and pharmacies. After several months, Adrienne begins to worry about her opioid intake. She notices that when the drugs begin to wear off she starts to feel very sick and needs to take more. She knows she is experiencing withdrawal from opioids and also knows that her tolerance for the drugs has increased substantially. Adrienne finally confided in a friend about her behavior, and her friend told her that she needed to get help for her addiction. Adrienne did a quick internet search and found the closest treatment facility was in the next town over (about 45 minutes away). Additionally, that facility only offered detoxification and stabilization. If she wanted to pursue an outpatient treatment program (which offered counseling and the option of medication-assisted treatment), she would have to travel even further (about an hour and a half). Adrienne turned off her computer, feeling dejected. As a part-time employee, she did not have medical insurance and knew she would not be able to afford any of the treatment programs. She did not know how she would be able to keep her jobs if she had to drive 45 minutes or 1.5 hours away for treatment. Moreover, Adrienne did not know what she would do with her children if she tried to go to treatment (particularly several days in a detox unit) given that she does not have any relatives nearby. Adrienne decided that she would have to try to manage her opioid use by herself.

What are your reactions to the case of Adrienne? What might advocacy entail?

SUMMARY

Individuals with addiction face a variety of barriers to their wellness including stigma, lack of quality, accessible treatment, and acute care models rather than sustained recovery management. Additionally, mental health professionals may lack training in addictions counseling or hold biases related to clients with addiction. It is imperative that counselors embrace their role as advocates to give voice to the needs of clients with addiction. The New Recovery Advocacy Movement has made great strides in serving individuals with addiction. From important legislation to assist with treatment coverage, to recovery schools, to CRPs, the advocacy movement is working to create a new paradigm and culture of recovery. Counselors can join this movement and build upon the foundation that has been laid to work with and on behalf of those with addiction to ensure high-quality, affordable, accessible treatment and continuous care and recovery support. The ACA Advocacy Competencies (Toporek & Daniels, 2018; Toporek et al., 2009) can provide guidance for how counselors can advocate within various domains to remove obstacles that impede individuals with addiction from reaching their wellness goals.

RESOURCES

Association of Recovery in Higher Education: https://collegiaterecovery.org/
Association of Recovery Schools: https://recoveryschools.org/

Earnshaw, V. A. (2020). Stigma and substance use disorders: A clinical, research, and advocacy agenda. *American Psychologist, 75*(9), 1300–1311. https://doi.org/10.1037/amp0000744
Faces & Voices of Recovery: https://facesandvoicesofrecovery.org/
Mulvaney-Day, N., Gibbons, B. J., Alikhan, S., & Karakus, M. (2019). Mental Health Parity and Addiction Equity Act and the use of outpatient behavioral health services in the United States, 2005–2016. *American Journal of Public Health, 109*, 190–196. https://doi.org/10.2105/AJPH.2019.305023
National Council on Alcoholism and Drug Dependence: https://ncaddms.org/
Ouellette, P., & Rose, R. V. (2020). Analyzing the first Eliminating Kickbacks in Recovery Act (EKRA) enforcement action and its application to federal and state false claim statuses. *Health Lawyer, 32*, 8–12.
Recovery Is Everywhere: https://recoveryiseverywhere.wordpress.com/
Scott, C. K., Dennis, M. L., & White, W. L. (2004). Recovery management checkups: A future function of addiction professionals? *Addiction Professional, 2*(5), 33–39.
White, W. L. (2007). The new recovery advocacy movement in America. *Addiction, 102*(5), 696–703. https://doi.org/10.1111/j.1360-0443.2007.01808.x
White, W. L. (2014). *Slaying the dragon: The history of addiction treatment and recovery in America* (2nd ed.). Chestnut Health Systems.

KEY REFERENCES

Only key references appear in the print edition. The full reference list appears in the digital product on Springer Publishing Connect: connect.springerpub.com/content/book/978-0-8261-3586-5/chapter/ch15

Association of Recovery in Higher Education. (2019). *Standards and recommendations.* https://collegiaterecovery.org/standards-recommendations/
Bugbee, B. A., Caldeira, K. M., Soong, A. M., Vincent, K. B., & Arria, A. M. (2016). *Collegiate recovery programs: A win-win proposition for students and colleges.* Center on Young Adult Health and Development. https://doi.org/10.13140/RG.2.2.21549.08160
Busch, S. H., Epstein, A. J., Harhay, M. O., Fiellin, D. A., Un, H., Leader, D., & Barry, C. L. (2014). The effects of federal parity on substance use disorder treatment. *American Journal of Managed Care, 20*(1), 76–82. PMID: 24512166.
Conner, S. R., & Anderson, J. R. (2020). Are we acute-care or recovery-oriented? Exploring ideals and practices expressed within the substance use treatment and correctional systems. *Substance Use and Misuse, 55*(14), 2278–2290. https://doi.org/10.1080/10826084.2020.1801742
Earnshaw, V. A. (2020). Stigma and substance use disorders: A clinical, research, and advocacy agenda. *American Psychologist, 75*(9), 1300–1311. https://doi.org/10.1037/amp0000744
Finch, A. J., Moberg, D. P., & Krupp, A. L. (2014). Continuing care in high schools: A descriptive study of recovery high school programs. *Journal of Child & Adolescent Substance Abuse, 23*(2), 116–129. https://doi.org/10.1080/1067828x.2012.751269
Harris, S. M. (2019). The Eliminating Kickbacks in Recovery Act of 2018—What does it mean? *Rheumatologist*, 1–4. https://www.the-rheumatologist.org/article/the-eliminating-kickbacks-in-recovery-act-of-2018-what-does-it-mean/
Laudet, A. B., Harris, K., Kimball, T., Winers, K. C., & Moberg, D. P. (2014). Collegiate recovery communities programs: What do we know and what do we need to know? *Journal of Social Work Practice in the Addictions, 14*(1), 84–100. https://doi.org/10.1080/1533256x.2014.872015
Leshner, A. I. (2001). Addiction is a brain disease. *Issues in Science and Technology, 17*(3), 75–80.
Polcin, D. L. (2014). Addiction science advocacy: Mobilizing political support to influence public policy. *International Journal of Drug Policy, 25*(2), 329–331. https://doi.org/10.1016/j.drugpo.2013.11.002
Scott, C. K., Dennis, M. L., & White, W. L. (2004). Recovery management checkups: A future function of addiction professionals? *Addiction Professional, 2*(5), 33–39.
Toporek, R. L., & Daniels, J. (2018). *2018 update: American Counseling Association advocacy competencies.* https://www.counseling.org/docs/default-source/competencies/aca-advocacy-competencies-updated-may-2020.pdf?sfvrsn=f410212c_4
Toporek, R. L., Lewis, J. A., & Crethar, H. C. (2009). Promoting systemic change through the ACA advocacy competencies. *Journal of Counseling & Development, 87*(3), 260–268. https://doi.org/10.1002/j.1556-6678.2009.tb00105.x

White, W. L. (2007). The new recovery advocacy movement in America. *Addiction, 102*(5), 696–703. https://doi.org/10.1111/j.1360-0443.2007.01808.x

White, W. L., Kelly, J. F., & Roth, J. D. (2012). New addiction-recovery support institutions: Mobilizing support beyond professional addiction treatment and recovery mutual aid. *Journal of Groups in Addiction & Recovery, 7*(2–4), 297–317. https://doi.org/10.1080/1556035X.2012.705719

INDEX